HOLT GEOMETRY

Eugene D. Nichols

Mervine L. Edwards

E. Henry Garland

Sylvia A. Hoffman

Albert Mamary

William F. Palmer

HOLT GEOMETRY

Holt, Rinehart and Winston, Inc.
New York, Toronto, London, Sydney

About the Authors

Eugene D. Nichols is Professor and Head of the Department of Mathematics Education, and Lecturer of the Department of Mathematics, The Florida State University, Tallahassee, Florida.

Mervine L. Edwards is Chairman of the Mathematics Department, Shore Regional High School, West Long Branch, New Jersey.

E. Henry Garland is Head of the Mathematics Department at the Developmental Research School, and Associate Professor of Mathematics Education, The Florida State University, Tallahassee, Florida.

Sylvia A. Hoffman is Curriculum Development Specialist for the Office of the Superintendent of Public Instruction, State of Illinois.

Albert Mamary is Assistant Superintendent of Schools for Instruction, Johnson City Central School District, Johnson City, New York.

William F. Palmer is Associate Professor of Mathematics, Mercer University, Macon, Georgia.

Photo credits are on page viii.

ISBN: 0-03-091331-4

3456789012 071 987654321

CONTENTS

SPECIAL TOPICS

ACKNOWLEDGEMENTS FOR PHOTOGRAPHS

Page	26	U.S. Bureau of Reclamation
Page	39	Top: Hedrich-Blessing; center: Wide World Photos; bottom: UPI Photo
Page	40	Top: Wide World Photos; bottom: UPI Photo
Page	66	Top & bottom: U.S. Bureau of Reclamation
Page	73	Top: Hedrich-Blessing; bottom: Wide World Photos
Page	74	Top: UPI Photo; bottom: Hedrich-Blessing
Page	164	Top & bottom: USDA Photo
Page	170	Top: Courtesy of the American Museum of National History; bottom left: Mt. Wilson & Palomar Observatories; bottom right: D.S. Kennedy & Co.
Page	244	Top: U.S. Bureau of Reclamation; bottom: Irene Fertik
Page	486	Top: Irene Fertik; bottom: Courtesy of MIT

SYMBOL LIST

Symbol	Meaning	Page
$\overleftrightarrow{MN}$	line MN	1
$\overline{MN}$	segment MN	1
$\overrightarrow{MN}$	ray MN	1
$\angle AOB$	angle AOB	3
$A \cap B$	intersection of A and B	3
$A \cup B$	union of A and B	3
$\triangle XYZ$	triangle XYZ	4
$A \leftrightarrow 2$	A corresponds to 2	6
MN	distance between M and N	7
$\cong$	is congruent to	9
$m \angle AOB$	degree measure of $\angle AOB$	15
$\llcorner$	right angle	27
$\therefore$	therefore	41
$\perp$	is perpendicular to	50
$\not\perp$	is not perpendicular to	50
$\angle P\text{-}\overleftrightarrow{XY}\text{-}Q$	dihedral angle	60
$\parallel$	is parallel to	67
$\not\parallel$	is not parallel to	68
$\not\cong$	is not congruent to	75
A'	A prime	112
$R \triangle ABC$	region of $\triangle ABC$	146
$\square ABCD$	parallelogram $ABCD$	202
$\sim$	is similar to	253
$\not\sim$	is not similar to	268
$\doteq$	is approximately equal to	301
$\odot$	circle	315
$\overarc{AB}$	arc AB	327
$m\overarc{AB}$	degree measure of arc AB	328
P_1	P sub one	383
$P(x, y)$	Point P with coordinates (x, y)	401
$\vec{d}(RS)$	directed distance from R to S	411

Soap Bubble Surfaces

Dip in soapy water.

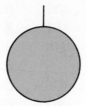

A soap bubble will form
over the surface.

The bubble will cover the smallest possible surface. This is the minimum surface of the formation.

Try this formation.

Closed curlycue

Closed curlycue
surface

Closed curlycue with
center region burst
Result is Mobius Strip.

Some more closed wire formations

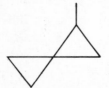

Tetrahedron with
two edges missing

Cube

Cube with
three sides missing

Construct your own wire formations. Dip them in soapy water and see
what you get.

Geometric Figures

OBJECTIVES
- To identify and name sets of points such as line, ray, or segment
- To identify and name unions and intersections of sets of points

 REVIEW CAPSULE

A set is a collection of objects.

$A \cup B$	$A \cap B$
↓	↓
A union B	*A intersection B*
is the set of all the elements in *A*, or *B*, or both *A* and *B*.	is the set of all the elements in both *A* and *B*.

Geometry is the study of sets of points.

	Point	Line	Segment
Name of set →	Point	Line	Segment
Picture →	•P	$l \overset{\longleftrightarrow}{\underset{M \quad N}{\bullet \quad \bullet}}$	$\underset{X \qquad Y}{\bullet\!\!-\!\!-\!\!-\!\!\bullet}$
Symbol →	P	ℓ, or $\overleftrightarrow{MN}$, or $\overleftrightarrow{NM}$	$\overline{XY}$ or $\overline{YX}$
Read. →	Point P	Line ℓ, or line *MN*, or line *NM*	Segment *XY*, or segment *YX*

	Ray	Plane
Name of set →	Ray	Plane
Picture →		
Symbol →	$\overrightarrow{TU}$	p
Read. →	Ray *TU*	Plane *p*

EXAMPLE 1 Name this set of points.

A ray is pictured. →

$\overrightarrow{AB}$, or $\overrightarrow{AC}$ is pictured.

A ray is named by its endpoint and one other point.

Thus, the set of points is ray *AB* ($\overrightarrow{AB}$).

EXAMPLE 2   Which of these sets are figures?

Each is a set of points. ──────→
A set of points may consist of one point.

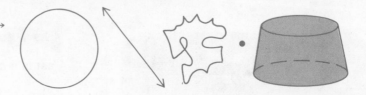

All are figures.

Definition of *geometric figure* ──────→ | A *geometric figure* is a set of points.

Each figure in Example 2 is a subset of space.

Definition of *space* ──────→ | *Space* is the set of all points.

EXAMPLE 3   Using the figure, find each of the following.

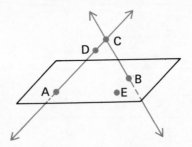

		Answers
A, D, C are on the same line. ──→	3 collinear points	{*A, D, C*}
A, E, B are in the same plane. ──→	3 coplanar points	{*A, E, B*}
There are other possible answers. ──→	3 noncollinear points	{*A, D, B*}
There are other possible answers. ──→	4 noncoplanar points	{*A, B, C, E*}

Definitions of *collinear* and
coplanar points ──────→ | *Collinear points* are points on the same line.
Coplanar points are points in the same plane.

EXAMPLE 4   Give all possible names for this line.

A line is named by any two of its
points. ──────→ $\overleftrightarrow{RJ}, \overleftrightarrow{RQ}, \overleftrightarrow{JQ}, \overleftrightarrow{QJ}, \overleftrightarrow{QR}, \overleftrightarrow{JR}$

EXAMPLE 5 Illustrate some possible intersections of two collinear rays. Give a simpler name for each, if possible.

The intersection can be the empty set. ————→

The intersection can be a set with one point. ————→

The intersection can be a segment. ————→

The intersection can be one of the rays. ————→

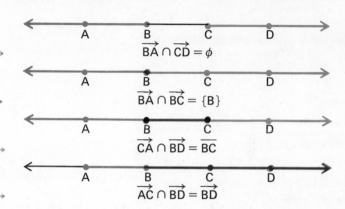

$\overrightarrow{BA} \cap \overrightarrow{CD} = \phi$

$\overrightarrow{BA} \cap \overrightarrow{BC} = \{B\}$

$\overrightarrow{CA} \cap \overrightarrow{BD} = \overline{BC}$

$\overrightarrow{AC} \cap \overrightarrow{BD} = \overrightarrow{BD}$

EXAMPLE 6 Illustrate some possible unions of two coplanar rays. Give a simpler name for each, if possible.

The union can be a line. ————→

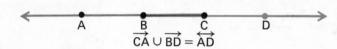

$\overrightarrow{CA} \cup \overrightarrow{BD} = \overleftrightarrow{AD}$

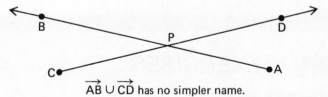

$\overrightarrow{BA} \cup \overrightarrow{CD}$ has no simpler name.

$\overrightarrow{OA}$ and $\overrightarrow{OB}$ have a common endpoint. Their union is an angle.

$\angle AOB$ is read angle AOB. ————→

$\overrightarrow{OA} \cup \overrightarrow{OB} = \angle AOB = \angle BOA$

$\overrightarrow{AB}$ and $\overrightarrow{CD}$ do not have a common endpoint. Their union is not an angle.

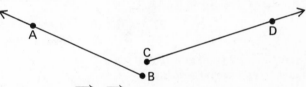

$\overrightarrow{AB} \cup \overrightarrow{CD}$ has no simpler name.

Definition of *angle* ————→

An angle is the union of two rays with a common endpoint.

EXAMPLE 7   Illustrate some possible unions of two or more
segments. Give a simpler name for each if possible.

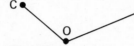

The union of two collinear segments
can be a segment. ————————→

$\overline{AC} \cup \overline{BD} = \overline{AD}$

The union of two segments is not
an angle. ————————————→

$\overline{OC} \cup \overline{OD}$ has no simpler name.

The union of three coplanar segments
can be a triangle. ————————→

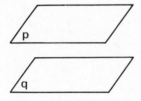

$\triangle XYZ$ is read triangle XYZ. ————→

$\overline{XY} \cup \overline{YZ} \cup \overline{ZX} = \triangle XYZ$

Definition of *triangle* ————————→

A *triangle* is the union of three noncollinear
segments, each two having a common endpoint.

EXAMPLE 8   Illustrate some possible intersections of two planes.
Give a simpler name for each if possible.

The drawing on the left shows that the
intersection can be the empty set.

The drawing on the right shows that
the intersection can be a line.

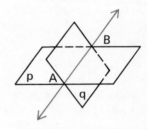

$$p \cap q = \phi \qquad p \cap q = \overrightarrow{AB}$$

ORAL EXERCISES

Name each figure.

1.

2.

3.

4.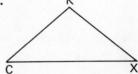

Give a simpler name.

5. $\overline{MO} \cup \overline{NP}$
7. $\overrightarrow{OM} \cap \overrightarrow{NP}$
9. $\overleftrightarrow{MO} \cap \overline{NP}$
11. $\overline{MP} \cup \overline{NO}$
13. $\overline{OP} \cap \overline{MN}$

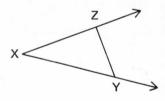

6. $\overline{MN} \cap \overline{NP}$
8. $\overrightarrow{NO} \cup \overrightarrow{OP}$
10. $\overline{NM} \cap \overrightarrow{OP}$
12. $\overrightarrow{MN} \cup \overrightarrow{OP}$
14. $\overrightarrow{OM} \cup \overrightarrow{NP}$

Give a simpler name.

15. $\overrightarrow{XZ} \cup \overrightarrow{XY}$

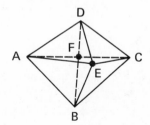

16. $\overline{XY} \cup \overline{YZ} \cup \overline{ZX}$

EXERCISES

PART A

1. Give three possible names
   for this line.

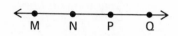

2. Give three segments
   contained in the line.

**Identify each set of points as *collinear*, *coplanar but not collinear*, or *not coplanar*.
(In the picture, *E* is not in the same plane as *A, B, C, D*, and *F*.)**

3. {D, E}
4. {A, B, E}
5. {A, E, C}
6. {A, B, C, D}
7. {B, D, F}
8. {B, C, D, E}

9. Which geometric figure is suggested by
   one edge of this page?

10. Which geometric figure is suggested by
    the top of your desk?

PART B

Draw pictures illustrating 3 possible intersections or unions of each.

11. Two collinear segments
13. A segment and a ray

12. Two noncollinear segments
14. A line and a plane

True or false? Draw pictures to illustrate each statement.

15. The union of two rays can be a line.
17. Two lines can intersect in exactly two
    points.
19. The union of two segments can be an
    angle.

16. The union of two rays can be an angle.
18. Two planes can intersect in exactly one
    point.
20. A line and a plane can intersect in
    exactly two points.

Coordinates and Distance

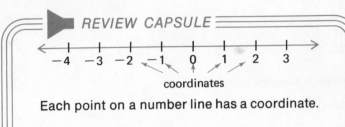

REVIEW CAPSULE

Each point on a number line has a coordinate.

$$|2| = 2 \qquad |-2| = 2 \qquad |0| = 0$$
$|2|$ is read the absolute value of 2.

EXAMPLE 1

On this number line, which point corresponds to each given coordinate?

There is a one-to-one correspondence between the points and the coordinates.

$-4 \leftrightarrow A$ means
-4 corresponds to point A.

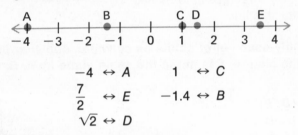

$$-4 \leftrightarrow A \qquad 1 \leftrightarrow C$$
$$\frac{7}{2} \leftrightarrow E \qquad -1.4 \leftrightarrow B$$
$$\sqrt{2} \leftrightarrow D$$

EXAMPLE 2

Give the coordinate for each point.

This number line is marked off in tenths.

Each point has exactly one coordinate.

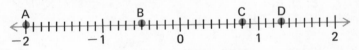

$$A \leftrightarrow -2 \qquad B \leftrightarrow -.5$$
$$C \leftrightarrow .8 \qquad D \leftrightarrow 1.3$$

EXAMPLE 3

Show two different one-to-one correspondences between the given points and coordinates.

Two different number lines are shown.

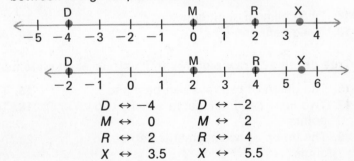

$$D \leftrightarrow -4 \qquad D \leftrightarrow -2$$
$$M \leftrightarrow 0 \qquad M \leftrightarrow 2$$
$$R \leftrightarrow 2 \qquad R \leftrightarrow 4$$
$$X \leftrightarrow 3.5 \qquad X \leftrightarrow 5.5$$

EXAMPLE 4   Find the distance between *P* and *Q*.

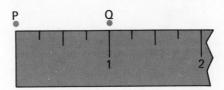

PQ means the distance between
P and *Q.* ——————————————→   *PQ* = 1 inch.

Moving the ruler does not change the distance.

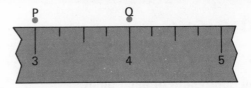

Symbol for absolute value
$PQ = \overset{\frown}{|4-3|}$, or $|3-4|$ ——————————→   *PQ* = 1 inch.

Definition of *distance* ——————————→   The distance (*AB*) between two points *A* and *B* with
$|b-a| = |a-b|$ coordinates *a* and *b* is $|b-a|$, or $|a-b|$.

EXAMPLE 5   Find the length of $\overline{PQ}$. Use both an inch ruler and a
centimeter ruler.

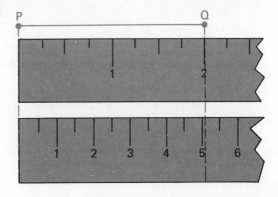

The length of a segment is the distance
between its endpoints.

The length of a segment depends on the
ruler used to measure it.   *PQ* = 2 inches,   or   *PQ* = 5.1 centimeters.

Definition of *length* ——————————→   The *length* of a segment *PQ* is the distance (*PQ*)
between the points *P* and *Q*.

EXAMPLE 6 Find the length of each given segment. Use the number line as a ruler.

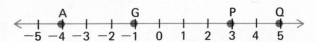

Find the distance between the endpoints.

Segment		Length	
$\overline{PQ}$	$PQ = \|5 - 3\|$		$= 2$
$\overline{GP}$	$GP = \|3 - (-1)\|$		$= 4$
$\overline{AG}$	$AG = \|-1 - (-4)\|$		$= 3$
$\overline{PA}$	$PA = \|-4 - 3\|$		$= 7$

EXERCISES

PART A

Give the coordinate of each point.

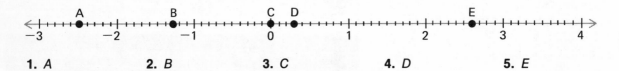

1. A   **2.** B   **3.** C   **4.** D   **5.** E

Find the length of each segment in inches and in centimeters. (Use a ruler.)

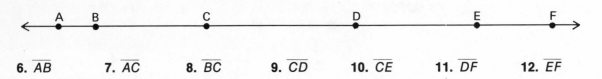

6. $\overline{AB}$ **7.** $\overline{AC}$ **8.** $\overline{BC}$ **9.** $\overline{CD}$ **10.** $\overline{CE}$ **11.** $\overline{DF}$ **12.** $\overline{EF}$

Find the length of each segment. Use the number line as a ruler.

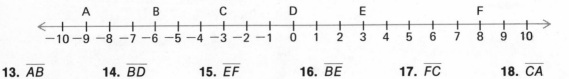

13. $\overline{AB}$ **14.** $\overline{BD}$ **15.** $\overline{EF}$ **16.** $\overline{BE}$ **17.** $\overline{FC}$ **18.** $\overline{CA}$

PART B

Complete each statement. Use the number line.

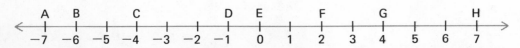

19. $AB = $ _____?_____   **20.** $GF = F$ _____?_____   **21.** $AC = F$ _____?_____   **22.** $AD = $ _____?_____ E

Congruence of Segments

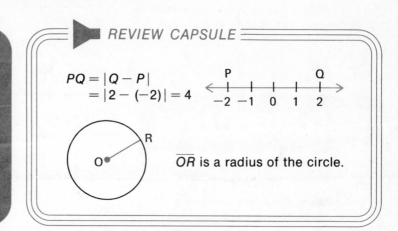

REVIEW CAPSULE

$$PQ = |Q - P|$$
$$= |2 - (-2)| = 4$$

$\overline{OR}$ is a radius of the circle.

EXAMPLE 1

Using a ruler, show that $\overline{AB}$ and $\overline{CD}$ have the same length.

$AB = 2$ cm, $CD = 2$ cm ⟶

Definition of *congruent segments* ⟶

Two segments are *congruent* if they have the same length.

EXAMPLE 2   Show that $\overline{PQ}$ and $\overline{TU}$ are congruent.

$$PQ = |-2 - (-5)| = 3, \qquad TU = |4 - 1| = 3$$

$\overline{PQ} \cong \overline{TU}$ means $\overline{PQ}$ is congruent to $\overline{TU}$. ⟶ **Thus, $\overline{PQ} \cong \overline{TU}$.**

EXAMPLE 3   Show that $\overline{AC} \cong \overline{DB}$.

$$AC = |0 - (-6)| = 6, \qquad DB = |-2 - 4| = 6$$

$\overline{AC} \cong \overline{DB}$ means $AC = DB$.   **Thus, $\overline{AC} \cong \overline{DB}$.**

A compass can be adjusted to *construct* a segment congruent to a given segment.

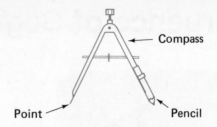

Compass

Point ← → Pencil

construction

A segment congruent to a given segment

STRATEGY

Adjust the compass opening to correspond to the end points of $\overline{ST}$.

———————
S   T

GIVEN
$\overline{ST}$

CONSTRUCT
$\overline{XY} \cong \overline{ST}$ on line ℓ

Adjust compass to correspond to S and T.

Place compass point on X. Mark Y with compass pencil.

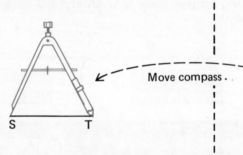

S   T

Move compass.

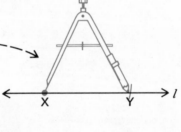

X   Y ℓ

Conclusion: $\overline{XY} \cong \overline{ST}$

EXAMPLE 4 Construct a segment with a length equal to the sum of the lengths of the two given segments.

J ———————— N

T ———————— H

Construct $\overline{XY} \cong \overline{JN}$.
Construct $\overline{YZ} \cong \overline{TH}$.

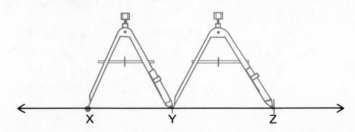

X   Y   Z

Thus, $XZ = JN + TH$.

EXAMPLE 5

$PG = PH$ ⟶ Construct a point P equidistant from points G and H.

G ·   H ·

Open compass wider than one half of GH.

With compass point on G, draw an arc. ⟶ ✕ P ← With compass point on H and same opening, draw an arc which intersects the first arc.

The two arcs intersect at P.

G ·   H ·

Different compass openings will give different points.

Definition of midpoint of a segment ⟶

A *midpoint* of a segment divides it into two congruent segments.

A —————————————•————————————— B
                    M

M is the midpoint of $\overline{AB}$.

construction

The midpoint of a given segment

S ——————————————— T

GIVEN
$\overline{ST}$
CONSTRUCT
M, the midpoint of $\overline{ST}$

STRATEGY

Connect two points equidistant from S and T.

Construct P, such that $SP = TP$.

S ——————————— T

Construct Q different from P such that $SQ = TQ$.

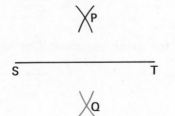

S ——————————— T

Draw $\overleftrightarrow{PQ}$ intersecting $\overline{ST}$ at M.

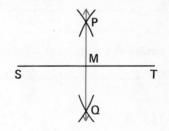

S ——————————— T

Conclusion: M is the midpoint of $\overline{ST}$.

Bisect means divide into two congruent segments. ⟶ The midpoint of a segment bisects the segment.

EXAMPLE 6   Find the coordinate of the midpoint of $\overline{AB}$.

$$\frac{5 + (-3)}{2} = 1$$

Find the point M that makes $\overline{AM} \cong \overline{MB}$. ———————→

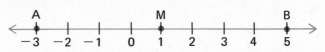

If M has coordinate 1, then $AM = 4 = MB$.
Thus, the coordinate of the midpoint is 1.

EXERCISES

PART A

Which pairs of segments are congruent? Use a ruler to decide.

1.    **2.**   **3.**    **4.**

Which pairs of segments are congruent? Use a compass to decide.

5.    **6.**   **7.**    **8.**

On the given number line, which pairs of segments are congruent?

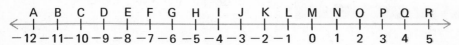

9. $\overline{AB}$ and $\overline{EG}$ **10.** $\overline{CM}$ and $\overline{FP}$ **11.** $\overline{GP}$ and $\overline{EN}$
12. $\overline{DK}$ and $\overline{GN}$ **13.** $\overline{PC}$ and $\overline{RE}$ **14.** $\overline{BP}$ and $\overline{IA}$

Construct a segment congruent to the given segment. Construct a point equidistant from its endpoints.

15. ———————————————
A   B

16. ———————————————————
X   Y

Construct a segment congruent to the given segment. Construct the midpoint of the segment.

17. ———————————————
R   S

18. ———————————————————
H   J

PART B

Find the coordinate of the midpoint of the segment whose endpoints have the given coordinates.

19. 0 and 10   **20.** 3 and 19   **21.** 6 and −6
22. 15 and −7   **23.** −4 and 9   **24.** 5.6 *and* 8.4

25. Construct a segment whose length is
$AB + CD$.

A ——————— B   C ——————————— D

26. Construct a segment whose length is
$PQ - RS$.

P ———————————— Q   R ——— S

27. Construct a segment twice as long as $\overline{TU}$.

T ——————— U

28. Construct a segment whose length is
one fourth of GH.

G ———————————————————— H

PART C

On the number line, find the other endpoint of a segment congruent to the given segment.

A B C D E F G H I J K L M N O P Q R
-8 -7 -6 -5 -4 -3 -2 -1 0 1 2 3 4 5 6 7 8 9

EXAMPLE $\overline{EN}$, point G.
Since $EN = |5 - (-4)| = 9,$ $|x - (-2)| = 9$
$x = 7$

$|7 - (-2)| = 9$

Thus, P is the required point, since $GP = 9$.

29. $\overline{BL}$, point D **30.** $\overline{KC}$, point P **31.** $\overline{DQ}$, point B
32. $\overline{IP}$, point J **33.** $\overline{EF}$, point R **34.** $\overline{CH}$, point L.

Algebra Review

OBJECTIVE
■ To solve linear equations

To solve a linear equation:
1. Remove parentheses.   2. Combine like terms.
3. Get the variable alone.

EXAMPLE   Solve $6(x + 2) = 4 - (3 - 2x) - 1$.
$6x + 12 = 4 - 3 + 2x - 1$
$6x + 12 = 2x$
$4x = -12$
$x = -3$

$-(3 - 2x) = -1(3 - 2x) = -3 + 2x \longrightarrow$

Solve.

1. $2(x + 1) = x + 5$
2. $3x - 4 = x - 5 + 7$
3. $x - (2x + 1) = 3 + 3x - 8$
4. $3x - 4 = 3(x - 1) - x$
5. $x - (2x + 1) = 3 - (3x + 6)$
6. $2 - (x - 5) = 3(x + 3)$
7. $x + 4(x + 1) = 2(4 + x)$
8. $7x - 5 - 3x = 5 - 2x - 7$
9. $5x + 13 = 2(x + 9) - 2$
10. $\frac{2}{3}(6x + 9) = 2 + x + 1$
11. $3(x + 2) - 1 = x(4 - 2) + 7$
12. $5x - (7 + x) = 3x + 4 - x$

Angles and their Measures

REVIEW CAPSULE

An angle is the union of two rays with a common endpoint.

$\angle AOB = \overrightarrow{OA} \cup \overrightarrow{OB}$

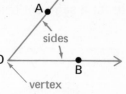

Each angle has two sides and a vertex.

EXAMPLE 1   Name the sides and the vertex of $\angle ZXT$.

The sides are rays. ⟶ Sides: $\overrightarrow{XZ}$ and $\overrightarrow{XT}$
The vertex is a point. ⟶ Vertex: X

EXAMPLE 2   Give four different names for this angle.

The vertex is always in the middle of the name. ⟶ $\angle YOT$, $\angle VOT$, $\angle TOY$, and $\angle XOV$ are four names.

A protractor is used to measure an angle.

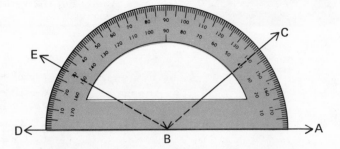

The measure of $\angle ABC$ is 40°.
The measure of $\angle ABE$ is 150°.

Definition of *degree measure* ⟶ Every angle has a *degree measure m*, such that $0 < m \le 180$.

EXAMPLE 3   Find the measure of ∠AOB. Use a protractor.

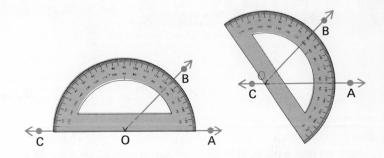

$m∠AOB$ means measure of ∠AOB in degrees. ──────────────→   **Thus, $m∠AOB = 45$.**

EXAMPLE 4   Draw an ∠XYZ with $m∠XYZ = 150$. Use a protractor.

1. Draw a ray, $\overrightarrow{YX}$.
2. Place the protractor point on Y with $\overrightarrow{YX}$ pointing to 0.
3. Mark Z at 150. Draw $\overrightarrow{YZ}$.

EXAMPLE 5   Show that $m∠TUV = m∠XYZ$.

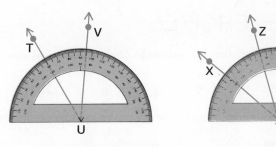

$m∠TUV = 95 - 60$, $m∠XYZ = 75 - 40$ ──→ $m∠TUV = 35$ $m∠XYZ = 35$

Thus, $m∠TUV = m∠XYZ$.

Congruent angles have the same measure.

∠TUV ≅ ∠XYZ
∠TUV is congruent to ∠XYZ.

Definition of congruent angles ──────→   Angles having the same measure are *congruent* angles.

An angle congruent to a given angle

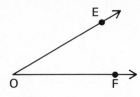

GIVEN
∠ EOF
CONSTRUCT
∠ MVH ≅ ∠ EOF

Draw an arc with center O. Use a radius of any length.	On a line, pick a point V. Using a radius of the same length, draw an arc with center V.	Set the compass with radius ≅ TU. Draw an arc with center H. Draw $\overrightarrow{VM}$.
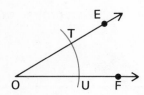	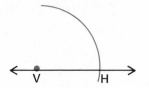	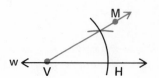

Conclusion: ∠ MVH ≅ ∠ EOF

ORAL EXERCISES

Without using a protractor estimate the measure of each angle.

1.
2.
3.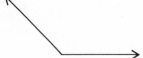
4.

EXERCISES

PART A

1. Name the vertex and sides of ∠XRT.

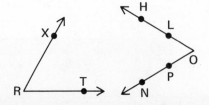

2. Give three other names for ∠HON.

Find the measure of each angle. Use a protractor.

3.

4.

5.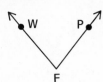

6.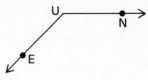

Draw angles having the given measure. Use a protractor.

7. $m \angle BOC = 38$

8. $m \angle IVT = 76$

9. $m \angle NOT = 45$

10. $m \angle XYZ = 90$

11. $m \angle SOA = 125$

12. $m \angle BCD = 172$

Determine which pairs are congruent. Use a protractor.

13.

14.

15.

Construct an angle congruent to the given angle.

16.

17.

18.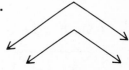

Using the protractor pictured, find the measure of each angle.

19. $\angle AOC$
20. $\angle DOB$
21. $\angle COE$
22. $\angle EOB$
23. $\angle AOF$
24. $\angle COF$

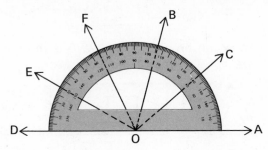

25. Construct an angle whose measure is $m \angle AOB + m \angle CQD$.

26. Construct an angle whose measure is $m \angle XYZ - m \angle RST$.

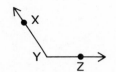

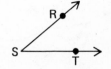

ANGLES AND THEIR MEASURES   **17**

Can You Draw This

Can you draw this figure
without lifting your pencil?
without crossing a part already
drawn? Without retracing any
portion?

(You may approach another part ➤◄
but not cross it ✖ .)

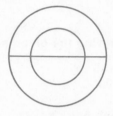

(See below.)

Which of the following figures can be drawn this way?

yes

yes

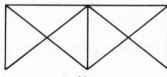

No

No

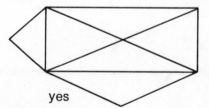

yes

Can you predict which figures can be drawn this way? Is there a definite pattern? (Yes, there is.) Try your hunch on these.

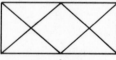

A

B

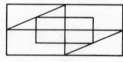

C

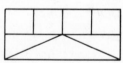

D

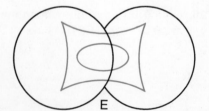

E

Answer

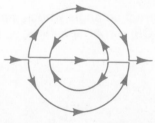

Interiors and Exteriors

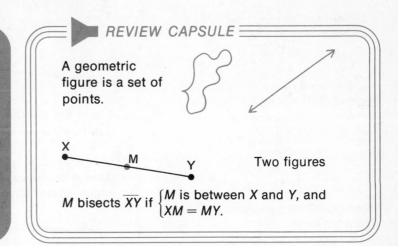

A line extends infinitely far.

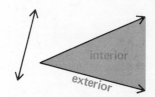

Lines are contained in the exterior, but not in the interior of each figure above.

Definition of *interior* and *exterior* ⟶ If a figure separates a plane into two parts, the *interior* is the part which contains no lines. The *exterior* is the other part.

EXAMPLE 1 Shade the interior of the figure below.

The interior is completely surrounded by the figure.

This figure is also called a closed curve.

EXAMPLE 2 Which points are in the interior of each figure?
Which points are in the exterior of each figure?

The arrows show that the figures
continue without end.

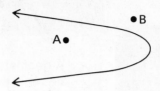
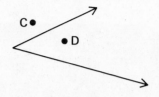

These figures are also called *open*
curves. They are also continuous.

A is in the interior.　　　　C is in the exterior
B is in the exterior.　　　　D is in the interior.

EXAMPLE 3 Draw a continuous figure and a discontinuous figure
which do not have interiors.

The figures do not separate the plane
into two parts.

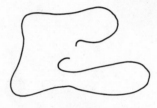

Continuous　　　　Discontinuous

EXAMPLE 4 Draw a figure which separates a plane into two parts
but which does not have an interior.

Both parts contain lines.

EXAMPLE 5 $\overrightarrow{OC}$ bisects $\angle AOB$.
What are the properties of $\overrightarrow{OC}$?

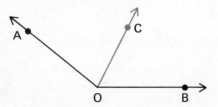

∠AOC and ∠COB have the same
measure.

$\overrightarrow{OC}$ is in the interior of $\angle AOB$.
$\angle AOC \cong \angle COB$

Definition of angle bisector ———————→ $\overrightarrow{OP}$ bisects $\angle AOB$ if $\begin{cases} P \text{ is in the interior of } \angle AOB, \\ \text{and } \angle AOP \cong \angle POB. \end{cases}$

$\overrightarrow{OP}$ is the *bisector* of $\angle AOB$.

EXAMPLE 6 $\angle GOJ \cong \angle JOH$. Is $\overrightarrow{OJ}$ the bisector of $\angle GOH$?

No. $\overrightarrow{OJ}$ is not in the interior of $\angle GOH$.

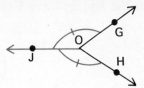

EXAMPLE 7 $\overrightarrow{TL}$ bisects $\angle JTC$.
$m\angle JTL = 2x + 4$, $m\angle LTC = 3x - 13$.
Find $m\angle JTL$.

 indicates that the two angles are congruent.

$$m\angle JTL = m\angle LTC$$
$$2x + 4 = 3x - 13$$
$$-x = -17$$
$$x = 17$$

$m\angle JTL = 2x + 4$ ———————→ **Thus,** $m\angle JTL = 2(17) + 4$, or 38.

construction

The bisector of a given angle

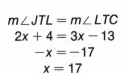

GIVEN
$\angle XYZ$
CONSTRUCT
$\overrightarrow{YP}$, the bisector of $\angle XYZ$

Draw an arc with center Y.	Use $\overline{RQ}$ as a radius. Draw an arc with center R. Draw an arc with center Q.	Draw $\overrightarrow{YP}$.
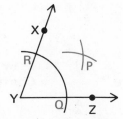		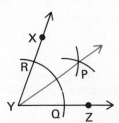

Conclusion $\overrightarrow{YP}$ is the bisector of $\angle XYZ$.

ORAL EXERCISES

Which of the figures have interiors?

1. 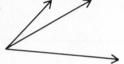 **2.** **3.** **4.**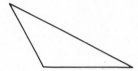

Which pictures show an angle and its bisector?

5. **6.** **7.**

EXERCISES

PART A

Which points are in the interior of each angle?

1. $\angle AOB$ **2.** $\angle BOF$

3. $\angle COA$ **4.** $\angle BOC$

5. $\angle FOD$ **6.** $\angle COE$

7. $\angle AOE$ **8.** $\angle AOD$

9. $\angle AOC$ **10.** $\angle AOF$

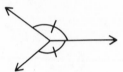

11. Draw an angle with a measure of 60°. Construct its bisector.

12. Draw an angle with a measure of 130°. Construct its bisector.

13. $\overrightarrow{SU}$ bisects $\angle RST$. $m\angle RSU = 5x + 3$, $m\angle UST = 6x - 2$. Find $m\angle RSU$.

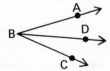

14. $\overrightarrow{SU}$ bisects $\angle RST$. $m\angle RSU = 8x + 4$, $m\angle UST = 9x - 3$. Find $m\angle RST$.

PART B

15. Draw an angle with a measure of 80°. Construct an angle with $\frac{1}{4}$ this measure.

16. Draw an angle with a measure of 140°. Construct an angle with $\frac{1}{8}$ this measure.

17. $\overrightarrow{BD}$ bisects $\angle ABC$. $m\angle ABC = 3x - 10$, $m\angle DBC = \frac{1}{2}x + 7$. Find $m\angle ABD$.

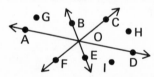

18. $\overrightarrow{BD}$ bisects $\angle ABC$. $m\angle ABD = \frac{1}{6}x - 4$, $m\angle DBC = 188 - \frac{5}{6}x$. Find $m\angle ABC$.

Patterns in Pie Cutting

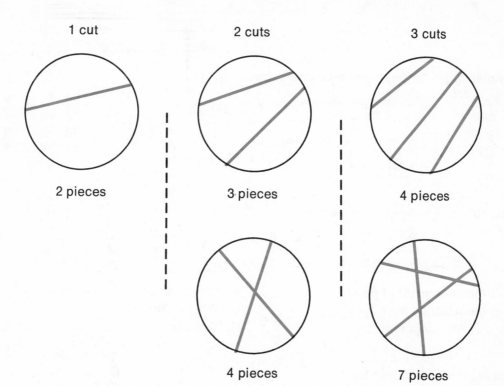

1 cut

2 pieces

2 cuts

3 pieces

4 pieces

3 cuts

4 pieces

7 pieces

Complete the chart.

Rules

- Use only straight cuts.
- The pieces can be any shape or size.
- Count the cuts and the pieces.

Number of Cuts	Smallest Number of Pieces	Largest Number of Pieces
1		2
2	3	
3		7
4		
5		
6		
.		
.		
.		
n		

Chapter One Review

Name each figure. [p. 1]

1.

2.

3.
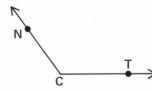

4.

Give a simpler name for each union or intersection. [p. 1]

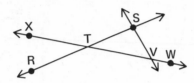

5. $\overleftrightarrow{XV} \cup \overleftrightarrow{TW}$
7. $\overleftrightarrow{RS} \cap \overleftrightarrow{XW}$
9. $\overleftrightarrow{TS} \cup \overleftrightarrow{TV}$
11. $\overleftrightarrow{XW} \cap \overrightarrow{VW}$

6. $\overrightarrow{TX} \cup \overrightarrow{TV}$
8. $\overrightarrow{VX} \cap \overrightarrow{TV}$
10. $\overleftrightarrow{TX} \cap \overline{TR}$
12. $\overline{TV} \cup \overline{VS} \cup \overline{ST}$

Use the number line below for questions 13–18. [p. 6, 9]

13. What is the coordinate of point *L*?
15. What is the distance from *E* to *N*?
17. Are $\overline{DI}$ and $\overline{GL}$ congruent?

14. What point has the coordinate 0?
16. What is the length of $\overline{GP}$?
18. Complete: $\overline{AO} \cong \overline{C\ ?}$

Use the protractor at the right for questions 19–21. [p. 14]

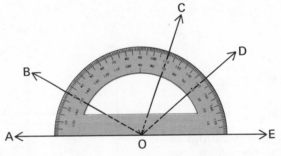

19. What is $m \angle AOB$?
20. What is $m \angle BOD$?
21. Are $\angle BOC$ and $\angle DOE$ congruent?

Which of the following figures have interiors? [p. 19]

22.

23.
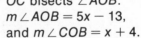

24. $\overrightarrow{OC}$ bisects $\angle AOB$.
$m \angle AOB = 5x - 13$,
and $m \angle COB = x + 4$.
Find $m \angle AOB$. [p. 19]

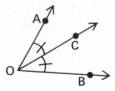

25. Draw a segment 5 centimeters long.
Construct its midpoint. [p. 9]

26. Draw an angle with a measure of
120°. Construct its bisector. [p. 19]

Chapter One Test

Name each figure.

1.
S ●————————————● T

2.
←————●————————————●————→
   L   J

3.
←————●————————————●————→
   A   B

Give a simpler name for each union or intersection.

4. $\overline{AB} \cup \overline{BD}$

6. $\overline{AB} \cap \overrightarrow{BC}$

5. $\overleftrightarrow{AD} \cap \overrightarrow{BC}$

7. $\overrightarrow{BA} \cap \overline{CD}$

←——●————●————●————●——→
  A   B   C   D

Use the number line for questions 8–13.

```
    A  B  C  D  E  F  G  H  I  J  K  L  M  N  O
←——+——+——+——+——+——+——+——+——+——+——+——+——+——+——+——→
   -7 -6 -5 -4 -3 -2 -1  0  1  2  3  4  5  6  7
```

8. What is the coordinate of point *F*?

10. What is the distance from *D* to *J*?

12. Are $\overline{AD}$ and $\overline{HK}$ congruent?

9. What point has coordinate −5?

11. What is the length of $\overline{CM}$?

13. $\overline{DA} \cong \overline{G\ ?}$

Use the protractor at the right for questions 14–16.

14. What is $m \angle AOB$?

15. What is $m \angle COD$?

16. Are $\angle AOB$ and $\angle BOC$ congruent?

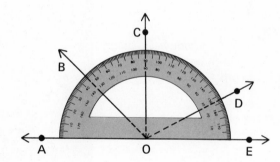

Which of the following figures have interiors?

17.

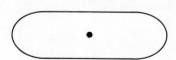

18.

19.

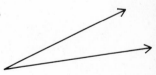

20. Find the length of the segment at the right in both inches and centimeters.

21. $\overrightarrow{QS}$ bisects $\angle PQR$.
$m \angle PQS = 6x - 5$,
and $m \angle SQR = 3x + 25$.
Find $m \angle PQR$.

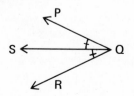

22. Draw a segment 8 centimeters long. Construct its midpoint.

23. Draw an angle with a measure of 90°. Construct its bisector.

Women in Engineering

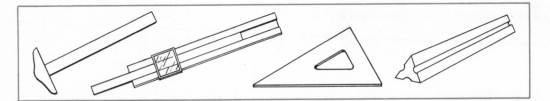

Shown here at work at the Bureau of Reclamation in Denver is one of the women engineers of the agency. She is a structural engineer on the technical staff.

Kinds of Angles

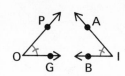

REVIEW CAPSULE

∠POG is congruent to ∠AIB.
∠POG ≅ ∠AIB
means
m∠POG = m∠AIB

The degree measure, m, of an angle is between 0 and 180.

$$0 < m \le 180$$

Angles can be classified by their measures.

Kind of angle ⟶	Right angle	Acute angle	Obtuse angle
Measures ⟶	$m = 90$	$0 < m < 90$	$90 < m < 180$

Picture ⟶
The symbol ⌐ is used to indicate a right angle. ⟶

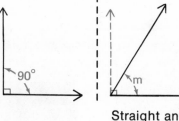

Kind of angle ⟶
Measure ⟶

Straight angle
$m = 180$

Picture ⟶

EXAMPLE 1   Measure each angle with a protractor. Classify it as an acute, right, obtuse, or straight angle.

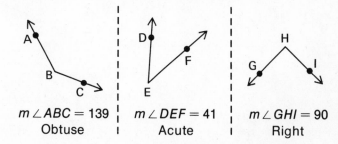

$m\angle ABC = 139$
Obtuse

$m\angle DEF = 41$
Acute

$m\angle GHI = 90$
Right

Some pairs of coplanar angles are adjacent.

Adjacent angles must have a common side. ⟶

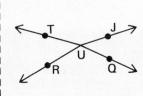

∠XOY are ∠YOZ are adjacent.

∠TUR and ∠JUQ are not adjacent.

In the figure on the right, ∠TUR and ∠JUQ have no common side.

The common side of adjacent angles must be between them.
In the figure on the right, ∠TWH and ∠BWH have no common side between them.

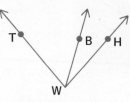

∠TWB and ∠BWH are adjacent.

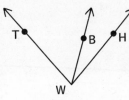

∠TWH and ∠BWH are not adjacent.

Adjacent angles must have a common vertex.

In the figure on the right, ∠NIV and ∠VTC have no common vertex.

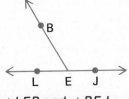

∠LEB and ∠BEJ are adjacent.

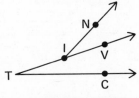

∠NIV and ∠VTC are not adjacent.

Definition of adjacent angles. ⟶

Adjacent angles are angles which { are coplanar, have a common vertex have a common side between them.

EXAMPLE 2   Which pairs of angles are adjacent?

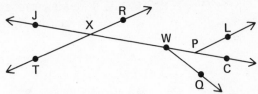

	Answers
∠JXR and ∠TXJ	Adjacent
∠LPC and ∠CWQ	Not adjacent
∠JXT and ∠RXC	Not adjacent

No common vertex. ⟶
No common side. ⟶

Vertical angles are formed by two intersecting lines.

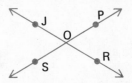

Two lines form two pairs of vertical angles.

$\angle JOS$ and $\angle POR$
$\angle JOP$ and $\angle SOR$ } are vertical angles.

Definition of vertical angles. ⟶ | Vertical angles are nonadjacent angles formed by two intersecting lines.

EXAMPLE 3   Complete the naming of a pair of vertical angles.

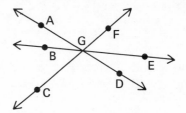

Vertical angles are not adjacent angles. $\angle AGB$ and $\underline{\angle EGD}$ $\angle FGD$ and $\underline{\angle AGC}$

ORAL EXERCISES

Classify each angle as acute, right, obtuse, or straight.

1.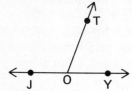
2.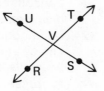
3.
4.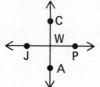

Complete the naming of a pair of adjacent angles.

Complete the naming of a pair of vertical angles.

5.
6.
7.
8.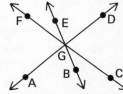

$\angle JOT$ and _____ $\angle RVS$ and _____ $\angle JWC$ and _____ $\angle FGE$ and _____

EXERCISES

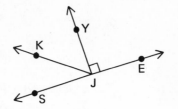

1. Name an acute angle.
   Find its measure.
3. Name a right angle.

2. Name an obtuse angle.
   Find its measure.
4. Name a straight angle.

Which are pairs of adjacent angles? If they are not, explain why not.

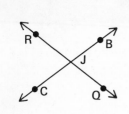 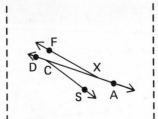 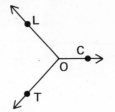 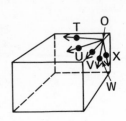

5. $\angle RJC$ and $\angle QJC$
6. $\angle CJQ$ and $\angle RJB$

7. $\angle FXD$ and $\angle XCS$
8. $\angle FXA$ and $\angle DCS$

9. $\angle LOC$ and $\angle LOT$
10. $\angle TOC$ and $\angle LOC$

11. $\angle TOV$ and $\angle VOX$
12. $\angle VOW$ and $\angle WOX$

Make drawings to illustrate each of the following.

13. Two adjacent angles.
15. Two angles with a common vertex but not a common side

14. Two vertical angles.
16. Two angles with a common side and vertex which are not adjacent

True or false? For each false statement draw a picture to show that it is false.

17. An acute angle and an obtuse angle cannot be adjacent.
19. Two obtuse angles cannot be adjacent.
21. If $\angle XOY$ and $\angle YOZ$ are adjacent, and if $m \angle XOY = 45$ and $m \angle YOZ = 60$, then $m \angle XOZ = 105$.

23. The common side (except the vertex) of any two adjacent angles is in the interior of the angle formed by their noncommon sides.

25. If the noncommon sides of two adjacent angles are collinear, then the sum of their measures is 180.

18. An acute angle and an obtuse angle cannot be vertical angles.
20. Any two intersecting lines form adjacent angles.
22. If two angles are adjacent, then the measure of the angle formed by their noncommon sides is the sum of their measures.

24. If the noncommon sides of two adjacent angles are collinear, and if one of the angles is acute, then the other angle is obtuse.

26. Two angles that are adjacent cannot also be vertical angles.

Supplements and Complements

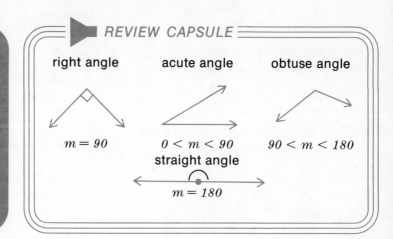

REVIEW CAPSULE

right angle   acute angle   obtuse angle

$m = 90$ $0 < m < 90$ $90 < m < 180$

straight angle

$m = 180$

$\angle ABC$ and $\angle DEF$ are supplementary.
$\angle RSX$ and $\angle XST$ are supplementary.

$m\angle ABC + m\angle DEF = 180$
$m\angle RSX + m\angle XST = 180$

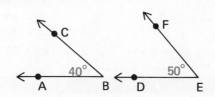

$\angle ABC$ is a supplement of $\angle DEF$.

$\angle RSX$ is a supplement of $\angle XST$.

Definition of *supplementary angles* $\longrightarrow$ | Two angles are *supplementary* if the sum of their measures is 180°.

$\angle ABC$ and $\angle DEF$ are complementary.
$\angle LQR$ and $\angle RQN$ are complementary.

$m\angle ABC + m\angle DEF = 90$
$m\angle LQR + m\angle RQN = 90$

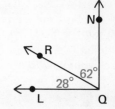

$\angle ABC$ is a complement of $\angle DEF$.

$\angle LQR$ is a complement of $\angle RQN$.

Definition of *complementary angles* $\longrightarrow$ | Two angles are complementary if the sum of their measures is 90°.

EXAMPLE 1   Find the measure of a complement of each angle. Find the measure of a supplement.

Measure of Angle	Measure of a Complement	Measure of a Supplement
30°	60°	150°
75°	15°	105°
23°	67°	157°
100°	none	80°

Sum of measures of complements is 90°.
Sum of measures of supplements is 180°.

EXAMPLE 2   Find the measure of an angle if its measure is 30° more than that of its complement.

The sum of measures is 90°. ————————→
The measure is 30° more than the measure of its complement.

$$\text{Let} \quad m = \text{measure of the angle}$$
$$90 - m = \text{measure of its complement}$$
$$m = (90 - m) + 30$$
$$2m = 120$$
$$m = 60 \qquad \textbf{Thus,} \text{ the angle measures } 60°.$$

EXAMPLE 3   Find the measure of an angle if its measure is twice that of its supplement.

The sum of measures is 180°. ————————→
The measure is twice the measure of its supplement.

Check your solution. ————————→

$$\text{Let} \quad m = \text{measure of the angle}$$
$$180 - m = \text{measure of its supplement}$$
$$m = 2(180 - m)$$
$$m = 360 - 2m$$
$$3m = 360$$
$$m = 120 \qquad \textbf{Thus,} \text{ the angle measures } 120°.$$

EXAMPLE 4   Find the measure of an angle if its measure is 22° less than three times the measure of its complement.

$3(90 - m) = 270 - 3m$ ————————→

Check your solution. ————————→

$$\text{Let} \quad m = \text{measure of the angle}$$
$$90 - m = \text{measure of its complement}$$
$$m = 3(90 - m) - 22$$
$$m = 270 - 3m - 22$$
$$4m = 248$$
$$m = 62 \qquad \textbf{Thus,} \text{ the angle measures } 62°.$$

ORAL EXERCISES

Which are measures of complementary angles? supplementary angles? neither?

1. 30° and 60°   **2.** 140° and 40°   **3.** 57° and 123°   **4.** 88° and 2°
5. 63° and 37°   **6.** 93° and 93°   **7.** 45° and 45°   **8.** 78° and 12°
9. 46° and 133°   **10.** 92° and 98°   **11.** 75° and 15°   **12.** 37° and 143°

Give the measure of a supplement.

13. 90°   **14.** 60°   **15.** 170°   **16.** 83°   **17.** 7°

Give the measure of a complement.

18. 45°   **19.** 30°   **20.** 87°   **21.** 56°   **22.** 39°

EXERCISES

PART A

Using a protractor, draw an angle which is a supplement of each given angle.

1. 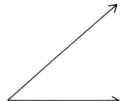   **2.**    **3.**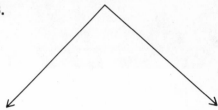

Using a protractor, draw an angle which is a complement of each given angle.

4.    **5.**    **6.**

Find the measure of the angle if its measure is as indicated.

7. 40° more than that of its complement
8. 70° more than that of its supplement.
9. 17° less than that of its supplement
10. 81° less than that of its complement
11. Twice that of its complement.
12. Four times that of its supplement.
13. Equal to that of its supplement.
14. Equal to that of its complement.

PART B

Find the measure of the angle.

15. The measure of its complement is one-third that of its supplement.

16. The measure of its supplement is 4 times that of its complement.

17. Its measure is 47° less than twice that of its complement.

18. Its measure is 63° more than twice that of its supplement.

19. Its measure is 22° less than three times that of its complement.

20. Its measure is 62° more than half that of its supplement.

21. The measure of its supplement is 47° more than twice that of its complement.

22. The measure of its supplement is 4° less than three times that of its complement.

Points, Lines, and Planes

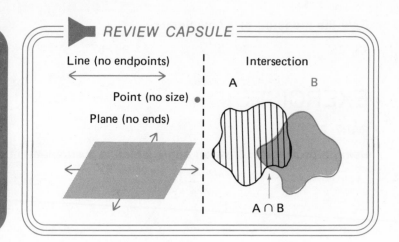

REVIEW CAPSULE

Line (no endpoints)

Point (no size)

Plane (no ends)

Intersection

A   B

A ∩ B

We accept this without proof. ⟶ Two points are contained in exactly one line.

Lines are straight. ⟶

$\longleftrightarrow$
P   Q   not

EXAMPLE 1 True or false? Two lines can intersect in two points. Give an argument to support your answer.

2 possibilities

True   or   False

Two lines intersect in two points.

If ℓ and m intersect in P and Q,

then P and Q are contained in ℓ and P and Q are contained in m.

Assuming that the statement is true leads to a contradiction. ⟶

Contradiction. (Two points are contained in exactly one line.)
Thus, the statement is false.

Some basic statements, called *postulates,* are not based on other statements. They are assumed to be true without any proof.

Postulate 1

For any two points, there is exactly one line containing them.

Other statements, called *theorems*, are based on an argument using accepted or proved ideas.

Example 1 is a proof of this theorem. ⌐

Theorem 2.1

Two lines intersect in at most one point.

EXAMPLE 2 How many different planes contain two given points? three given noncollinear points?

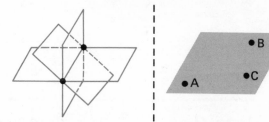

Many planes contain two given points.

Only one plane contains three noncollinear points.

Example 2 suggests another postulate.

Postulate 2

Three noncollinear points are contained in exactly one plane.

EXAMPLE 3 How many different planes contain a line and a point not on the line?

Draw a diagram. ───────→

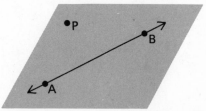

Line ℓ has at least two points. Name these A and B.

P is not on line ℓ. ───────→ P, A, and B are 3 noncollinear points.

Use Postulate 2. ───────→ So, P, A, and B are contained in exactly one plane.

Thus, only one plane contains a line and point not on it.

(See Exercise 19.)

Theorem	2.2	A line and a point not on the line are contained in exactly one plane.
Theorem	2.3	Two intersecting lines are contained in exactly one plane.

EXAMPLE 4 What are the possible intersections of a line and a plane?

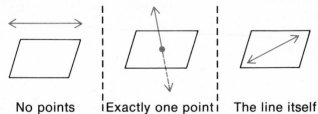

No points | Exactly one point | The line itself

Example 4 suggests these. ⌐

Postulate 3		If two points of a line are in a given plane, then the line itself is contained in the plane.
Theorem	2.4	If a line intersects a plane, but is not contained in the plane, then the intersection is exactly one point.

(Example 4 and Exercise 20)

EXAMPLE 5 What are the possible intersections of two planes?

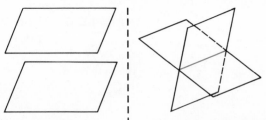

The planes do not intersect. | The planes intersect in a line.

Example 5 suggests this. ⌐

Postulate 4	If two planes intersect, then their intersection is exactly one line.

The constructions for copying a segment or angle suggest these postulates.

Postulate 5

Given a line and a point on it, there is a segment congruent to any given segment with the given point as endpoint.

Postulate 6

Given a line and a point on it, there is an angle congruent to any given angle with the given point as vertex.

Two other constructions suggest additional postulates.

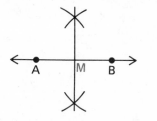

M is the midpoint of $\overline{AB}$. | $\overrightarrow{QS}$ bisects $\angle PQR$.

Postulate 7

Every segment has exactly one midpoint.

Postulate 8

Every angle, except a straight angle, has exactly one bisector.

EXAMPLE 6   How many different planes contain a given angle? Draw a picture to support your answer.

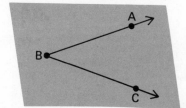

A, B, and *C* are 3 noncollinear points.

Use Postulate 2. ⟶ **Thus,** only one plane contains a given angle.

EXAMPLE 7   True or false? If a plane contains two points of a line, then it contains the segment joining them.

Use Postulate 3. ⟶ The plane contains the entire line and the segment is a subset.
Thus, the statement is true.

EXERCISES

Draw pictures to support your answers.

1. How many different lines are determined by four noncollinear points?
2. How many different planes are determined by four noncoplanar points?
3. Is it possible for exactly one line to contain three given points?
4. Is it possible for exactly two lines to be determined by three points?
5. Is it possible for more than one plane to contain three given points?
6. Is it possible for two planes to intersect in exactly one point?
7. Is it possible for a line and a plane to intersect in exactly two points?
8. Is it possible for three points not to be coplanar?
9. Is it possible for a curve to intersect a plane in exactly two points?
10. Is it possible for two planes to intersect in exactly two points?

True or false?

11. Any four points are coplanar.
12. No four points are coplanar.
13. Any three points are collinear.
14. No three points are collinear.
15. The intersection of a line and a plane can be the empty set.
16. The intersection of a plane and space can be the empty set.
17. Any two lines are contained in exactly one plane.
18. Any two points are contained in exactly one line.

PART B

19. Using Postulate 2, give an argument to prove Theorem 2.3.
20. Using Postulate 3, give an argument to prove Theorem 2.4.

Algebra Review

OBJECTIVE

■ To evaluate expressions

Order of Operations
1. Find powers.
2. Do all multiplications and divisions.
3. Do all additions and subtractions.

EXAMPLE Evaluate $x^2 - 2x^3 + 5$ if $x = -2$.
$$(-2)^2 - 2(-2)^3 + 5$$
$$4 - 2(-8) + 5 = 4 + 16 + 5, \text{ or } 25$$

Evaluate.

1. $x^2 + x - 5$ if $x = 3$
2. $3x^2 - 6x + 7$ if $x = -3$
3. $6x^3 + 5x^2 - 3x + 2$ if $x = 1$
4. $(x - 5)^2 + 3$ if $x = 7$
5. $x(x + 1) + x^3 - 2$ if $x = 3$
6. $2(x + 3)^2 + (5 - x)$ if $x = -5$

Geodesic Domes

The buildings shown here are examples of *geodesic domes.* These domes have many structural advantages. They can be made of polyester fiber, glass, aluminum, weather-proofed cardboard, plastic or even bamboo.

Such domes are structurally unlimited in size. They need no obstructing columns to hold them up and require less structural material to cover more space than any other building devised.

Astrodome in Houston, Texas

The Climatron, in St. Louis, Missouri, is a house of botanical wonders. Fluctuating air currents inside the dome permit plants from all over the world to be grown here.

Inventor of the Geodesic Dome

R. Buckminster Fuller, posing with his *dymaxion globe.*

Richard Buckminster Fuller, who is often called the *first poet of technology,* is the inventor of the geodesic dome. Fuller is an American and was born in 1899. He has devoted his life to the search for a *geometry of energy.* He developed the geodesic dome by experimenting with spheres as models of energy fields. In his sphere-shaped domes, the weight applied at any point is transmitted widely throughout the structure, giving a phenomenal strength-to-weight ratio.

Fuller designed the U.S. exhibit for the World's Fair in Canda. His geodesic dome became a symbol of Expo '67. Although he is most known for his globes, Fuller also designed the *dymaxion car,* a three-wheeled car which can turn in circles.

Simple Geometric Proofs

OBJECTIVES
- To draw conclusions from given information
- To prove simple theorems using properties of algebra

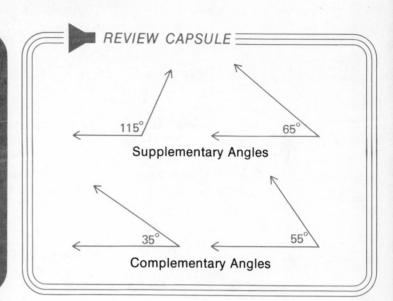

115°   65°

Supplementary Angles

35°   55°

Complementary Angles

$\angle ABC \cong \angle DEF$ means $m\angle ABC = m\angle DEF$. ⟶

To show that angles are congruent, show that their measures are equal.

EXAMPLE 1   Show that $\angle B \cong \angle E$.

The angle measures are equal. ⟶

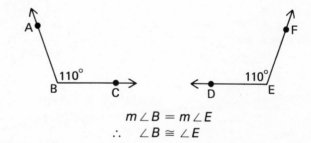

Angles can be named by their vertex point.
∴ is read therefore. ⟶

$m\angle B = m\angle E$
∴ $\angle B \cong \angle E$

EXAMPLE 2   If $\overrightarrow{OP}$ bisects $\angle AOB$, show that $m\angle AOP = m\angle POB$.

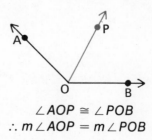

A bisector forms two congruent angles.
Use the definition of angle bisector. ⟶

$\angle AOP \cong \angle POB$
∴ $m\angle AOP = m\angle POB$

SUMMARY OF BASIC ALGEBRAIC PROPERTIES

Property	Statement	Algebraic Example	Geometric Application
Reflexive	$a = a$	$2 = 2$	$\angle XYZ \cong \angle XYZ$
Symmetric	If $a = b$, then $b = a$.	If $3 = 2 + 1$, then $2 + 1 = 3$	If $\angle XYZ \cong \angle ABC$, then $\angle ABC \cong \angle XYZ$.
Transitive	If $a = b$ and $b = c$, then $a = c$.	If $2x + 3 = y$ and $y = 5x - 4$, then $2x + 3 = 5x - 4$.	If $\overline{AC} \cong \overline{BD}$ and $\overline{BD} \cong \overline{EF}$, then $\overline{AC} \cong \overline{EF}$.
Substitution	If $a = b$, then b can be substituted for a.	If $5 = 4 + 1$, then $9 + ⑤ = 9 + (④ + ①)$.	If $AC = BD$, then $TF + \widehat{AC} = TF + \widehat{BD}$.

Algebraic properties can be used in geometric proofs.

EXAMPLE 3 Given: $m\angle A = m\angle B$ and $m\angle B = m\angle C$
Prove: $m\angle A = m\angle C$

This format is usually used in geometric proofs.

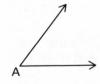

Proof

The two given statements lead to the conclusion in step 3.

Statements	Reasons
1. $m\angle A = m\angle B$	1. Given
2. $m\angle B = m\angle C$	2. Given
3. $\therefore m\angle A = m\angle C$	3. Transitive property

EXAMPLE 4 Given: $m\angle R = 47$, $m\angle N = 47$
Prove: $\angle R \cong \angle N$

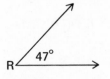 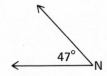

Proof

Reasons are given for every step in the proof.

Statements	Reasons
1. $m\angle R = 47$	1. Given
2. $m\angle N = 47$	2. Given
3. $m\angle R = m\angle N$	3. Substitution property
4. $\therefore \angle R \cong \angle N$	4. Definition of $\cong$ angles

SUMMARY OF BASIC PROPERTIES FOR EQUATIONS

Property	Statement	Example
Addition property	If $a = b$, then $a + c = b + c$.	If $x = 5$, then $x + 2 = 5 + 2$.
Subtraction property	If $a = b$, then $a - c = b - c$.	If $AC = 9$, then $AC - 3 = 9 - 3$.
Multiplication property	If $a = b$, then $ac = bc$.	If $m \angle B = 20$, then $\frac{1}{2} m \angle B = \frac{1}{2} \cdot 20$
Division property	If $a = b$, then $\frac{a}{c} = \frac{b}{c}$, $(c \neq 0)$.	If $7x = 21$, then $x = 3$.

Basic properties of equations can also be used in geometric proofs.

EXAMPLE 5 Given: $m \angle AOB + m \angle BOC = m \angle COD + m \angle BOC$
Prove: $\angle AOB \cong \angle COD$

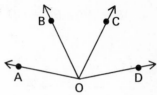

The colored arrows help show how statements follow from other statements.

Proof

Statements	Reasons
1. $m \angle AOB + m \angle BOC = m \angle COD + m \angle BOC$	**1.** Given
2. $m \angle AOB = m \angle COD$	**2.** Subtraction property
3. $\therefore \angle AOB \cong \angle COD$	**3.** Definition of congruent angles

Subtract $m \angle BOC$.

EXAMPLE 6 $\angle C \cong \angle D$ and $\angle C$ and $\angle D$ are supplements. What conclusion can you draw?

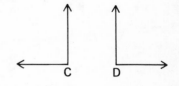

$\angle C \cong \angle D$ → $m \angle C = m \angle D$
Def. of supplementary $\angle$'s → $m \angle C + m \angle D = 180$
$m \angle C + m \angle D = m \angle C + m \angle C$ → So, $2m \angle C = 180$

Thus, $m \angle C = m \angle D = 90$.

EXAMPLE 7 Draw a diagram based on the given information.

Use only the given information. Mark the diagram.

Given: $\overrightarrow{BD}$ bisects $\angle ABC$.
   $m \angle ABD = 30$
Prove: $m \angle DBC = 30$

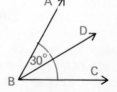

EXERCISES

PART A

What conclusions can you draw based on the given information? What are the reasons for your conclusions?

1. $\overrightarrow{UT}$ bisects $\angle DUB$.

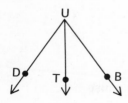

2. B is in the interior of $\angle AOC$. $\angle AOB \cong \angle BOC$.

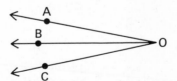

3. $\angle MON \cong \angle NOP$, $\angle NOP \cong \angle POQ$.

4. $AB + BC = BC + CD$

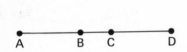

5. $\angle X \cong \angle Y$, $\angle X$ and $\angle Y$ are complements.

6. $m\angle XOY + m\angle YOZ = m\angle ZOW + m\angle YOZ$

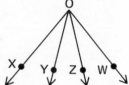

Write a proof. (Use the pattern shown in this lesson.)

7. Given: $m\angle XYZ = m\angle ABC$, $m\angle ABC = m\angle GHJ$
Prove: $\angle XYZ \cong \angle GHJ$

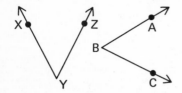

8. Given: $m\angle A = 88$, $m\angle B = 88$
Prove: $m\angle A = m\angle B$

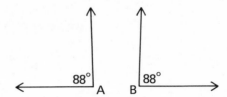

PART B

Draw a diagram. Then write a proof.

9. Given: $m\angle DEF = 113$,
$m\angle QRS = 113$
Prove: $\angle DEF \cong \angle QRS$

10. Given: $m\angle A + m\angle B = m\angle C + m\angle B$
Prove: $\angle A \cong \angle C$

11. Given: $m\angle T + m\angle M = 175$, $m\angle L + m\angle M = 175$
Prove: $m\angle T = m\angle L$

12. Given: $m\angle YVW + m\angle RST = 57$, $m\angle LMN + m\angle RST = 57$
Prove: $\angle YVW \cong \angle LMN$

13. Given: $m\angle O - m\angle Q = 21$, $m\angle P - m\angle Q = 21$
Prove: $\angle O \cong \angle P$

14. Given: $m\angle H = 40$, $m\angle N = 2(m\angle H)$, $m\angle O = 80$
Prove: $m\angle N = m\angle O$

Classifying Angles

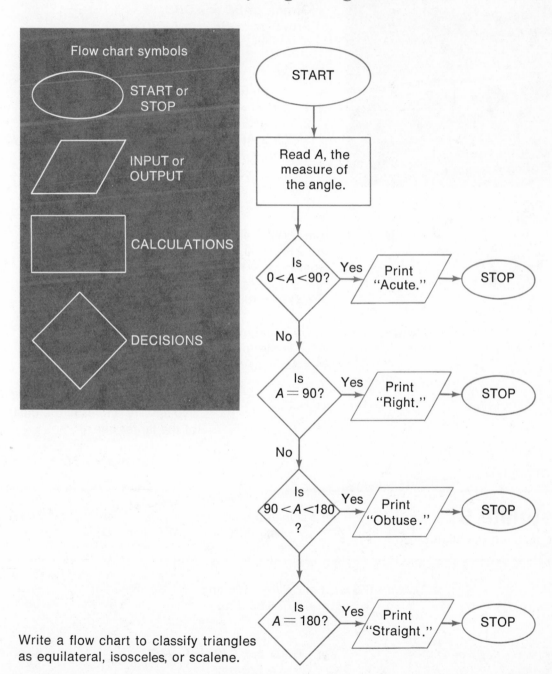

Flow chart symbols

START or STOP

INPUT or OUTPUT

CALCULATIONS

DECISIONS

START

Read A, the measure of the angle.

Is $0 < A < 90$? — Yes → Print "Acute." → STOP

No ↓

Is $A = 90$? — Yes → Print "Right." → STOP

No ↓

Is $90 < A < 180$? — Yes → Print "Obtuse." → STOP

↓

Is $A = 180$? — Yes → Print "Straight." → STOP

Write a flow chart to classify triangles as equilateral, isosceles, or scalene.

Measures of Segments and Angles

OBJECTIVES
- To apply the angle addition postulate
- To apply the segment addition postulate

▶ REVIEW CAPSULE

Given: $\angle ABE \cong \angle CBD$
Prove: $m\angle ABE + m\angle EBD = m\angle CBD + m\angle EBD$.

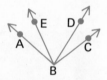

Proof

Statements	Reasons
1. $\angle ABE \cong \angle CBD$	1. Given
2. $m\angle ABE = m\angle CBD$	2. Def. of congruence
3. $\therefore m\angle ABE + m\angle EBD = m\angle CBD + m\angle EBD$	3. Addition property of equations

EXAMPLE 1 If $m\angle XYZ = 40$ and $m\angle ZYW = 60$, what is $m\angle XYW$?

$m\angle XYW = 100$

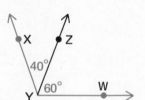

EXAMPLE 2 $\overrightarrow{BD}$ is in the interior of $\angle ABC$.
What is the relationship between the measures of $\angle ABC$, $\angle ABD$, and $\angle DBC$?

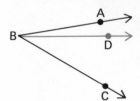

The sum of the measures of the two smaller angles is the measure of the larger one.

$$m\angle ABC = m\angle ABD + m\angle DBC.$$

Postulate 9
(Angle addition postulate)

If $\overrightarrow{BD}$ is in the interior of $\angle ABC$, then
$$m\angle ABC = m\angle ABD + m\angle DBC.$$

EXAMPLE 3 If $m\angle RJS = 126$ and $m\angle RJT = 86$, find $m\angle TJS$.

$m\angle RJS = m\angle RJT + m\angle TJS$

$m\angle TJS = m\angle RJS - m\angle RJT$
$= 126 - 86$
$= 40$

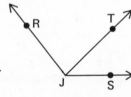

Angles are often named with a single letter or number.

EXAMPLE 4

Write other names for
∠1 and ∠3.

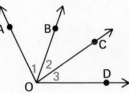

Do not use ∠O since both angles have
the same vertex.

∠1   ∠AOB
∠3   ∠COD

EXAMPLE 5

Given: $m\angle 1 = m\angle 3$
Prove: $\angle QRT \cong \angle WRS$

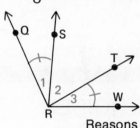

Analysis:
Add $m\angle 2$ to $m\angle 1$ to get $m\angle QRT$.
Add $m\angle 2$ to $m\angle 3$ to get $m\angle WRS$.

Proof

Statements	Reasons
1. $m\angle 1 = m\angle 3$	1. Given
2. $m\angle 1 + m\angle 2 = m\angle 3 + m\angle 2$	2. Addition property of equations
3. $m\angle QRT = m\angle 1 + m\angle 2$	3. Angle addition postulate
4. $m\angle WRS = m\angle 2 + m\angle 3$	4. Angle addition postulate
5. $m\angle QRT = m\angle WRS$	5. Substitution
6. $\therefore \angle QRT \cong \angle WRS$	6. Definition of congruent angles

EXAMPLE 6

If $AB = 5$ cm and
$BC = 7$ cm, find AC.

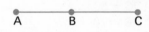

The sum of the measures of the
smaller segments is the measure of the
larger segment.

$$AC = AB + BC$$
$$= 5 + 7$$
$$= 12$$

Thus, $AC = 12$ cm.

Postulate 10
(Segment addition postulate)

If point P is between points
A and B, then $AB = AP + PB$.

EXAMPLE 7

If $AB = 6$ in., $BC = 8$ in.,
and $CD = AB$, find BD.

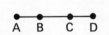

Segment addition postulate ⟶
Substitution property ⟶

$$BD = BC + CD$$
$$= BC + AB$$
$$= 8 + 6$$
$$= 14$$

Thus, $BD = 14$ in.

EXAMPLE 8 Given: $AB = CD$
Prove: $AC = BD$

Proof

Statements	Reasons
1. $AB = CD$	**1.** Given
2. $AB + BC = CD + BC$	**2.** Addition property for equations
3. $AC = AB + BC$	**3.** Segment addition postulate
4. $BD = BC + CD$	**4.** Segment addition postulate
5. $\therefore AC = BD$	**5.** Substitution property

EXERCISES

PART A

Give another name for each angle.

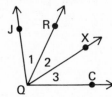

1. $\angle 1$
2. $\angle 2$
3. $\angle 3$

Find the missing segment lengths.

4. $RJ = 8$ cm, $JQ = 9$ cm, $RQ = $?
5. $RQ = 19$ cm, $JQ = 8$ cm, $RJ = $?

$\overrightarrow{OC}$ **is in the interior of** $\angle AOB$. **Find the missing measure.**

6. $m\angle AOC = 50$,
$m\angle COB = 70$.
Find $m\angle AOB$.

7. $m\angle AOB = 110$,
$m\angle COB = 40$.
Find $m\angle AOC$.

8. $m\angle AOC = 10$,
$m\angle AOB = 90$.
Find $m\angle COB$.

9. $m\angle x = 55$, $m\angle y = 20$,
$m\angle z = m\angle x$.
Find $m\angle BOJ$.

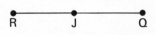

10. $m\angle x = m\angle z$, $m\angle BOJ = 78$.
Find $m\angle ROH$.

11. $TJ = 4$ cm, $JW = 7$ cm,
$WN = TJ$.
Find JN.

12. $TJ = WN$, $TW = 9$ in.
Find JN.

13. Given: $m\angle 1 = m\angle 3$
Prove: $m\angle NCX = m\angle TCD$

14. Given: $m\angle NCX = m\angle TCD$
Prove: $m\angle 1 = m\angle 3$

15. Given: $RP = EY$
Prove: $RE = PY$

16. Given: $RE = PY$
Prove: $RP = EY$

PART B

17. Given: $\angle 1 \cong \angle 3$
Prove: $\angle LVC \cong \angle RVQ$

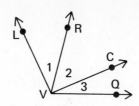

18. Given: $\angle LVC \cong \angle RVQ$
Prove: $\angle 1 \cong \angle 3$

19. Given: $\overline{BR} \cong \overline{CS}$, $\overline{RV} \cong \overline{SV}$
Prove: $\overline{BV} \cong \overline{CV}$

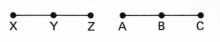

20. Given: $\overline{BV} \cong \overline{CV}$, $\overline{BR} \cong \overline{CS}$
Prove: $\overline{RV} \cong \overline{SV}$

21. Given: $\overline{XZ} \cong \overline{AC}$
$XY = \frac{1}{2}XZ$, $AB = \frac{1}{2}AC$
Prove: $\overline{XY} \cong \overline{AB}$

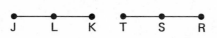

22. Given: $\overline{XY} \cong \overline{AB}$
$XY = \frac{1}{2}XZ$, $AB = \frac{1}{2}AC$
Prove: $\overline{XZ} \cong \overline{AC}$

PART C

23. Given: L bisects $\overline{JK}$, S
bisects $\overline{TR}$, $\overline{JK} \cong \overline{TR}$.
Prove: $\overline{JL} \cong \overline{SR}$

24. Given: $JL = LK$, $JL = TS$,
$JK = TR$
Prove: S bisects $\overline{TR}$.

Algebra Review

The Distributive Property
$$a(b + c) = ab + ac$$

$$3x(x^2 + 5) = 3x^3 + 15x$$

EXAMPLE   Multiply $(2x + 3)(x - 2)$.

Two possible ways

$(2x + 3)(x - 2)$
$(2x + 3)x + (2x + 3)(-2)$
$2x^2 + 3x - 4x - 6$
$2x^2 - x - 6$

or

$$
\begin{array}{r}
2x + 3 \\
x - 2 \\
\hline
2x^2 + 3x \\
-4x - 6 \\
\hline
2x^2 - x - 6
\end{array}
$$

Multiply.

1. $3(x + y)$
2. $5x(2x^2 + 3x)$
3. $4x^2(2x^3 - 5y)$
4. $(3x - 2y)(-5)$
5. $(7x^2 - 4x)(-3x^3)$
6. $(2x^3 + 4xy)(2xy^2)$
7. $(2x + 1)(x - 3)$
8. $(2x - 5)(x - 4)$
9. $(3x - 5)(2x + 3)$
10. $(3x + 4)(3x + 4)$
11. $(5x + 2y)(5x + 2y)$
12. $(6x + 3y^2)(6x + 3y^2)$
13. $(a - b)(a + b)$
14. $(3x - 5)(3x + 5)$
15. $(2a^2 - 3b)(2a^2 + 3b)$

Perpendiculars

OBJECTIVES
- To identify perpendicular lines, rays, and segments
- To prove statements about perpendiculars
- To construct perpendiculars

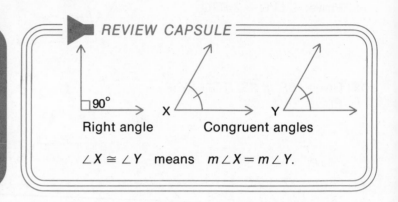

REVIEW CAPSULE

90°

Right angle

Congruent angles

$\angle X \cong \angle Y$ means $m\angle X = m\angle Y$.

$\overleftrightarrow{AB} \perp \overleftrightarrow{XY}$ means $\overleftrightarrow{AB}$ is perpendicular to $\overleftrightarrow{XY}$.

$\overleftrightarrow{AB}$ is perpendicular to $\overleftrightarrow{XY}$.

$$\overleftrightarrow{AB} \perp \overleftrightarrow{XY}$$

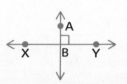

Definition of *perpendicular lines* ⟶

Two lines are *perpendicular* if they intersect to form a right angle.

EXAMPLE 1 Using a protractor, find which pairs of lines are perpendicular.

$m\angle CEB = 90$
$m\angle HJG = 100$
$m\angle NOL = 95$

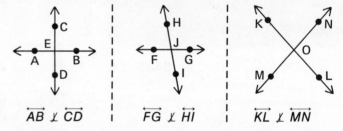

$\cancel{\perp}$ means is not perpendicular to. ⟶

$\overleftrightarrow{AB} \cancel{\perp} \overleftrightarrow{CD}$ | $\overleftrightarrow{FG} \cancel{\perp} \overleftrightarrow{HI}$ | $\overleftrightarrow{KL} \cancel{\perp} \overleftrightarrow{MN}$

Segments and rays are perpendicular if they are subsets of perpendicular lines.

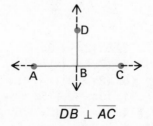

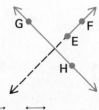

The lines containing the segments or rays are $\perp$.

$\overline{DB} \perp \overline{AC}$

$\overrightarrow{EF} \perp \overleftrightarrow{GH}$

EXAMPLE 2 Which of the following appear to be perpendicular?

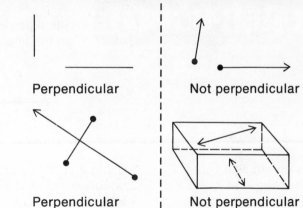

Perpendicular   Not perpendicular

⊥ lines must intersect. ⟶

Perpendicular   Not perpendicular

Methods for constructing perpendicular lines provide ways to construct right angles.

construction

A line perpendicular to a given line through a point not on the line

•P

Given
Line ℓ and point P not on ℓ
CONSTRUCT
$\overleftrightarrow{PQ} \perp \ell$

$l \longleftrightarrow$

Draw an arc with center P intersecting ℓ at X and Y.

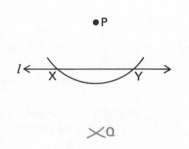

Using X and Y as centers, and the same radius, draw arcs intersecting at Q.

Draw $\overleftrightarrow{PQ}$.

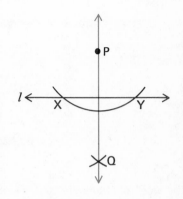

Conclusion: $\overleftrightarrow{PQ} \perp \ell$

A line perpendicular to a given line through a point on the line

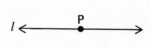

Given
Line ℓ and point P on ℓ
CONSTRUCT
$\overleftrightarrow{QP} \perp \ell$

Draw an arc with center P intersecting ℓ at X and Y.

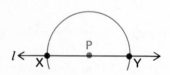

Using X and Y as centers, and congruent radii, draw arcs intersecting at Q.

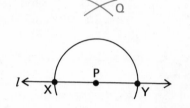

Draw $\overleftrightarrow{QP}$.

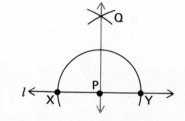

Conclusion: $\overleftrightarrow{QP} \perp \ell$

Postulate 11

Given a point and a line in a plane, there is exactly one line through the point perpendicular to the given line.

EXAMPLE 3 Construct a 45° angle.

Construct $\overleftrightarrow{TP} \perp \overrightarrow{PQ}$.
$m \angle TPQ = 90$
Bisect $\angle TPQ$.

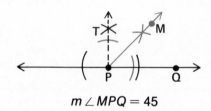

$m \angle MPQ = 45$

EXAMPLE 4 Using a protractor, find
$m \angle AOB + m \angle BOC + m \angle COD$.

The sides of straight $\angle AOD$ are on $\overleftrightarrow{AD}$.

$$m \angle AOB + m \angle BOC + m \angle COD$$
$$\downarrow \qquad\quad \downarrow \qquad\quad \downarrow$$
$$90 \quad + \quad 30 \quad + \quad 60$$

Thus, $m \angle AOB + m \angle BOC + m \angle COD = 180$.

Postulate 12

The sum of the measures of the angles with the same vertex on one side of a line is 180°.

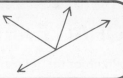

EXAMPLE 5

If $m\angle RSV = 49$ and $m\angle VSW = 70$, find $m\angle WST$.

$m\angle RSV + m\angle VSW + m\angle WST = 180$

$$m\angle WST = 180 - (49 + 70)$$
$$= 180 - 119$$
$$= 61$$

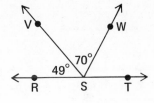

EXAMPLE 6

$\angle XTC \cong \angle RTC$. What conclusion would you draw about $\angle XTC$?

Since $m\angle XTC = m\angle RTC$ and $m\angle XTC + m\angle RTC = 180$,
$$m\angle XTC = 90.$$
$\therefore \angle XTC$ is a right angle.

Example 6 suggests Theorem 2.5.

Theorem 2.5

If two lines form congruent adjacent angles, then they are perpendicular.

ANALYSIS

Lines are perpendicular if a right angle (90°) is formed.

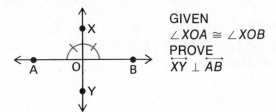

GIVEN
$\angle XOA \cong \angle XOB$
PROVE
$\overleftrightarrow{XY} \perp \overleftrightarrow{AB}$

PROOF

STATEMENTS	REASONS
1. $\angle XOA \cong \angle XOB$	1. Given
2. $m\angle XOA = m\angle XOB$	2. Definition of congruent angles
3. $m\angle XOA + m\angle XOB = 180$	3. Sum of measures of angles with the same vertex on one side of a line is 180°.
4. $2m\angle XOA = 180$	4. Substitution property
5. $m\angle XOA = 90$	5. Division property
6. $\angle XOA$ is a right angle	6. Definition of right angle
7. $\therefore \overleftrightarrow{XY} \perp \overleftrightarrow{AB}$	7. Definition of perpendicular lines

ORAL EXERCISES

Which of the following appear to be perpendicular lines, rays, or segments?

1.
2.
3.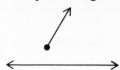
4.

5.
6.
7.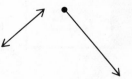
8.

EXERCISES

PART A

Use a protractor to determine which of the following are perpendicular.

1.
2.
3.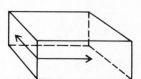
4.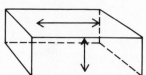

5. In the given figure, which pairs of rays are perpendicular?

6. Given: ∠DOC and ∠COB are complements.
Prove: $\overrightarrow{OD} \perp \overleftrightarrow{AB}$

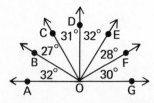

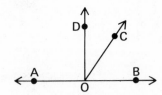

7. Draw a line and a point not on the line. Construct a perpendicular to the line through the point.

8. Draw a line. At a given point on the line construct a line perpendicular to the given line.

PART B

9. Construct a 135° angle.

10. Construct a $22\frac{1}{2}°$ angle.

11. Given: $\overleftrightarrow{TW} \perp \overleftrightarrow{XY}$ intersecting at R
Prove: $\angle TRX \cong \angle TRY$

12. Given: $\overleftrightarrow{TW} \perp \overleftrightarrow{XY}$ intersecting at R
Prove: $m\angle TRX + m\angle YRW = 180$

Theorems About Angles

REVIEW CAPSULE

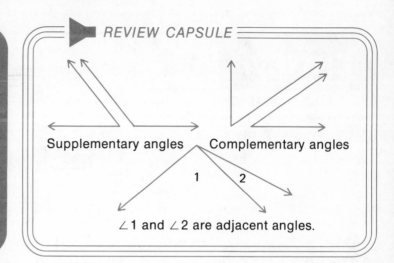

Supplementary angles   Complementary angles

∠1 and ∠2 are adjacent angles.

Theorem 2.6

Supplements of congruent angles are congruent.

ANALYSIS

Angles are congruent if their measures are equal.

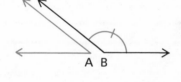

A B

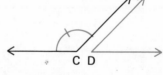

C D

GIVEN
∠A is a supplement of ∠B.
∠D is a supplement of ∠C.
∠B ≅ ∠C

PROVE
∠A ≅ ∠D

PROOF

STATEMENTS	REASONS
1. $m\angle A + m\angle B = 180$	1. Definition of supplements
2. $m\angle D + m\angle C = 180$	2. Definition of supplements
3. $m\angle A + m\angle B = m\angle D + m\angle C$	3. Substitution property
4. $\angle B \cong \angle C$	4. Given
5. $m\angle B = m\angle C$	5. Definition of congruent angles
6. $m\angle A = m\angle D$	6. Subtraction property for equations
7. ∴ $\angle A \cong \angle D$	7. Definition of congruent angles

A *corollary* of a theorem is a theorem whose proof requires only a few simple statements in addition to the proof of the original theorem.

Corollary

Supplements of the same angle are congruent.

Theorem 2.7

Complements of congruent angles are congruent.

ANALYSIS

Angles are congruent if they have the same measure.

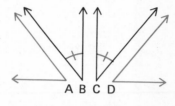

A B C D

GIVEN

∠A is a complement of ∠B.
∠D is a complement of ∠C.
∠B ≅ ∠C

PROVE

∠A ≅ ∠D

PROOF

STATEMENTS	REASONS
1. $m\angle A + m\angle B = 90$	1. Definition of complements
2. $m\angle D + m\angle C = 90$	2. Definition of complements
3. $m\angle A + m\angle B = m\angle D + m\angle C$	3. Substitution property
4. $\angle B \cong \angle C$	4. Given
5. $m\angle B = m\angle C$	5. Definition of congruent angles
6. $m\angle A = m\angle D$	6. Subtraction property for equations
7. $\therefore \angle A \cong \angle D$	7. Definition of congruent angles

Corollary

Complements of the same angle are congruent.

EXAMPLE 1

$m\angle AOB = 30$,
$m\angle BOC = 30$, $\overrightarrow{OB} \perp \overleftrightarrow{XY}$.
What conclusion can you draw about ∠XOA and ∠YOC ?

Complements of congruent angles are congruent. ⟶ ∠XOA ≅ ∠YOC

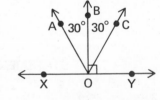

EXAMPLE 2

$m\angle NCJ = 70$. What conclusion can you draw about ∠XCN and ∠JCB ?

Sum of measures of angles with the same vertex on one side of a line is 180°. ⟶

$m\angle XCN = 110$
$m\angle JCB = 110$
$\therefore \angle XCN \cong \angle JCB$

∠XCN and ∠JCB are vertical angles.

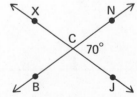

Example 2 suggests a theorem about vertical angles.

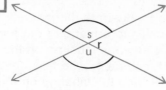

Theorem 2.8

Vertical angles are congruent.

ANALYSIS
Show that ∠s and ∠u are both supplements of ∠r. Use the corollary to Th. 2.6.

GIVEN
∠s and ∠u are vertical angles.
PROVE
∠s ≅ ∠u

PROOF

STATEMENTS

1. $m\angle s + m\angle r = 180$
   $m\angle u + m\angle r = 180$
2. ∠s and ∠r are supplements.
   ∠u and ∠r are supplements.
3. ∠s ≅ ∠u

REASONS

1. Sum of measures of angles with the same vertex on one side of a line is 180°.
2. Definition of supplements
3. Supplements of the same angle are congruent.

EXAMPLE 3 Which angles shown are congruent?

Vertical angles are congruent.

∠RHM ≅ ∠AHQ
∠RHQ ≅ ∠AHM

EXAMPLE 4
$m\angle CNS = 3x$,
$m\angle ZNK = 4x - 25$.
Find $m\angle CNS$.

Vertical angles are congruent. ⟶

$m\angle CNS = m\angle ZNK$
$3x = 4x - 25$
$-x = -25$
$x = 25$

$m\angle CNS = 3x$ ⟶ $3x = 75$

Thus, $m\angle CNS = 75$.

EXAMPLE 5 Draw a labeled diagram. State what is given and state what is to be proved.
The bisectors of two adjacent supplementary angles are perpendicular.

Draw a diagram.
Write what is given and what is to be proved in terms of the diagram.

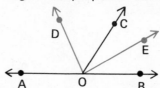

Given: $m\angle AOC + m\angle COB = 180$, $\overrightarrow{OD}$ bisects $\angle AOC$, $\overrightarrow{OE}$ bisects $\angle COB$.
Prove: $\overrightarrow{OD} \perp \overrightarrow{OE}$

To Prove a Theorem

1. Draw a diagram to illustrate the theorem. Label the diagram.
2. Determine the given information from the verbal statement.
   Write the GIVEN. Use the labeling on the diagram.
3. Determine what is to be proved from the verbal statement.
   Write the PROVE. Use the labeling on the diagram.
4. Outline a plan for the argument. (Analysis)
5. Give specific reasons for each step in the proof. Use
   a. definitions   **b.** postulates   **c.** theorems already proved.

ORAL EXERCISES

Complete each statement.

1.

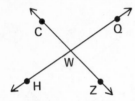

∠ *CWH* ≅ _____

2.

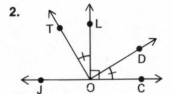

∠ *JOT* ≅ _____

3.

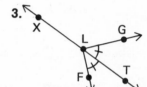

∠ *XLG* ≅ _____

4.

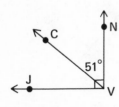

m ∠ *JVC* = _____

5.

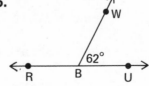

m ∠ *RBW* = _____

6.

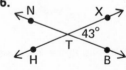

m ∠ *NTH* = _____

EXERCISES

PART A

Find the unknown angle measures.

1. $m \angle AOD = 8x$,
   $m \angle BOC = 6x + 30$.
   Find $m \angle AOD$.
3. $m \angle AOD = 3x$,
   $m \angle BOC = 2x + 10$.
   Find $m \angle AOD$.

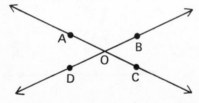

2. $m \angle AOB = 4x - 2$,
   $m \angle DOC = 3x + 6$.
   Find $m \angle AOB$.
4. $m \angle AOB = x + 30$,
   $m \angle DOC = 34 + 2x$.
   Find $m \angle DOC$.

58   THEOREMS ABOUT ANGLES

What conclusions can you draw about angles in each exercise?

5. Given: $\angle AOB \cong \angle COD$

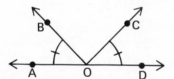

6. Given: $\angle x$ and $\angle y$ are complements, $\angle x$ and $\angle z$ are complements.

7. Given: $\angle 2 \cong \angle 3$

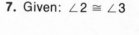

Give a complete proof.

8. Given: $\angle TOP \cong \angle TOQ$
Prove: $\angle POX \cong \angle QOX$

9. Given: $\angle 1 \cong \angle 4$
Prove: $\angle 2 \cong \angle 3$

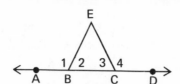

10. Given: $\angle 2$ and $\angle 4$ are supplements
Prove: $\angle 2 \cong \angle 3$

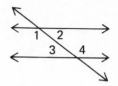

PART B

Draw a labeled diagram. State what is given, and state what is to be proved.

11. If two angles have congruent complementary angles, then they have congruent supplementary angles.

12. If two angles have congruent supplementary angles, then they have congruent complementary angles.

13. Given: $\angle CBE \cong \angle CDE$
Prove: $\angle ABF \cong \angle CDE$

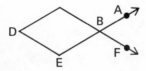

14. Given: $\angle CDE \cong \angle ABF$
Prove: $\angle CBA$ is a supplement of $\angle CDE$

15. Prove: If two angles are supplements and congruent, then each angle is a right angle.

16. Prove: If two lines are perpendicular, then they form congruent adjacent angles.

PART C

In each of the following, not enough information is given to prove the stated conclusion. One more condition must be given. State that condition and prove.

17. Given: $\angle DOC$ is a complement of $\angle BOC$.
Prove: $\angle AOB \cong \angle DOC$

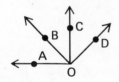

18. Given: $\overrightarrow{EB}$ bisects $\angle CED$.
Prove: $\angle EAC \cong \angle EAD$

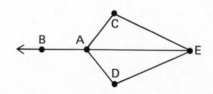

Dihedral Angles and Perpendiculars

OBJECTIVES

■ To describe and measure dihedral angles
■ To recognize perpendicular lines and planes in space

▶ *REVIEW CAPSULE*

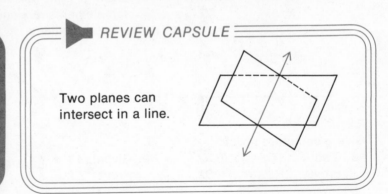

Two planes can intersect in a line.

Two lines intersect to form four *angles.*

Two planes intersect to form four *dihedral angles.*

Each dihedral angle has two faces and an edge.

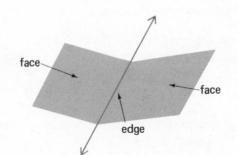

face

face

edge

Parts of a dihedral angle

Dihedral angles are named by a point in each face and by the edge.

The edge is a line.
The faces are half-planes.

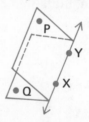

P

Y

X

Q

∠P − $\overleftrightarrow{XY}$ − Q

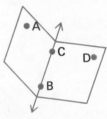

A

C   D

B

∠A − $\overleftrightarrow{BC}$ − D

EXAMPLE 1   List two common examples of objects that are models of dihedral angles.

A dihedral angle actually extends infinitely far.

1. Two adjacent walls of a room
2. The inside part of a cake after a slice has been cut out

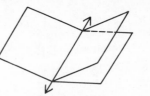

EXAMPLE 2   Draw a picture of two adjacent dihedral angles.

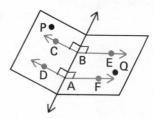

A dihedral angle is measured by its *plane angles*.

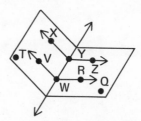

Two plane angles of dihedral angle
$P - \overleftrightarrow{AB} - Q$
$\overrightarrow{BC} \perp$ edge $\overleftrightarrow{AB}$ from B
$\overrightarrow{BE} \perp$ edge $\overleftrightarrow{AB}$ from B

$\angle CBE$ and $\angle DAF$ are plane angles.
The union of the two perpendicular rays from a point on the edge, one ray in each face, is a plane angle.

This can be proved. ——————————→ | **Any two plane angles of a dihedral angle are congruent.** |

EXAMPLE 3   If $\angle XYZ$ is a plane angle of $\angle T - \overleftrightarrow{YW} - Q$, and if $m\angle XYZ = 135$, what is $m\angle T - \overleftrightarrow{YW} - Q$?

Any two plane angles of a dihedral angle are congruent. ——————————→

$$m\angle T - \overleftrightarrow{YW} - Q = 135$$

The measure of a dihedral angle is the measure of any one of its plane angles.

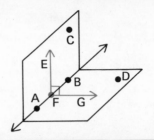

$$m \angle EFG = 90$$
$$m \angle C - \overleftrightarrow{AB} - D = 90$$

Definition of perpendicular planes ——→

Perpendicular planes are planes whose dihedral angle is a right angle.

EXAMPLE 4   If plane $p \perp$ plane q, what is $m \angle ABC$?

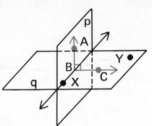

The dihedral angle of perpendicular planes is a right angle. ——→

$$m \angle A - \overleftrightarrow{BX} - Y = 90$$
$\angle ABC$ is a plane angle.

The measure of the dihedral $\angle$ is the meas. of a plane $\angle$. ——→

Thus, $m \angle ABC = 90$.

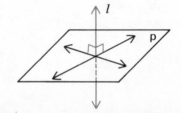

line $\ell \perp$ plane p ——————→

Definition of a line perpendicular to a plane ——————————→

A line perpendicular to a plane is a line which is perpendicular to all lines in the plane which intersect it.

EXERCISES

PART A

1. If $m \angle JBC = 78$, what is $m \angle T - \overrightarrow{RW} - 0$?

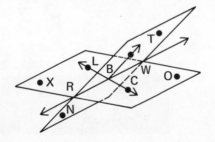

2. If $m \angle X - \overleftrightarrow{RW} - T = 141$, what is $m \angle LBJ$?

3. If $m \angle JBC = 76$, what is $m \angle T - \overleftrightarrow{RW} - X$?

4. If $m \angle X - \overleftrightarrow{RW} - T = 138$, what is $m \angle JBC$?

PART B

Planes _p_ and _q_ are perpendicular intersecting in $\overleftrightarrow{AB}$. ∠ _COE_ is a plane angle of ∠ _C_ — $\overleftrightarrow{AB}$ — _E_. _m_∠ _FOE_ = 40. Give the measure of each angle, if possible. If not enough information is given, write "too little information."

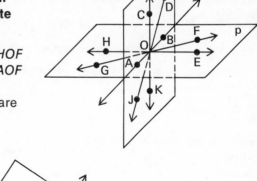

5. ∠ _COE_   6. ∠ _COF_   7. ∠ _BOF_   8. ∠ _HOF_

9. ∠ _DOE_   10. ∠ _COB_   11. ∠ _DOF_   12. ∠ _AOF_

13. List three common examples of objects that are models of a line perpendicular to a plane.

True or false?

14. All plane angles of a given dihedral angle are congruent.
15. All angles with vertices on the edge of a dihedral angle and sides in its faces are congruent.
16. If a plane is perpendicular to a given plane, then it is perpendicular to every line of the second plane.

PART C

17. Draw a labeled diagram, state what is given, and state what is to be proved for the statement in Exercise 16.

18. Prove: If a line is perpendicular to a plane, then every plane that contains the line is also perpendicular to the given plane.

Algebra Review

$$-2x^2 + 4x^3 + 3x^2 - x$$

Like terms
To simplify polynomials, combine like terms.

EXAMPLE   Simplify $(2x^2 + 3x^4 - x^3) - (7x^2 + 3x - x^4)$.

$(2x^2 + 3x^4 - x^3) - 1(7x^2 + 3x - x^4)$

$2x^2 + 3x^4 - x^3 - 7x^2 - 3x + x^4$

$4x^4 - x^3 - 5x^2 - 3x$

Simplify.

1. $4x^2 + x^4 - 2) - (x^4 + 4x^2 - 7)$
2. $(6x + 4x^3 - 3) - (x^3 - 4x^2 + x)$
3. $(4 + x^2 - 5x^3) + (3x^3 - 4x^2 + 2)$
4. $(x + x^3 + x^5) - (2 + x^2 - x^4)$
5. $(4x^4 + 2x^2 - x) - (2x^4 + 2x^2 + x)$
6. $(3x^4 + 2x + 5) - (x^4 + 3x^2 - 2x)$

Chapter Two Review

Classify each angle as straight, acute, right, or obtuse. [p. 27]

1. $m\angle XTN = 38$

2. $m\angle RJV = 132$

3. $m\angle CVP = 180$

Classify each pair of angles as complementary, supplementary, or neither. [p. 31]

4. $m\angle JTP = 43$
$m\angle CTL = 57$

5. $m\angle LCD = 123$
$m\angle TNQ = 57$

6. $m\angle XYZ = 8$
$m\angle RST = 82$

True or false? [p. 34]

7. Two lines can intersect in two points.

8. There is exactly one plane which contains two given points.

9. Any line which intersects a plane at more than one point is contained in the plane.

10. Any three points are contained in a single line.

11. Given: $\angle RWS \cong \angle SWT$,
$\angle SWT \cong \angle TWU$
Prove: $\angle RWS \cong \angle TWU$ [p. 41]

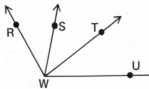

12. Given: $\angle RWS \cong \angle TWU$
Prove: $\angle RWT \cong \angle SWU$
[p. 41]

13. Given: $LC = PQ$
Prove: $LC + CP = PQ + CP$
[p. 46]

14. Given: $\overline{LP} \cong \overline{CQ}$
Prove: $\overline{LC} \cong \overline{PQ}$ [p. 46]

15. Find the measure of an angle if its measure is 40° more than that of a supplement. [p. 31]

16. Find the measure of an angle if its measure is 30° less than three times the measure of a complement. [p. 31]

Find the missing measures. [p. 50]

17. $m\angle AOB = 90$, $m\angle x = 50$
$\angle y \cong \angle w$.
Find $m\angle w$.

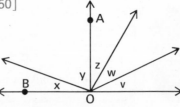

18. $m\angle x = 20$, $m\angle z = 30$,
$m\angle w = 35$, $\overrightarrow{OA} \perp \overrightarrow{BO}$.
Find $m\angle v$.

Draw a labeled diagram. State what is given, and state what is to be proved.

19. Two intersecting lines are contained in exactly one plane. [p. 34].

20. If two lines form congruent adjacent angles, then they are perpendicular.
[p. 50]

21. Construct a line perpendicular to a given line from a point not on it. [p. 50]

22. Construct an angle with a measure of $22\frac{1}{2}°$. [p. 50]

23. Draw a 3-in. segment. Construct a line which is perpendicular to the segment and bisects it.
[p. 50]

Chapter Two Test

Classify each angle as straight, acute, right, or obtuse.

1. $m \angle ABC = 140$

2. $m \angle DEF = 79$

3. $m \angle XYZ = 180$

Classify each pair of angles as complementary, supplementary, or neither.

4. $m \angle ABC = 60$
$m \angle PQR = 30$

5. $m \angle KLM = 120$
$m \angle MLN = 30$

6. $m \angle BCD = 178$
$m \angle JKL = 2$

True or false?

7. If two lines intersect, then they intersect in exactly one point.

9. Three points may be contained in more than one plane.

11. If two angles are complements, then they are also adjacent.

8. If two planes intersect, then they intersect in exactly one point.

10. Two angles can be both supplements and complements.

12. Complements of congruent angles are congruent.

13. Given: $\overline{CS} \cong \overline{NT}$
Prove: $\overline{CN} \cong \overline{ST}$

14. Given: $\angle ABE \cong \angle DCF$
Prove: $\angle CBE \cong \angle BCF$

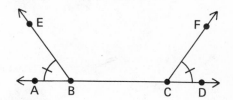

15. Find the measure of an angle if its measure is 60° more than that of a supplement.

16. Find the measure of an angle if its measure is 30° less than twice the measure of a complement.

Find the missing measures.

17. $m \angle x = 38$, $m \angle y = 63$,
$\angle x \cong \angle z$.
Find $m \angle z$.

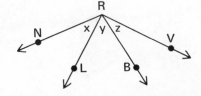

18. $m \angle y = 72$, $m \angle z = 29$,
$\angle x \cong \angle z$.
Find $m \angle NRB$.

Draw a labeled diagram, state what is given, and state what is to be proved.

19. If two non-common sides of adjacent angles are perpendicular, then the angles are complements.

21. Construct an angle with a measure of 45°.

20. Two right angles are both supplementary and congruent.

Mathematics in Reclamation

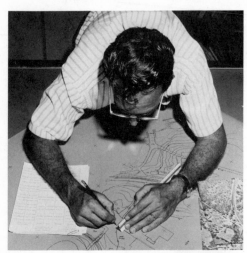

Shown here is an engineer from the Bureau of Reclamation's Central Valley Project in California. He is compiling a topographic map by photogrammetry.

A hydraulic engineer (left) and a hydrologic technician are checking the computer plot on a ground-water map.

Parallel Lines and Skew Lines

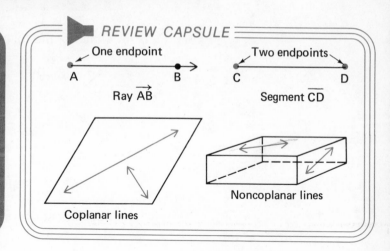

▶ *REVIEW CAPSULE*

Ray $\overrightarrow{AB}$

Segment $\overline{CD}$

Coplanar lines

Noncoplanar lines

Parallel lines do not intersect. ⟶

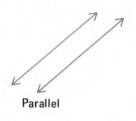

Parallel

Not parallel

Parallel lines are coplanar. ⟶

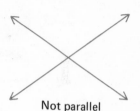

Parallel

Not parallel

Definition of *parallel lines* ⟶

Parallel lines are coplanar lines which do not intersect.

EXAMPLE 1 Which of the following are parallel lines?

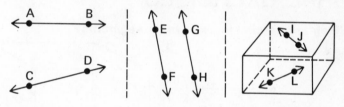

$\overleftrightarrow{EF} \parallel \overleftrightarrow{GH}$ means $\overleftrightarrow{EF}$ is parallel to $\overleftrightarrow{GH}$. ⟶

$\overleftrightarrow{EF} \parallel \overleftrightarrow{GH}$

Definition of *skew lines*	**Skew lines** are noncoplanar lines.

EXAMPLE 2 Which of the following are skew lines?

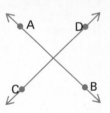 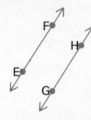 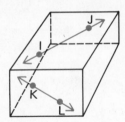

$\overrightarrow{IJ}$ and $\overleftrightarrow{KL}$ are noncoplanar. ——→ $\overrightarrow{IJ}$ and $\overleftrightarrow{KL}$ are skew lines.

Segments or rays can also be parallel.

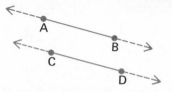 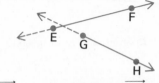

Say. ——→ $\overline{AB}$ is parallel to $\overline{CD}$. $\overrightarrow{EF}$ is not parallel to $\overrightarrow{GH}$.

Write. ——→ $\overline{AB} \parallel \overline{CD}$ $\overrightarrow{EF} \not\parallel \overrightarrow{GH}$

Definition of *parallel* rays or segments ——→	Rays or segments are *parallel* if the lines which contain them are parallel.

EXAMPLE 3 True or false? Draw a picture to defend your answer. Two segments which do not intersect are parallel.

The lines containing $\overline{AB}$ and $\overline{CD}$ do intersect. ——→

False.
$\overline{AB}$ does not intersect $\overline{CD}$.
But, $\overline{AB} \not\parallel \overline{CD}$.

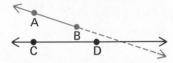

ORAL EXERCISES

Which are parallel lines, rays, or segments?

1.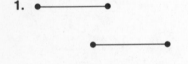

2.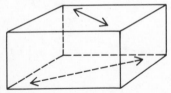

3.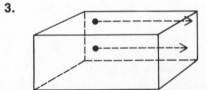

EXERCISES

PART A

In each figure, which pairs of lines, rays, or segments appear to be parallel? Which appear to be skew?

1.
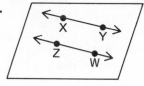

2.
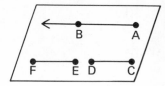

3.
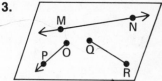

4.
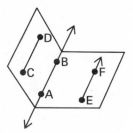

5.
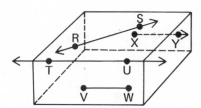

6.
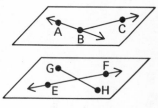

True or false? Draw a picture to defend your answer.

7. All lines which do not intersect are parallel.

8. If two rays are contained in parallel lines, then they are parallel.

9. Two lines which are not parallel are skew.

10. Two lines which are not coplanar are skew.

11. Two coplanar lines are parallel.

12. Two parallel lines are coplanar.

13. Two rays which are parallel do not intersect.

14. Two rays which do not intersect are parallel.

PART B

Always true, sometimes true, or never true?

15. A ray that does not intersect a line is parallel to the line.

16. Two lines are either parallel or they intersect.

17. Two intersecting lines are coplanar.

18. Skew lines do not intersect.

19. Two coplanar segments which do not intersect are parallel.

20. Two lines parallel to a third line are parallel to each other.

21. Two rays which are not parallel and do not intersect are skew.

22. If two lines are perpendicular to the same line, then they are parallel.

23. No coplanar lines are skew lines.

24. No skew lines are coplanar.

Transversals

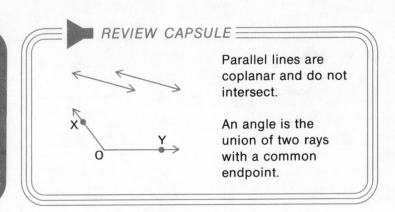

REVIEW CAPSULE

Parallel lines are coplanar and do not intersect.

An angle is the union of two rays with a common endpoint.

Coplanar lines can be intersected by a transversal.

$$\overleftrightarrow{XY} \cap \overleftrightarrow{AB} = \{E\}$$
$$\overleftrightarrow{XY} \cap \overleftrightarrow{CD} = \{F\}$$
$$\overrightarrow{PQ} \cap \overleftrightarrow{MN} = \{R\}$$
$$\overrightarrow{PQ} \cap \overleftrightarrow{ST} = \{V\}$$

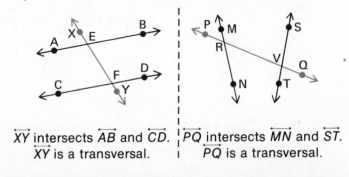

$\overleftrightarrow{XY}$ intersects $\overleftrightarrow{AB}$ and $\overleftrightarrow{CD}$.
$\overleftrightarrow{XY}$ is a transversal.

$\overrightarrow{PQ}$ intersects $\overleftrightarrow{MN}$ and $\overleftrightarrow{ST}$.
$\overrightarrow{PQ}$ is a transversal.

Definition of a *transversal* ⎯⎯⎯⎯⎯⟶ A *transversal* is a line which intersects two coplanar lines in two distinct points.

EXAMPLE 1

Identify the transversals.

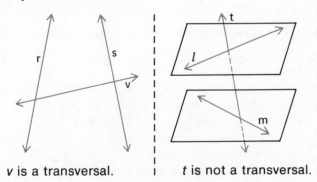

In the second picture, ℓ and m are not coplanar.

v is a transversal.

t is not a transversal.

EXAMPLE 2   Identify the transversals in each picture.

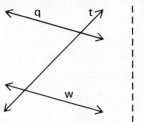

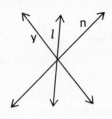

In the second picture, there is only one point of intersection.

t is a transversal.   ℓ is not a transversal.

**Special Pairs of Angles
Formed by Two Lines and a Transversal**

Alternate Interior Angles   Corresponding Angles   Alternate Exterior Angles

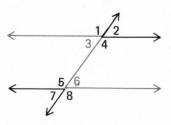   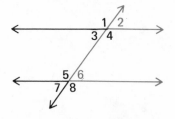   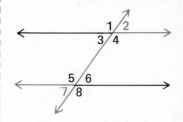

∠3 and ∠6 are alternate interior angles.

∠2 and ∠6 are corresponding angles.

∠2 and ∠7 are alternate exterior angles.

Other pairs: ∠4 and ∠5

Other pairs: ∠1 and ∠5, ∠4 and ∠8, ∠3 and ∠7

Other pairs: ∠1 and ∠8

EXAMPLE 3   Identify each given pair of angles as alternate interior, corresponding, alternate exterior, or none of these.

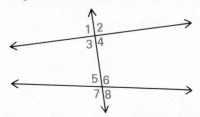

Use the patterns in the above display to decide.

	Answers
∠1 and ∠5	Corresponding angles
∠3 and ∠6	Alternate interior angles
∠2 and ∠7	Alternate exterior angles
∠4 and ∠8	Corresponding angles
∠3 and ∠5	None of these
∠2 and ∠8	None of these

ORAL EXERCISES

1. Name the transversal.

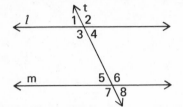

2. Name each pair of corresponding angles.

3. Name each pair of alternate interior angles.

4. Name each pair of alternate exterior angles.

EXERCISES

PART A

Identify the transversals.

1.

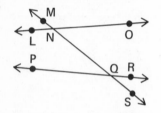

2.

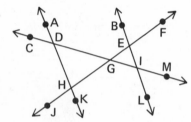

3.

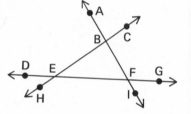

Identify each given pair of angles as alternate interior, corresponding, alternate exterior, or none of these.

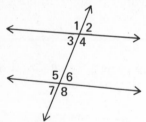

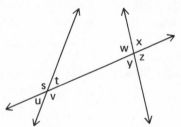

4. ∠1 and ∠3
5. ∠2 and ∠5
6. ∠1 and ∠8
7. ∠4 and ∠5
8. ∠3 and ∠7

9. ∠t and ∠y
10. ∠v and ∠z
11. ∠u and ∠z
12. ∠v and ∠w
13. ∠s and ∠w

14. ∠5 and ∠9
15. ∠1 and ∠11
16. ∠3 and ∠10
17. ∠1 and ∠7
18. ∠2 and ∠6

PART B

19. If alternate interior angles form a letter N or Z, what letters do corresponding angles form?

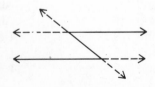

20. Given two lines and a transversal, how many pairs of alternate interior angles are formed? corresponding angles? alternate exterior angles? vertical angles?

Geometry in Architecture

The Union Tank Car Company
Roundhouse in Baton Rouge, Louisiana
is shaped like part of a sphere.

The John Hancock Building in Chicago
is shaped like a truncated pyramid
(pyramid with the top cut off). The
x-shaped lattice structure gives extra
support to the building.

Lake Point Towers, an apartment complex in Chicago, has a base and roof shaped like a three-leafed clover. This design affords every tenant a view of Lake Michigan.

Marina City Towers in Chicago are shaped like two truncated circular cylinders. Many similarly shaped buildings have been patterned after these.

Congruent Angles and Parallel Lines

REVIEW CAPSULE

Alternate interior angles:
$\angle u$ and $\angle x$
$\angle v$ and $\angle w$

Corresponding angles:
$\angle s$ and $\angle w$, $\angle t$ and $\angle x$
$\angle u$ and $\angle y$, $\angle v$ and $\angle z$

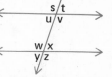

EXAMPLE 1

$\ell \parallel m$.
List the pairs of alternate interior angles. Find the measure of each angle.

Use a protractor to measure each angle.

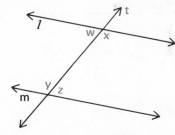

Pairs of alternate interior angles

$\angle w \cong \angle z; \angle x \cong \angle y$

$\angle w$ and $\angle z$	$\angle x$ and $\angle y$
$m\angle w = 59$ $m\angle z = 59$	$m\angle x = 121$ $m\angle y = 121$

EXAMPLE 2

$\ell \not\parallel m$.
List the pairs of alternate interior angles. Find the measure of each angle.

$\ell \not\parallel m$ means line ℓ is not parallel to line m.

Use a protractor to measure each angle.

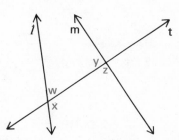

Pairs of alternate interior angles

$\angle w \not\cong \angle z, \angle x \not\cong \angle y$

$\angle w$ and $\angle z$	$\angle x$ and $\angle y$
$m\angle w = 65$ $m\angle z = 91$	$m\angle x = 115$ $m\angle y = 89$

Examples 1 and 2 suggest this.

Postulate 13

If two parallel lines are intersected by a transversal, then alternate interior angles are congruent.

EXAMPLE 3 $\ell \parallel m$, $m \angle x = 140$.
Find $m \angle z$.

$\angle x$ and $\angle z$ are corresponding angles.

$\angle x \cong \angle y$ So, $m \angle y = 140$.
$\angle y \cong \angle z$ So, $m \angle z = 140$.

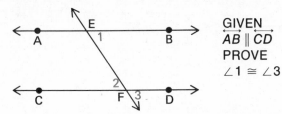

Example 3 suggests this.

Thus, $m \angle z = 140$.

Theorem 3.1

If two parallel lines are intersected by a transversal, then corresponding angles are congruent.

ANALYSIS
Vert. $\angle$'s are $\cong$. Alt. int.
$\angle$'s of $\parallel$ lines are $\cong$.

GIVEN
$\overleftrightarrow{AB} \parallel \overleftrightarrow{CD}$
PROVE
$\angle 1 \cong \angle 3$

PROOF

STATEMENTS	REASONS
1. $\angle 1 \cong \angle 2$	1. Alt. int. $\angle$'s of $\parallel$ lines are $\cong$.
2. $\angle 2 \cong \angle 3$	2. Vert. $\angle$'s are $\cong$.
3. $\therefore \angle 1 \cong \angle 3$	3. Transitive property for $\cong$.

EXAMPLE 4 $\ell \parallel m$, $m \angle 1 = 3x + 20$,
$m \angle 2 = 2x + 40$. Find $m \angle 1$.

Corr. $\angle$'s of $\parallel$ lines are $\cong$. $\longrightarrow$ $m \angle 1 = m \angle 2$
Substitution property $\longrightarrow$ $3x + 20 = 2x + 40$
$x = 20$
Thus, $m \angle 1 = 3(20) + 20$, or 80.

EXAMPLE 5 $\ell \parallel m$, $m \angle 1 = 52$.
Find $m \angle 2$.

Corr. $\angle$'s of $\parallel$ lines are $\cong$. $\longrightarrow$ $m \angle 3 = m \angle 1 = 52$
$\angle 2$ and $\angle 3$ are supp. $\angle$'s. $\longrightarrow$ $m \angle 2 = 180 - m \angle 3 = 128$

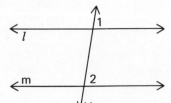

<table>
<tr>
<td>

Theorem   3.2

(See Ex. 20.)

</td>
<td>

If two parallel lines are intersected by a transversal, then interior angles on the same side of the transversal are supplementary.

</td>
</tr>
</table>

EXAMPLE 6 $\overrightarrow{PQ} \parallel \overrightarrow{RS}$, $m\angle y = 3x - 10$, $m\angle z = 2x + 40$.
Find $m\angle y$.

Use Th. 3.2. ⟶

$$m\angle y + m\angle z = 180$$
$$(3x - 10) + (2x + 40) = 180$$

Combine like terms. ⟶
$5x = 150$

$$5x + 30 = 180$$
$$x = 30$$

Thus, $m\angle y = 3(30) - 10$, or 80.

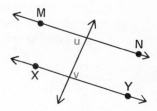

EXAMPLE 7

Is enough information given?
$m\angle u = 81$. Find $m\angle v$.

The lines must be parallel to use Post. 13 or Th 3.1 or Th. 3.2.

No. We must also know that $\overleftrightarrow{MN} \parallel \overleftrightarrow{XY}$.

EXAMPLE 8

Given: $\overrightarrow{AD} \parallel \overrightarrow{EG}$ and $\overrightarrow{BF} \parallel \overrightarrow{CH}$
Prove: $\angle 1 \cong \angle 4$

Analysis: Show $\angle 1 \cong \angle 2$, $\angle 2 \cong \angle 3$, and $\angle 3 \cong \angle 4$. Use the transitive property.

Proof

Statements	Reasons
1. $\angle 1 \cong \angle 2$	1. Alt. int. $\angle$'s of $\parallel$ lines are $\cong$.
2. $\angle 2 \cong \angle 3$	2. Corr. $\angle$'s of $\parallel$ lines are $\cong$.
3. $\angle 3 \cong \angle 4$	3. Vert. $\angle$'s are $\cong$.
4. $\therefore \angle 1 \cong \angle 4$	4. Transitive property for $\cong$.

ORAL EXERCISES

Find the unknown angle measures.

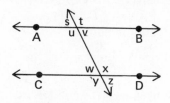

1. $\overleftrightarrow{AB} \parallel \overleftrightarrow{CD}$, $m\angle v = 63$
$m\angle w = ?$ $m\angle z = ?$

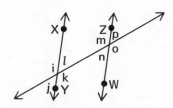

2. $\overleftrightarrow{XY} \parallel \overleftrightarrow{ZW}$, $m\angle k = 128$
$m\angle o = ?$ $m\angle n = ?$

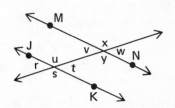

3. $\overleftrightarrow{MN} \parallel \overleftrightarrow{JK}$, $m\angle r = 42$
$m\angle w = ?$ $m\angle x = ?$

EXERCISES

Find the measure of each angle.

1. $\overleftrightarrow{BD} \parallel \overleftrightarrow{HJ}$, $m \angle x = 59$

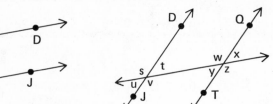

2. $\overleftrightarrow{DJ} \parallel \overleftrightarrow{QT}$, $m \angle z = 134$

3. $\overleftrightarrow{EU} \parallel \overleftrightarrow{BL}$, $\overleftrightarrow{NT} \parallel \overleftrightarrow{CS}$, $m \angle t = 49$

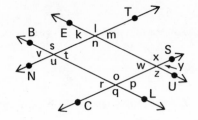

4. If $\overleftrightarrow{AF} \parallel \overleftrightarrow{GL}$, name 3 pairs of congruent angles in the figure at the right, and give a reason for each congruence.

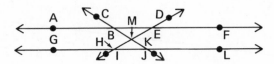

5. If $\overleftrightarrow{AB} \parallel \overleftrightarrow{CD}$, $m \angle u = 2x + 10$, and $m \angle v = 3x - 20$, find $m \angle u$.

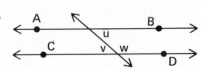

6. If $\overleftrightarrow{AB} \parallel \overleftrightarrow{CD}$, $m \angle u = x$, and $m \angle w = 5x$, find $m \angle u$ and $m \angle w$.

Based on the information given, what angles can be proved congruent? What angle measures can be found?

7. Given: $\overleftrightarrow{VU} \parallel \overleftrightarrow{SX}$

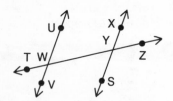

8. Given: $\overline{AE} \parallel \overline{CD}$, $\overline{AE} \perp \overline{FB}$

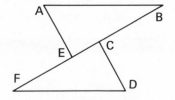

9. Given: $\overleftrightarrow{AC} \parallel \overrightarrow{DG}$, $m \angle BEF + m \angle BFE = 158$.

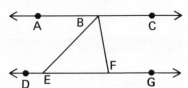

10. Given: $\overleftrightarrow{AD} \parallel \overleftrightarrow{EK}$, $\overleftrightarrow{CG} \parallel \overleftrightarrow{JH}$
Prove: $\angle ABC \cong \angle HIK$

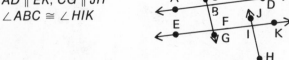

11. Given: $\overleftrightarrow{AD} \parallel \overleftrightarrow{EK}$, $\overleftrightarrow{CG} \parallel \overleftrightarrow{JH}$
Prove: $\angle DBG$ is a supplement of $\angle JIK$

12. Given: $\overleftrightarrow{AC} \parallel \overleftrightarrow{DF}$, $\overleftrightarrow{DF} \parallel \overleftrightarrow{GJ}$
Prove: $m \angle BEH = m \angle CBE + m \angle EHJ$

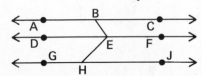

13. Given: $\overleftrightarrow{AC} \parallel \overleftrightarrow{DF}$, $\overleftrightarrow{DF} \parallel \overleftrightarrow{GJ}$, $\overline{BE} \perp \overline{EH}$
Prove: $\angle CBE$ is a complement of $\angle EHJ$

Find the measure of each angle. Use only the information given.

14. $\overrightarrow{PQ} \parallel \overrightarrow{RS}$, $m\angle m = 63$, $\angle n$ and $\angle q$ are supplements.

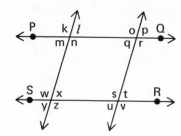

15. $\ell \parallel m \parallel n$, $\angle 1 \cong \angle 2$, $\angle 2 \cong \angle 3$.

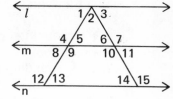

16. $\overleftrightarrow{AB} \parallel \overleftrightarrow{CD}$, $m\angle t = 2y$, $m\angle j = 3y - 10$, $m\angle v = 2y + 15$ $m\angle \ell = 3y - 7$.

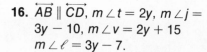
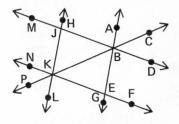

17. Given: $\overrightarrow{AB} \parallel \overrightarrow{CD} \parallel \overrightarrow{EF}$
Prove: $m\angle w + m\angle x + m\angle y + m\angle z = 360$

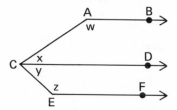

18. Given: $\overleftrightarrow{TR} \parallel \overleftrightarrow{XW}$
Prove: $m\angle 2 + m\angle 4 + m\angle 5 = 180$

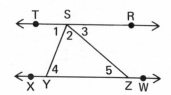

19. Given: $\overleftrightarrow{AG} \parallel \overleftrightarrow{HL}$, $\overrightarrow{MD} \parallel \overrightarrow{NF}$, $\angle PBG \cong \angle NEA$, $\overrightarrow{BP}$ bisects $\angle MBG$.
Prove: $\overrightarrow{BM}$ bisects $\angle ABP$.

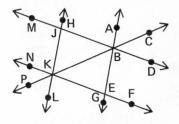

20. Prove Theorem 3.2.

21. Prove: If two parallel lines are intersected by a transversal, then alternate exterior angles are congruent.

22. Prove: If two parallel lines are intersected by a transversal, then exterior angles on the same side of the transversal are supplements.

23. Prove: If a transversal is perpendicular to one of two parallel lines, then it is perpendicular to the other.

Contradictory information is given for each figure below. Determine what is contradictory.

24. $\overleftrightarrow{AF} \parallel \overleftrightarrow{GM}$, $\angle ABC \cong \angle DEF$, $\angle JBF$ is a supplement of $\angle AEK$, $m\angle MLK = 87$.

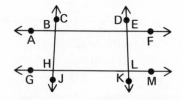

25. $\overleftrightarrow{AF} \parallel \overleftrightarrow{GM}$, $\overrightarrow{CJ} \parallel \overrightarrow{DK}$, $m\angle ABC = 48$, $m\angle DLM = 132$, $\angle AED$ is a complement of $\angle JHM$. $\angle AED$

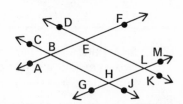

26. $\overleftrightarrow{AB} \parallel \overleftrightarrow{EC}$, $\angle v$ is a complement of $\angle w$, $m\angle x = 47$, and $m\angle z = 98$. $m\angle z$

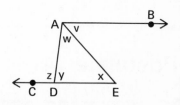

Parallel Lines and Congruent Angles

OBJECTIVES

■ To form converses of statements
■ To prove lines are parallel

 REVIEW CAPSULE

If parallel lines are intersected by a transversal, then

1. alternate interior angles are congruent,
2. corresponding angles are congruent,
3. interior angles on the same side of the transversal are supplementary.

The following two statements are converses of each other.

The "if" clause becomes the "then" clause, and the "then" clause becomes the "if" clause.

If it is raining, then the streets are wet.

If the streets are wet, then it is raining.

EXAMPLE 1   Write the converse of, "If two lines are parallel, then the alternate interior angles are congruent."

To form a converse, interchange the "if" and the "then" clauses.

The converse is, "If the alternate interior angles are congruent, then the lines are parallel."

EXAMPLE 2   Write a statement that is true, but whose converse is false.

The converse of a statement is not necessarily true.

Statement: "If an animal is a dog, then it has four legs."
Converse: "If an animal has four legs, then it is a dog."

We will accept the converse of Postulate 13 as another postulate.

Postulate 14

If two lines are intersected by a transversal so that two alternate interior angles are congruent, then the lines are parallel.

EXAMPLE 3   Which lines are parallel?

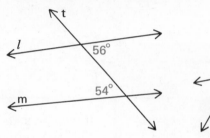

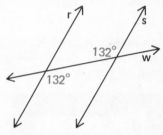

If alt. int. ∠'s are ≅, then lines are ∥. ⟶ $r \parallel s$

The converse of Theorem 3.1 can be proved.

Theorem   3.3   If two lines are intersected by a transversal so that corresponding angles are congruent, then the lines are parallel.

ANALYSIS

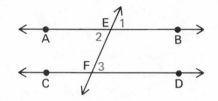

GIVEN
∠1 ≅ ∠3
PROVE
$\overleftrightarrow{AB} \parallel \overleftrightarrow{CD}$

Vert. ∠'s are ≅.
Lines are ∥ if alt. int. ∠'s are ≅.

PROOF

STATEMENTS	REASONS
1. ∠2 ≅ ∠1	**1.** Vert. ∠'s are ≅.
2. ∠1 ≅ ∠3	**2.** Given
3. ∠2 ≅ ∠3	**3.** Transitive prop. for ≅
4. ∴ $\overleftrightarrow{AB} \parallel \overleftrightarrow{CD}$	**4.** If alt. int. ∠'s are ≅, then lines are ∥.

EXAMPLE 4 $\overleftrightarrow{AB} \perp \overleftrightarrow{EH}$ and $\overleftrightarrow{CD} \perp \overleftrightarrow{EH}$
What conclusion would you draw about $\overleftrightarrow{AB}$ and $\overleftrightarrow{CD}$?

⊥'s form ≅ rt. ∠'s. ⟶ $m\angle AFG = 90$ and $m\angle CGH = 90$.
So, ∠AFG ≅ ∠CGH.
Use Th. 3.3. ⟶ **Thus, $\overleftrightarrow{AB} \parallel \overleftrightarrow{CD}$.**

Corollary

Two coplanar lines perpendicular to the same line are parallel.

EXAMPLE 5 $m\angle z = 70$, $m\angle y = 110$.
Show $\ell \parallel m$.

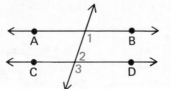

$\angle x$ and $\angle y$ are supplementary. $\longrightarrow$ $m\angle x = 180 - 110 = 70$
$m\angle x = m\angle z$ $\longrightarrow$ $\angle x \cong \angle z$
Use Th. 3.3. $\longrightarrow$ $\therefore \ell \parallel m$

Theorem   3.4

If two lines are intersected by a transversal so that two interior angles on the same side of the transversal are supplementary, then the lines are parallel.

ANALYSIS

Lines are $\parallel$ if corr. $\angle$'s are $\cong$.
Sum of meas. of $\angle$'s on one side of line = 180°.

GIVEN
$m\angle 1 + m\angle 2 = 180$
PROVE
$\overleftrightarrow{AB} \parallel \overleftrightarrow{CD}$

PROOF

(See Exercise 18.)

EXAMPLE 6   Given: $\angle 1$ and $\angle 4$ are supplements.
Prove: $\ell \parallel m$

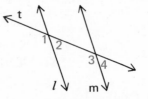

Analysis: show corr. $\angle$'s $\cong$.

Proof

Statements	Reasons
1. $\angle 3$ and $\angle 4$ are supplements.	1. Sum of meas. of $\angle$'s with the same vertex on one side of line = 180°.
2. $\angle 1$ and $\angle 4$ are supplements.	2. Given
3. $\angle 3 \cong \angle 1$	3. Supp. of same $\angle$ are $\cong$.
4. $\therefore \ell \parallel m$	4. If corr. $\angle$'s are $\cong$, then lines are $\parallel$.

Th. 3.4 could also be used to prove this.

ORAL EXERCISES

Write the converse of each statement.

1. If Mary practices, then she will become a good tennis player.

2. If glogs glig, then blobs blab.

Which lines are parallel?

3.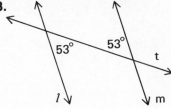

4.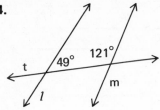

5.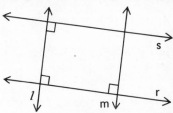

6.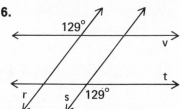

7.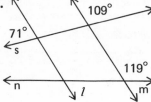

8.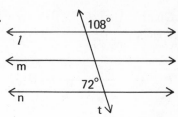

EXERCISES

PART A

Write the converse. Determine if the converse is true or false.

1. If two angles are supplementary, then the sum of their measures is 180°.

2. If two lines form a right angle, then they are perpendicular.

3. If two coplanar lines are perpendicular to the same line, then they are parallel.

4. If two interior angles on the same side of a transversal are supplementary, then the two lines are parallel.

Which lines are parallel? Which angles are congruent? Use only the information given to decide.

5. $\angle ACB \cong \angle EFG$

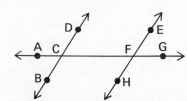

6. $\overrightarrow{VY} \perp \overrightarrow{RS}$, $\overrightarrow{VY} \perp \overrightarrow{TU}$

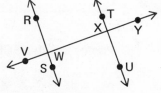

7. $\overrightarrow{BE}$ bisects $\angle ABH$, $\overrightarrow{HF}$ bisects $\angle BHI$, $\overleftrightarrow{AD} \parallel \overleftrightarrow{GI}$.

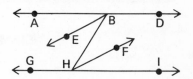

8. Given: $\overleftrightarrow{AB} \parallel \overleftrightarrow{CD}$, $\angle ALR \cong \angle CNV$
Prove: $\overleftrightarrow{RS} \parallel \overleftrightarrow{VW}$

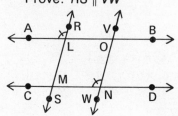

9. Given: $\overleftrightarrow{AB} \perp \overleftrightarrow{HK}$, $\overleftrightarrow{AB} \perp \overleftrightarrow{LP}$, $\overleftrightarrow{CD} \perp \overleftrightarrow{HK}$
Prove $\overleftrightarrow{CD} \perp \overleftrightarrow{LP}$

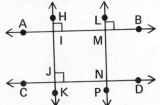

10. Given: $\overleftrightarrow{MT} \parallel \overleftrightarrow{SR}$, $\angle S$ and $\angle M$ are supplements.
Prove: $\overleftrightarrow{MV} \parallel \overleftrightarrow{SP}$

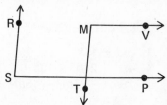

Which lines cannot be parallel?

11. $m\angle v = 128$, $m\angle w = 62$

13. $m\angle y = 74$, $m\angle z = 116$

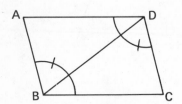

12. $m\angle w = 78$, $m\angle x = 81$

14. $m\angle v = 114$, $m\angle y = 112$

PART B

15. Given: $\overline{AD} \parallel \overline{BC}$, $\angle ABC \cong$ $\angle ADC$
Prove: $\overline{AB} \parallel \overline{DC}$

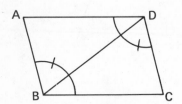

16. Given: $\angle 1 \cong \angle 2$, $\angle 5 \cong \angle 1$, $\overrightarrow{FC}$ bisects $\angle BFG$.
Prove: $\overleftrightarrow{AD} \parallel \overleftrightarrow{EG}$

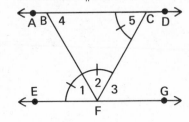

17. Given: $\ell \parallel n$, $\angle 1 \cong \angle 4$
Prove: $m \parallel n$

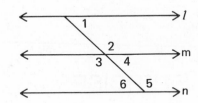

18. Prove Theorem 3.4.

Algebra Review

To factor out the greatest common monomial
1. Factor out the greatest common whole number factor other than 1.
2. Factor out the greatest common variable factor, if any.

EXAMPLE

Factor out the GCF from $6x^4 - 9x$.

$6x^4 - 9x = 2 \cdot 3 \cdot x^4 - 3 \cdot 3 \cdot x$
Greatest common   Greatest common
number factor: 3   variable factor: x
GCF is $3x$

Use the distributive property. ⟶ **Thus,** $6x^4 - 9x = 3x(2x^3 - 3)$.

Factor out the GCF.

1. $3x^3 - 15x$

2. $8a^3 - 25a^2$

3. $8a^4 - 32a^2$

4. $4b^3 - 24b^2 + 48b$

5. $5x^2 - 20x + 35$

6. $4p^3 - 12p^2 + 16p$

7. $18m^4 - 27m^3 - 45m^2 + 36m$

8. $6y^3 - 18y^2 - 13$

9. $6a^4 - 12a^3 - 24a^2 + 3a$

Women of Mathematics

Amalie Noether was born in Germany on March 23, 1882. Her girlhood was typical. Three years after leaving high school, Noether took the tests for prospective school teachers of French and English. This stimulated her interest in university studies, and she became one of two female students at the University of Erlangen and later at the University of Göttingen. Somewhere along the way, Noether's interest was transferred from language to mathematics.

Amalie Noether
(1882-1935)

Noether was sponsored for a faculty position at the University of Göttingen, but failed to receive it because of opposition to women lecturers. Nevertheless, she gave lectures which were announced under the name of the famous mathematician, Hilbert, free of charge. In 1922, she was promoted and allowed to give lectures under her own name, but she did not receive any salary for this honor.

In 1933, Germany was on the verge of a national revolution and Noether, along with many other academic persons, was prohibited from participating in academic activities. So she came to the United States, where she again found respect and friendship among her peers. Noether died on April 14, 1935 at the peak of her career.

The Parallel Postulate

OBJECTIVE

■ To apply the parallel postulate

▶ REVIEW CAPSULE

If $\vec{PB}$ is in the interior of $\angle APC$, then $m\angle APC = m\angle APB + m\angle BPC$.

If $\ell \parallel n$, then $m \nparallel n$.

The picture suggests that there is only one line through point P which is parallel to line n.

EXAMPLE 1 If $\overleftrightarrow{AP} \parallel \overleftrightarrow{CD}$ and $\overleftrightarrow{BP} \parallel \overleftrightarrow{CD}$, what conclusion would you draw about $\angle APC$ and $\angle BPC$?

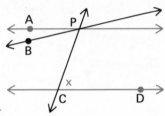

Alt. int. $\angle$'s of $\parallel$ lines are $\cong$. ⟶ $\begin{cases} \text{If } \overleftrightarrow{AP} \parallel \overleftrightarrow{CD}, \text{ then } \angle APC \cong \angle x. \\ \text{If } \overleftrightarrow{BP} \parallel \overleftrightarrow{CD}, \text{ then } \angle BPC \cong \angle x. \end{cases}$

Transitive prop. of $\cong$ ⟶ **Thus,** $\angle APC \cong \angle BPC$.

EXAMPLE 2 On the basis of Example 1, is it possible for both $\overleftrightarrow{AP}$ and $\overleftrightarrow{BP}$ to be parallel to $\overleftrightarrow{CD}$?

Suppose $\overleftrightarrow{AP} \parallel \overleftrightarrow{CD}$ and $\overleftrightarrow{BP} \parallel \overleftrightarrow{CD}$.
From Example 1, $m\angle APC = m\angle BPC$.

Since $\vec{PB}$ is in the interior of $\angle APC$, $m\angle APC = m\angle APB + m\angle BPC$. ⟶ But, $m\angle APC > m\angle BPC$. Contradiction.

Ex. 1 and 2 suggest this. ⟶ **Thus,** $\overleftrightarrow{AP}$ and $\overleftrightarrow{BP}$ are not both parallel to $\overleftrightarrow{CD}$.

Postulate 15
(The Parallel Postulate)

Through point P not on line ℓ, there is exactly one line parallel to ℓ.

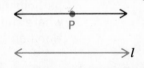

EXAMPLE 3   Complete the blank with
=, ≠, or "cannot tell."
If $\ell \parallel m$, and $m \angle w = 40$,
then $m \angle z$ _____ 140.

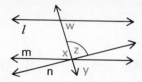

$n \nparallel \ell.$ ⟶ $m \angle z \neq 140$

ORAL EXERCISES

Complete each blank with ∥, ∦, or "cannot tell."

1. If $s \parallel \ell$, then m _____ ℓ.

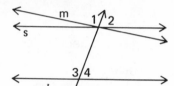

2. If $m \nparallel \ell$, then s _____ ℓ.

3. If $\angle 1 \cong \angle 3$, then m _____ ℓ.

4. If $\angle 1 \cong \angle 3$, then s _____ ℓ.

5. If $\angle 2 \ncong \angle 4$, then m _____ ℓ.

6. If $\angle 2 \ncong \angle 4$, then s _____ ℓ.

EXERCISES

PART A

Complete each blank with =, ≠, or "cannot tell."

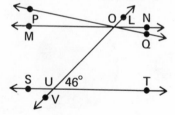

Given: $\overleftrightarrow{MN} \parallel \overleftrightarrow{ST}$
$m \angle LUT = 46$

1. $m \angle QOV$ _____ 134

2. $m \angle LON$ _____ 46

3. $m \angle LOQ$ _____ 46

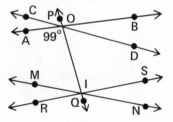

Given: $\overleftrightarrow{AB} \parallel \overleftrightarrow{RS}$, $\overleftrightarrow{CD} \parallel \overleftrightarrow{MN}$,
$m \angle AOQ = 99$

4. $m \angle BOQ$ _____ 99

5. $m \angle RIQ$ _____ 99

6. $m \angle SIQ$ _____ 81

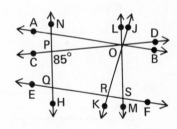

Given: $\overleftrightarrow{AB} \parallel \overleftrightarrow{EF}$,
$m \angle HPD = 85$

7. $m \angle COM$ _____ 95

8. $m \angle FQH$ _____ 85

9. $m \angle COL$ _____ 85

PART B

Complete each blank with ∥, ∦, or cannot tell.

10. If $\overleftrightarrow{JT} \nparallel \overleftrightarrow{VN}$, then $\overleftrightarrow{JT}$ _____ $\overleftrightarrow{SB}$.

12. If $\angle JOW$ and $\angle APB$ are
supplements, then $\overrightarrow{JT}$ _____ $\overrightarrow{NV}$.

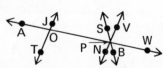

11. If $\overleftrightarrow{JT} \perp \overleftrightarrow{AW}$ and $\overleftrightarrow{VN} \perp \overleftrightarrow{AW}$,
then $\overleftrightarrow{JT}$ _____ $\overleftrightarrow{SB}$.

13. If $\overleftrightarrow{JT} \parallel \overleftrightarrow{VN}$ then $\overleftrightarrow{SB}$ _____ $\overleftrightarrow{JT}$.

About the Parallel Postulate

Three Geometries

Euclidean
- Named after Euclid, a famous Greek geometer
- Assumes a unique parallel line through a given point
- Usable for ordinary distances

Lobachevskian
- Named after the Russian mathematician, Lobachevski
- Assumes more than one parallel line through a point
- Usable for molecular distances

Riemannian
- Named after the German mathematician, Riemann
- Assumes no parallel lines
- Usable for astronomical distances.

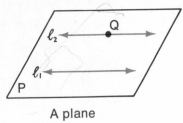

A plane

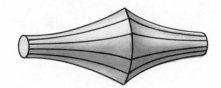

A pseudosphere

A sphere

Do parallel lines actually exist?

Astronomers have found some evidence, in studying light from far off stars, that there may not be any such thing as parallel lines. If this is true, then a geometry in which there are no parallel lines would be used to analyze astronomical distances. Strange as it may seem, it is impossible to prove that only one line can be drawn parallel to a given line, through a given point. However if we assume that two lines can intersect in only one point, then it becomes possible to prove that parallel lines do exist.

Using Parallel Lines

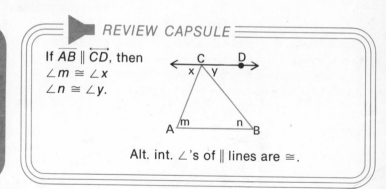

◣ *REVIEW CAPSULE*

If $\overleftrightarrow{AB} \parallel \overleftrightarrow{CD}$, then
$\angle m \cong \angle x$
$\angle n \cong \angle y$.

Alt. int. $\angle$'s of $\parallel$ lines are $\cong$.

EXAMPLE 1 $\overleftrightarrow{AB} \parallel \overleftrightarrow{CD}$. Find $m \angle ACB$.

$\overleftrightarrow{AB} \parallel \overleftrightarrow{CD} \longleftarrow \begin{array}{l} \angle x \cong \angle A \\ \angle y \cong \angle B \end{array}$

$m \angle x + m \angle ACB + m \angle y = 180$
$$60 + m \angle ACB + 48 = 180$$

Thus, $m \angle ACB = 72$

Auxiliary means "helping."

Example 1 suggests an auxiliary line that can be drawn to help prove the following theorem.

Theorem 3.5

The sum of the measures of the three angles of a triangle is 180°.

ANALYSIS

Sum of meas. of $\angle$'s with the same vertex on one side of line = 180°.
Use an auxiliary line $\parallel \overline{AB}$.

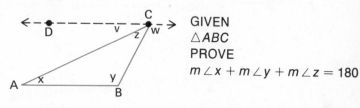

GIVEN
$\triangle ABC$
PROVE
$m \angle x + m \angle y + m \angle z = 180$

PROOF

STATEMENTS

1. Draw $\overleftrightarrow{DC} \parallel \overline{AB}$.
2. $m \angle x = m \angle v$
3. $m \angle y = m \angle w$
4. $m \angle v + m \angle z + m \angle w = 180$
5. $\therefore m \angle x + m \angle z + m \angle y = 180$

REASONS

1. Parallel postulate
2. Alt. int. $\angle$'s of $\parallel$ lines are $\cong$.
3. Alt. int. $\angle$'s of $\parallel$ lines are $\cong$.
4. Sum of meas. of $\angle$'s with the same vertex on one side of a line = 180°
5. Substitution property

EXAMPLE 2 $m\angle A = x$, $m\angle B = 2x + 20$,
$m\angle C = 5x - 16$.
Find the measure of each angle.

Sum of meas. of $\angle$'s of a $\triangle = 180°$. ⟶ $x + (2x + 20) + (5x - 16) = 180$
Combine like terms. ⟶ $8x + 4 = 180$
Subtract 4 from each side. ⟶ $8x = 176$
Divide each side by 8. ⟶ $x = 22$
$2x + 20 = 64$
$5x - 16 = 94$

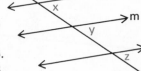

Check: $22 + 64 + 94 = 180$. ⟶ **Thus,** $m\angle A = 22$, $m\angle B = 64$, and $m\angle C = 94$.

EXAMPLE 3 $m \parallel \ell$, $n \parallel \ell$, $m\angle x = 43$.
Find $m\angle y$ and $m\angle z$
Show that $m \parallel n$.

Corr. $\angle$'s of $\parallel$ lines are $\cong$. ⟶ $m\angle y = m\angle x$ So, $m\angle y = 43$.
$m\angle z = m\angle x$ So, $m\angle z = 43$.

$\angle d$ and $\angle e$ are corr. $\angle$'s. Use Th. 3.3. ⟶ **Thus,** $m \parallel n$.

Theorem 3.6

In a plane, two lines parallel to the same line are parallel to each other.

ANALYSIS

Assume $\overleftrightarrow{AB} \not\parallel \overleftrightarrow{CD}$ and find a contradiction.

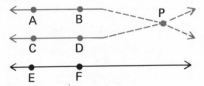

GIVEN
$\overleftrightarrow{AB} \parallel \overleftrightarrow{EF}$, $\overleftrightarrow{CD} \parallel \overleftrightarrow{EF}$
$\overleftrightarrow{AB}$, $\overleftrightarrow{CD}$, and $\overleftrightarrow{EF}$ are coplanar.
PROVE
$\overleftrightarrow{AB} \parallel \overleftrightarrow{CD}$

PROOF

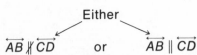

$\rightarrowtail \overleftrightarrow{AB}$ intersects $\overleftrightarrow{CD}$ at a point P.
$\rightarrowtail \overleftrightarrow{AB}$ and $\overleftrightarrow{CD}$ are two lines through $P \parallel \overleftrightarrow{EF}$.
$\rightarrowtail$ This contradicts the parallel postulate.

Since $\overleftrightarrow{AB} \not\parallel \overleftrightarrow{CD}$ leads to a contradiction, then the only other possibility is that $\overleftrightarrow{AB} \parallel \overleftrightarrow{CD}$.

The proof of Theorem 3.6 is an example of an indirect proof.

EXAMPLE 4 Prove: A triangle cannot have two right angles.

State the Given and Prove. ──────→ Given: △ABC
Prove: ∠A and ∠B are not both right angles.

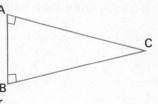

Analysis: Use an indirect proof.

Proof

Either or

∠A and ∠B are rt. ∠'s.   ∠A and ∠B are not both
m∠A + m∠B = 180   rt. ∠'s.
m∠A + m∠B + m∠C > 180

Sum of meas. of ∠'s of a △ = 180°. ──────→ This contradicts Theorem 3.5.

∠A and ∠B being rt. ∠'s leads to a contradiction. The only other possibility is that ∠A and ∠B are not both right angles.

ORAL EXERCISES

Find the measure of the third angle in each triangle.

1.
60° 60°

2.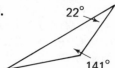
45°
90°

3.
77° 46°

4.
37°
42°

5.
87° 45°

6.
22°
141°

7.
84°
12°

8.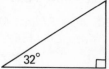
32°

EXERCISES

PART A

Find the measure of each angle in △ABC.

1. $m\angle A = x$
$m\angle B = x$
$m\angle C = 2x$

3. $m\angle A = x + 10$
$m\angle B = x + 20$
$m\angle C = x + 30$

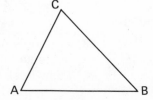

2. $m\angle A = x + 30$
$m\angle B = 3x - 10$
$m\angle C = 2x + 70$

4. $m\angle A = x + 50$
$m\angle B = 2x - 10$
$m\angle C = 2x + 25$

Use the information given to find the measure of the stated angle. If not enough information if given, write "too little information."

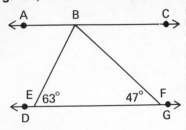

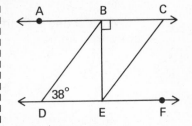

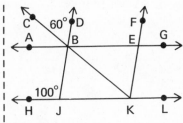

$m \angle BEG = 63$
$m \angle DFB = 47$
5. $m \angle EBF = ?$
6. $m \angle BFG = ?$
7. $m \angle ABE = ?$
8. $m \angle CBE = ?$

$\overrightarrow{AB} \parallel \overrightarrow{DE}, \overrightarrow{BD} \parallel \overrightarrow{EC},$
$\overline{EB} \perp \overline{AC}, m \angle BDE = 38$
9. $m \angle DBE = ?$
10. $m \angle ACE = ?$
11. $m \angle ABC = ?$
12. $m \angle ABD = ?$

$\overrightarrow{AG} \parallel \overrightarrow{HL}, \overrightarrow{JD} \parallel \overrightarrow{KF},$
$m \angle HJD = 100, m \angle CBD = 60$
13. $m \angle JBK = ?$
14. $m \angle HKC = ?$
15. $m \angle ABC = ?$
16. $m \angle AEK = ?$

17. Given: $\overline{BC} \perp \overline{CA}$
    Prove: $m \angle A + m \angle B = 90$

18. Given: $\angle R \cong \angle T,$
    $\angle N \cong \angle J$
    Prove: $\angle Q \cong \angle V$

19. Given: $A, C,$ and E are collinear.
    Prove: $m \angle s = m \angle x + m \angle y$

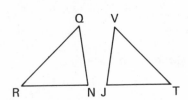

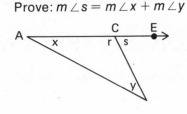

PART B

For each figure, determine whether or not contradictory information is given. If so, which information is contradictory?

20. $\overrightarrow{AC} \nparallel \overrightarrow{FJ}, m \angle ABD = 28, m \angle HBK = 103,$
    $m \angle EGJ = 49.$

21. $\overrightarrow{AE} \parallel \overrightarrow{JM}, \overrightarrow{CL} \perp \overrightarrow{AE}, \angle CKM$ is a supplement of $\angle CBE, m \angle QGC + m \angle ADQ = 180,$
    $m \angle PKC = 85.$

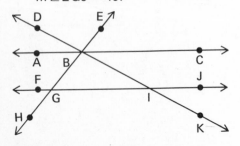

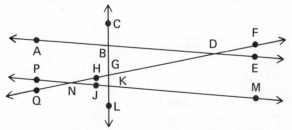

Give an indirect proof of each of the following:

22. A triangle cannot have more than one obtuse angle.

23. A triangle cannot have both a right angle and an obtuse angle.

24. A triangle cannot have two parallel sides.

25. Skew lines do not intersect.

Constructing Parallel Lines

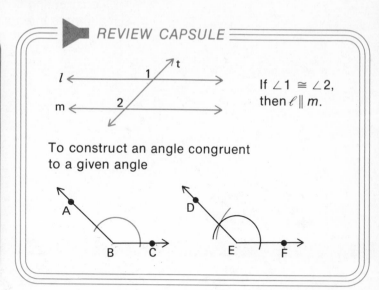

REVIEW CAPSULE

If ∠1 ≅ ∠2, then ℓ ‖ m.

To construct an angle congruent to a given angle

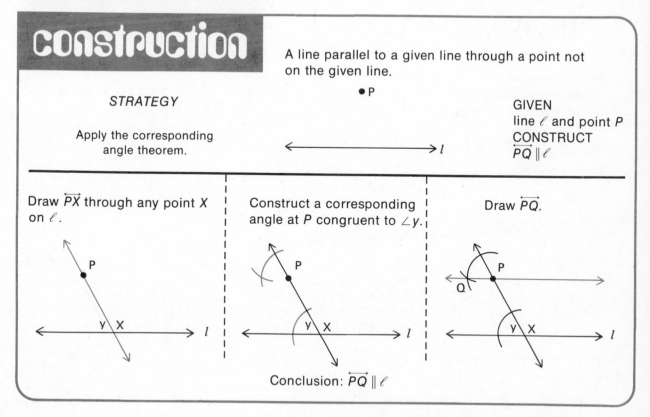

construction

A line parallel to a given line through a point not on the given line.

• P

⟷ ℓ

GIVEN
line ℓ and point P
CONSTRUCT
$\overleftrightarrow{PQ} \parallel \ell$

STRATEGY

Apply the corresponding angle theorem.

Draw $\overrightarrow{PX}$ through any point X on ℓ.

Construct a corresponding angle at P congruent to ∠y.

Draw $\overleftrightarrow{PQ}$.

Conclusion: $\overleftrightarrow{PQ} \parallel \ell$

The construction could have been done using the alternate interior angle postulate.

EXAMPLE Through C construct a line parallel to $\overline{AB}$ by constructing congruent alternate interior angles.

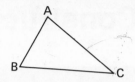

Use $\overline{AC}$ as a transversal.

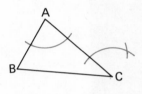

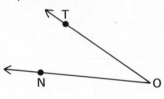

Lines are ‖ if alt. int. ∠'s are ≅.

$\overleftrightarrow{CD} \parallel \overline{AB}$

EXERCISES

PART A

Copy each diagram.

1. Construct a line through P parallel to ℓ.

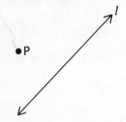

2. Construct a line through K parallel to $\overline{SM}$.

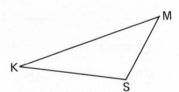

3. Construct a line through N parallel to $\overrightarrow{OT}$.

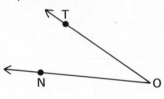

PART B

Copy each diagram.

4. Construct $\overleftrightarrow{CD} \parallel \overline{AB}$ and $\overleftrightarrow{BE} \parallel \overline{AC}$.

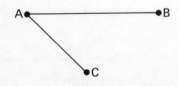

5. Construct M, the midpoint of $\overline{AB}$. Through M, construct $\overleftrightarrow{MX} \parallel \overline{AC}$ and $\overleftrightarrow{MY} \parallel \overline{BC}$.

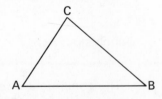

6. Construct $\triangle PQR$ such that $\overline{PQ} \parallel \overline{AB}$, $\overline{QR} \parallel \overline{BC}$, and $\overline{RP} \parallel \overline{AC}$.

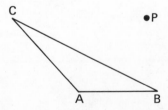

Parallel Planes

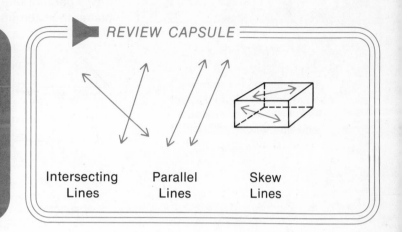

REVIEW CAPSULE

Intersecting   Parallel   Skew
Lines   Lines   Lines

Two planes intersect in a line.

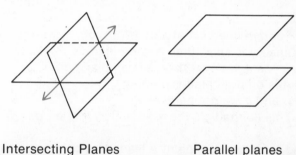

Intersecting Planes   Parallel planes

Definition of parallel planes ———————▶ | *Parallel planes* are planes which do not intersect.

EXAMPLE 1   Draw a plane p parallel to a plane q.
Draw a plane r intersecting both p and q.
Are the lines of intersection parallel or intersecting or skew?

Two planes intersect in a line.

$p \cap r = \ell$
$q \cap r = t$

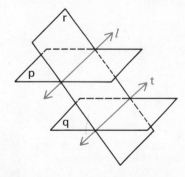

ℓ and t seem to be parallel.

3.7

If two parallel planes are intersected by a third plane, then the lines of intersection are parallel.

ANALYSIS

Two lines are ∥ if they are coplanar and do not intersect. Assume ℓ and m intersect and find a contradiction. (Use an indirect proof.)

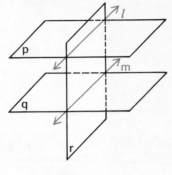

GIVEN
plane p ∥ plane q
$p \cap r = \ell$, $q \cap r = m$
PROVE
$\ell \parallel m$

PROOF

ℓ and m are coplanar since they both lie in plane r.

Either

ℓ and m intersect at a point A, or

ℓ and m do not intersect

Since A is on ℓ, then A is on plane p.
Since A is on m, then A is on plane q.
A is on both planes p and q.
p and q are not parallel.
This contradicts the assumption that $p \parallel q$.

ℓ and m intersect at point A leads to a contradiction.
The only other possibility is that ℓ and m do not intersect.

∴ $\ell \parallel m$

EXAMPLE 2   Draw pictures showing the three possible intersections of a line and a plane.

The line can be completely contained in the plane. ⟶

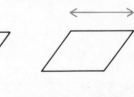

The line itself   A point   The empty set

Definition of a parallel line and plane.

A line and plane are *parallel* if they have no points in common.

EXAMPLE 3   True or false? Draw a picture to support your answer.
If two lines are parallel, every plane containing
one of the lines is parallel to every plane
containing the other.

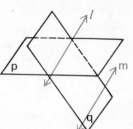

$\ell \parallel m$
Plane p contains ℓ.
Plane q contains m.

But, plane $p \nparallel$ plane q.

This picture shows a counterexample.   **Thus,** the statement is false.

EXERCISES
PART A

True or false? Draw a picture to support your answer.

1. Any two planes parallel to the same plane are parallel to each other.
2. Any two planes perpendicular to the same plane are parallel to each other.
3. Any two planes parallel to the same line are parallel to each other.
4. Any two planes perpendicular to the same line are parallel to each other.
5. A plane and a line parallel to the same line are parallel to each other.
6. Any line parallel to a plane is parallel to each line contained in the plane.
7. Any line parallel to the intersection of two planes is parallel to each of the planes.
8. Any plane parallel to one of two intersecting planes intersects the other plane.
9. Any line in one of two parallel planes is parallel to any line in the second plane.
10. Any plane which intersects one of two parallel planes intersects the second plane.
11. Any line parallel to a second line is parallel to any plane containing the second line.
12. Any two lines in space parallel to a third line are parallel to each other.

PART B

13. Given: plane $p \parallel$ plane q, line ℓ on p
    Prove: $\ell \parallel q$

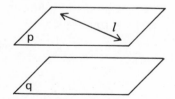

14. Given: $\ell \parallel p$, ℓ on q, $p \cap q = t$
    Prove: $\ell \parallel t$

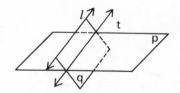

15. Give an indirect proof: If a line intersects a plane in a point, then it is not parallel to any line contained in the plane.

16. Skew lines were defined. Is there a need to define skew planes? Why or why not?

Chapter Three Review

1. $\ell \parallel m.\ m\angle q = 50.$
Find $m\angle x$ and $m\angle v.$
[p. 75]

3. $\ell \parallel m.\ m\angle s = 5a - 10$
and $m\angle w = 3a + 50.$
Find $m\angle s.$ [p. 75]

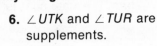
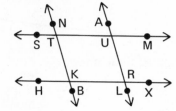

2. $\ell \parallel m.\ m\angle r = 150,$
$\angle t \cong \angle z.$
Find $m\angle u.$ [p. 75]

4. $\ell \parallel m.\ m\angle q = 90 - a,$
$m\angle y = 4a + 45.$
Find $m\angle v.$ [p. 75]

Which lines are parallel? Use only the given information. [p. 80]

5. $m\angle EFB = 138$
$m\angle FGD = 138$

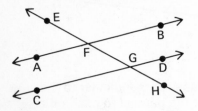

6. $\angle UTK$ and $\angle TUR$ are
supplements.

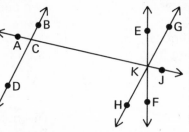

7. $m\angle OWZ = 72, m\angle WZD = 72,$
$m\angle NOW = 118$

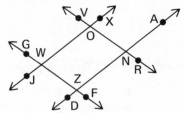

True or false?

8. Any two nonintersecting lines are
parallel. [p. 67]

9. Any two nonparallel lines are skew
lines. [p. 67]

10. If two lines are intersected by a
transversal such that alternate
interior angles are congruent, then
the lines are parallel. [p. 80]

11. If two parallel lines are intersected by
a transversal, then interior angles
on the same side of the transversal
are complements. [p. 75]

Complete each blank with
$\parallel, \not\parallel,$ **or cannot tell.** [p. 86]

12. If $\overleftrightarrow{BD} \parallel \overleftrightarrow{EF}$, then $\overleftrightarrow{BD}$ __ $\overleftrightarrow{GH}$.

13. If $\overleftrightarrow{BD} \perp \overleftrightarrow{AJ}$, and $\overleftrightarrow{EF} \perp \overleftrightarrow{AJ}$,
then $\overleftrightarrow{BD}$ __ $\overleftrightarrow{EF}$. [p. 80]

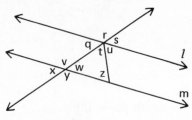

14. Write the converses
of the statements
in Items 10 and 11. [p. 80]

15. Given: $\angle 1 \cong \angle 2, \angle 3 \cong \angle 4$
Prove: $\overrightarrow{RU} \parallel \overrightarrow{QP}$ [p. 80]

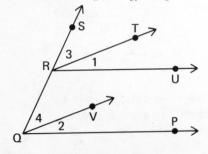

16. Give an indirect proof:
A right triangle cannot
have an obtuse angle. [p. 89]

17. Copy the diagram.
Construct a line through
E parallel to $\overline{AB}$. [p. 93]

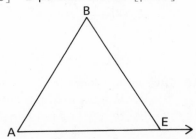

Chapter Three Test

1. $\overleftrightarrow{AG} \parallel \overleftrightarrow{HL}$, $\overleftrightarrow{MD} \parallel \overleftrightarrow{NF}$,
$m \angle HJD = 110$,
$m \angle KBE = 64$.
Find $m \angle MBP$ and
$m \angle JKB$.

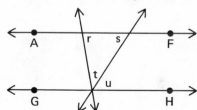

2. $\overleftrightarrow{AG} \parallel \overleftrightarrow{HL}$, $\overleftrightarrow{BK}$ bisects $\angle EBJ$,
$m \angle BJK = 80$.
Find $m \angle EBK$ and
$m \angle JBK$.

3. $\overleftrightarrow{AF} \parallel \overleftrightarrow{GH}$, $m \angle r = 100$,
and $m \angle u = 20$.
Find $m \angle t$.

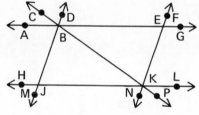

4. $\overleftrightarrow{AF} \parallel \overleftrightarrow{GH}$, $m \angle r = 45 - 3x$,
$m \angle t = x + 10$, and
$m \angle s = 10x + 85$.
Find $m \angle u$.

True or false?

5. Any two coplanar lines which do not intersect are parallel.

6. Any two coplanar rays which do not intersect are parallel.

7. If two lines intersected by a transversal are not parallel, then alternate interior angles formed are not congruent.

8. The sums of the measures of the angles of any two triangles are equal.

9. Any two noncoplanar lines are skew lines.

10. If two lines are parallel to the same line, then they are parallel to each other.

11. Through point X not on line m, there are many lines parallel to m.

12. Write the converse of "If lines are parallel, then they are coplanar."

13. Draw a line and a point not on the line. Construct a line through the point parallel to the given line.

14. Prove: The sum of the measures of the angles of a triangle is 180.

15. Give an indirect proof: A triangle cannot have two obtuse angles.

16. Given: $\overline{AB} \parallel \overline{CD}$,
$\qquad \angle BAD \cong \angle DCB$
Prove: $\overline{AD} \parallel \overline{BC}$

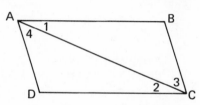

Who Did It?

Clue:

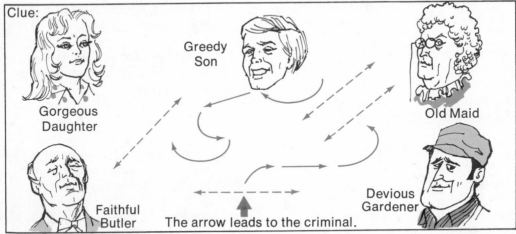

Gorgeous
Daughter

Greedy
Son

Old Maid

Faithful
Butler

Devious
Gardener

The arrow leads to the criminal.

The Inspector finds that

means *slide* in this
direction the length of
the arrow

means *turn* in this
direction the amount
of the arrow

means *flip* over
this line as shown.

Classification of Triangles

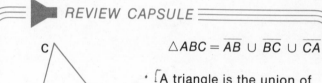

▶ *REVIEW CAPSULE*

$$\triangle ABC = \overline{AB} \cup \overline{BC} \cup \overline{CA}$$

- A triangle is the union of three noncollinear segments. Each pair of segments has a common end point.
- Each segment is a side.
- Each endpoint is a vertex.

side   vertex

Triangles can be classified by their sides.

	Equilateral	Isosceles	Scalene
Kind of triangle	Equilateral	Isosceles	Scalene
Special property	Three congruent sides	At least two congruent sides	No congruent sides
Picture			

≅ sides are marked.

EXAMPLE 1   Classify each triangle by its sides.

The markings tell which sides are congruent.

Scalene   Equilateral   Isosceles

EXAMPLE 2   Name the vertex, legs, base, and base angles of isosceles triangle *ABC*.

The legs are the ≅ sides.
Base ∠'s are opposite the legs.

Vertex: *A*, legs: $\overline{AB}$ and $\overline{AC}$,
base: $\overline{BC}$, base ∠'s: ∠*B* and ∠*C*

Triangles can be classified by their angles.

Kind of triangle ⟶ Acute | Obtuse

Special property ⟶ Three acute angles | One obtuse angle

Kind of triangle ⟶ Right | Equiangular

Special property ⟶ One right angle | Three congruent angles

≅ ∠'s are marked.

EXAMPLE 3   Classify each triangle by its angles.

Obtuse | Right | Equiangular

EXAMPLE 4   True or False? Some obtuse triangles are isosceles. Make a sketch to support your answer.

True.

· The obtuse ∠ is included between the legs.

ORAL EXERCISES

Classify each triangle by its sides.

1.

2.

3.

4.

Classify each triangle by its angles.

5.

6.

7.

8.

EXERCISES

PART A

Draw a picture of a triangle with the given properties.

1. Both obtuse and scalene
2. Both right and isosceles
3. Both acute and isosceles
4. Both right and scalene

True or false? Make a sketch to support your answer.

5. Each equilateral triangle is isosceles.
6. Some obtuse triangles are equilateral.
7. No scalene triangle is isosceles.
8. Some right triangles are equilateral.
9. Each equiangular triangle is equilateral.
10. Each right triangle is scalene.
11. Each acute triangle is scalene.
12. Each equilateral triangle is equiangular.
13. Some isosceles triangles are equiangular.
14. No equilateral triangle is obtuse.
15. Some right triangles are obtuse.
16. Each scalene triangle is acute.

Name the vertex, legs, base, and base angles of each isosceles triangle shown.

17.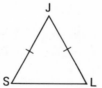

18.

PART B

Use the set diagram for all problems.

$U = \{$all triangles$\}$
$A = \{$all isosceles triangles$\}$
$B = \{$all equilateral triangles$\}$
$C = \{$all right triangles$\}$
$D = \{$all scalene triangles$\}$

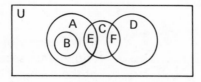

19. If set $E = A \cap C$, what triangles are in E?
20. If set $F = C \cap D$, what triangles are in F?
21. To which set or sets do acute triangles belong?
22. To which set or sets do obtuse triangles belong?

PART C

Prove each statement. Use an indirect proof.

23. An equiangular triangle cannot be an obtuse triangle.
24. A scalene triangle cannot be an isosceles triangle.

Sums of Angle Measures

OBJECTIVES
- To apply theorems about triangle angle measures
- To find the measures of exterior angles of triangles

▶ REVIEW CAPSULE

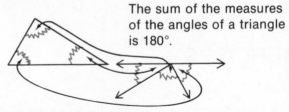

The sum of the measures of the angles of a triangle is 180°.

The sum of the measures of the angles with the same vertex on one side of a line is 180°.

EXAMPLE 1 $\angle A \cong \angle F, \angle B \cong \angle E$
$m\angle C = 40$.
Find $m\angle D$.

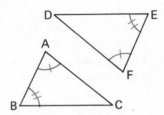

Sum of meas. of ∠'s of △ = 180°. ⟶ $m\angle A + m\angle B + m\angle C = m\angle F + m\angle E + m\angle D$
$m\angle A = m\angle F, m\angle B = m\angle E$ ⟶ $m\angle A + m\angle B \quad\quad = m\angle F + m\angle E$
Subtraction property ⟶ $\quad\quad\quad m\angle C = \quad\quad\quad\quad m\angle D$
Substitution property ⟶ $\quad\quad\quad m\angle D = 40$

Example 1 suggests a proof of the following theorem.

Theorem 4.1

(See Ex. 12.)

If two angles of a triangle are congruent to two angles of a second triangle, then the third angles of the triangles are also congruent.

EXAMPLE 2 $\angle A \cong \angle D, \angle G \cong \angle E,$
$m\angle C = 2x - 30, m\angle B = x + 5.$
Find $m\angle C$.

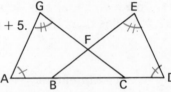

Use Theorem 4.1 ⟶ $\quad\quad m\angle C = m\angle B$
$\quad\quad 2x - 30 = x + 5$
Solve for x. ⟶ $\quad\quad\quad\quad x = 35$
$2x - 30 = 2(35) - 30$ ⟶ **Thus,** $\quad m\angle C = 40$.

Each triangle has six exterior angles. There are two congruent exterior angles at each vertex.

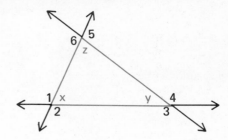

∠1 and ∠2 are ≅ vert. ∠'s.
∠3 and ∠4 are ≅ vert. ∠'s.
∠5 and ∠6 are ≅ vert. ∠'s.

Exterior Angle	Adjacent Angle	Opposite Interior Angles
∠1	∠x	∠y and ∠z
∠2	∠x	∠y and ∠z
∠3	∠y	∠z and ∠x
∠4	∠y	∠z and ∠x
∠5	∠z	∠x and ∠y
∠6	∠z	∠x and ∠y

Definition of exterior angle ⟶

> An *exterior angle* of a triangle is an angle which is adjacent and supplementary to an angle of the triangle.

EXAMPLE 3 $m\angle A = 42$, $m\angle B = 114$. Find the measure of exterior $\angle ACD$.

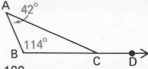

Sum of meas. of ∠'s of △ = 180°. ⟶ $m\angle A + m\angle B + m\angle ACB = 180$

$$m\angle A + m\angle B = 156$$

Subtraction property ⟶ $m\angle ACB = 34$

∠ACD and ∠ACB are supplementary. ⟶ $m\angle ACD + m\angle ACB = 180$

Thus, $m\angle ACD = 156$.

Theorem 4.2
(See Ex. 13.)

The measure of an exterior angle of a triangle is the sum of the measures of its two opposite interior angles.

Corollary

The measure of an exterior angle of a triangle is greater than the measure of either of its opposite interior angles.

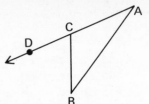

EXAMPLE 4 $m\angle A = x + 10$, $m\angle B = 3x - 5$,
$m\angle BCD = 2x + 23$.
Find $m\angle BCD$.

$\angle BCD$ is an exterior angle. ──────→

$$m\angle BCD = m\angle A + m\angle B$$
$$2x + 23 = (x + 10) + (3x - 5)$$
$$2x + 23 = 4x + 5$$
$$18 = 2x$$
$$x = 9$$

$2x + 23 = 2(9) + 23$ ──────────→ **Thus,** $m\angle BCD = 41$.

EXAMPLE 5   Show that $\overleftrightarrow{PT}$ and $\overleftrightarrow{PQ}$ cannot
both be perpendicular to ℓ.
Suppose $\overleftrightarrow{PT} \perp \ell$ and $\overleftrightarrow{PQ} \perp \ell$.
$\angle PTS$ is an exterior angle of $\triangle PQT$.

Use the corollary to Th. 4.2. ──────→ So, $m\angle PTS > m\angle PQT$.
$m\angle PQT = m\angle PTS$ But, $\angle PQT$ and $\angle PTS$ are
both right angles.

Assuming that both are perpendicular   Contradiction.
to ℓ leads to a contradiction. ──────→ **Thus,** $\overleftrightarrow{PT}$ and $\overleftrightarrow{PQ}$ cannot both be perpendicular to ℓ.

Theorem **4.3**

There is at most one line perpendicular to a given line from a given point.

(See Ex. 14.)

ORAL EXERCISES

What is the measure of each exterior angle pictured?

1.
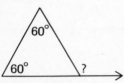

2.
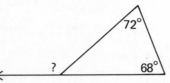

3.
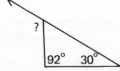

Complete each sentence with =, <, or >.

4.
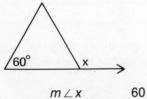

$m\angle x$ ____ 60

5.
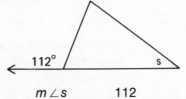

$m\angle s$ ____ 112

6.
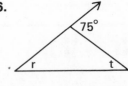

$m\angle r + m\angle t$ ____ 75

EXERCISES

PART A

Find the indicated angle measure.

1.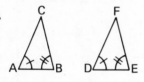

$\angle A \cong \angle D$, $\angle B \cong \angle E$
$m \angle C = x$, $m \angle F = 2x - 30$
Find $m \angle C$.

2.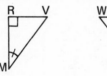

$\overline{MR} \perp \overline{RV}$, $\overline{NS} \perp \overline{WS}$
$\angle M \cong \angle N$, $m \angle V = 2x + 30$,
$m \angle W = 9x - 5$
Find $m \angle W$.

3.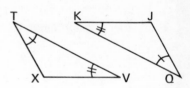

$\angle T \cong \angle Q$, $\angle V \cong \angle K$
$m \angle X = y + 80$, $m \angle J = 4y + 20$
Find $m \angle J$.

4.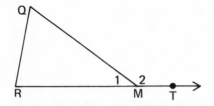

$m \angle 1 = x$, $m \angle 2 = 4x$
Find $m \angle 2$.

5.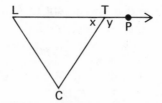

$m \angle x = 2a + 10$, $m \angle y = 5a - 5$
Find $m \angle y$.

6.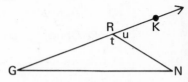

$m \angle t = 6y - 1$, $m \angle u = 2y - 3$
Find $m \angle u$.

PART B

7. Given: $\angle D \cong \angle C$
 Prove: $\angle A \cong \angle E$

8. Given: $\angle A \cong \angle B$, $\overrightarrow{CD}$
 bisects $\angle ACB$
 Prove: $\overline{CD} \perp \overline{AB}$

9. Given: $\angle A \cong \angle B$, $\overrightarrow{CD} \perp \overline{AB}$
 Prove: $\overrightarrow{CD}$ bisects $\angle ACB$

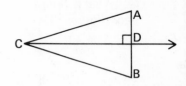

10. Given: $\angle CDE \cong \angle CED$
 $\angle A \cong \angle B$
 Prove: $\overline{DE} \parallel \overline{AB}$

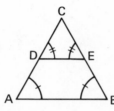

11. Given: $\overline{FD} \perp \overline{AB}$
 $\angle A \cong \angle B$
 Prove: $\angle F \cong \angle CEF$

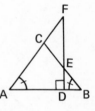

PART C

12. Prove Theorem 4.1.

13. Prove Theorem 4.2.

14. Prove Theorem 4.3.

Reflections

EXPERIMENT

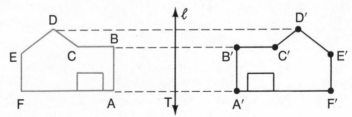

1. Copy the figure and line ℓ.

2. Draw $\overline{AT} \perp \ell$. Extend the segment to A' so that $\overline{AT} \cong \overline{TA'}$.
   Repeat for points B, C, D, E, and F.

3. Connect points A', B', C', D', E', and F'.

4. Compare this image with the original figure.

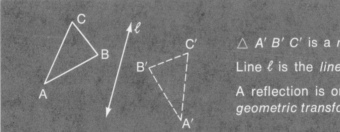

$\triangle\, A'\, B'\, C'$ is a *reflection* of $\triangle\, A\, B\, C$.

Line ℓ is the *line of symmetry*.

A reflection is one type of
geometric transformation.

Copy each figure and the line of symmetry. Draw the reflection of
each figure.

1.

2.

3.

4.

5.

6.

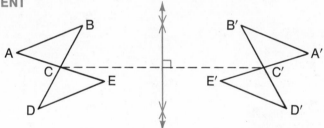

1. Copy the figure and its reflection.

2. Construct the perpendicular bisector of $\overline{CC'}$.

3. This line is the line of symmetry of the figure and its reflection.

4. Explain how to use paperfolding instead of construction to find the line of symmetry.

Copy each figure and its reflection. Construct the line of symmetry.

7.

8.

9.

10.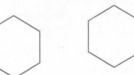

Copy each pair of figures. By folding the paper, find out which are reflections of each other.

11.

12.

13.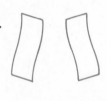

Men of Mathematics

Benjamin Banneker (1731-1806), was born in Maryland. His father was a prosperous farmer with 120 acres outside of Baltimore. Banneker attended school and also did much reading on his own, especially in astronomy, geology and physics. In 1789, Banneker was one of the two surveyors to survey and assess the land designated to become the city of Washington, D.C.

Benjamin Banneker had little formal education but his capacity for learning enabled him to become a respected authority in the fields of geology, astronomy and physics.

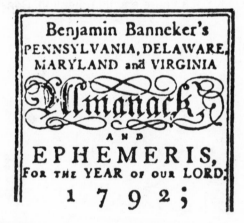

Benjamin Banneker's
PENNSYLVANIA, DELAWARE,
MARYLAND and VIRGINIA
Almanack
AND
EPHEMERIS,
FOR THE YEAR OF OUR LORD;
1 7 9 2;

In 1792 an almanac entitled "Benjamin Banneker's Almanac and Ephemeris" was published and continued for a period of seven years. His almanacs contained commentaries on school problems as well as factual material. Banneker reported his 17 year cycle calculation for the locust plagues in his almanac.

Congruent Triangles

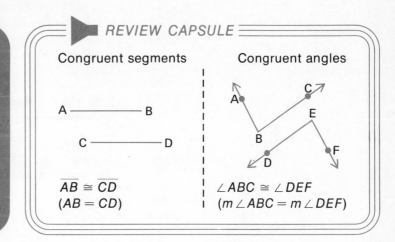

REVIEW CAPSULE

Congruent segments

Congruent angles

$\overline{AB} \cong \overline{CD}$
$(AB = CD)$

$\angle ABC \cong \angle DEF$
$(m \angle ABC = m \angle DEF)$

Congruent sides and congruent angles are marked.

$\triangle ABC \cong \triangle DEF$

Read: Triangle *ABC* is congruent to triangle *DEF*. ⟶

$\triangle ABC \cong \triangle DEF$

Corresponding ∠'s are ≅. Corresponding sides are ≅.

$\angle A \cong \angle D$	$\overline{AB} \cong \overline{DE}$
$\angle B \cong \angle E$	$\overline{BC} \cong \overline{EF}$
$\angle C \cong \angle F$	$\overline{CA} \cong \overline{FD}$

Congruent triangles have the same
size   and   shape.
Sides determine size.   Angles determine shape.

Definition of *congruent triangles* ⟶

Two triangles are *congruent* if corresponding angles are congruent and corresponding sides are congruent.

EXAMPLE 1

$\triangle XTN \cong \triangle JEP$

If $\triangle XTN \cong \triangle JEP$, which sides and which angles are corresponding?

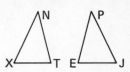

Corresponding sides ⟶ $\overline{XT}$ and $\overline{JE}$, $\overline{TN}$ and $\overline{EP}$, $\overline{NX}$ and $\overline{PJ}$
Corresponding angles ⟶ $\angle X$ and $\angle J$, $\angle T$ and $\angle E$, $\angle N$ and $\angle P$

EXAMPLE 2   Is $\triangle TJR \cong \triangle PCM$?

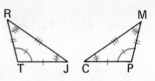

$\triangle TJR \cong \triangle PCM$

From the diagram,
$\angle T \cong \angle P$ $\overline{TJ} \cong \overline{PC}$
$\angle J \cong \angle C$ $\overline{JR} \cong \overline{CM}$
$\angle R \cong \angle M$ $\overline{RT} \cong \overline{MP}$

Corr. sides are $\cong$. Corr. $\angle$'s are $\cong$. ———→ **Thus,** $\triangle TJR \cong \triangle PCM$.

Example 2 shows that triangles do not have to be turned the same way to be congruent.

EXAMPLE 3   Complete the statement: $\triangle ZAQ \cong$ _____.
Use only the markings shown.

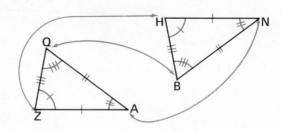

From the diagram
$\angle Z \cong \angle H$ $\overline{ZA} \cong \overline{HN}$
$\angle A \cong \angle N$ $\overline{AQ} \cong \overline{NB}$
$\angle Q \cong \angle B$ $\overline{QZ} \cong \overline{BH}$

Put corresponding parts in similar positions. ———————————→ $\triangle ZAQ \cong \triangle HNB$

A special lettering scheme is sometimes used to show congruent triangles.

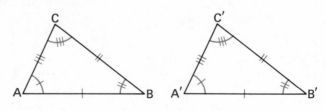

A' is read A prime.

$A \leftrightarrow A'$
$B \leftrightarrow B'$
$C \leftrightarrow C'$

$\triangle ABC \cong \triangle A'B'C'$

EXAMPLE 4   Complete the statement: $\triangle LDM \cong$ _____.
Use only the markings shown.

$\angle$'s L, D, F, and J are all $\cong$.
$L \leftrightarrow F$ or $L \leftrightarrow J$
$D \leftrightarrow J$ or $D \leftrightarrow F$
$M \leftrightarrow W$

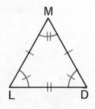

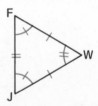

$\triangle LDM \cong \triangle FJW$, or $\triangle LDM \cong \triangle JFW$

EXERCISES

1. Which triangle seems to be congruent to △ABC?

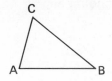
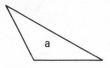

2. Which triangle does not seem congruent to the other three?

Complete the congruence statement. Use only the markings shown.
Is more than one statement possible for any pair?

3.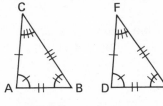

△ABC ≅ _____

4.

△MNO ≅ _____

5.

△TNZ ≅ _____

6.

_____ ≅ △RVX

7.

_____ ≅ △RST

8.

_____ ≅ △BUZ

Draw labeled diagrams to illustrate each.

9. △ABC ≅ △XYZ

10. △XYZ ≅ △X′Y′Z′

11. △RXA ≅ △BFJ

12. △LVC ≅ △MPI,
LV = 3x + 2, MP = 5x − 8.
Find LV.

13. △LVC ≅ △MPI,
m∠C = 3x − 23, m∠I = 2x − 5.
Find m∠I.

S S S Congruence

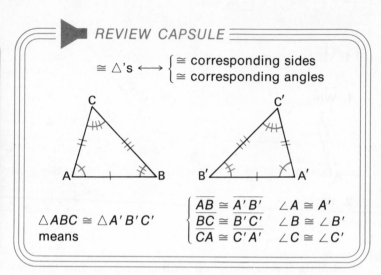

REVIEW CAPSULE

$$\cong \triangle\text{'s} \longleftrightarrow \begin{cases} \cong \text{ corresponding sides} \\ \cong \text{ corresponding angles} \end{cases}$$

$\triangle ABC \cong \triangle A'B'C'$ means

$$\begin{cases} \overline{AB} \cong \overline{A'B'} & \angle A \cong \angle A' \\ \overline{BC} \cong \overline{B'C'} & \angle B \cong \angle B' \\ \overline{CA} \cong \overline{C'A'} & \angle C \cong \angle C' \end{cases}$$

EXAMPLE 1 The three sticks represent the sides of a triangle. Connect the loose ends. How many different triangles can you make?

Only one triangle is possible.

EXAMPLE 2 Fasten the three sticks together to make a triangle. How many different triangles can be made out of the three sticks?

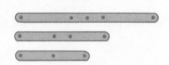

Try this experiment with sticks of several different sizes.

Only one triangle is possible.

construction

A triangle, given the three sides

A ——————— B
C ————— D
E ———— F

GIVEN
Segments $\overline{AB}$, $\overline{CD}$, $\overline{EF}$
CONSTRUCT
$\triangle A'B'C'$ with sides
congruent to $\overline{AB}$, $\overline{CD}$, $\overline{EF}$

STRATEGY
Copy the three segments,
joining each pair
at a common vertex.

Copy $\overline{AB}$:
Construct $\overline{A'B'} \cong \overline{AB}$

Copy $\overline{CD}$ and $\overline{EF}$.
Using center A' and radius $\overline{CD}$,
draw an arc.
Using center B' and radius $\overline{EF}$
draw another arc.

Complete $\triangle A'B'C'$.
Draw $\overline{A'C'}$ and $\overline{B'C'}$.

Conclusion: $\triangle A'B'C'$ is the desired triangle.

Examples 1 and 2 and the construction suggest this.

Postulate 16
(S S S for $\cong$ $\triangle$'s)

Two triangles are congruent if the three sides of
one are congruent respectively to the three sides
of the other. (side-side-side congruence)

EXAMPLE 3   Which two triangles are congruent?
Use only the markings shown.

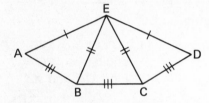

The three sides of $\triangle AEB$ are $\cong$ to the
three sides of $\triangle DEC$.
Use Postulate 16. ————————→

$\overline{AE} \cong \overline{DE}$, $\overline{AB} \cong \overline{DC}$, $\overline{BE} \cong \overline{CE}$
Thus, $\triangle AEB \cong \triangle DEC$.

EXAMPLE 4

Analysis: Show that three sides of △ABP are ≅ to three sides of △CDP.

A bisector divides a segment into two ≅ segments.

Postulate 16 ──────────────────────→

Given: P bisects $\overline{AC}$, P bisects $\overline{BD}$, $\overline{AB} \cong \overline{CD}$.
Prove: △ABP ≅ △CDP

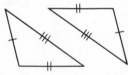

Proof

Statements	Reasons
1. $\overline{AP} \cong \overline{CP}$	1. Def. of bisector
2. $\overline{BP} \cong \overline{DP}$	2. Same as 1
3. $\overline{AB} \cong \overline{CD}$	3. Given
4. ∴ △ABP ≅ △CDP	4. S S S for ≅ △'s

EXERCISES

PART A

Tell whether each pair of triangles is congruent. Use only the markings shown.

1.

2.

3.

4.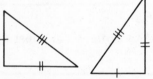

5.

6.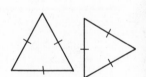

Are the given triangles congruent? Explain your reasoning.

7. $\overline{AB} \cong \overline{DE}$, $\overline{BC} \cong \overline{EF}$, $\overline{AC} \cong \overline{DF}$

8. Isosceles △'s MNO and PQR, $\overline{MO} \cong \overline{PR}$

9. $\overline{MR} \cong \overline{XL}$, Q bisects $\overline{RX}$ and $\overline{ML}$

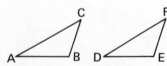

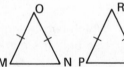

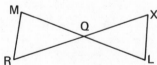

Find the unknown lengths.

10. △KLM ≅ △RST, KL = 5. Find RS.

11. △PQR ≅ △XYZ, △PQR is equilateral, PQ = 7. Find QR and XZ.

12. △NZV ≅ △TZL, NT = 12 Find NZ.

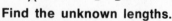

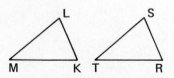

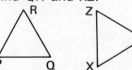

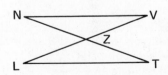

13. Given $\overline{MP} \cong \overline{ON}$, $\overline{OP} \cong \overline{MN}$
Prove: $\triangle MNO \cong \triangle OPM$

14. Given: $\overline{RU} \cong \overline{TU}$, $\overline{RS} \cong \overline{TS}$
Prove: $\triangle URS \cong \triangle UTS$

15. Given: $\overline{MT} \cong \overline{XR}$, V bisects $\overline{MX}$ and $\overline{RT}$
Prove: $\triangle MVT \cong \triangle XVR$

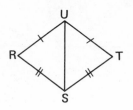

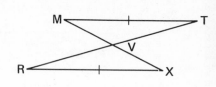

16. If $\triangle SMN \cong \triangle VPR$, then which sides are congruent?

17. If $\triangle ANQ \cong \triangle MVX$, then which angles are congruent?

18. Draw a picture of an acute triangle. Construct a triangle congruent to it.

19. Draw a picture of an obtuse triangle. Construct a triangle congruent to it.

PART B

20. Given: $\triangle HJK$ and $\triangle CQD$ are equilateral, $\overline{HJ} \cong \overline{CQ}$.
Prove: $\triangle HJK \cong \triangle CQD$

21. Given: $\triangle MXV$ is equilateral, $\overline{MX} \cong \overline{MT}$, $\overline{VX} \cong \overline{VT}$.
Prove: $\triangle MTV$ is equilateral.

22. Given: $\overline{JP} \cong \overline{WL}$, $\overline{JA} \cong \overline{WN}$, $\overline{AL} \cong \overline{NP}$
Prove: $\triangle JAL \cong \triangle WNP$

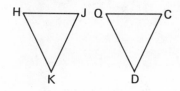

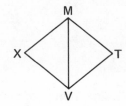

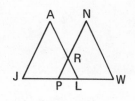

23. Construct an equilateral $\triangle ABC$ with $\overline{AB} \cong \overline{RN}$.

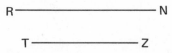

24. Construct an isosceles $\triangle WXY$ with $\overline{WX} \cong \overline{RN}$ and $\overline{XY} \cong \overline{YW} \cong \overline{TZ}$.

PART C

25. Given: $\triangle XYZ$, $\triangle XYW$, $\triangle XWZ$, and $\triangle YZW$ are all equilateral.
Prove: $\triangle XYZ \cong \triangle XYW$ $\cong \triangle XWZ \cong \triangle YZW$

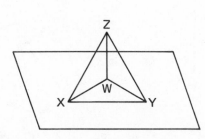

26. Given: $\triangle XYZ$ is equilateral, $\overline{XW} \cong \overline{YW} \cong \overline{ZW}$.
Prove: $\triangle XWY \cong \triangle YWZ$ $\cong \triangle ZWX$

Slides

1. Copy the figure and parallel lines ℓ and m.
2. Find the reflection of the figure about line ℓ. Find the reflection of this new figure about line m.
3. Compare this last figure with the original figure.

△ X′ Y′ Z′ is a *slide image* of △ X Y Z.

$\overrightarrow{Y Y'}$ is a *slide arrow*. It shows the path of the slide.

Two reflections about parallel lines of symmetry give a slide.

Copy each figure and the parallel lines of symmetry. Find the slide image.

1.

2.

3.
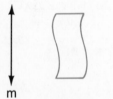

4.

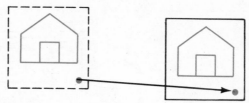

1. Copy the figure. Place a dot at the end of the slide arrow.

2. Slide the dot on the copy along the slide arrow to the arrowhead. Use carbon paper to trace the image.

3. This image is the slide image with respect to the given slide arrow.

Copy each figure and slide arrow. Find the slide image with respect to the given slide arrow.

5.

6.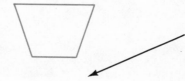

7.

8.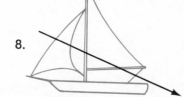

Copy each figure and slide arrows m and n. Find the slide image with respect to m, and then with respect to n.

9.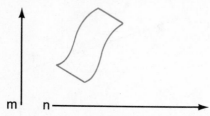

10.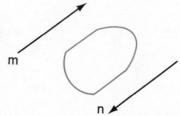

Rotations

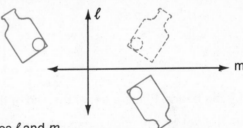

EXPERIMENT

1. Copy the figure and lines ℓ and m.

2. Find the reflection of the figure about line ℓ. Find the reflection of this new figure about line m.

3. Compare this last figure with the original figure.

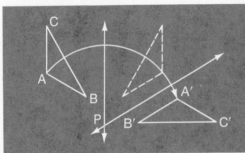

$\triangle A'B'C'$ is the *rotation image* of $\triangle ABC$ about P with respect to the turn arrow $\overrightarrow{AA'}$.

Two reflections about intersecting lines of symmetry give a rotation.

Copy each figure and the intersecting lines of symmetry. Find the rotation image.

1.

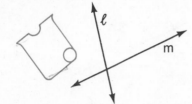

2.

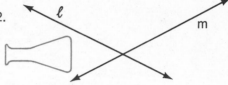

3.

4.

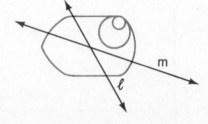

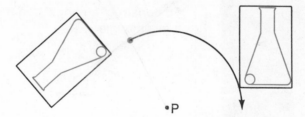

1. Copy the figure. Place a dot at the end of the turn arrow.

2. Turn the copy about *P* until the dot is at the other end of the turn arrow. Use carbon paper to trace the image.

3. This image is the rotation image about *P* with respect to the given turn arrow.

Copy each figure, turn center, and turn arrow. Find the rotation image about *P* with respect to the given turn arrow.

5.

6.

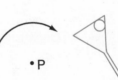

7.

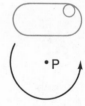

8.

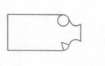

9.

10. Copy the figures and find the turn center.

11. Copy the figures. Is there more than one turn center?

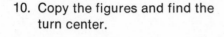

S A S and A S A Congruence

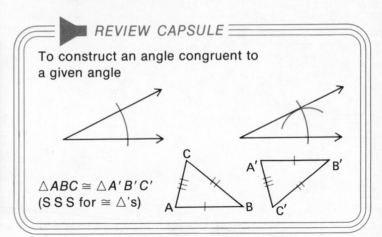

▶ REVIEW CAPSULE

To construct an angle congruent to a given angle

$\triangle ABC \cong \triangle A'B'C'$
(S S S for $\cong \triangle$'s)

EXAMPLE 1   Construct $\triangle A'B'C'$ so that $\overline{A'B'} \cong \overline{AB}$, $\angle B' \cong \angle B$, and $\overline{B'C'} \cong \overline{BC}$. Does $\triangle A'B'C'$ appear to be congruent to $\triangle ABC$?

1. Copy $\overline{AB}$:
Construct $\overline{A'B'} \cong \overline{AB}$.

2. Copy $\angle B$ at vertex B':
Construct $\angle A'B'D \cong \angle ABC$

$\angle A'B'D$ is copied from the original $\triangle ABC$.

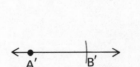

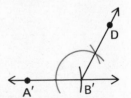

3. Copy $\overline{BC}$ along $\overrightarrow{B'D}$:
Construct $\overline{B'C'} \cong \overline{BC}$.

4. Draw $\overline{A'C'}$.

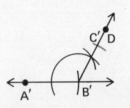

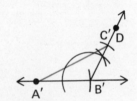

Tracing $\triangle A'B'C'$ and fitting it on top of $\triangle ABC$ will show that they have the same size and shape. ───────→

Conclusion: $\triangle A'B'C'$ is the required triangle. $\triangle A'B'C'$ appears congruent to $\triangle ABC$.

Postulate 17
(S A S for ≅ △'s)

Two triangles are congruent if two sides and an included angle of one are congruent respectively to two sides and an included angle of the other.

∠R is the included ∠ for sides $\overline{RV}$ and $\overline{RT}$.
∠S is the included ∠ for sides $\overline{SM}$ and $\overline{SJ}$.

SAS for ≅ △'s. ⟶

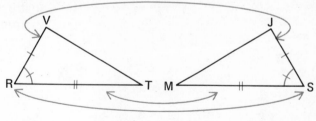

△VRT ≅ △JSM

EXAMPLE 2   In △XYZ, which angle is included between each pair of sides?

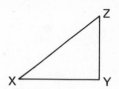

The vertex of the included angle is the common endpoint of the two sides.

Pair of sides	Included angle
$\overline{XY}$ and $\overline{YZ}$	∠Y
$\overline{YZ}$ and $\overline{ZX}$	∠Z
$\overline{ZX}$ and $\overline{XY}$	∠X

EXAMPLE 3   Are the triangles congruent? If so, write a congruence statement.

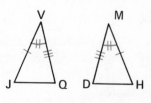

SAS for ≅ △'s. ⟶   Yes. △JVQ ≅ △HMD.

EXAMPLE 4   Given: O is the midpoint of $\overline{RK}$ and $\overline{HS}$
Prove: △ROH ≅ △KOS

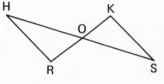

Analysis: △'s can be proved congruent by S A S. Midpoints determine ≅ segments.

Proof

Statements		Reasons
1. $\overline{RO} \cong \overline{KO}$	(S)	1. Def. of midpoint
2. ∠ROH ≅ ∠KOS	(A)	2. Vert. ∠'s are ≅.
3. $\overline{HO} \cong \overline{SO}$	(S)	3. Same as 1.
4. ∴ △ ROH ≅ △KOS		4. SAS for ≅ △'s

∠ROH is included between $\overline{RO}$ and $\overline{HO}$.

EXAMPLE 5 Construct $\triangle A'B'C'$ so that $\angle A' \cong \angle A$, $A'B' \cong AB$, and $\angle B' \cong \angle B$. Does $\triangle A'B'C'$ appear to be congruent to $\triangle ABC$?

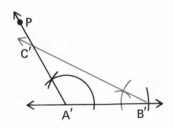

1. Copy $\angle A$ and $\overline{AB}$:
   Construct $A'B' \cong \overline{AB}$,
   Construct $\angle PA'B' \cong \angle CAB$

2. Copy $\angle B$:
   Construct $\angle A'B'C' \cong \angle ABC$

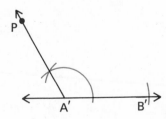

Tracing $\triangle A'B'C'$ and fitting it on top of $\triangle ABC$ will show that they have the same size and shape.

Conclusion: $\triangle A'B'C'$ is the required triangle. $\triangle A'B'C'$ appears congruent to $\triangle ABC$.

Theorem 4.4
(ASA for $\cong$ $\triangle$'s)

Two triangles are congruent if two angles and an included side of one are congruent respectively to two angles and an included side of the other.

The endpoints of the included side are the vertices of the two angles.

$\overline{BG}$ is included between $\angle B$ and $\angle G$.
$\overline{GS}$ is included between $\angle G$ and $\angle S$.
$\overline{SB}$ is included between $\angle S$ and $\angle B$.

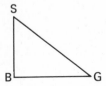

EXAMPLE 6 Given: $\overline{NP}$ bisects $\angle LNM$, $NP \perp LM$
Prove: $\triangle LPN \cong \triangle MPN$

Analysis: $\triangle$'s can be proved $\cong$ by ASA. $\angle$ bisector forms $\cong$ $\angle$'s.

$\angle$ bisector forms two $\cong$ $\angle$'s.

Proof

Statements	Reasons
1. $\angle 1 \cong \angle 2$	1. Def. of $\angle$ bisector
2. $\overline{NP} \cong \overline{NP}$	2. Reflexive prop.
3. $\angle 3$ and $\angle 4$ are rt. $\angle$'s	3. $\perp$ lines form rt. $\angle$'s.
4. $\angle 3 \cong \angle 4$	4. All rt. $\angle$'s are $\cong$.
5. $\therefore \triangle LPN \cong \triangle MPN$	5. ASA for $\cong$ $\triangle$'s

ORAL EXERCISES

For each pair of sides of each triangle, tell which angle is the included angle.

1. 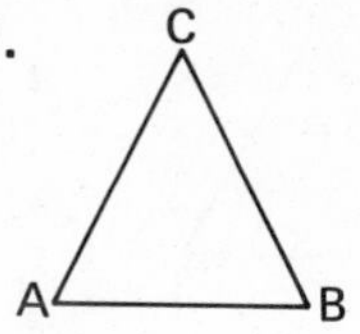

2. 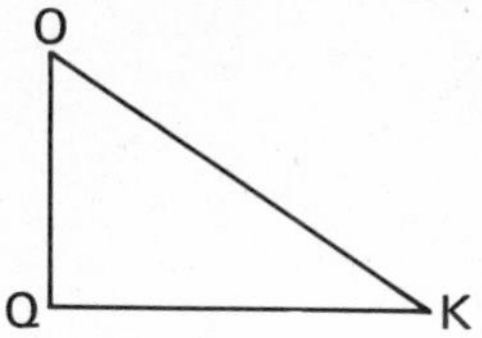

3. 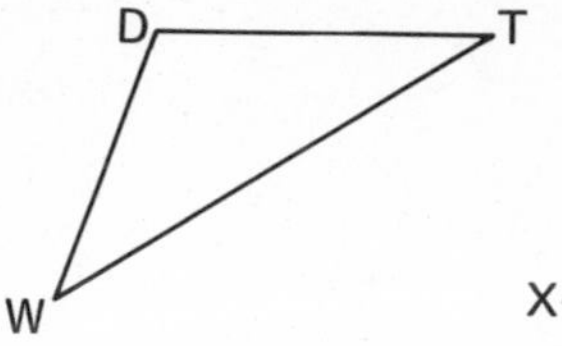

4. 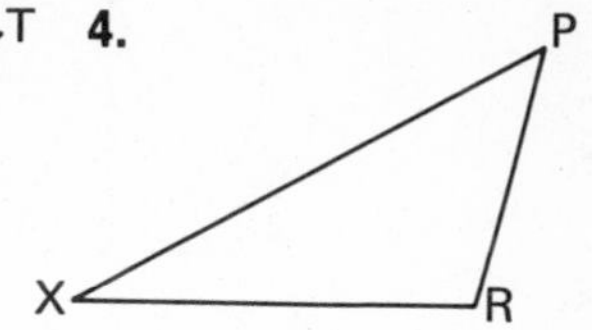

For each pair of angles of each triangle, tell which side is the included side.

5. 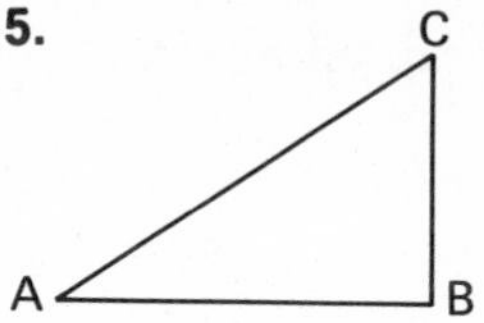

6. 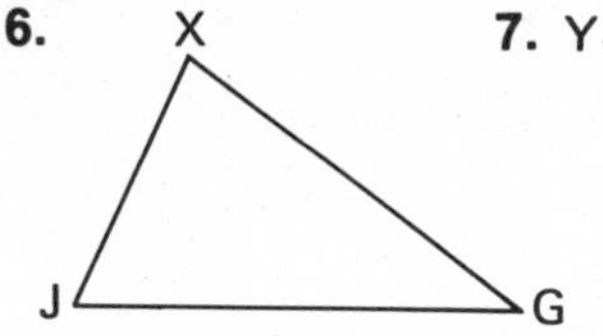

7. 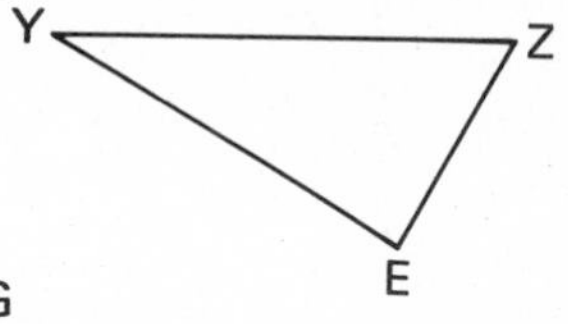

8. 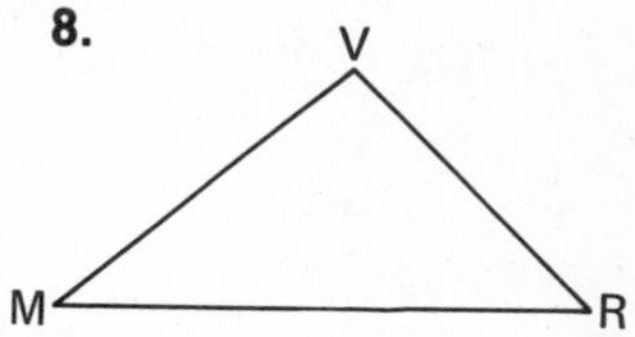

EXERCISES

PART A

1. If $\triangle LJK \cong \triangle CPQ$, which sides are congruent? **2.** If $\triangle XTN \cong \triangle GKJ$, which angles are congruent?

Are the triangles congruent? Explain your reasoning.

3. $\overline{AB} \cong \overline{DE}$, $\overline{BC} \cong \overline{EF}$, $\overline{CB} \perp \overline{AB}$, $\overline{FE} \perp \overline{DE}$.

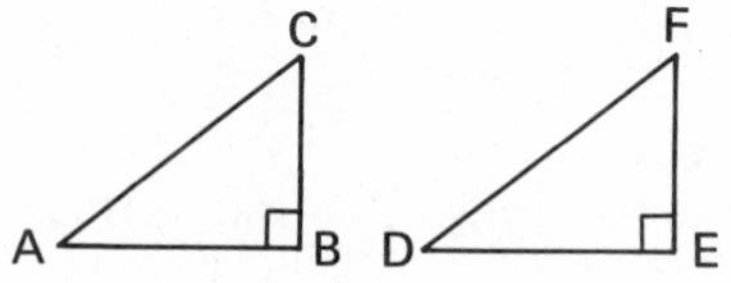

4. $\triangle XYZ$ and $\triangle RST$ are both equiangular.

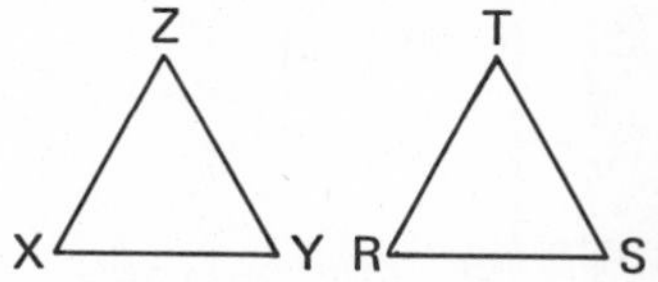

5. $\triangle APQ$ and $\triangle CXY$ are both right $\triangle$'s, $m\angle P = 47$ $m\angle X = 47$, $\overline{PQ} \cong \overline{XY}$.

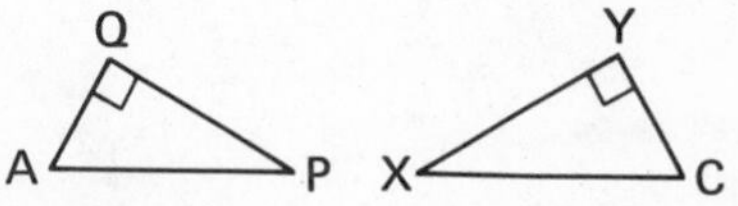

6. Draw an acute triangle. Construct a triangle congruent to it by SAS. By ASA.

7. Draw an obtuse triangle. Construct a triangle congruent to it by SAS. By ASA.

8. Given: $\overline{AE} \cong \overline{CE}$, $\overline{DE} \cong \overline{BE}$
Prove: $\triangle ADE \cong \triangle CBE$

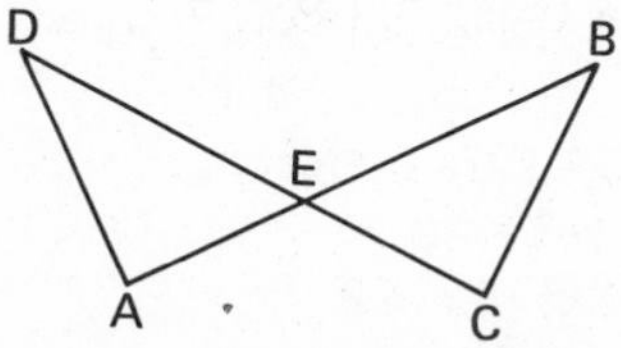

9. Given: E bisects $\overline{AB}$, $\angle A \cong \angle B$.
Prove: $\triangle AED \cong \triangle BEC$

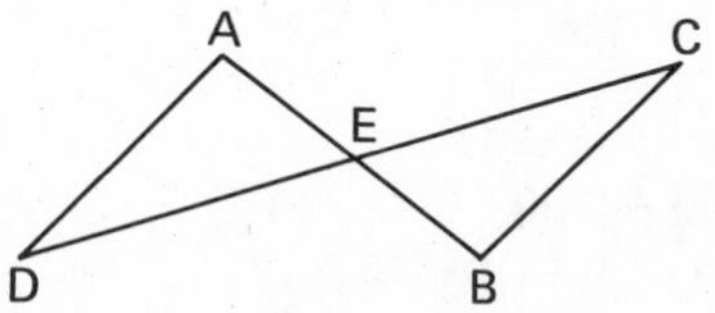

10. Given: $\angle RUS \cong \angle TUS$, $\overline{RU} \cong \overline{TU}$
Prove: $\triangle RUS \cong \triangle TUS$

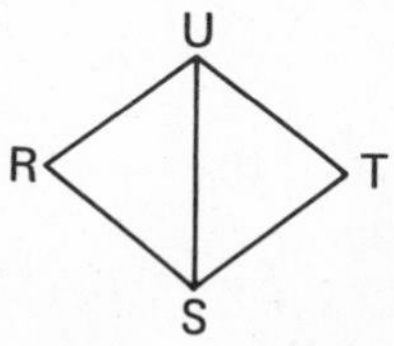

PART B

11. Given: $\overline{AC} \cong \overline{BC}$, $\overline{CD}$ bisects $\angle ACB$.
Prove: $\triangle ADC \cong \triangle BDC$

12. Given: $\overline{ZW} \perp \overline{XY}$; $\overline{ZW}$ bisects $\overline{XY}$.
Prove: $\triangle XWZ \cong \triangle YWZ$

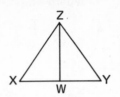

13. Given: $\overline{RU} \parallel \overline{ST}$, $\overline{RS} \parallel \overline{UT}$
Prove: $\triangle RUS \cong \triangle TSU$

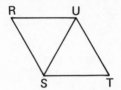

14. Construct a triangle with sides congruent to $\overline{GH}$ and $\overline{MN}$ and the included angle congruent to $\angle A$.

G ———————————— H

M ——————————————— N

15. Construct a triangle with angles congruent to $\angle A$ and $\angle B$ and the included side congruent to $\overline{MN}$.

PART C

16. Given: $\overline{ZW} \perp$ all lines in plane p through W. $\overline{XW}$ and $\overline{YW}$ are in p. $\angle ZXW \cong \angle YZW$.
Prove: $\triangle XWZ \cong \triangle YWZ$

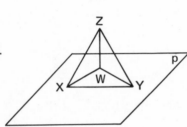

17. Given: $\triangle XYZ$, $\triangle XYW$, $\triangle XWZ$, $\triangle WYZ$ are all equiangular.
Prove: $\triangle XYZ \cong \triangle XYW \cong \triangle XWZ \cong \triangle WYZ$

Algebra Review

To factor a trinomial like $x^2 - 7x + 12$
1. Try factors of x^2 and 12.
2. Determine signs for correct middle term.

$(1x)(\boxminus 2) = -2x$
$(\boxminus 3)(1x) = -3x$
$(-2x) + (-3x) = -5x$

EXAMPLE   Factor $x^2 - 5x + 6$.

1x ⟋ □2
1x ⟍ □3

Thus, $x^2 - 5x + 6 = (x - 2)(x - 3)$.

Factor $9x^2 - 25$.
↑
Difference of squares
$(3x)^2 - (5)^2$
Thus, $9x^2 - 25 = (3x + 5)(3x - 5)$.

Factor.

1. $x^2 - 7x + 10$

2. $x^2 - x - 12$

3. $x^2 + 9x + 18$

4. $x^2 - 36$

5. $x^2 - 100$

6. $4x^2 - 49$

7. $2x^2 - 7x + 3$

8. $2x^2 + 11x + 15$

9. $3x^2 - x - 2$

Other Triangle Congruences

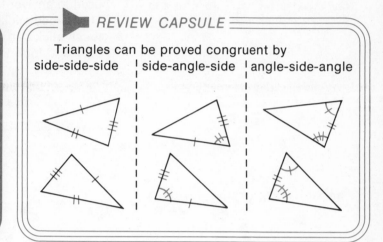

▶ *REVIEW CAPSULE*

Triangles can be proved congruent by

| side-side-side | side-angle-side | angle-side-angle |

EXAMPLE 1

$\angle M \cong \angle X$, $\angle Q \cong \angle L$, $\overline{QD} \cong \overline{LH}$

Is $\triangle MQD \cong \triangle XLH$?

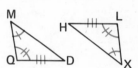

$\overline{QD}$ is not included between $\angle M$ and $\angle Q$.
$\overline{LH}$ is not included between $\angle X$ and $\angle L$.

The information given does not fit any of the three congruence patterns already used.

Use Theorem 4.1.
ASA for $\cong \triangle$'s.

However, since $\angle M \cong \angle X$ and $\angle Q \cong \angle L$, then $\angle D \cong \angle H$.

Therefore, $\triangle MQD \cong \triangle XLH$.

This suggests another congruence theorem.

Theorem 4.5

(AAS for $\cong \triangle$'s)

Two triangles are congruent if two angles and a side opposite one of them are congruent respectively to two angles and the corresponding side of the other.

ANALYSIS
Show that $\angle C \cong \angle C'$.
Then use ASA for $\cong \triangle$'s.

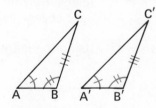

GIVEN
$\angle A \cong \angle A'$, $\angle B \cong \angle B'$, $\overline{BC} \cong \overline{B'C'}$

PROVE
$\triangle ABC \cong \triangle A'B'C'$

PROOF

(See Exercise 20.)

| | EXAMPLE 2 | Is side-side-angle a triangle congruence pattern? |

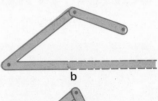

The hinged sticks have two sides and one angle (not included) fixed.

A hinged stick can be used to answer this. The hinged stick *s* can touch stick *b* in two places to form triangles.

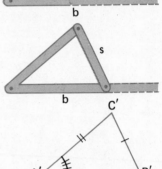

Two different triangles are formed.

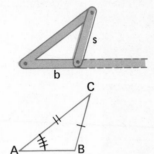

△ABC and △A′B′C′ are not congruent by SSA.

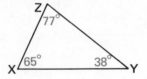

$$\triangle ABC \not\cong \triangle A'B'C'$$

Side-side-angle is not a triangle congruence pattern.

Two triangles with two sides and a nonincluded angle of one congruent respectively to two sides and a nonincluded angle of the other are *not* necessarily congruent.

EXAMPLE 3   Is angle-angle-angle a triangle congruence pattern?

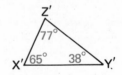

△XYZ and △X′Y′Z′ are not congruent.

No. ∠X ≅ ∠X′, ∠Y ≅ ∠Y′, ∠Z ≅ ∠Z′. But, △XYZ ≇ △X′Y′Z′.

Angle-angle-angle is not a triangle congruence pattern.

Two triangles with all three angles of one congruent respectively to the three angles of the other are *not* necessarily congruent.

EXAMPLE 4   Using the markings, tell if the triangles are congruent.

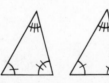

No. Angle-angle-angle is not a congruence pattern.

Yes. Angle-angle-side is a congruence pattern.

SUMMARY

You can prove triangles congruent by

 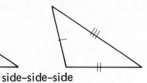

side-side-side

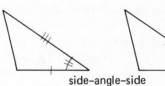

side-angle-side

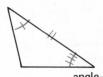 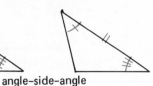

angle-side-angle

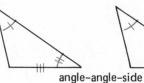

angle-angle-side

You cannot prove triangles congruent by

 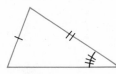

side-side-angle

angle-angle-angle

ORAL EXERCISES

Using the markings, tell which triangles are congruent. Explain your reasoning.

1.

2.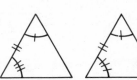

3.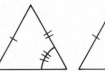

4.

5.

6.

7.

8.

9.

EXERCISES

PART A

According to the information given, is △*RVX* ≅ △*HLT*? If so, why?

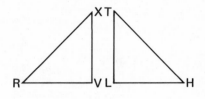

1. $\overline{RV} \cong \overline{HL}$, $\overline{VX} \cong \overline{LT}$, $\angle V \cong \angle L$
2. $\angle X \cong \angle T$, $\angle R \cong \angle H$, $\overline{XV} \cong \overline{TL}$
3. $\overline{RX} \cong \overline{HT}$, $\overline{RV} \cong \overline{HL}$, $\angle X \cong \angle T$
4. $\angle R \cong \angle H$, $\angle V \cong \angle L$, $\angle X \cong \angle T$
5. $\angle R \cong \angle H$, $\overline{XV} \cong \overline{TL}$, $\angle X \cong \angle T$
6. $\overline{RX} \cong \overline{HT}$, $\overline{RV} \cong \overline{HL}$, $\overline{VX} \cong \overline{LT}$
7. $\angle V \cong \angle L$, $\angle R \cong \angle H$, $\overline{VR} \cong \overline{LH}$
8. $\overline{RX} \cong \overline{HT}$, $\angle X \cong \angle T$, $\overline{XV} \cong \overline{TL}$
9. $\overline{XV} \perp \overline{RV}$, $\overline{TL} \perp \overline{HL}$, $\overline{RV} \cong \overline{HL}$
10. $\overline{RX} \cong \overline{HT}$, $\angle R \cong \angle H$, $\angle X \cong \angle T$

11. Given: *X* is the midpoint of $\overline{TC}$, $\angle T \cong \angle C$
    Prove: △*XAT* ≅ △*XVC*

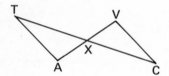

12. Given: $\overline{QL}$ bisects $\angle RQV$,
    $\angle R \cong \angle V$
    Prove: △*RLQ* ≅ △*VLQ*

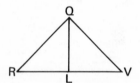

13. Given: $\overline{NT} \cong \overline{WQ}$, $\overline{WT} \cong \overline{NQ}$,
    Prove: △*NTW* ≅ △*WQN*

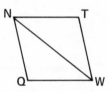

14. Given: $\overline{RL} \cong \overline{XL}$, $\angle R \cong \angle X$
    Prove: △*RLG* ≅ △*XLB*

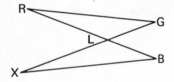

15. Given: $\overline{GH} \perp \overline{MB}$;
    $\overline{GH}$ bisects $\overline{MB}$.
    Prove: △*MHG* ≅ △*BHG*

16. Given: $\overline{DH} \parallel \overline{SM}$, $\angle S \cong \angle H$
    Prove: △*DSM* ≅ △*MHD*

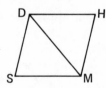

PART B

17. Given: $\overline{VT} \parallel \overline{QP}$, $\overline{QA} \parallel \overline{ST}$,
    $\angle V \cong \angle P$, $\overline{QA} \cong \overline{TS}$
    Prove: △*VAQ* ≅ △*PST*

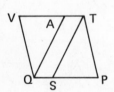

18. Given: $\overline{VQ} \parallel \overline{AG}$, $\angle 1 \cong \angle 3$
    $\angle J \cong \angle S$, $\overline{JQ} \cong \overline{SA}$
    Prove: △*VQJ* ≅ △*GAS*

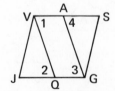

19. Given: $\angle ALT \cong \angle AHT$
    $\overline{AL} \cong \overline{TH}$, $\overline{GL} \cong \overline{VH}$
    Prove: △*AGL* ≅ △*TVH*

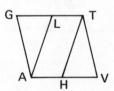

20. Prove Theorem 4.5.

Congruent Triangles and Transformations

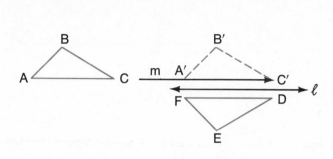

$\triangle DEF$ is the image of $\triangle ABC$.
A slide followed by a reflection.

$\triangle UVW$ is the image of $\triangle RST$.
A rotation followed by a slide.

> *Congruent triangles* are triangles which are images of each other by a reflection, slide, rotation, or a combination of these.

Show that the pairs of triangles are congruent by finding the slide, rotation, reflection, or combination.

1.
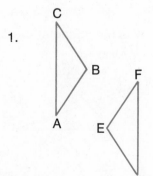

2.
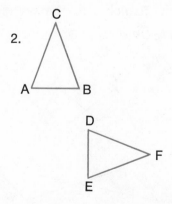

3.
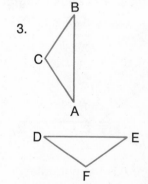

Chapter Four Review

Classify each triangle by its sides and by its angles. [p. 101]

1.

2.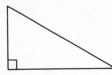

3.

4.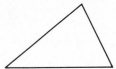

Find *m*∠x. [p. 104]

5.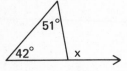

6.

7.

8.

Using the markings, which triangles are congruent? Explain your reasoning. [p. 111]

9.

10.

11.

12. Draw a triangle which is both obtuse and scalene. Construct a triangle congruent to it. [p. 101, 122]

13. Draw two triangles which have congruent corresponding angles but are not congruent triangles. [p. 127]

14. *m*∠q = 3x − 2, *m*∠r = 2x + 14, *m*∠y = 6x − 2. Find *m*∠y. [p. 104]

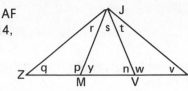

AF

15. ∠q ≅ ∠v, ∠y ≅ ∠n, *m*∠r = 5x + 5, *m*∠t = 6x − 10. Find *m*∠r. [p. 104]

Are the given triangles congruent? Explain your reasoning. [p. 127]

16. $\overline{RW} \cong \overline{NK}$, $\overline{WT} \cong \overline{KC}$, $\overline{TR} \cong \overline{CN}$

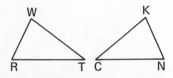

17. $\overline{CK} \cong \overline{BJ}$, ∠C ≅ ∠B, $\overline{CY} \cong \overline{BX}$

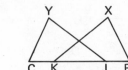

18. W is the midpoint of $\overline{LB}$. $\overline{UB} \cong \overline{JL}$

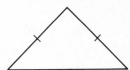

19. Given: F is the midpoint of $\overline{PW}$ and $\overline{CJ}$. Prove: △CFP ≅ △JFW [p. 127]

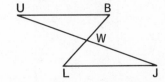

20. Given: ∠P ≅ ∠W, $\overline{CF} \cong \overline{JF}$ Prove: △CPF ≅ △JWF [p. 127]

Chapter Four Test

Classify each triangle by its sides and by its angles.

1.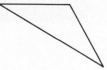

2.

3.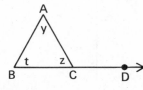

4.

Find $m \angle x$.

5.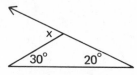

6.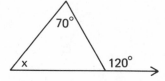

7.

Using the markings, which triangles are congruent? Explain your reasoning.

8.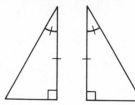

9.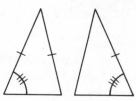

10.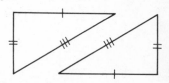

11. Draw a triangle which is both obtuse and isosceles.

12. Draw an equilateral triangle. Construct a triangle congruent to it.

Find the indicated angle measures.

13. $m \angle ACD = 5x + 10$,
$m \angle t = 40$, $m \angle y = x + 30$.
Find $m \angle z$.

14. $\angle t \cong \angle z$,
$m \angle y = 30$.
Find $m \angle ACD$.

15. Given: Z is the midpoint of $\overline{JN}$ and $\overline{KC}$
Prove: $\triangle JZC \cong \triangle NZK$

16. Given: $\overline{MO} \parallel \overline{TL}$, $\overline{TM} \parallel \overline{LO}$
Prove: $\triangle TOM \cong \triangle OTL$

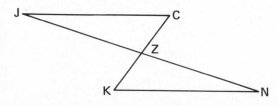

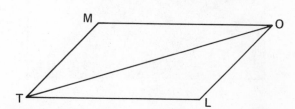

USING CONGRUENT TRIANGLES

How Many Ways?

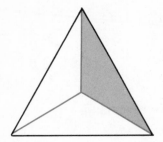 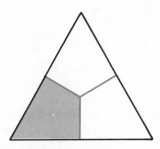 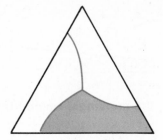

How many other ways can you find to
divide an equilateral triangular
region into three congruent regions?

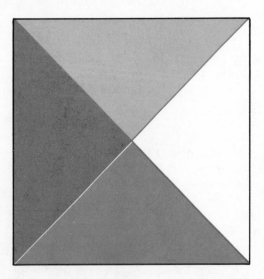

Can you show some other ways to
divide a square into four congruent
regions?

Corresponding Parts of Triangles

▶ REVIEW CAPSULE

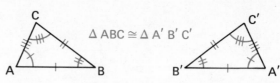

$\triangle ABC \cong \triangle A'B'C'$

In congruent triangles, corresponding sides are $\cong$ and corresponding angles are $\cong$.

The definition of $\cong \triangle$'s tells this.

$$\triangle ABC \cong \triangle A'B'C'$$
means

$\overline{AB} \cong \overline{A'B'}$	$\angle A \cong \angle A'$
$\overline{BC} \cong \overline{B'C'}$	$\angle B \cong \angle B'$
$\overline{CA} \cong \overline{C'A'}$	$\angle C \cong \angle C'$

This gives a new way of proving segments or angles congruent.

Corresponding parts of congruent triangles are congruent.

EXAMPLE 1 $\triangle SJC \cong \triangle NQP$. Name the congruent corresponding angles. Draw a diagram.

$\triangle SJC \cong \triangle NQP$

$\leftrightarrow$ means corresponds to.

$\angle S \leftrightarrow \angle N$
$\angle J \leftrightarrow \angle Q$
$\angle C \leftrightarrow \angle P$

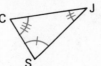

EXAMPLE 2   Given: $\angle 2 \cong \angle 4$, $\angle 3 \cong \angle 1$
Prove: $\overline{AB} \cong \overline{CD}$

ANALYSIS

Corr. sides of $\cong \triangle$'s are $\cong$.

$\overline{AC}$ and $\overline{CA}$ are two names for the common side.

Proof

Statements	Reasons
1. $\angle 2 \cong \angle 4$ (A)	1. Given
2. $\overline{AC} \cong \overline{CA}$ (S)	2. Reflexive property
3. $\angle 3 \cong \angle 1$ (A)	3. Given
4. $\triangle ABC \cong \triangle CDA$	4. ASA for $\cong \triangle$'s
5. $\therefore \overline{AB} \cong \overline{CD}$	5. Corr. sides of $\cong \triangle$'s are $\cong$.

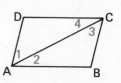

EXAMPLE 3 $\overline{AD}$ bisects $\overline{BC}$; $\overline{AD} \perp \overline{BC}$;
$m \angle BAD = 28$.
Find $m \angle C$.

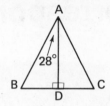

$\overline{AD}$ bisects $\overline{BC}$. $\longrightarrow$	$\overline{BD} \cong \overline{CD}$
$\overline{AD} \perp \overline{BC}$ $\longrightarrow$	$\angle ADB \cong \angle ADC$
	$\overline{AD} \cong \overline{AD}$
SAS for $\cong$ $\triangle$'s $\longrightarrow$	$\triangle ADB \cong \triangle ADC$
Corr. $\angle$'s of $\cong$ $\triangle$'s are $\cong$. $\longrightarrow$	$\angle C \cong \angle B$
$m \angle B + 28 + 90 = 180$ $\longrightarrow$	$m \angle B = 62$

Thus, $m \angle C = 62$.

EXAMPLE 4   Given: $\overline{RS} \cong \overline{VT}$, $\overline{VR} \cong \overline{TS}$
Prove: $\overline{RS} \parallel \overline{VT}$

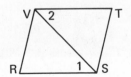

ANALYSIS

Lines are $\parallel$ if alt. int. $\angle$'s are $\cong$.
    Corr. $\angle$'s of $\cong$ $\triangle$'s are $\cong$.

$\overline{SV}$ is the same seg. as $\overline{VS}$. $\longrightarrow$

$\angle 1$ and $\angle 2$ are alt. int. $\angle$'s.

Proof

Statements	Reasons
1. $\overline{RS} \cong \overline{VT}$ (S)	1. Given
2. $\overline{SV} \cong \overline{SV}$ (S)	2. Reflexive property
3. $\overline{VR} \cong \overline{TS}$ (S)	3. Given
4. $\triangle VRS \cong \triangle STV$	4. SSS for $\cong$ $\triangle$'s
5. $\angle 1 \cong \angle 2$	5. Corr. $\angle$'s of $\cong$ $\triangle$'s are $\cong$.
6. $\therefore$ $\overline{RS} \parallel \overline{VT}$	6. Lines are $\parallel$ if alt. int. $\angle$'s are $\cong$.

ORAL EXERCISES

Name the corresponding sides of each pair of congruent triangles.

1.

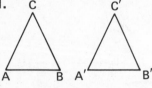

$\triangle ABC \cong \triangle A'B'C'$

2.

$\triangle JQB \cong \triangle ZNX$

3.

$\triangle CHV \cong \triangle LQI$

Complete each statement.

4.

5.

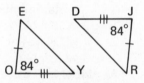

6.

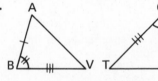

$\overline{TR}$ corresponds to _____.

$\angle E$ corresponds to _____.

$\angle V$ corresponds to _____.

EXERCISES

Give the measure of the corresponding side or angle.

1. $\triangle ABC \cong \triangle RST$
$m\angle A = 68$

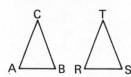

2. $\triangle LTV \cong \triangle ARQ$
$TV = 8$ in.

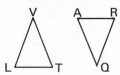

3. $\triangle PCM \cong \triangle JFW$
$\overline{PC} \cong \overline{MC}$, $PC = 3$ cm

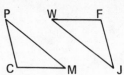

Name the corresponding congruent sides and the corresponding congruent angles. Draw a diagram.

4. $\triangle QZP \cong \triangle JTL$

5. $\triangle RNW \cong \triangle VCQ$

6. $\triangle AXZ \cong \triangle BJL$

7. Given: $\overline{AP} \cong \overline{SM}$,
$\angle 1 \cong \angle 3$
Prove: $\overline{AM} \cong \overline{SP}$

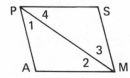

8. Given: $\angle 1 \cong \angle 2$, $\angle 4 \cong \angle 3$
Prove: $\overline{LT} \cong \overline{VR}$

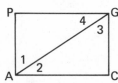

9. Given: $\overline{WQ} \parallel \overline{CH}$, $\angle 2 \cong \angle 4$
Prove: $\overline{WH} \cong \overline{CQ}$

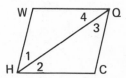

10. $\overline{AC} \cong \overline{BC}$, $\angle x \cong \angle y$,
$m\angle A = 72$.
Find $m\angle B$.

11. D is the midpoint of $\overline{AB}$,
$\overline{CD} \perp \overline{AB}$, $m\angle x = 32$.
Find $m\angle B$.

12. Given: $\overline{PG} \cong \overline{CA}$, $\angle 4 \cong \angle 2$
Prove: $\overline{AP} \parallel \overline{CG}$

13. Given: $\overline{AP} \perp \overline{PG}$,
$\angle 1 \cong \angle 3$, $\angle 2 \cong \angle 4$
Prove: $\overline{GC} \perp \overline{AC}$

14. Given: $\overline{CD} \perp \overline{AD}$,
$\overline{CD} \perp \overline{BD}$, $\overline{AD} \cong \overline{BD}$
Prove: $\triangle ACB$ is isosceles.

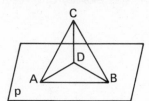

15. Given: $\overline{PS} \perp \overline{JS}$,
$\overline{PS} \perp \overline{QS}$, $\angle PJS \cong \angle PQS$
Prove: $\triangle JSQ$ is isosceles.

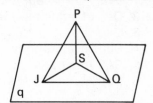

16. Given: $\overline{LM} \perp \overline{RM}$,
$\overline{LM} \cong \overline{TM}$, $\overline{LR} \cong \overline{TR}$
Prove: $\overline{TM} \perp \overline{RM}$

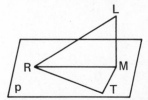

Properties of Isosceles Triangles

REVIEW CAPSULE

Isosceles triangles

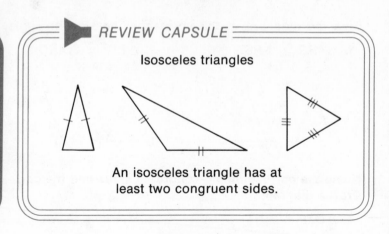

An isosceles triangle has at least two congruent sides.

EXAMPLE 1

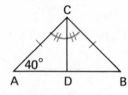

$\triangle ABC$ is isosceles with $\overline{AC} \cong \overline{BC}$. $\overline{CD}$ bisects $\angle ACB$, $m \angle A = 40$. Find $m \angle B$.

$\overline{CD}$ bisects $\angle ACB$.
SAS for $\cong \triangle$'s ——————————→
Corr. $\angle$'s of $\cong \triangle$'s are $\cong$. ——————→
$m \angle A = 40$ ————————————————→

$\overline{AC} \cong \overline{BC}$, $\angle ACD \cong \angle BCD$, $\overline{CD} \cong \overline{CD}$
$\triangle ADC \cong \triangle BDC$
$\angle A \cong \angle B$
Thus, $m \angle B = 40$

Theorem 5.1

If two sides of a triangle are congruent, then the angles opposite these sides are congruent.

ANALYSIS

Corr. $\angle$'s of $\cong \triangle$'s are $\cong$. The bis. of $\angle ACB$ forms $\cong \angle$'s.

GIVEN
$\overline{AC} \cong \overline{BC}$
PROVE
$\angle A \cong \angle B$

PROOF

STATEMENTS	REASONS
1. Draw $\overrightarrow{CD}$ bisecting $\angle ACB$.	1. Every $\angle$, except a straight $\angle$, has exactly one bisector.
2. $\angle x \cong \angle y$	2. Def. of angle bisector
3. $\overline{AC} \cong \overline{BC}$	3. Given
4. $\overline{CD} \cong \overline{CD}$	4. Reflexive property
5. $\triangle ACD \cong \triangle BCD$	5. SAS for $\cong \triangle$'s
6. $\therefore \angle A \cong \angle B$	6. Corr. $\angle$'s of $\cong \triangle$'s are $\cong$.

Base ∠'s are opposite the ≅ sides. ──────→ Theorem 5.1 is sometimes stated:
"Base angles of an isosceles triangle are congruent."

EXAMPLE 2   In $\triangle ABC$, $\overline{AB} \cong \overline{BC}$. $m\angle B = x$, $m\angle A = 2x - 30$.
Find $m\angle B$.

Draw a picture. ∠'s opp. ≅ sides of a
△ are ≅. ──────────────────→

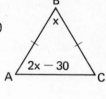

$$\angle A \cong \angle C$$
$$m\angle C = 2x - 30$$
$$m\angle A + m\angle B + m\angle C = 180$$
Substitution property ──────────→ $(2x - 30) + (x) + (2x - 30) = 180$
$$5x - 60 = 180$$
$$5x = 240$$
$$x = 48$$

$m\angle B = x$ ────────────────→ **Thus, $m\angle B = 48$.**

EXAMPLE 3   Find the measure of each angle
of an equilateral triangle.

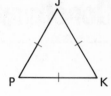

All 3 sides are ≅. ──────────────→ $\overline{PJ} \cong \overline{PK}$ and $\overline{PK} \cong \overline{JK}$
∠'s opp. ≅ sides of △ are ≅. ──────→ So, $\angle K \cong \angle J$ and $\angle J \cong \angle P$.
$$m\angle K = 60$$
All 3 ∠'s are ≅.⎫ $$m\angle J = 60$$
$180 \div 3 = 60$ ⎭ $$m\angle P = 60$$

Example 3 suggests a corollary to Theorem 5.1. ⌐↓

Corollary

An equilateral triangle is also equiangular.

The converse of Theorem 5.1 can be proved.

Theorem   5.2

If two angles of a triangle are congruent, then the
sides opposite these angles are congruent.

ANALYSIS

Corr. sides of ≅ △'s are ≅. The ⊥
to $\overline{AB}$ forms ≅ △'s by AAS.

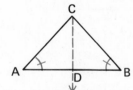

GIVEN
$\angle A \cong \angle B$
PROVE
$\overline{AC} \cong \overline{BC}$

PROOF
(See Exercise 9.)

EXAMPLE 4 $\angle Q \cong \angle C$, $QC = 15$ cm,
the perimeter of $\triangle QCV$
is 41 cm.
Find CV.

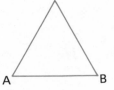

The perimeter is the sum of the lengths
of the sides. ──────────────────→

$$QV + QC + CV = 41$$
$$QV + 15 + CV = 41$$
$$QV + CV = 26$$

Sides opp. $\cong \angle$'s of a $\triangle$ are $\cong$. ────→
Substitution property ────────→

$$\text{But,} \quad QV = CV$$
$$2CV = 26$$
$$CV = 13$$

Thus, CV is 13 cm.

This is the converse of the corollary to Theorem 5.1. ⌐

Corollary

An equiangular triangle is also equilateral.

EXAMPLE 5 $m\angle A = 2x + 10$, $m\angle B = 3x - 15$,
$m\angle C = 4(x - 10)$, $\angle A \cong \angle B$.
Show that $\triangle ABC$ is equilateral.

$\angle A \cong \angle B$ ──────────────────→

$$2x + 10 = 3x - 15$$
$$25 = x$$

$2(25) + 10 = 60$ ──────────→ $m\angle A = 60$
$3(25) - 15 = 60$ ──────────→ $m\angle B = 60$
$4(25 - 10) = 60$ $m\angle C = 60$
An equiangular $\triangle$ is equilateral. ────→ **Thus,** $\triangle ABC$ is equilateral.

ORAL EXERCISES

Find the unknown angle measures in each isosceles triangle.

1.

2.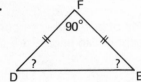

3.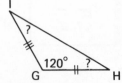

4.

True or false?

5. All angles of an isosceles triangle are congruent.

6. All sides of an isosceles triangle are congruent.

7. An equilateral triangle is also isosceles.

8. An equiangular triangle is also isosceles.

9. Base angles of an isosceles triangle are congruent.

10. A right triangle cannot be isosceles.

EXERCISES

PART A

Find the measure of each angle in △XYZ.

1. $\overline{XZ} \cong \overline{YZ}$ $m \angle X =$
$3y + 4$, $m \angle Z = 2y - 4$

2. $\overline{XZ} \cong \overline{YZ}$ $m \angle Y =$
$3t + 3$, $m \angle Z = 4t - 16$

Find the measures of the indicated angles.

3. $\overline{XZ} \cong \overline{YZ}$, $m \angle Z = 48$.
Find $m \angle t$, $m \angle r$.

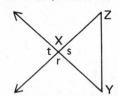

4. $\overline{RT} \cong \overline{ST}$, $m \angle R = 57$.
Find $m \angle S$, $m \angle x$, $m \angle y$.

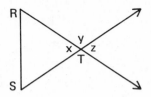

5. $\overline{VS} \perp \overline{SM}$, $\overline{VS} \cong \overline{SM}$.
Find $m \angle V$, $m \angle M$.

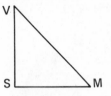

6. Given: $\overrightarrow{TW} \parallel \overline{XS}$, $\overline{XT} \cong \overline{ST}$
Prove: $\angle 1 \cong \angle 2$

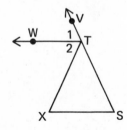

7. Given: $\overrightarrow{RG} \parallel \overline{VN}$, $\angle 1 \cong \angle 2$
Prove: △VRN is isosceles.

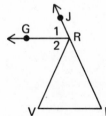

8. Given: $\angle 1 \cong \angle 2$
Prove: △MHV is isosceles.

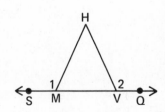

PART B

9. Prove Theorem 5.2.

10. Prove the corollary to Theorem 5.2.

11. Given: $\overline{RT} \parallel \overline{HM}$, $\overline{HQ} \cong \overline{MQ}$
Prove: $\overline{RQ} \cong \overline{TQ}$

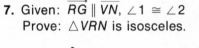
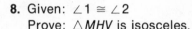

12. Given: $\overline{RT} \parallel \overline{HM}$, $\overline{QR} \cong \overline{QT}$
Prove: $\overline{RH} \cong \overline{MT}$

13. Given: $\overline{RH} \cong \overline{FH}$, $\angle 1 \cong \angle 3$
Prove: $\overline{HM} \cong \overline{HQ}$

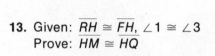
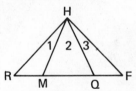

14. Given: $\overline{HM} \cong \overline{HQ}$, $\angle 1 \cong \angle 3$
Prove: $\overline{RH} \cong \overline{FH}$

A Puzzle in Shapes

Describe the intersections of two triangular regions.

Make cutouts from colored plastic to find the possible intersections.

1.   A triangular and a quadrilateral region

2.   Two quadrilateral regions

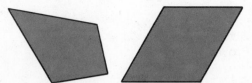

Overlapping Triangles

<table>
<tr><td>

OBJECTIVES

- To identify and name overlapping triangles
- To prove overlapping triangles congruent

</td><td>

▶ REVIEW CAPSULE

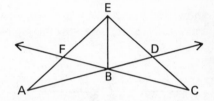

$m\angle POR = m\angle POQ + m\angle QOR$ if
1. $\angle POQ$ and $\angle QOR$ are adjacent, and
2. $\overrightarrow{OQ}$ is in the interior of $\angle POR$.

$HK = HJ + JK$ if
1. H, J, and K are collinear, and
2. J is between H and K.

</td></tr>
</table>

EXAMPLE 1   Name each triangle in the figure.

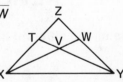

There are eight triangles. ⟶ $\triangle ABF$, $\triangle ABE$, $\triangle ADE$, $\triangle BEF$, $\triangle CBD$, $\triangle CBE$, $\triangle CFE$, $\triangle DEB$

EXAMPLE 2 $\triangle XYT$ and $\triangle XYW$ are overlapping triangles. Redraw the picture using different colors for each triangle.

Overlapping triangles have parts of their interiors in common.

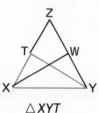

$\triangle XYW$ and $\triangle XYT$ share side $\overline{XY}$.

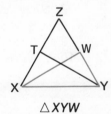

$\triangle XYW$ $\triangle XYT$

EXAMPLE 3   Given: $\angle ZXY \cong \angle ZYX$, $\overline{XT} \cong \overline{YW}$
Prove: $\triangle TXY \cong \triangle WYX$

ANALYSIS

$\triangle TXY$ and $\triangle WYX$ overlap. Redraw the figure.

Proof

Statements	Reasons
1. $\overline{XT} \cong \overline{YW}$	1. Given
2. $\angle ZXY \cong \angle ZYX$	2. Given
3. $\overline{XY} \cong \overline{XY}$	3. Reflexive property
4. $\therefore \triangle TXY \cong \triangle WYX$	4. SAS for $\cong$ $\triangle$'s

EXAMPLE 4   Given: $\overline{AC} \cong \overline{AD}$, $\angle C \cong \angle D$
Prove: $\overline{AE} \cong \overline{AB}$

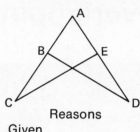

ANALYSIS

Show $\triangle AEC$ and $\triangle ABD$ are $\cong$. $\triangle AEC$ and $\triangle ABD$ overlap. Redraw the figure.

Proof

Statements	Reasons
1. $\angle C \cong \angle D$ (A)	1. Given
2. $\overline{AC} \cong \overline{AD}$ (S)	2. Given
3. $\angle A \cong \angle A$ (A)	3. Reflexive property
4. $\triangle AEC \cong \triangle ABD$	4. ASA for $\cong$ $\triangle$'s
5. $\therefore \overline{AE} \cong \overline{AB}$	5. Corr. sides of $\cong$ $\triangle$'s are $\cong$.

EXAMPLE 5   Given: $\overline{WJ} \parallel \overline{NT}$, $\overline{WJ} \perp \overline{SA}$, $\overline{SJ} \cong \overline{AT}$, $\overline{CS} \cong \overline{CA}$
Prove: $\overline{NT} \cong \overline{WJ}$

ANALYSIS

Show $\triangle NTS$ and $\triangle WJA$ are $\cong$. $\triangle WJA$ and $\triangle NTS$ overlap. Redraw the figure.

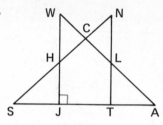

$SJ + JT = ST$ and $AT + JT = AJ$ ⟶

$\overline{CS} \cong \overline{CA}$ ⟶

Proof

Statements	Reasons
1. $\angle WJA$ is a rt. $\angle$.	1. $\overline{WJ} \perp \overline{SA}$
2. $\angle NTS$ is a rt. $\angle$.	2. Int. $\angle$'s of $\parallel$ lines on same side of trans. are suppl.
3. $\angle NTS \cong \angle WJA$ (A)	3. All rt. $\angle$'s are $\cong$.
4. $SJ = AT$	4. $\cong$ seg. have = lengths.
5. $SJ + JT = AT + JT$	5. Addition prop. of equality
6. $ST = AJ$	6. Segment addition post.
7. $\overline{ST} \cong \overline{AJ}$ (S)	7. Def. of congruence
8. $\angle S \cong \angle A$ (A)	8. $\angle$'s opp. $\cong$ sides are $\cong$.
9. $\triangle NTS \cong \triangle WJA$	9. ASA for $\cong$ $\triangle$'s.
10. $\therefore \overline{NT} \cong \overline{WJ}$	10. Corr. sides of $\cong$ $\triangle$'s are $\cong$.

ORAL EXERCISES

Name all the different triangles in each figure.

1.

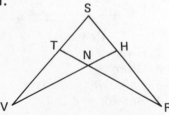

2.

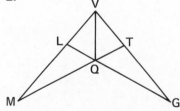

3.

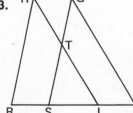

EXERCISES

PART A

Make drawings using different colors to show clearly the overlapping triangles.

1.

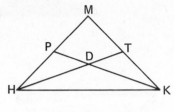

△HTM and △KPM

2.

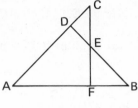

△ABD and △AFC

3.

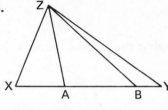

△XBZ and △AYZ

4. Given: $\overline{KM} \cong \overline{LM}$, $\overline{HL} \cong \overline{JK}$
Prove: △HLM ≅ △JKM

5. Given: ∠X ≅ ∠Y, $\overline{XT} \cong \overline{YR}$
Prove: △XZT ≅ △YZR

6. Given: $\overline{DA} \perp \overline{AB}$, $\overline{CB} \perp \overline{AB}$
$\overline{AD} \cong \overline{BC}$, $\overline{AE} \cong \overline{BF}$
Prove: △DAF ≅ △CBE

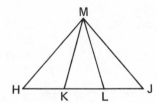

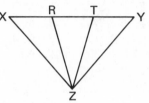

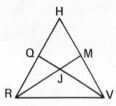

7. Given: $\overline{AE} \cong \overline{BE}$,
∠A ≅ ∠B
Prove: $\overline{AC} \cong \overline{BD}$

8. Given: $\overline{AB} \perp \overline{BC}$,
∠1 ≅ ∠2, ∠A ≅ ∠D
Prove: $\overline{DC} \perp \overline{BC}$

9. Given: ∠HRV ≅ ∠HVR,
$\overline{QR} \cong \overline{MV}$
Prove: ∠QVR ≅ ∠MRV

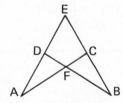

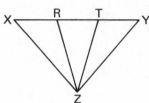

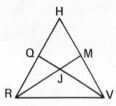

PART B

10. Given: ∠1 ≅ ∠6,
∠2 ≅ ∠5, $\overline{RH} \cong \overline{JK}$
Prove: △RKL ≅ △JHL

11. Given: $\overline{AG} \cong \overline{CG}$,
$\overline{BE} \cong \overline{DE}$, $\overline{BF} \cong \overline{CF}$
Prove: $\overline{AG} \parallel \overline{BE}$

12. Given: $\overline{BF} \parallel \overline{CE}$,
$\overline{CA} \parallel \overline{DG}$, $\overline{AG} \cong \overline{EF}$
Prove: △AFB ≅ △GED

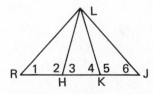

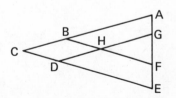

$R \triangle ABC$ means region of $\triangle ABC$. ⟶ $R \triangle ABC$ is $\triangle ABC$ and its interior

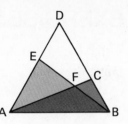

EXAMPLE Write a simpler name for
$R \triangle ABC \cap R \triangle ABE$.

The double shading shows the
intersection.

$R \triangle ABC \cap R \triangle ABE = R \triangle ABF$

Using the picture, write a simpler name for each of the following.

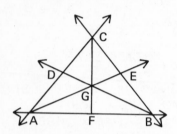

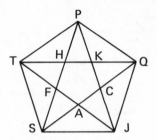

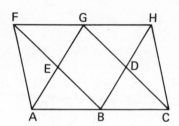

13. $R \triangle FBC \cap R \triangle AEC$	**18.** $R \triangle SJC \cup R \triangle JAQ$	**23.** $R \triangle ACG \cap R \triangle BCD$
14. $R \triangle AGF \cup R \triangle FGB$	**19.** $R \triangle TAQ \cap R \triangle PJQ$	**24.** $R \triangle ABF \cap R \triangle ACG$
15. $R \triangle AGC \cap R \triangle DGC$	**20.** $R \triangle TQP \cap R \triangle PSJ$	**25.** $R \triangle AEF \cup R \triangle ABE$
16. $R \triangle ABD \cap R \triangle ABE$	**21.** $R \triangle TSQ \cap R \triangle SJQ$	**26.** $R \triangle ABE \cap R \triangle BCD$
17. $R \triangle AFC \cap R \triangle ABG$	**22.** $R \triangle PKQ \cup R \triangle PSQ$	**27.** $R \triangle GCH \cap R \triangle BCH$

Algebra Review

OBJECTIVE

■ To write a fraction in
simplest form

To write a fraction in simplest form:
1. Factor both numerator and denominator.
2. Divide out common factors.

EXAMPLE Simplify $\dfrac{x^2 - 5x + 6}{x^2 - 4}$.

$x^2 - 5x + 6 = (x - 2)(x - 3)$ ⟶

$x^2 - 4 = (x - 2)(x + 2)$ ⟶

$$\frac{\overset{1}{\cancel{(x - 2)}}(x - 3)}{\underset{1}{\cancel{(x - 2)}}(x + 2)}$$

$$\frac{x - 3}{x + 2}$$

Simplify.

1. $\dfrac{x^2 - 7x + 12}{x^2 - 9}$

2. $\dfrac{a^2 + 8a + 15}{2a + 6}$

3. $\dfrac{2x^2 - 50}{x^2 + 8x + 15}$

4. $\dfrac{3b^2 - 15b + 18}{b^2 - b - 6}$

5. $\dfrac{4x^3y^2}{20x^2y^4}$

6. $\dfrac{4x - 4y}{x^2 - y^2}$

Congruence of Right Triangles

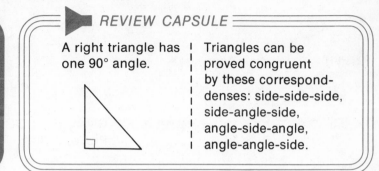

▶ *REVIEW CAPSULE*

A right triangle has one 90° angle.

Triangles can be proved congruent by these correspondences: side-side-side, side-angle-side, angle-side-angle, angle-angle-side.

Sides of right triangles have special names.

The *hypotenuse* is the side opposite the right angle. The *legs* are the other two sides.

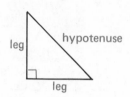
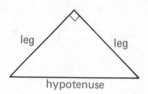

EXAMPLE 1

True or false? Two right triangles are congruent if their legs are congruent.

True.

$\triangle CAB \cong \triangle YZX$ by SAS for $\cong \triangle$'s. ⟶

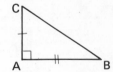
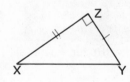

EXAMPLE 2

True or false?
Two right triangles are congruent if a leg and acute angle of one are congruent to the corresponding leg and acute angle of the other.

True.

$\triangle LJK \cong \triangle RTS$ by AAS for $\cong \triangle$'s. ⟶

There is another possibility.

$\triangle LJK \cong \triangle RTS$ by ASA for $\cong \triangle$'s. ⟶

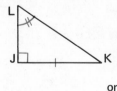

or

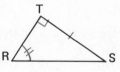

EXAMPLE 3   True or false? Two right triangles are congruent if the hypotenuse and an acute angle of one are congruent to the hypotenuse and an acute angle of the other.

True.

△*BVG* ≅ △*CWK* by AAS for ≅ △'s. ⟶

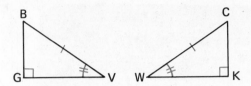

EXAMPLE 4   Given: $\overline{AC} \perp \overline{BD}$, $\overline{AB} \cong \overline{AD}$
Prove: △*BCA* ≅ △*DCA*

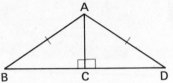

ANALYSIS

△'s are ≅ by AAS, ∠'s opp. ≅ sides of a △ are ≅.

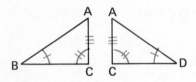

Proof

Statements	Reasons
1. $\overline{AB} \cong \overline{AD}$	1. Given
2. ∠*B* ≅ ∠*D* (A)	2. ∠'s opp. ≅ sides of a △ are ≅.
3. ∠*BCA* and ∠*DCA* are rt. ∠'s.	3. ⊥'s form rt. ∠'s.
4. ∠*BCA* ≅ ∠*DCA* (A)	4. All rt. ∠'s are ≅.
5. $\overline{AC} \cong \overline{AC}$ (S)	5. Reflexive property
6. ∴ △*BCA* ≅ △*DCA*	6. AAS for ≅ △'s

Theorem 5.3

(HL for ≅ rt. △'s)

Two right triangles are congruent if the hypotenuse and a leg of one are congruent respectively to the hypotenuse and a leg of the other.

ANALYSIS

Construct △*SUR* with $\overline{RS} \cong \overline{NX}$. Show △*TNX* ≅ △*URS* and △*TNX* ≅ △*URH*.

GIVEN
△'s *TNX* and *URH*, ∠*TNX* and ∠*URH* are rt. ∠'s $\overline{TN} \cong \overline{UR}$, $\overline{TX} \cong \overline{UH}$.

Prove
△*TNX* ≅ △*URH*

OUTLINE OF PROOF

1. Extend $\overline{HR}$ to *S* so that $\overline{RS} \cong \overline{NX}$.
2. Draw *SU*.
3. ∠*URH* + ∠*URS* = 180°
4. ∠*URS* = 90°
5. ∠*TNX* is a rt. ∠.
6. ∠*TNX* ≅ ∠*URS*
7. $\overline{TN} \cong \overline{UR}$
8. △*TNX* ≅ △*URS*

9. $\overline{TX} \cong \overline{US}$
10. $\overline{TX} \cong \overline{UH}$
11. $\overline{US} \cong \overline{UH}$
12. ∠*UHR* ≅ ∠*USR*
13. ∠*TXN* ≅ ∠*USR*
14. ∠*TXN* ≅ ∠*UHR*
15. ∴ △*TNX* ≅ △*URH*

148   CONGRUENCE OF RIGHT TRIANGLES

Leg-leg	Leg-acute angle	Hypotenuse-acute angle	Hypotenuse-leg
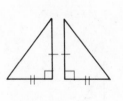	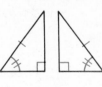	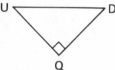	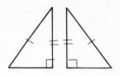
(SAS for ≅ △'s)	(ASA) or (AAS)	(AAS)	

ORAL EXERCISES

Name the hypotenuse and legs in each right triangle.

1. 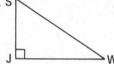   **2.**    **3.** 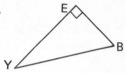   **4.**

True or false?

5. The hypotenuse of a right triangle is opposite the right angle.

6. A leg of a right triangle is opposite an acute angle.

7. The hypotenuse of a right triangle is longer than either leg.

8. The right angle of a right triangle is larger than either of the other angles.

Is right △ BPT congruent to right △ MCV? Why? Use only the given information.

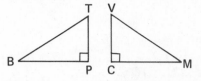

9. $\overline{BP} \cong \overline{MC}$, $\overline{BT} \cong \overline{MV}$

10. $\angle B \cong \angle M$, $\overline{BP} \cong \overline{MC}$

11. $\angle B \cong \angle M$, $\angle T \cong \angle V$

12. $\overline{BP} \cong \overline{MC}$, $\overline{PT} \cong \overline{CV}$

13. $\overline{BT} \cong \overline{MV}$, $\angle T \cong \angle V$

14. $\overline{BT} \cong \overline{MV}$, $\overline{TP} \cong \overline{VC}$

Tell whether the right triangles in each pair are congruent.

15.   **16.** 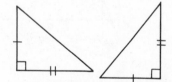   **17.**

EXERCISES

PART A

Based on the given information, name the pairs of congruent triangles.

1. $\overline{AC} \perp \overline{DB}$ at O, $\overline{AD} \cong \overline{CB}$,
$\overline{AO} \cong \overline{CO}$

2. $\overline{XZ} \perp \overline{WY}$, $\overline{XZ}$ bisects $\overline{WY}$,
$\overline{WZ} \cong \overline{YZ}$.

3. $\overline{FT} \perp \overline{AR}$, $\overline{AF} \cong \overline{RF}$

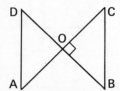

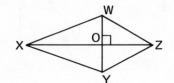

4. Given: $\overline{AZ} \perp \overline{BX}$, $\overline{BY} \perp \overline{AX}$,
$\overline{AY} \cong \overline{BZ}$
Prove: $\triangle ABZ \cong \triangle BAY$

5. Given: $\overline{AZ} \perp \overline{BX}$, $\overline{BY} \perp \overline{AX}$
$\angle ZAB \cong \angle YBA$
Prove: $\triangle ABZ \cong \triangle BAY$

PART B

6. Given: $\overline{ZW}$ is $\perp$ bisector of $\overline{XY}$.
Prove: $\triangle XYZ$ is isosceles.

7. Given: $\overline{ZW} \perp \overline{XY}$, $\overline{ZW}$
bisects $\angle XZY$.
Prove: $\triangle XYZ$ is isosceles.

8. Given: $\overline{KS} \perp \overline{JQ}$, $\overline{JR} \perp \overline{KQ}$,
$\overline{JQ} \cong \overline{KQ}$
Prove: $\overline{JR} \cong \overline{KS}$

9. Given: $\overline{KS} \perp \overline{JQ}$, $\overline{JR} \perp \overline{KQ}$,
$\overline{SQ} \cong \overline{RQ}$
Prove: $\overline{JR} \cong \overline{KS}$

10. Given: $\triangle HJL \cong \triangle CRT$,
$\overline{LN} \perp \overline{HJ}$, $\overline{TQ} \perp \overline{CR}$
Prove: $\overline{LN} \cong \overline{TQ}$

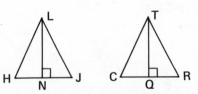

11. Given: $\triangle HJL \cong \triangle CRT$
$\overline{LN} \perp \overline{HJ}$, $\overline{TQ} \perp \overline{CR}$,
$\overline{LN}$ bisects $\angle HLJ$.
Prove: $\overline{TQ}$ bisects $\angle CTR$.

PART C

Given: $\overline{PQ} \perp$ plane t at Q
$\overline{QA}$ and $\overline{QB}$ are in t.
$\overline{AP} \cong \overline{BP}$

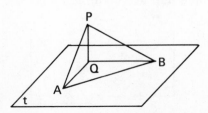

12. Prove: $\triangle APQ \cong \triangle BPQ$
13. Prove: $\angle PAB \cong \angle PBA$
14. Prove: $\triangle QAB \cong \angle QBA$

Flow Chart: Congruent Triangles

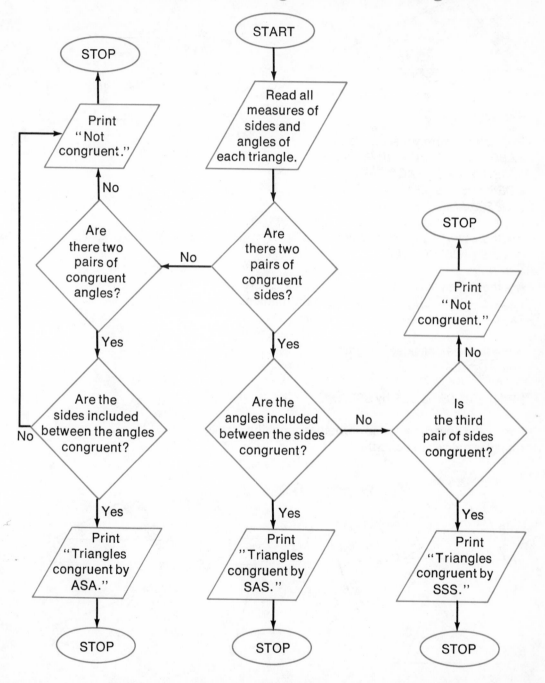

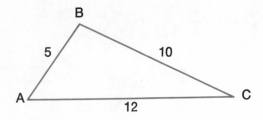

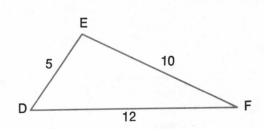

Example

Read all measures of each triangle.

$\triangle ABC$ $AB = 5$, $BC = 10$, $AC = 12$

$\angle ABC$, $\angle CAB$, $\angle ACB$

$\triangle DEF$ $DE = 5$, $EF = 10$, $DF = 12$

$\angle DEF$, $\angle FDE$, $\angle EFD$

Are there two pairs of congruent sides?

Yes. $\overline{AB} \cong \overline{DE}$, $\overline{BC} \cong \overline{EF}$

Are the angles between the pairs of sides congruent?

i.e. is $\angle ABC \cong \angle DEF$? Insufficient information.

Say No.

Is the third pair of sides congruent?

Yes. $\overline{AC} \cong \overline{DF}$

PRINT $\triangle ABC \cong \triangle DEF$ by SSS.

Follow the flow chart to show whether or not the triangles below are congruent.

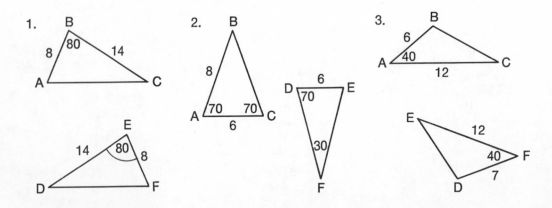

Using Corresponding Parts

REVIEW CAPSULE

Ways of showing segments congruent:	Ways of showing angles congruent:
1. Bisector of segment	1. Angle bisector
2. Sides opposite ≅ ∠'s of a △	2. ∠'s opposite ≅ sides of a △
3. Corresponding sides of ≅ △'s	3. Corresponding angles of ≅ △'s

EXAMPLE 1

Given: △AFD ≅ △BFE
$\overline{BD} \perp \overline{AC}$, $\overline{AE} \perp \overline{BC}$
Prove: △ABD ≅ △BAE

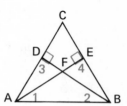

ANALYSIS

△'s are ≅ by AAS. rt. ∠'s are ≅.
∠'s opp. ≅ sides of a △ are ≅.

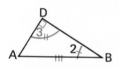

Proof

Statements	Reasons
1. △AFD ≅ △BFE	1. Given
2. $\overline{AF} \cong \overline{BF}$	2. Corr. sides of ≅ △'s are ≅.
3. ∠1 ≅ ∠2 (A)	3. ∠'s opp. ≅ sides of a △ are ≅.
4. ∠3 ≅ ∠4 (A)	4. ⊥'s form right ∠'s.
5. $\overline{AB} \cong \overline{AB}$ (S)	5. Reflexive prop.
6. ∴ △ABD ≅ △BAE	6. AAS for ≅ △'s

EXAMPLE 2

Given: $\overline{JK}$ and $\overline{HL}$ bisect each other at R.
Prove: △JKL ≅ △KJH

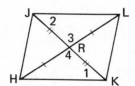

ANALYSIS

△'s are ≅ by SAS. First show △JRL ≅ △KRH, then $\overline{JL} \cong \overline{KH}$ and ∠2 ≅ ∠1.

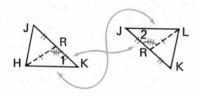

Proof

Statements	Reasons
1. $\overline{JR} \cong \overline{KR}$	1. $\overline{HL}$ bisects $\overline{JK}$ at R.
2. ∠3 ≅ ∠4	2. Vert. ∠'s are ≅.
3. $\overline{LR} \cong \overline{HR}$	3. $\overline{JK}$ bisects $\overline{HL}$ at R.
4. △JRL ≅ △KRH	4. SAS for ≅ △'s
5. $\overline{JL} \cong \overline{KH}$ (S)	5. Corr. sides of ≅ △'s are ≅.
6. ∠2 ≅ ∠1 (A)	6. Corr. ∠'s of ≅ △'s are ≅.
7. $\overline{JK} \cong \overline{KJ}$ (S)	7. Reflexive property
8. ∴ △JKL ≅ △KJH	8. SAS for ≅ △'s

EXERCISES

PART A

Copy the diagram. Mark the pairs of congruent segments and angles in the given congruent triangles. Name another pair of triangles which can be proved congruent.

1. △ABE ≅ △CDE

2. △JTC ≅ △LQC

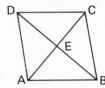

3. △HLJ ≅ △CJL

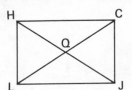

4. Given: △HJL ≅ △CRT, LN ⊥ HJ, TQ ⊥ CR
Prove: △LNJ ≅ △TQR

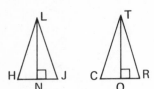

5. Given: △BJQ ≅ △VTQ, NT ∥ JC
Prove: △JCT ≅ △TNJ

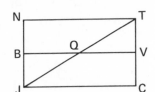

6. Given: △XRC ≅ △XMH, MH ⊥ RX, RC ⊥ MX
Prove: △RMH ≅ △MRC

7. Given: RQ ≅ KA, RV ≅ KJ, VQ ≅ JA, QM ⊥ RV, AC ⊥ JK
Prove: QM ≅ AC

8. Given: ZG ⊥ RT, WV ⊥ PB, ZG ≅ WV, ZT ≅ WP, RT ≅ BP
Prove: ZR ≅ WB

9. Given: AO ⊥ BC, OX ⊥ BA, OY ⊥ CA, OB ≅ OC
Prove: OX ≅ OY

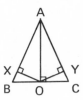

PART B

Find the measure of the indicated angle. If not enough information is given, state what is needed.

10. △HLJ ≅ △CJL, HL ⊥ LJ, m∠CLJ = 36.
Find m∠LHJ.

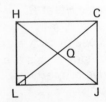

11. △CTV ≅ △NJV, m∠VJT = 74, m∠CVN = 112.
Find m∠VNJ.

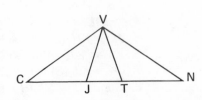

12. △QXB ≅ △JXW, QW ⊥ JL, m∠L = 40.
Find m∠QXJ.

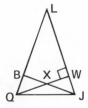

13. Given: $\overline{AD} \cong \overline{BC}$, $\overline{DE} \perp \overline{AB}$,
$\overline{CF} \perp \overline{AB}$, $\overline{DE} \cong \overline{CF}$
Prove: $\overline{AC} \cong \overline{BD}$

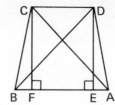

14. Given: $\overline{DE} \perp \overline{AB}$, $\overline{CF} \perp \overline{AB}$,
$\overline{DE} \cong \overline{CF}$, $\overline{AC} \cong \overline{DB}$
Prove: $\overline{AD} \cong \overline{BC}$

Given: $\overline{AD} \perp \overline{AB}$, $\overline{BC} \perp \overline{AB}$,
$\overline{AD} \cong \overline{BC}$

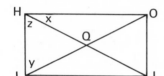

15. Prove: $\overline{AC} \cong \overline{BD}$
16. Prove: $\triangle AOB$ is isosceles.
17. Prove: $\overline{OD} \cong \overline{OC}$
18. Prove: $\overline{AB} \parallel \overline{DC}$
19. Prove: $\overline{AD} \perp \overline{DC}$ and $\overline{BC} \perp \overline{DC}$
20. Prove: $\triangle AOB \cong \triangle COD$
21. Prove: $\overline{AO} \cong \overline{BO} \cong \overline{CO} \cong \overline{DO}$

Contradictory information is given in some of the following exercises. Which information is contradictory?

22. $\triangle HLJ \cong \triangle OJL$, $\overline{HJ} \cong \overline{LO}$,
$m \angle x = 42$, $m \angle y = 48$,
$m \angle z = 42$

23. $\overline{QJ}$ and $\overline{XC}$ bisect each
other, $QJ = 8$, $XC = 10$,
$m \angle x = 42$, $m \angle y = 42$.

24. $\overline{NA} \perp \overline{DZ}$, $\overline{DR} \perp \overline{NZ}$,
$m \angle x = 38$, $m \angle y = 38$,
$m \angle w = 14$

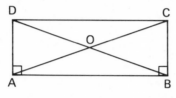

PART C

25. Given: $\overline{XY} \cong \overline{XZ}$, M is midpoint of $\overline{YZ}$, $\angle WMY \cong$
$\angle TMZ$.
Prove: $\overline{YT} \cong \overline{ZW}$

26. Given: $\overline{OW} \cong \overline{OT}$, $\overline{OX} \cong \overline{OY}$
Prove: $\overline{XZ} \cong \overline{YZ}$

27. Given: $\overline{AB} \cong \overline{DB}$, $\overline{AC} \cong \overline{DC}$
Prove: $\triangle AED$ is isosceles.

28. Given: $\overline{TZ} \cong \overline{TY}$, $XZ = XY$
Prove: $\overline{ZW} \cong \overline{YW}$

29. Given: $\angle ZXW \cong \angle YXW$
$\angle XZT \cong \angle XYT$
Prove: $\angle XZW \cong \angle XYW$

Bisectors

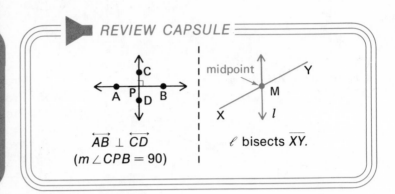

REVIEW CAPSULE

$\overleftrightarrow{AB} \perp \overleftrightarrow{CD}$
$(m \angle CPB = 90)$

ℓ bisects $\overline{XY}$.

EXAMPLE 1 Which point bisects $\overline{DL}$?

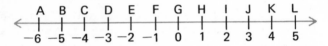

DH is the length of $\overline{DH}$.
$DH = |1 - (-3)| = 4$
$HL = |5 - 1| = 4$

Point H bisects $\overline{DL}$, since $DH = HL$.

EXAMPLE 2 Which ray bisects $\angle AOE$?

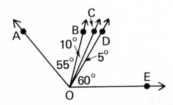

$m \angle AOC = 65$
$m \angle COE = 65$

$\overrightarrow{OC}$ bisects $\angle AOE$, since $m \angle AOC = m \angle COE$.

SUMMARY

Every segment has a bisector.

M is the bisector (or midpoint) of $\overline{AB}$.

$\begin{cases} M \text{ is between } A \text{ and } B. \\ AM = MB \quad (\overline{AM} \cong \overline{MB}) \end{cases}$

Every angle has a bisector.

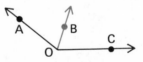

$\overrightarrow{OB}$ is the bisector of $\angle AOC$.

$\begin{cases} \overrightarrow{OB} \text{ (except } O) \text{ is in the interior of } \angle AOC. \\ m \angle AOB = m \angle BOC \quad (\angle AOB \cong \angle BOC) \end{cases}$

EXAMPLE 3 $\angle AOC$ and $\angle BOC$ are right angles. $AO = 7$ cm. $OB = 7$ cm. What is the relationship between $\overline{AB}$ and $\overleftrightarrow{CD}$?

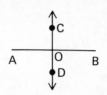

$\overleftrightarrow{CD} \perp \overline{AB}$, and $\overleftrightarrow{CD}$ bisects $\overline{AB}$. ————→ $\overleftrightarrow{CD}$ is the perpendicular bisector of $\overline{AB}$.

EXAMPLE 4 Draw a diagram and label it. State what is given, and state what is to be proved.
"A point on the perpendicular bisector of a segment is equidistant from the endpoints of the segment."

$\overleftrightarrow{CM} \perp \overline{AB}$

M is the midpoint of $\overline{AB}$.

PA is the distance between P and A.
PB is the distance between P and B.

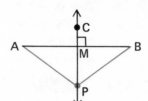

Given: $\overleftrightarrow{CM}$ is $\perp$ bisector of $\overline{AB}$, P is a point on $\overleftrightarrow{CM}$.
Prove: $PA = PB$

EXAMPLE 5 Give an analysis for a proof of Example 4.

$\overline{AM} \cong \overline{BM}$, $\angle AMP \cong \angle BMP$, and $\overline{PM}$ is a common side. ————→

Analysis: $\overline{PA}$ and $\overline{PB}$ are corresponding sides of $\triangle PAM$ and $\triangle PBM$. Show $\triangle PAM \cong \triangle PBM$ by using SAS for $\cong \triangle$'s.

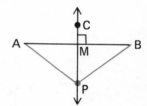

Theorem 5.4

A point on the perpendicular bisector of a segment is equidistant from the endpoints of the segment.

EXAMPLE 6 Draw a diagram and label it. State what is given, and state what is to be proved.
"Two points each equidistant from the endpoints of a segment determine the perpendicular bisector of the segment."

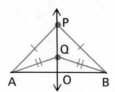

Given: $\overline{AP} \cong \overline{BP}$, $\overline{AQ} \cong \overline{BQ}$
Prove: Prove $\overleftrightarrow{PQ}$ is the $\perp$ bisector of $\overline{AB}$.

EXAMPLE 7   Give an analysis for a proof of Example 6.

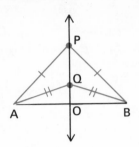

Analysis: Show $\overline{AO} \cong \overline{OB}$ by proving $\triangle APO \cong \triangle BPO$. To do this, show $\angle APQ \cong \angle BPQ$. (Prove $\triangle APQ \cong \triangle BPQ$ by SSS for $\cong \triangle$'s.) Then show $\overset{\cdot}{PQ} \perp AB$ by showing $\angle AOQ \cong \angle BOQ$. (Use $\triangle APO \cong \triangle BPO$.)

Two lines which meet to form $\cong$ adjacent $\angle$'s are $\perp$. ⟶

| **Theorem** | **5.5** | Two points each equidistant from the endpoints of a segment determine the perpendicular bisector of the segment. |

ORAL EXERCISES

Identify any bisectors or perpendicular bisectors.

1. 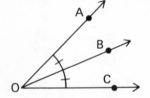   **2.** 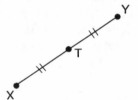   **3.**   **4.**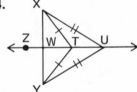

Which point bisects each segment?

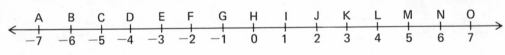

5. $\overline{IO}$ **6.** $\overline{HL}$ **7.** $\overline{DL}$ **8.** $\overline{CK}$ **9.** $\overline{ND}$

EXERCISES

PART A

Name any other bisectors which can be shown from the given information.

1. $\overline{TQ}$ bisects $\angle STM$, $\overline{ST} \cong \overline{MT}$.   **2.** $\overline{TQ}$ bisects $\overline{SM}$, $\overline{ST} \cong \overline{MT}$.   **3.** $\overline{TQ} \perp \overline{SM}$, $\overline{ST} \cong \overline{MT}$

For each of the following statements, draw a diagram and label it. State what is given, and state what is to be proved in terms of the diagram.

4. The bisector of the vertex angle of an isosceles triangle bisects the base of the triangle.

5. The bisector of the base of an isosceles triangle bisects the vertex angle of the triangle.

6. If a perpendicular segment from the vertex angle of a triangle to the base of the triangle bisects the vertex angle, then the triangle is isosceles.

7. The bisector of the vertex angle of an isosceles triangle is the perpendicular bisector of the base.

PART B

8. Write a proof for Exercise 4.
10. Write a proof for Exercise 6.
12. Prove Theorem 5.4.

9. Write a proof for Exercise 5.
11. Write a proof for Exercise 7.
13. Prove Theorem 5.5.

Prove.

14. All points in the bisector of an angle are equidistant from the sides of the angle. (Note: the distance from a point to a line is measured along the perpendicular from the point to the line.)

15. Perpendicular segments from the midpoints of the legs of an isosceles triangle to the base are congruent.

PART C

Prove.

16. Segments of the bisectors of base angles of isosceles triangles cut off by the legs of the triangle are congruent.

17. Given: $\overline{BD}$ is the $\perp$ bisector of $\overline{AC}$.
Prove: $\angle BAD \cong \angle BCD$

18. Given: $\overline{EB} \perp$ plane p, $\overline{ED}$ is a $\perp$ bisector of $\overline{AC}$.
Prove: $\overline{BD}$ is a $\perp$ bisector of $\overline{AC}$.

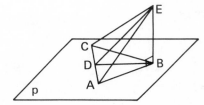

19. Given: $\overline{EB} \perp$ plane p, $\overline{ED}$ bisects $\angle CEA$, $\overline{CE} \cong \overline{AE}$.
Prove: $\overline{BD}$ bisects $\angle CBA$.

20. Given: $\angle ABC \cong \angle ADC$, $\angle 1 \cong \angle 2$
Prove: $\overline{AC}$ is the $\perp$ bisector of $\overline{BD}$.

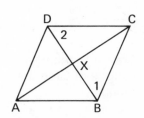

21. Given: $\angle ABC \cong \angle ADC$, $\angle 1 \cong \angle 2$
Prove: $\overline{AC}$ is the bisector of $\angle DAB$.

Altitudes and Medians

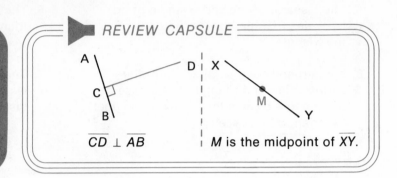

REVIEW CAPSULE

$\overline{CD} \perp \overline{AB}$

M is the midpoint of $\overline{XY}$.

An altitude can be in the interior of a △.

An altitude can be in the exterior of a △.

An altitude of a rt. △ can be a leg of the △.

$\overline{CD}$ is an altitude of △ABC.

$\overline{ZW}$ is an altitude of △XYZ.

$\overline{TS}$ is an altitude of △RST.

Definition of *altitude of a triangle* ⟶

An *altitude of a triangle* is a segment from a vertex of the triangle perpendicular to the line containing the opposite side of the triangle.

EXAMPLE 1   Draw the three altitudes of △ABC.

There is an altitude from each vertex to the opposite side.

EXAMPLE 2   Draw a triangle with an altitude outside the triangle.

Obtuse △'s have altitudes which are outside the △'s.

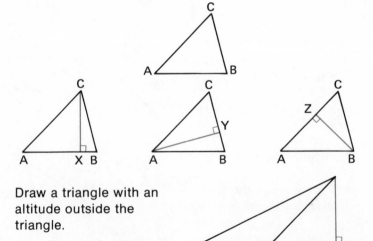

Medians are always in the interior of a △.

$\overline{CE}$ is a median | $\overline{ZV}$ is a median | $\overline{TU}$ is a median
of △ABC. | of △XYZ. | of △RST.

Definition of *median of a triangle* ⟶ A *median of a triangle* is a segment from a vertex of the triangle to the midpoint of the opposite side of the triangle.

EXAMPLE 3

Prove: Corresponding medians of congruent triangles are congruent.

Draw and label a diagram.
Write the "Given" and "Prove."
ANALYSIS
Show △CAD ≅ △C'A'D' by using △ABC ≅ △A'B'C' and the definition of median.

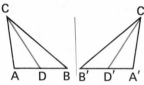

Given: △ABC ≅ △A'B'C',
$\overline{CD}$ is a median of △ABC,
$\overline{C'D'}$ is a median of △A'B'C'.
Prove: $\overline{CD} ≅ \overline{C'D'}$

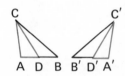

D is the midpoint of $\overline{AB}$. ⟶

≅ segments have the same meas. ⟶

△ABC ≅ △A'B'C'

$\overline{CD}$ and $\overline{C'D'}$ are corresponding medians. ⟶

Proof

Statements	Reasons
1. $\overline{AB} ≅ \overline{A'B'}$ and $AB = A'B'$	1. Corr. sides of ≅ △'s are ≅.
2. $AD = \frac{1}{2}AB$ $A'D' = \frac{1}{2}A'B'$	2. Def. of median
3. $AD = A'D'$	3. Trans. and mult. prop.
4. $\overline{AD} ≅ \overline{A'D'}$ (S)	4. Def. of ≅ seg.
5. $\angle A ≅ \angle A'$ (A)	5. Corr. ∠'s of ≅ △'s are ≅.
6. $\overline{CA} ≅ \overline{C'A'}$ (S)	6. Same as 1
7. △CAD ≅ △C'A'D'	7. SAS for ≅ △'s
8. ∴ $\overline{CD} ≅ \overline{C'D'}$	8. Same as 1

A similar proof shows that corresponding altitudes of congruent triangles are congruent.

EXAMPLE 4

△XYZ ≅ △PQR, $\overline{ZM}$ and $\overline{RN}$ are corresponding altitudes. $ZM = 5x - 40$, $RN = 2x + 50$.
Find ZM.

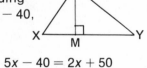

Corr. alt. of ≅ △'s are ≅. ⟶
Subtraction and addition prop. ⟶

$ZM = 5(30) - 40$ ⟶

$5x - 40 = 2x + 50$
$3x = 90$
$x = 30$

Thus, $ZM = 110$.

EXERCISES

PART A

1. $\triangle RJN \cong \triangle CLQ$, $\overline{JT}$ and $\overline{LX}$ are corresponding medians, $JT = 6y + 2$, $LX = 8y - 14$. Find JT. *50*

2. $\triangle CSL \cong \triangle AJP$, $\overline{CH}$ and $\overline{AX}$ are corresponding altitudes, $CH = 3(y + 3)$, $AX = 4(2y + 1)$. Find CH. *12*

3. $\triangle DPW \cong \triangle YKE$, $\overline{WA}$ and $\overline{EN}$ are corresponding medians, $WA = 9x - 2$, $EN = 4(x + 2)$. Find WA. *16*

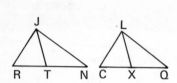 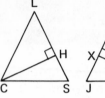 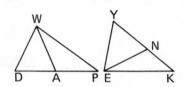

4. $\triangle ZWT \cong \triangle LJQ$. Name the corresponding medians.

5. $\triangle TWI \cong \triangle BVR$. Name the corresponding altitudes.

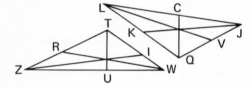 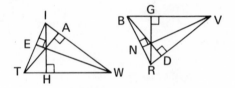

6. Given: $\overline{AC}$ is an altitude of $\triangle ABD$.
Prove: $m\angle 1 + m\angle 2 = m\angle 3 + m\angle 4$

7. Given: $\overline{JM} \perp \overline{MW}$, $\angle J \cong \angle 1$
Prove: $\overline{MX}$ is an altitude of $\triangle JWM$.

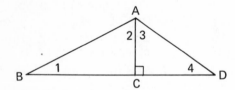 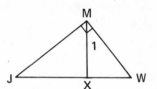

PART B

8. Given: $\triangle XYZ \cong \triangle BAC$, $\overline{TQ}$ is the $\perp$ bisector of $\overline{XY}$, $\overline{JH}$ is the $\perp$ bisector of $\overline{AB}$.
Prove: $\overline{TQ} \cong \overline{JH}$

9. Given: $\triangle ABC \cong \triangle YXZ$, $\overrightarrow{AT}$ bisects $\angle CAB$, $\overrightarrow{YQ}$ bisects $\angle XYZ$.
Prove: $\overline{AT} \cong \overline{YQ}$

10. Given: $\overline{FD}$ is the $\perp$ bisector of $\overline{AC}$, $\overline{GE}$ is the $\perp$ bisector of $\overline{BC}$, $\overline{FD} \cong \overline{GE}$.
Prove: $\overline{AC} \cong \overline{BC}$

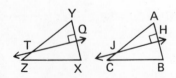 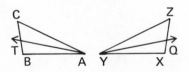

For each of the following statements, draw a diagram and label it. State what is given, and state what is to be proved in terms of the diagram. Prove the statement.

11. Corresponding altitudes of congruent triangles are congruent.

12. Any two altitudes of an equilateral triangle are congruent.

13. Any two medians of an equilateral triangle are congruent.

14. The altitude to the base of an isosceles triangle is also a median.

15. The median to the base of an isosceles triangle is also an altitude.

16. The altitude to the base of an isosceles triangle is the bisector of the vertex angle.

17. The median to the base of an isosceles triangle is the bisector of the vertex angle.

18. If two altitudes of a triangle are congruent, then the triangle is isosceles.

PART C

Determine if each of the following is a true statement. If so, prove it. If not, show a counterexample.

19. If a median of a triangle is perpendicular to the side to which it is drawn, then the triangle is isosceles.

20. If the medians of a triangle are congruent, then the triangle is isosceles.

21. If a median of a triangle bisects the vertex angle, then the triangle is isosceles.

22. If an altitude of a triangle also bisects an angle of the triangle, then the triangle is isosceles.

23. Given: $\overline{EB} \perp$ plane p, $\overline{ED}$ is a $\perp$ bisector of $\overline{AC}$.
Prove: $\overline{BD}$ is a $\perp$ bisector of $\overline{AC}$.

24. Given: $\overline{EB} \perp$ plane p, $\overline{ED}$ bisects $\angle CEA$, $\overline{CE} \cong \overline{AE}$.
Prove: $\overline{BD}$ bisects $\angle CBA$.

25. Given: $\triangle CXR \cong \triangle ZXR$, $\overline{CT}$ is an altitude of $\triangle CXR$.
Prove: $\overline{ZT}$ is an altitude of $\triangle ZXR$.

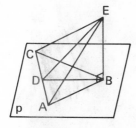

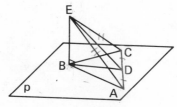

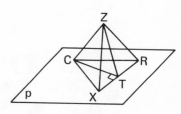

Given: $\overline{XT}$ and $\overline{YT}$ are $\perp$ bisectors of $\overline{ZW}$.

26. Prove: $\triangle WXT \cong \triangle ZXT$

27. Prove: $\triangle WYT \cong \triangle ZYT$

28. Prove: $\triangle ZXY \cong \triangle WXY$

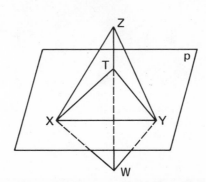

Given: $\triangle XYT$ in plane p, $\overline{ZW} \perp p$ at T, $\overline{TZ} \cong \overline{TW}$, $\overline{XZ} \cong \overline{YZ}$.

29. Prove: $\overline{XT} \cong \overline{YT}$

30. Prove: $\overline{XW} \cong \overline{YW}$

Mathematics in Dairying

A beef research leader checks over part of a herd. This once abandoned farmland was donated by farmers in 40 counties of Indiana for use as an outdoor laboratory. Plant and animal researchers are seeking to improve land and increase forage and animal yields.

Pictured above is a dairy scientist examining comparison studies of sire-son pairs of dairy cattle.

Constructions

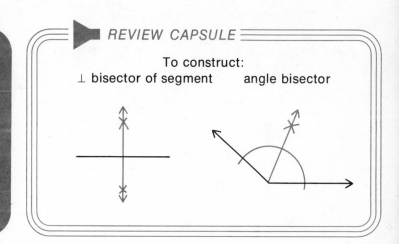

REVIEW CAPSULE

To construct:
⊥ bisector of segment   angle bisector

We can use basic constructions to construct other figures.

EXAMPLE 1 Draw an obtuse △ABC, with obtuse ∠A. Construct the median to side $\overline{BC}$.

Find the midpoint M of $\overline{BC}$ using the the ⊥ bisector construction.

Draw $\overline{AM}$.

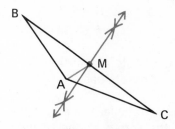

$\overline{AM}$ is the required median.

EXAMPLE 2 Draw an acute △XYZ. Construct the altitude to side $\overline{YZ}$.

From X, contruct a line perpendicular to $\overline{YZ}$.

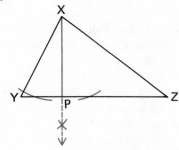

$\overline{XP}$ is the required altitude.

EXAMPLE 3 True or false? Check by making the necessary constructions. "The vertex angle bisector of an isosceles triangle bisects the base."

Draw isosceles △ABC.
Construct $\overrightarrow{BD}$ bisecting ∠B.

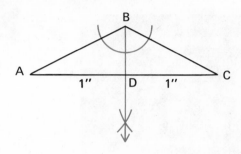

Measure $\overline{AD}$ and $\overline{CD}$. ⟶

$AD = 1$ in. $CD = 1$ in.
$\overrightarrow{BD}$ bisects $\overline{AC}$.

Thus, it seems that the statement is true.

One example does not prove that a statement is true.

The drawing in Example 3 suggests that the statement might be true. It does not prove it is true.

EXERCISES

PART A

1. Draw an acute triangle. Construct the median to one of the sides.

2. Draw an obtuse triangle. Construct the median to a side opposite an acute angle.

3. Draw an obtuse triangle. Construct the altitude from the vertex of one of the acute angles.

4. Draw an acute triangle. Construct the altitude to one of the sides.

5. Draw an acute triangle. Construct the perpendicular bisector of one side of the triangle.

6. Draw a scalene triangle. Construct the altitude from one vertex, the median from the same vertex, the angle bisector of the angle with this vertex, and the perpendicular bisector of the side opposite this vertex. Are any of these four the same?

7. Draw an obtuse triangle. Construct the angle bisector of the obtuse angle. Is this the same as the median?

True or false? Check by making the necessary constructions.

8. The median to the base of an isosceles triangle is also an altitude.

9. The bisector of an angle of a triangle also bisects the opposite side.

10. An altitude of a triangle is also a perpendicular bisector of a side of the triangle.

11. A median of a triangle can never be the perpendicular bisector of a side of the triangle.

12. An angle bisector of a triangle can never be an altitude of the triangle.

13. A perpendicular bisector of a side of a triangle can also bisect an angle.

PART B

14. Draw three triangles: one acute, one obtuse, and one right. Construct the three altitudes of each triangle. What conclusions would you draw about the intersections of these altitudes?

15. Repeat exercise 14, constructing the three medians.

16. Repeat Exercise 14, constructing the three angle bisectors.

17. Repeat Exercise 14, constructing the three perpendicular bisectors of the sides.

Algebra Review

OBJECTIVE
■ To multiply and divide fractions

To multiply fractions:
1. Use $\dfrac{a}{b} \cdot \dfrac{c}{d} = \dfrac{a \cdot c}{b \cdot d}$.
2. Factor both numerator and denominator.
3. Divide out common factors.

To divide fractions:
1. Use the reciprocal of the divisor.
2. Multiply.

EXAMPLE   Divide $\dfrac{x^2 - 5x + 6}{x - 4} \div \dfrac{x - 2}{x^2 - 16}$.

Use the reciprocal of $\dfrac{x - 2}{x^2 - 16}$ and multiply.

Use $\dfrac{a}{b} \cdot \dfrac{c}{d} = \dfrac{a \cdot c}{b \cdot d}$. $\longrightarrow$

$$\dfrac{x^2 - 5x + 6}{x - 4} \cdot \dfrac{x^2 - 16}{x - 2}$$
$$\dfrac{(x^2 - 5x + 6)(x^2 - 16)}{(x - 4)(x - 2)}$$

Factor and divide out common factors. $\longrightarrow$

$$\dfrac{\overset{1}{(x - 2)}(x - 3)\overset{1}{(x - 4)}(x + 4)}{\underset{1}{(x - 4)}\underset{1}{(x - 2)}}$$

$$\dfrac{(x - 3)(x + 4)}{1}, \text{ or } x^2 + x - 12$$

Simplify.

1. $\dfrac{y^2 - 16}{9y^2 - 25} \div \dfrac{y - 4}{3y + 5}$

2. $\dfrac{4x + 8}{6x + 18} \cdot \dfrac{5x + 15}{x^2 - 4}$

3. $\dfrac{a^2 - 3a - 10}{a^2 + 3a + 2} \cdot \dfrac{a^2 + 8a + 7}{a^2 - 6a + 5}$

4. $\dfrac{x^2 + 2x - 15}{x^2 + x - 2} \cdot \dfrac{x^2 + 5x - 6}{x^2 + 11x + 30}$

5. $\dfrac{6x + 12}{3x - 9} \div \dfrac{2x + 4}{x^2 - 9}$

6. $\dfrac{a^2 - a - 6}{a^2 + 3a + 2} \cdot \dfrac{a^2 + 7a + 6}{a^2 - 4a + 3}$

Chapter Five Review

1. $\triangle XRT \cong \triangle QLS$. List the pairs of congruent sides. [p. 135]

2. $\triangle XRT \cong \triangle QLS$. List the pairs of congruent angles. [p. 135]

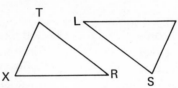

3. In each right triangle, identify the hypotenuse and the legs. [p. 147]

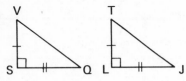 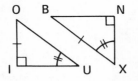 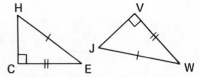

Which pairs of right triangles are congruent? What is the reason? [p. 147]

4.
5.
6.

7. In each triangle, is $\overline{AX}$ an altitude or a median? [p. 160]

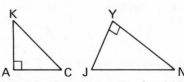

8. Given: $\overline{AJ} \cong \overline{AR}$, $\overline{AQ}$ bisects $\angle RAJ$.
   Prove: $\overline{JQ} \cong \overline{RQ}$ [p. 156]

9. Given: $\overline{AQ}$ bisects $\angle RAJ$.
   Prove: $m\angle 1 + m\angle 3 = m\angle 2 + m\angle 4$ [p. 156]

10. Given: $\triangle TCQ \cong \triangle TPJ$, $\overline{JP} \perp \overline{TQ}$
    Prove: $\overline{CJ} \cong \overline{PQ}$ [p. 143, 153]

11. Given: $\overline{QC}$ and $\overline{JP}$ are altitudes of $\triangle TJQ$, $\angle CQJ \cong \angle PJQ$.
    Prove: $\triangle TJQ$ is isosceles. [p. 160]

12. Isosceles $\triangle RJP$, $\overline{JR} \cong \overline{JP}$, $m\angle R = 3x - 5$, $m\angle P = 2x + 20$.
    Find $m\angle J$. [p. 138]

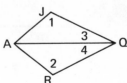

13. $\angle R \cong \angle P$, $RJ = 7x - 4$, $PJ = 5x + 2$.
    Find RJ. [p. 138]

For each statement, draw a diagram and label it. State what is given, and state what is to be proved in terms of the diagram.

14. All altitudes of an equilateral triangle are congruent. [p. 160]

15. If two medians of a triangle are congruent, then the triangle is isoscles.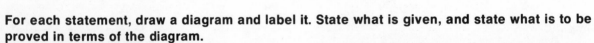

16. Draw an obtuse triangle. Construct the altitude from the vertex of one of the acute angles. [p. 165]

17. Draw an obtuse triangle. Construct the median to the side opposite the obtuse angle. [p. 165]   [p. 160]

Chapter Five Test

1. $\triangle PQR \cong \triangle XYZ$. List the pairs of congruent sides.

2. $\triangle PQR \cong \triangle XYZ$. List the pairs of congruent angles.

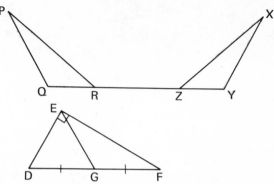

3. Identify the hypotenuse and legs of right $\triangle DEF$.

4. Which segment is an altitude of $\triangle DEF$? Which segment is a median?

Which pairs of right triangles are congruent? What is the reason?

5.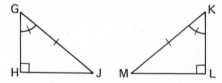

6.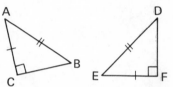

For each statement, draw a diagram and label it. State what is given, and state what is to be proved in terms of the diagram.

7. Two altitudes of an isosceles triangle are congruent.

8. Two right triangles are congruent if a leg and hypotenuse of one are congruent to a leg and hypotenuse of the other.

9. Given: Isosceles $\triangle RNP$, $\overline{RP} \cong \overline{NP}$, $m \angle R = 3x + 4$, $m \angle N = 5x - 22$. Find $m \angle N$.

10. $\angle R \cong \angle N$, $RP = 3x - 1$, $PN = 2x + 4$. Find RP.

11. Given: $\overline{JQ}$ bisects $\angle PQR$, $JQ \perp PR$. Prove: $\triangle PQR$ is isosceles.

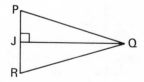

12. Given: $\triangle LCD \cong \triangle HGQ$, DT and QN are altitudes. Prove: $\overline{LT} \cong \overline{HN}$

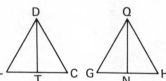

13. Given: $\overline{SC}$ is an altitude of $\triangle SJR$. Prove: $m \angle 1 + m \angle 4 = m \angle 2 + m \angle 3$

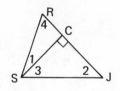

14. Draw an obtuse triangle. Construct the median to the longest side.

Mathematics in Astronomy

Detailed scale maps depict the relationships of the stars.

An important tool of the astronomer is the telescope. Pictured below is the Palomar Hale 200-inch telescope.

Radio telescopes have greatly increased the range of radiations intercepted from outer space. This has enabled man to gain more knowledge of the composition and structure of the universe.

Polygons

OBJECTIVES

■ To identify and name polygons

■ To identify sides and vertices of polygons

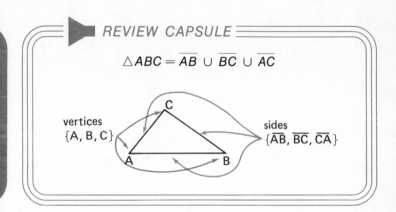

▶ *REVIEW CAPSULE*

$$\triangle ABC = \overline{AB} \cup \overline{BC} \cup \overline{AC}$$

vertices
{A, B, C}

sides
$\{\overline{AB}, \overline{BC}, \overline{CA}\}$

Poly means *many*. A *polygon* has many sides.

A polygon is a union of three or more segments.

Definition of polygon ————————→

Both conditions must be met.

> A *polygon* is the union of three or more coplanar segments which intersect only at their endpoints, and each endpoint is shared by exactly two segments.

EXAMPLE 1   Tell why each is not a polygon.

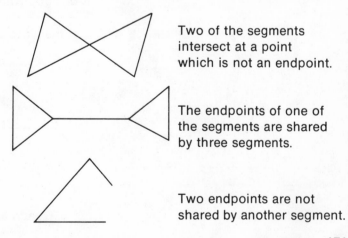

Two of the segments intersect at a point which is not an endpoint.

The endpoints of one of the segments are shared by three segments.

Two endpoints are not shared by another segment.

EXAMPLE 2 Which of the following are polygons? Why are the others not polygons?

You can trace a polygon by starting at any point and without lifting the pencil or retracing any points return to the starting point.

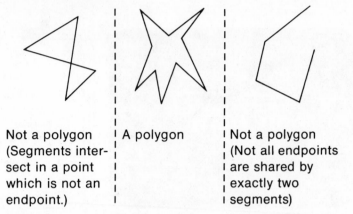

Not a polygon (Segments intersect in a point which is not an endpoint.) | A polygon | Not a polygon (Not all endpoints are shared by exactly two segments)

The *sides* of a polygon are its segments.
The *vertices* of a polygon are the endpoints.

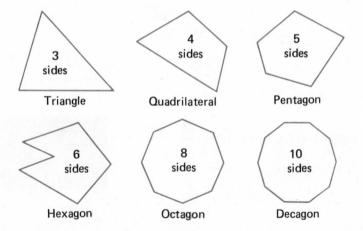

The number of vertices of a polygon is the same as the number of sides.

Triangle — 3 sides
Quadrilateral — 4 sides
Pentagon — 5 sides
Hexagon — 6 sides
Octagon — 8 sides
Decagon — 10 sides

A polygon with *n* sides is called an *n-gon*.

EXAMPLE 3 List the sides and vertices. Name the polygon.

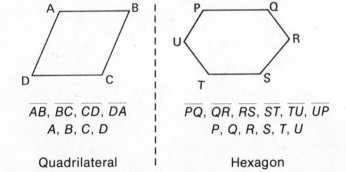

Sides ⟶ $\overline{AB}, \overline{BC}, \overline{CD}, \overline{DA}$ | $\overline{PQ}, \overline{QR}, \overline{RS}, \overline{ST}, \overline{TU}, \overline{UP}$

Vertices ⟶ A, B, C, D | P, Q, R, S, T, U

Name ⟶ Quadrilateral | Hexagon

ORAL EXERCISES

Name the sides and vertices of each polygon.

1.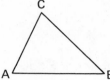

2.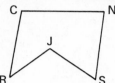

3.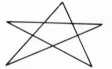

4.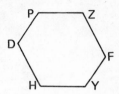

Which of the following are polygons?

5.

6.

7.

8.

EXERCISES

PART A

Which of the following are polygons. Tell why the others are not.

1.

2.

3.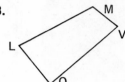

4.

5.

6.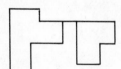

7.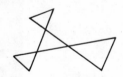

8.

Name each of the following polygons.

9.

10.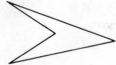

11.

12.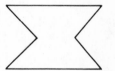

PART B

How many sides does the polygon have? (Use a dictionary, if necessary.) Draw a picture.

13. Heptagon   **14.** Nonagon   **15.** Dodecagon

Convex and Concave Polygons

OBJECTIVE
■ To identify convex and concave sets of points

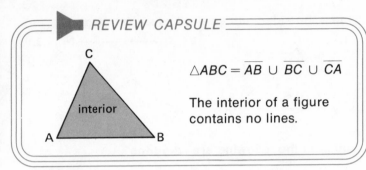

▶ *REVIEW CAPSULE*

$$\triangle ABC = \overline{AB} \cup \overline{BC} \cup \overline{CA}$$

The interior of a figure contains no lines.

Convex and Concave Sets

These sets are convex.   These sets are concave.

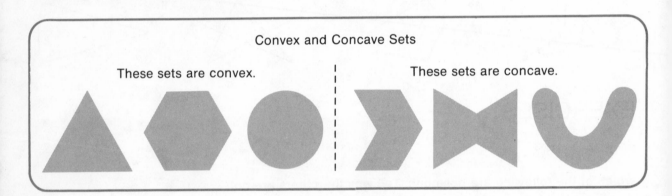

Definition of *convex set* ⟶

Definition of *concave* set ⟶

A set of points is *convex* if the segment *XY* joining any two points of the set is in the set. If the set is not convex, then it is *concave.*

Convex   Concave

EXAMPLE 1   Which are convex sets? Which are concave sets?

In a convex set, the segment joining *any* pair of points must be in the set.

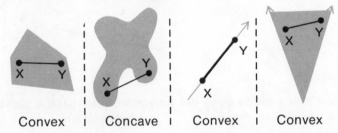

Convex | Concave | Convex | Convex

EXAMPLE 2 Draw a quadrilateral region and an octagonal region.

The polygon is the border of the region.

Quadrilateral region | Octagonal region

The region determined by a polygon is the union of the interior of the polygon and the polygon itself.

EXAMPLE 3 Which is a convex set, a triangle or a triangular region?

The triangle is shown in red. *X* and *Y*

The triangle *is not* a convex set since all the points of *XY* are not on the triangle.

The triangular region is shown in red. *X* and *Y* are points in the region.

The triangular region is a convex set since the segment joining any two points of the region is in the region.

Definition of convex polygon ⟶

A *convex polygon* is a polygon that determines a convex region. A polygon that is not convex is concave.

EXAMPLE 4 Which are convex polygons? Which are concave?

A convex polygon is not convex itself. The region is convex.

Convex | Concave | Concave

ORAL EXERCISES

Which are convex sets? Which are concave sets?

1.

2.

3.

4.

Which are convex polygons? Which are concave?

5. 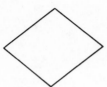 6.   7.   8.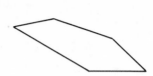

EXERCISES

PART A

Copy each of the following. Draw an appropriate segment to show whether each is a convex or a concave set.

1.  2.   3.  4.

5.  6.   7.   8.

Copy each of the following. Pick two appropriate points in each and draw the connecting segment to show that it is not a convex set.

9.   10.  11.   12.

Make drawings of each of the following.

13. A convex quadrilateral 14. A concave quadrilateral 15. A convex pentagon
16. A concave pentagon 17. A convex hexagon 18. A concave decagon

PART B

True or false? Draw pictures to defend your answers.

19. The union of any two convex sets is a convex set.
20. The intersection of any two convex sets is a concave set.
21. The union of any two concave sets is a concave set.
22. The intersection of any two concave sets is a concave set.
23. The union of a convex set and a concave set is a convex set.
24. The intersection of a convex set and a concave set is a concave set.

Sprouts

Here is a three-dot sprouts game.

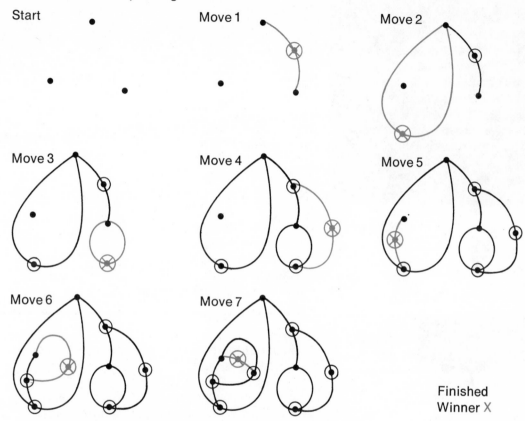

Start

Move 1

Move 2

Move 3

Move 4

Move 5

Move 6

Move 7

Finished
Winner X

The game of sprouts begins with any number, n, of dots.
A move consists of drawing a line connecting two dots or a dot with itself and placing a new dot on the line.

Players: Two or more.

Rules: 1. A line cannot cross itself, any other line, or any more than two dots.

2. Any dot on more than three lines is out of play.

3. The winner is the last person able to play.

Try playing a four-dot sprouts game. How many moves can you make?

Can you discover a formula for the maximum number of moves for a game of any number of dots?

Interior Angles of Convex Polygons

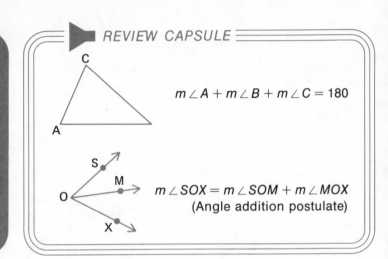

▶ *REVIEW CAPSULE*

$$m \angle A + m \angle B + m \angle C = 180$$

$$m \angle SOX = m \angle SOM + m \angle MOX$$
(Angle addition postulate)

EXAMPLE 1 Draw a quadrilateral. Measure each angle. Find the sum of the angle measures.

$$132 + 66 + 100 + 62 = 360$$

62°   100°
132°
66°

Theorem 6.1

The sum of the measures of the angles of a convex quadrilateral is 360°.

ANALYSIS
Sum of meas. of ∠'s of a △ = 180°.
A diagonal determines 2 △'s.

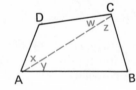

GIVEN
convex quadrilateral *ABCD*
PROVE
$$m \angle A + m \angle B + m \angle C + m \angle D = 360$$

PROOF

STATEMENTS	REASONS
1. Draw diagonal $\overline{AC}$.	1. Two points are contained in exactly one line.
2. $m \angle DAB = m \angle x + m \angle y$	2. Angle addition postulate
3. $m \angle DCB = m \angle z + m \angle w$	3. Same as 2
4. $m \angle A + m \angle B + m \angle C + m \angle D = m \angle x + m \angle y + m \angle B + m \angle z + m \angle w + m \angle D$	4. Subst. prop.
5. $m \angle x + m \angle w + m \angle D = 180$	5. Sum of meas. of ∠'s of a △ = 180°.
6. $m \angle y + m \angle B + m \angle z = 180$	6. Same as 5
7. ∴ $m \angle A + m \angle B + m \angle C + m \angle D = 360$	7. Subst. and addition properties

EXAMPLE 2 $m\angle A = 5x + 5$, $m\angle B = 6x - 8$, $m\angle C = 4x + 13$, $m\angle D = 4x + 8$. Find $m\angle A$ and $m\angle C$.

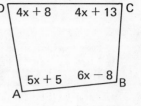

Sum of meas. of $\angle$'s of quad. = 360°. $\longrightarrow$

$$(5x + 5) + (6x - 8) + (4x + 13) + (4x + 8) = 360$$
$$19x + 18 = 360$$
$$19x = 342$$
$$x = 18$$

$m\angle A = 5(18) + 5$ $\longrightarrow$ $\qquad\qquad m\angle A = 95$
$m\angle C = 4(18) + 13$ $\longrightarrow$ $\qquad\qquad m\angle C = 85$

EXAMPLE 3 For each polygon draw all the diagonals from a single vertex. How many sides does the polygon have? How many triangles are formed?

A *diagonal* of a polygon is a segment joining any two nonconsecutive vertices.

4 sides | 6 sides | 8 sides
2 triangles | 4 triangles | 6 triangles

In each of these polygons, the number of triangles formed by the diagonals is two less than the number of sides.

EXAMPLE 4 If a polygon has n sides, how many triangles are formed by the diagonals from a single vertex?

The number of triangles is two less than the number of sides. $\longrightarrow$

$(n - 2)$ triangles are formed.

EXAMPLE 5 Find the sum of the measures of the angles of each polygon.

The angles are sometimes called interior angles.

n sides
$(n - 2)$ triangles
$\angle$ meas. sum = $(n - 2)(180)$ $\longrightarrow$

5 sides | 6 sides | 7 sides
3 triangles | 4 triangles | 5 triangles
540° | 720° | 900°

INTERIOR ANGLES OF CONVEX POLYGONS **179**

Example 5 suggests a proof of the following.

Theorem 6.2
(See Ex. 24.)

The sum of the measures of the interior angles of a convex polygon with n sides is $(n-2)180$.

EXAMPLE 6

A 15-gon is a polygon with 15 sides.

Find the sum of the measures of the angles of a convex 15-gon.

n sides ⟶ 15 sides
$(n-2)180$ ⟶ $13(180) = 2{,}340$

Thus, the sum of the measures of the angles of a 15-gon is 2,340°.

EXAMPLE 7

How many sides does a convex polygon have if the sum of the measures of its angles is 1,620°?

n is the number of sides ⟶
$(n-2)180 = 180n - 360$ ⟶

$$(n-2)180 = 1{,}620$$
$$180n - 360 = 1{,}620$$
$$180n = 1{,}980$$
$$n = 11$$

The polygon is an 11-gon ⟶ **Thus,** the polygon has 11 sides.

ORAL EXERCISES

How many triangles can be formed by drawing all the diagonals from a single vertex of each of the following polygons?

1.   **2.**  **3.**  **4.**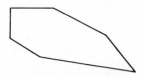

How many triangles can be formed by drawing all the diagonals from a single vertex of a polygon with the given number of sides?

5. 7   **6.** 11   **7.** 12   **8.** 18   **9.** 37   **10.** 122

EXERCISES

PART A

Find the measure of each angle of quadrilateral *ABCD*.

1. $m\angle A = 4x$, $m\angle B = 4x + 10$
$m\angle C = 5x - 10$, $m\angle D = 5x$

2. $m\angle A = 5x$, $m\angle B = 6x + 4$
$m\angle C = 3x - 1$, $m\angle D = 7x$

3. $m\angle A = 3x - 2$, $m\angle B = 4x$
$m\angle C = 2x + 25$, $m\angle D = 58$

For each of the following quadrilaterals, three of the angle measures are given. Find the measure of the fourth angle.

4. 38°, 96°, 103°   **5.** 83°, 117°, 135°   **6.** 90°, 90°, 90°

Compute the angle measure sum of each of the following polygons.

7. A pentagon   **8.** An octagon   **9.** A dodecagon
10. A fifty-gon   **11.** A 102-gon   **12.** A thousand-gon

Draw a picture of each of the following convex polygons. Using a protractor, measure each angle. Add these to determine the angle measure sum. Compare this with the sum found by the formula of Theorem 6.2.

13. A pentagon   **14.** A heptagon   **15.** An octagon

Find the number of sides of the polygon having the given angle measure sum.

16. 540°   **17.** 1,080°   **18.** 1,800°   **19.** 3,960°

PART B

20. If all the angles of a hexagon are congruent, then what is the measure of each angle?

21. If all the angles of an octagon are congruent, then what is the measure of each angle?

22. If all the angles of a 15-gon are congruent, then what is the measure of each angle?

23. If each angle of a polygon has a measure of 144°, then how many sides does the polygon have?

PART C

24. Give a complete proof of Theorem 6.2, using triangles formed by diagonals from a single vertex.

25. Find a formula for the measure of each angle of an *n*-gon if all angles are congruent.

26. In the the following figures, how is the number of triangles formed related to the number of sides? Prove Theorem 6.2 using an approach based on these pictures.

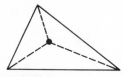 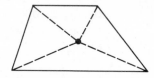

Using a protractor, measure each angle of each concave polygon below. Add these to determine the angle measure sum. Does the formula of Theorem 6.2 work for concave polygons? Is there a formula?

27.   **28.**    **29.**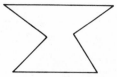

Exterior Angles of Convex Polygons

OBJECTIVES

■ To identify the exterior angles of a polygon
■ To develop and apply a formula for the sum of the measures of exterior angles of a convex polygon

▶ *REVIEW CAPSULE*

A triangle has two exterior angles at each vertex.

The two exterior angles at each vertex are congruent.

Vertical angles are congruent.

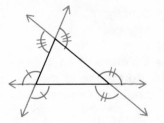

Every convex polygon has two congruent exterior angles at each vertex.

EXAMPLE 1   Draw a pentagon *ABCDE*. Draw and label all exterior angles.

A pentagon has 5 vertices.

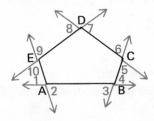

Angles 1 through 10 are the exterior angles.

EXAMPLE 2   One exterior angle is shown at each vertex of the pentagon below. Using a protractor, measure each of these. What is the sum of the measures of the exterior angles?

The interior and exterior angles at each vertex are supplementary.

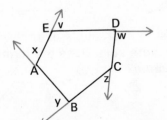

$m \angle x = 68$
$m \angle y = 87$
$m \angle z = 44$
$m \angle w = 98$
$m \angle v = \underline{63}$
$ 360$

The sum of the measures of the exterior angles is 360°.

EXAMPLE 3 Find $m \angle r + m \angle s + m \angle t + m \angle u + m \angle p$.

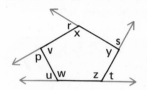

An exterior and interior $\angle$ at each vertex are supplementary. ⟶

$$(m \angle r + m \angle x) + (m \angle s + m \angle y) + (m \angle t + m \angle z) +$$
$$(m \angle u + m \angle w) + (m \angle p + m \angle v)$$
$$= \quad 180 \quad + \quad 180 \quad + \quad 180 \quad + \quad 180 \quad + \quad 180$$
$$= 5(180), \text{ or } 900$$

The sum of the measures of int. $\angle$'s is $(n - 2)$ 180. ⟶

But, $m \angle x + m \angle y + m \angle z + m \angle w + m \angle v = (5 - 2) 180$
$$= 540$$

(total of all $\angle$ meas.) − (total of int. $\angle$ meas.) = (total of ext. $\angle$ meas.) ⟶

Thus, $m \angle r + m \angle s + m \angle t + m \angle u + m \angle p =$
$$900 - 540, \text{ or } 360.$$

Theorem 6.3

(See Ex. 13.)

The sum of the measures of the exterior angles, one at each vertex, of any convex polygon is 360°.

EXAMPLE 4 What is the sum of the measures of the exterior angles, one at each vertex, of a convex 138-gon?

Use Theorem 6.3. ⟶ The sum of the measures is 360°.

ORAL EXERCISES

What is the sum of the measures of the exterior angles of the polygons shown below?

1.

2.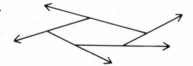

3.

EXERCISES

PART A

What is the sum of the measures of the exterior angles, one at each vertex, of each of the given convex polygons?

1. An octagon

2. A decagon

3. A 17-gon

Copy each polygon. Draw an exterior angle at each vertex. Use a protractor to measure each exterior angle. What is the sum of the measures of these exterior angles? Does the result agree with Theorem 6.3?

4.

5.

6.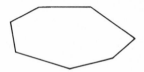

For each polygon, compute the sum of the measures of all pairs of interior and exterior angles (one at each vertex), and the sum of the measures of all interior angles. Use these sums to compute the sum of the measures of the exterior angles.

7. A heptagon

8. A decagon

9. A 30-gon

PART B

10. If all the angles of a hexagon are congruent, then what is the measure of each exterior angle?

11. If each exterior angles of a polygon has a measure of 30°, then how many sides does the polygon have?

12. If all the angles of an n-gon are congruent, then what is the measure of each exterior angle?

13. Give a complete proof of Theorem 6.3.

14. The measures of the exterior angles of a pentagon are $m \angle p = x$, $m \angle q = 2x$, $m \angle r = 3x$, $m \angle s = 4x$, and $m \angle t = 5x$. Find the measure of each angle.

15. The measures of the exterior angles of a hexagon are $m \angle p = 2x + 4$, $m \angle q = 8x + 7$, $m \angle r = 5x - 6$, $m \angle s = 6x + 9$, $m \angle t = 3x - 2$, $m \angle u = 5x$. Find the measure of each angle.

Algebra Review

OBJECTIVE
■ To add and subtract fractions

To add or subtract two fractions:
1. Change to equivalent fractions with a common denominator.
2. Combine the numerators.

EXAMPLE Simplify $\dfrac{3x}{x^2 - 4} - \dfrac{4}{x - 2}$.

$\dfrac{a}{b} - \dfrac{c}{d}$ means $\dfrac{a}{b} + \dfrac{-1(c)}{d}$ ───────→

$\dfrac{3x}{(x + 2)(x - 2)} + \dfrac{-1(4)(x + 2)}{(x - 2)(x + 2)}$

$\dfrac{3x - 4(x + 2)}{(x + 2)(x - 2)}$, or $\dfrac{-x - 8}{x^2 - 4}$

$LCD = (x + 2)(x - 2)$

Simplify.

1. $\dfrac{6}{y^2 - 16} - \dfrac{5}{y + 4}$

2. $\dfrac{6x + 1}{x^2 - 9} + \dfrac{3}{x - 3}$

3. $5 + \dfrac{8a - 6}{4}$

4. $\dfrac{9}{b + 8} - \dfrac{2}{b}$

Constant Width Curves

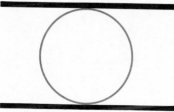

When a circular roller is turned between two parallel surfaces, it will always maintain contact with both surfaces.
A circle is a closed curve of constant width.

Another curve of constant width is the Reuleaux triangle. It is constructed by connecting the vertices of an equilateral triangle with arcs centered at the third vertex.

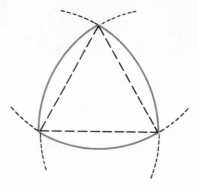

Construct several Reuleaux triangles of the same size of heavy cardboard. Attach them to an axle so they will roll along together. Balance a light book on top. Does the book move parallel to the horizontal surface?

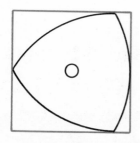

It is possible to make a drill that will cut a square hole. This was actually invented in 1914. Notice that the Reauleaux triangle can be turned in the square, still touching all four sides of the square. The amazing drill was based on this principle.

A constant width curve can be constructed by connecting the vertices of any regular polygon with an odd number of sides with arcs.
Try constructing a curve of constant width using a regular pentagon.

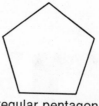

regular pentagon

Regular Polygons

Equilateral polygons have all sides congruent.

Equiangular polygons have all angles congruent.

Equilateral polygons | Equiangular polygons

EXAMPLE 1 Draw three polygons that are both equilateral and equiangular.

All sides are congruent and all angles are congruent.

A *regular polygon* is both equilateral and equiangular.

EXAMPLE 2 Find the measure of each interior angle of a regular octagon.

$n = 8$, $(n - 2)\,(180)$ ⟶ The sum of measures is $(8 - 2)\,(180) = 1{,}080°$.
$\frac{1{,}080}{8} = 135$, 8 congruent ∠'s. ⟶ **Thus,** each angle measures $135°$.

Theorem 6.4

The measure of an angle of a regular polygon with *n* sides is $\dfrac{(n - 2)\,180}{n}$.

EXAMPLE 3   Find the measure of each exterior angle of a regular hexagon.

A regular hexagon has $6 \cong \angle$'s.
The sum of measures is 360°. $\longrightarrow$ Each exterior angle measures $\frac{360}{6}$, or 60°.

Corollary

The measure of an exterior angle of a regular polygon with n sides is $\frac{360}{n}$.

EXAMPLE 4   How many sides does a regular polygon have if the measure of each angle is 150°?

Meas. of each $\angle$ is $\frac{(n-2)180}{n}$. $\longrightarrow$

$$150 = \frac{(n-2)(180)}{n}$$

Multiply each side by n. $\longrightarrow$
$(n-2)180 = 180n - 360$ $\longrightarrow$

$$150n = (n-2)(180)$$
$$150n = 180n - 360$$
$$-30n = -360$$
$$n = 12$$

A polygon with 12 sides is a dodecagon.   **Thus,** the polygon has 12 sides.

EXAMPLE 5   How many sides does a regular polygon have if the measure of each exterior angle is 72°?

Meas. of each $\angle$ is $\frac{360}{n}$. $\longrightarrow$

$$72 = \frac{360}{n}$$
$$72n = 360$$
$$n = 5$$

The polygon is a pentagon.   **Thus,** the polygon has 5 sides.

EXERCISES

PART A

Draw each of the following regular polygons.

1. Quadrilateral   2. Pentagon   3. Hexagon   4. Octagon

Find the measure of an interior angle of each of the following regular polygons.

5. Triangle   6. Quadrilateral   7. Pentagon   8. Hexagon
9. Heptagon   10. Decagon   11. 20-gon   12. 100-gon

Find the measure of an exterior angle of each of the following regular polygons.

13. Triangle   14. Quadrilateral   15. Pentagon   16. Heptagon
17. Dodecagon   18. 20-gon   19. 80-gon   20. 100-gon

Find the number of sides in a regular polygon with interior angles of the given measure.

21. 60° **22.** 135° **23.** 140° **24.** 162°

Find the number of sides in a regular polygon with exterior angles of the given measure.

25. 60° **26.** 36° **27.** 24° **28.** 20°

PART B

Which of the following are possible measure of interior angles of a regular polygon? If possible, how many sides does the polygon have?

29. 90° **30.** 100° **31.** $112\frac{1}{2}°$ **32.** 130° **33.** 144° **34.** 150°

Which of the following are possible measures of exterior angles of a regular polygon? If possible, how many sides does the polygon have?

35. 180° **36.** 150° **37.** 120° **38.** 72° **39.** 45° **40.** 20°

PART C

True or false? Draw pictures to illustrate.

41. An interior angle of a regular polygon cannot be congruent to an exterior angle.

42. For no value of n is an equilateral n-gon equiangular.

43. All equilateral polygons are convex.

44. All equiangular polygons are convex.

Algebra Review

OBJECTIVE
■ To solve fractional equations

To solve a fractional equation:
1. Multiply each side by the LCD.
2. Solve the resulting equation.

EXAMPLE Solve $\dfrac{2x-5}{3} = \dfrac{x+1}{2}$.

LCD = 6 ⟶

$$6\left(\frac{2x-5}{3}\right) = 6\left(\frac{x+1}{2}\right)$$
$$2(2x-5) = 3(x+1)$$
$$4x-10 = 3x+3$$
$$x = 13$$

Solve.

1. $\dfrac{3x+1}{4} = \dfrac{2x-3}{3}$

2. $\dfrac{5x-2}{4} = \dfrac{4x+1}{3}$

3. $\dfrac{5y-1}{3} = \dfrac{3y-2}{2}$

4. $\dfrac{n-7}{6} = \dfrac{3n}{4} - \dfrac{2n-1}{2}$

5. $\dfrac{2y-3}{7} - \dfrac{y+3}{14} = \dfrac{y}{2}$

6. $\dfrac{2a-1}{2} + \dfrac{5}{3} = \dfrac{3a+4}{12}$

7. $\dfrac{3}{x} + \dfrac{4}{5} = 2$

8. $\dfrac{3}{5y} + \dfrac{7}{2y} = 1$

9. $\dfrac{5}{3b} - \dfrac{1}{4} = \dfrac{7}{6b}$

Constructing Regular Polygons

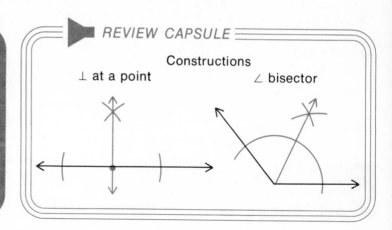

▶ *REVIEW CAPSULE*

Constructions

⊥ at a point   ∠ bisector

An equilateral triangle is the union of three congruent segments.

construction

An equilateral triangle

GIVEN
Segment $\overline{PQ}$
CONSTRUCT
An equilateral △ with sides ≅ $\overline{PQ}$

STRATEGY
Use the construction for a triangle given its three sides.

P ——————— Q

Set the compass with radius $\overline{PQ}$. Draw an arc with center P.

Use a congruent radius. Draw an arc with center Q.

Draw $\overline{PR}$ and $\overline{QR}$.

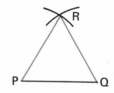

Conclusion: △PQR is equilateral.

Each angle of an equilateral tringle measures 60°. ——————————→ Each angle of the triangle constructed has a measure of 60°.

EXAMPLE 1   Construct a 30° angle.

Construct equilateral △ABC.
m ∠ A = 60

Bisect ∠ A.

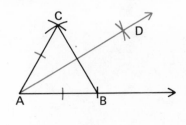

m ∠ BAD = 30

---

construction

A regular hexagon

STRATEGY
Draw a circle with radius
≅ PQ. Mark off arcs on
the circle with radii ≅ PQ.

P ———— Q

GIVEN
Segment PQ
CONSTRUCT
A regular hexagon with
sides ≅ PQ

Draw a circle with radius ≅ PQ.

Starting with any point X on the circle, mark off a series of arcs with radius ≅ PQ on the circle.

Draw the segments.

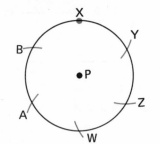

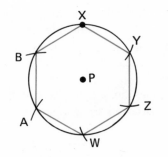

Conclusion: XYZWAB is a regular hexagon.

EXAMPLE 2   Construct a square with sides congruent to HJ.

A square is a regular quadrilateral.

Construct ⊥'s to form right angles.

Mark off segments ≅ HJ on the ⊥'s.

H ———— J

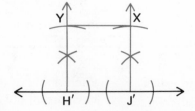

H'J'XY is a square.

EXAMPLE 3 Construct a 45° angle.

Start with any point *A* on a line.

Construct a perpendicular.

Bisect the 90° angle.

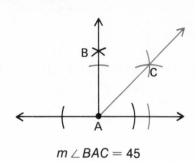

$m \angle BAC = 45$

EXERCISES

PART A

1. Draw a segment. Construct an equilateral triangle with sides congruent to the segment.

2. Draw a segment. Construct a square with sides congruent to the segment.

3. Draw a segment. Construct a regular hexagon with sides congruent to the segment.

Using the constructions for regular polygons and angle bisectors, construct an angle with the given measure.

4. 60°   5. 30°   6. 15°   7. 120°   8. 90°   9. 45°

PART B

EXAMPLE   Construct an angle with a measure of 135°.

$135 = 90 + 45$

$m \angle RPQ = 135$

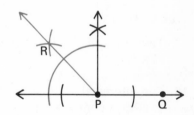

Construct an angle with each given measure.

10. 75°   11. $37\frac{1}{2}°$ 12. 165°   13. 150°   14. $157\frac{1}{2}°$ 15. 105°

16. Construct an equilateral triangle with sides twice a long as a given segment.

17. Construct a regular hexagon with sides half as long as a given segment.

PART C

18. Construct a regular octagon.
20. Construct a square with a diagonal congruent to a given segment.

19. Construct a regular dodecagon.
21. Give an argument to defend the construction for a regular hexagon.

Chapter Six Review

Which of the figures below are polygons? Why are the other figures not polygons? [p. 171]

1.
2.
3.
4.
5.

Which polygons are convex? Which are concave? [p. 174]

6.
7.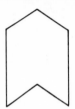
8.
9.
10.

11. Find the sum of the measures of the interior angles of a pentagon. [p. 178]
12. Find the sum of the measures of the interior angles of a 17-gon. [p. 178]
13. Find the sum of the measures of the exterior angles of an octagon. [p. 182]
14. Find the sum of the measures of the exterior angles of a 23-gon. [p. 182]
15. Find the measure of each interior angle of a regular hexagon. [p. 186]
16. Find the measure of each exterior angle of a regular dodecagon. [p. 182]

True or false?

17. Two sides of a polygon always intersect at a vertex. [p. 171]
18. If each exterior angle of a regular polygon has a measure of 90°, then the polygon is a square. [p. 186]
19. The intersection of two concave regions is always concave. [p. 174]
20. All the sides of an equiangular polygon are congruent. [p. 186]
21. In quadrilateral $ABCD$, $m \angle A = 5x + 20$, $m \angle B = 6x - 2$, $m \angle C = 9x - 8$, $m \angle D = 9x + 2$. Find the measure of each angle. [p. 178]
22. The measures of the exterior angles of a pentagon are $m \angle p = 4x + 4$, $m \angle q = 7x + 2$, $m \angle r = 6x - 9$, $m \angle s = 7x - 3$, $m \angle t = 2x + 2$. Find the measure of each angle. [p. 182]
23. Find the number of sides in a regular polygon each of whose interior angles measures 140°. [p. 186]
24. Draw a segment 2 inches long. Construct a regular hexagon with sides congruent to this segment. [p. 189]
25. Construct a 60° angle. [p. 189]
26. Construct a 30° angle. [p. 189]

Chapter Six Test

Tell which figures are polygons. Why are the other figures not polygons?

1.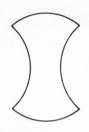

2.

3.

4.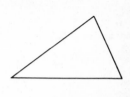

Which polygons are convex? Which are concave?

5.

6.

7.

8.

9. Find the sum of the measures of the interior angles of a 22-gon.

10. Find the sum of the measures of the exterior angles of a 37-gon.

11. Find the measure of each interior angle of a regular pentagon.

12. Find the measure of each exterior angle of a regular 20-gon.

True or false?

13. A decagon is a polygon with 12 sides.

14. If each interior angle of a regular polygon has a measure of 60°, then the polygon is a triangle.

15. In quadrilateral $XYZW$, $m \angle X = 4t$, $m \angle Y = 4t + 10$, $m \angle Z = 5t$, and $m \angle W = 5t - 10$. Find the measure of each angle.

16. The measures of the exterior angles of a triangle are $m \angle p = 2x + 20$, $m \angle q = 3x - 30$, $m \angle r = x + 70$. Find the measure of each exterior angle.

17. Find the number of sides in a regular polygon each of whose interior angles measures 144°.

18. Find the number of sides in a regular polygon each of whose exterior angles measures 18°.

19. Construct a regular hexagon.

20. Construct a 30° angle.

Angles in Concave Polygons

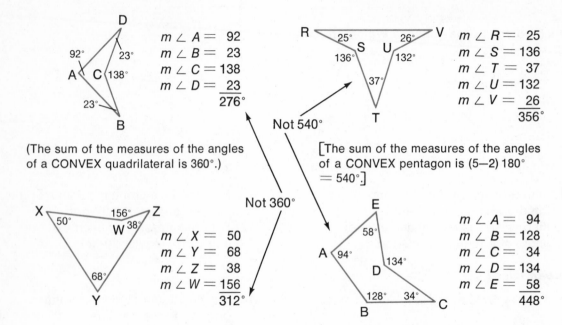

Concave Quadrilaterals

$m \angle A = 92$
$m \angle B = 23$
$m \angle C = 138$
$m \angle D = \underline{23}$
$276°$

(The sum of the measures of the angles of a CONVEX quadrilateral is 360°.)

$m \angle X = 50$
$m \angle Y = 68$
$m \angle Z = 38$
$m \angle W = \underline{156}$
$312°$

Concave Pentagons

$m \angle R = 25$
$m \angle S = 136$
$m \angle T = 37$
$m \angle U = 132$
$m \angle V = \underline{26}$
$356°$

Not 540°

Not 360°

[The sum of the measures of the angles of a CONVEX pentagon is (5−2) 180° = 540°.]

$m \angle A = 94$
$m \angle B = 128$
$m \angle C = 34$
$m \angle D = 134$
$m \angle E = \underline{58}$
$448°$

The angle formulas were proved for convex polygons.
They do not work for concave polygons.

Find the measure of the angle. [Hint: Divide into convex polygons.]

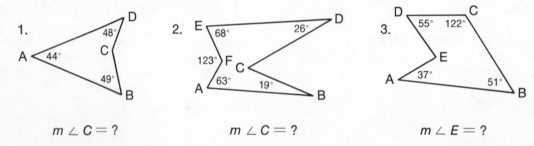

1.

$m \angle C = ?$

2.

$m \angle C = ?$

3.

$m \angle E = ?$

Properties of Quadrilaterals

REVIEW CAPSULE

A quadrilateral is a polygon with four sides.

$\angle A \cong \angle B$ means $m \angle A = m \angle B$.
$\overline{AB} \cong \overline{CD}$ means $AB = CD$.

Polygons have opposite and consecutive sides and angles.

Consecutive sides share a common vertex.

Opposite sides do not share a common vertex.

Vertices of *consecutive* angles are endpoints of the same side.

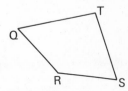

Opposite sides

Consecutive sides

Opposite angles

Consecutive angles

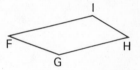

EXAMPLE 1

Consecutive angles are often labeled with consecutive letters of the alphabet.

List the pairs of consecutive sides and consecutive angles of quadrilateral QRST.

Consecutive sides
$\overline{QR}$ and $\overline{RS}$, $\overline{RS}$ and $\overline{ST}$, $\overline{ST}$ and $\overline{TQ}$, $\overline{TQ}$ and $\overline{QR}$

Consecutive angles
$\angle Q$ and $\angle R$, $\angle R$ and $\angle S$, $\angle S$ and $\angle T$, $\angle T$ and $\angle Q$

EXAMPLE 2

List the pairs of opposite sides and opposite angles of quadrilateral FGHI.

Opposite sides
$\overline{FG}$ and $\overline{HI}$, $\overline{GH}$ and $\overline{IF}$

Opposite angles
$\angle F$ and $\angle H$, $\angle G$ and $\angle I$

EXAMPLE 3 Draw a quadrilateral *PQRS*. Draw a segment connecting a pair of opposite vertices.

P and *R* are opposite vertices.

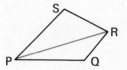

A *diagonal* connects opposite vertices. ⟶ $\overline{PR}$ is a *diagonal* of quadrilateral *PQRS*.

EXAMPLE 4 Are the diagonals of a quadrilateral congruent? Make a sketch to defend your answer.

Some figures have congruent diagonals.

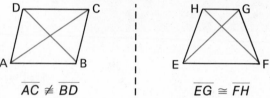

$$\overline{AC} \not\cong \overline{BD} \qquad \overline{EG} \cong \overline{FH}$$

Thus, the diagonals are not necessarily congruent.

EXAMPLE 5 Are opposite angles of a quadrilateral congruent? Make a sketch to defend your answer.

Some figures have congruent opposite angles.

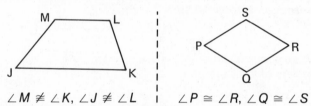

$$\angle M \not\cong \angle K, \angle J \not\cong \angle L \qquad \angle P \cong \angle R, \angle Q \cong \angle S$$

Thus, the opposite angles are not necessarily congruent.

EXAMPLE 6 Do the diagonals of a quadrilateral bisect each other? Make a sketch to defend your answer.

Diagonals of some figures bisect each other.

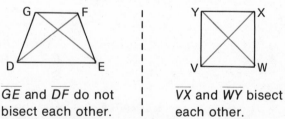

$\overline{GE}$ and $\overline{DF}$ do not bisect each other. $\overline{VX}$ and $\overline{WY}$ bisect each other.

Thus, the diagonals of a quadrilateral do not necessarily bisect each other.

Some quadrilaterals have special properties. Many of these quadrilaterals have special names. They will be examined in later lessons.

ORAL EXERCISES

Name the consecutive sides of each quadrilateral.

1.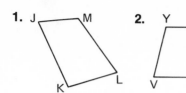

2.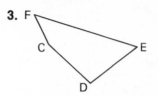

Name the consecutive angles of each quadrilateral.

3.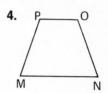

4.

5. Name the opposite sides of each quadrilateral above.

6. Name the opposite angles of each quadrilateral above.

EXERCISES

PART A

Name the diagonals of each quadrilateral. Do the diagonals intersect?

1.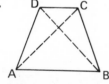

2.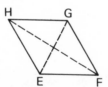

3.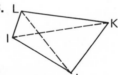

4.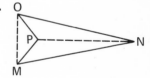

5. Draw a quadrilateral with congruent opposite sides.
7. Draw a quadrilateral with no congruent sides.

6. Draw a quadrilateral with congruent consecutive angles.
8. Draw a quadrilateral with no congruent angles.

PART B

For each of the following, draw pictures to defend your answer.

9. Are opposite sides of a quadrilateral necessarily congruent?
11. Are congruent triangles formed by the diagonals of a quadrilateral?
13. Do the segments which join the midpoints of consecutive sides of a quadrilateral necessarily have any special properties?

10. Do the diagonals of a quadrilateral bisect its angles?
12. Are any sides of a quadrilateral parallel?
14. Do the segments which join the midpoints of opposite sides of a quadrilateral necessarily have any special properties?

Congruence of Quadrilaterals

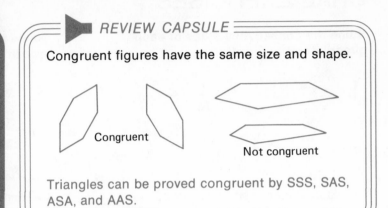

REVIEW CAPSULE

Congruent figures have the same size and shape.

Congruent

Not congruent

Triangles can be proved congruent by SSS, SAS, ASA, and AAS.

Size depends upon the lengths of the sides. Shape depends upon the angle measures.

Markings are used to show congruent sides and angles.

Congruent quadrilaterals have the same size and shape.

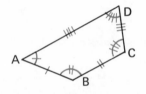

Quad. *ABCD* ≅ quad. *HGFE*

Definition of congruent quadrilaterals ⟶ | Two quadrilaterals are congruent if corresponding sides are congruent and corresponding angles are congruent.

EXAMPLE 1 Name the pairs of congruent sides and angles in the congruent quadrilaterals *ABCD* and *HGFE* above.

Congruent sides ⟶
Congruent angles ⟶

$$\overline{AB} \cong \overline{HG}, \overline{BC} \cong \overline{GF}, \overline{CD} \cong \overline{FE}, \overline{DA} \cong \overline{EH}$$
$$\angle A \cong \angle H, \angle B \cong \angle G, \angle C \cong \angle F, \angle D \cong \angle E$$

EXAMPLE 2 According to the markings on the pictures, what is a correct congruence statement?

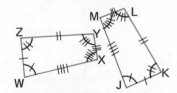

Corresponding vertices are named in the same order. ⟶ Quad. *WXYZ* ≅ quad. *JMLK*

Theorem 7.1

(SASAS for ≅ quadrilaterals)

Two quadrilaterals are congruent if any three sides and the included angles of one are congruent respectively to three sides and the included angles of the other.

ANALYSIS

Show corresponding sides are ≅ and corresponding ∠'s are ≅ by drawing diagonals and proving triangles are ≅.

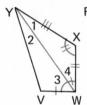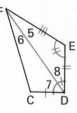

GIVEN

$VW \cong CD$, $\angle W \cong \angle D$,
$WX \cong DE$, $\angle X \cong \angle E$,
$XY \cong EF$

PROVE

Quad. $VWXY \cong$ quad. $CDEF$

PROOF

STATEMENTS

1. Draw diagonals YW and FD.

2. $\triangle WXY \cong \triangle DEF$
3. $\angle 1 \cong \angle 5$, $YW \cong FD$, $\angle 4 \cong \angle 8$
4. $\angle VWX \cong \angle CDE$
5. $\angle 3 \cong \angle 7$
6. $\triangle YVW \cong \triangle FCD$
7. $YV \cong FC$, $\angle 2 \cong \angle 6$
8. $\angle V \cong \angle C$
9. $\angle VYX \cong \angle CFE$
10. ∴ quad. $VWXY \cong$ quad. $CDEF$

REASONS

1. Two points are contained in exactly one line.
2. SAS for ≅ △'s (See Ex. 6.)
3. Corr. parts of ≅ △'s are ≅.
4. Given
5. (See Ex. 7.)
6. SAS for ≅ △'s
7. Corr. parts of ≅ △'s are ≅.
8. Same as 7
9. (See Ex. 7.)
10. Corr. sides are ≅. Corr. ∠'s are ≅.

EXAMPLE 3

Construct $A'B' \cong AB$.
Construct $\angle A' \cong \angle A$.
Construct $\angle B' \cong \angle B$.
Construct $A'D' \cong AD$.
Construct $B'C' \cong BC$.
Draw $D'C'$.

Construct a quadrilateral congruent to quadrilateral $ABCD$ using a SASAS correspondence.

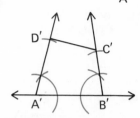

SASAS for ≅ quadrilaterals ⟶ Quad. $A'B'C'D' \cong$ quad. $ABCD$

EXAMPLE 4

According to the markings, what is a correct congruence statement?

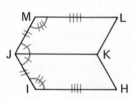

JK is common to both quad.
SASAS for ≅ quadrilaterals ⟶ Quad. $HIJK \cong$ quad. $LMJK$

ORAL EXERCISES

Which of the following quadrilaterals appear to be congruent?

1. 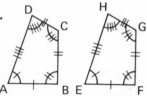   a   b   c

2. a   b   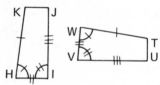 c

3. 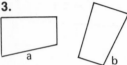 a   b   c

4. a   b   c

EXERCISES

PART A

On the basis of the markings shown, what is a correct congruence statement?

1.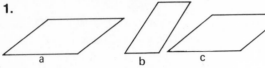

2.

3.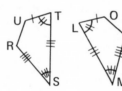

For each pair of congruent quadrilaterals, name all pairs of congruent sides and angles.

4. Quad. *BCDE* ≅ quad. *MNOP*

5. Quad. *TUVW* ≅ quad. *HIJK*

6. In the proof of Theorem 7.1, give a complete proof of step 2.

7. In the proof of Theorem 7.1, what are the reasons for steps 5 and 9?

8. Quad. *ABCD* ≅ quad. *EFGH*, *AB* = 10 cm, $m \angle E = 133$, *BC* = 8 cm, $m \angle F = 131$. Find *EF* and $m \angle A$.

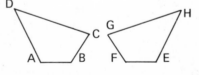

9. Quad. *ABCD* ≅ quad. *EFGH*, $m \angle A = 5x + 2$, $m \angle E = 6x - 26$. Find $m \angle A$.

10. Given: $\overline{FE}$ is the ⊥ bisector of $\overline{AB}$, $\overline{AD} \cong \overline{BC}$, $\angle A \cong \angle B$. Prove: Quad. *AEFD* ≅ quad. *BEFC*

11. Given: $\overline{EF}$ bisects $\angle DFC$, $\overline{DF} \cong \overline{CF}$, $\overline{FE}$ is the ⊥ bisector of $\overline{AB}$. Prove: Quad. *AEFD* ≅ quad. *BEFC*

PART B

12. Given: $\overline{DA} \cong \overline{CB}$,
$\overline{EA} \cong \overline{FB}$, $\angle A \cong \angle B$
Prove: Quad. $EABC \cong$
quad. $FBAD$

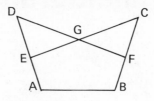

13. Given: $\triangle DEG \cong \triangle CFG$,
$\overline{EA} \cong \overline{FB}$
Prove: Quad. $EABC \cong$
quad. $FBAD$

14. Given: $\overline{AF} \cong \overline{BG}$,
$\triangle EFD \cong \triangle CBD$
Prove: Quad. $ABDE \cong$
quad. $GFDC$

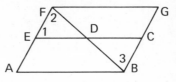

15. Given: $\triangle ABF \cong \triangle GFB$,
$\overline{FE} = \overline{AE}$, $\overline{GC} \cong \overline{BC}$,
$\overline{FD} \cong \overline{DB}$
Prove: Quad. $ABDE \cong$
quad. $GFDC$

16. Draw a quadrilateral. Construct a quadrilateral congruent to it using a SASAS correspondence.

17. Draw a quadrilateral. Construct a quadrilateral congruent to it using an ASASA correspondence.

PART C

18. Prove: Two quadrilaterals are congruent if any three angles and the included sides of one are congruent respectively to three angles and the included sides of the other. (ASASA for $\cong$ quadrilaterals)

19. A SSS congruence correspondence was sufficient to show that two triangles were congruent. Is a similar (SSSS) pattern sufficient to show that two quadrilaterals are congruent? Justify your answer.

Algebra Review

OBJECTIVE
■ To solve a proportion

If $\dfrac{a}{b} = \dfrac{c}{d}$, then $ad = bc$.

In a true proportion, the product of the extremes equals the product of the means.

EXAMPLE · Solve $\dfrac{x-3}{10} = \dfrac{2}{5}$.

If $\dfrac{a}{b} = \dfrac{c}{d}$, then $ad = bc$. $\longrightarrow$

$$5(x-3) = 10 \cdot 2$$
$$5x - 15 = 20$$
$$5x = 35$$
$$x = 7$$

Thus, the solution is 7.

Solve.

1. $\dfrac{a}{3} = \dfrac{4}{6}$

2. $\dfrac{y-3}{2} = \dfrac{y+5}{5}$

3. $\dfrac{3b}{b+4} = \dfrac{3b+9}{b+8}$

4. $\dfrac{x+10}{x+1} = \dfrac{x+4}{x-2}$

Properties of Parallelograms

REVIEW CAPSULE

If $\ell \parallel m$, then
$\angle 3 \cong \angle 6$ $\angle 1 \cong \angle 5$
$\angle 4 \cong \angle 5$ $\angle 2 \cong \angle 6$
$\angle 3 \cong \angle 7$
$\angle 4 \cong \angle 8$

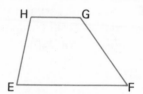

$\overline{AB} \parallel \overline{DC}$ and $\overline{AD} \parallel \overline{BC}$ ⟶

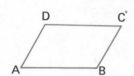

· *ABCD* is a parallelogram.
  $\square ABCD$

· *EFGH* is not a parallelogram.

· $\square ABCD$ means parallelogram *ABCD*. ⟶

Definition of parallelogram ⟶ · A *parallelogram* is a quadrilateral with each pair of opposite sides parallel.

Theorem 7.2

· Opposite sides of a parallelogram are congruent.

ANALYSIS

· Draw diagonal $\overline{DB}$.
· Prove $\triangle DAB \cong \triangle BCD$.

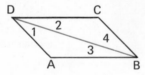

GIVEN
$\square ABCD$
PROVE
$\overline{AB} \cong \overline{CD}$ and $\overline{AD} \cong \overline{CB}$

PROOF

STATEMENTS	REASONS
· 1. Draw diagonal $\overline{DB}$.	· 1. Two points are contained in exactly one line.
2. $\overline{AB} \parallel \overline{DC}$ and $\overline{AD} \parallel \overline{BC}$	2. Def. of $\square$
3. $\angle 1 \cong \angle 4$	· 3. Alt. int. $\angle$'s of $\parallel$ lines are $\cong$.
4. $\angle 2 \cong \angle 3$	4. Same as 3
5. $\overline{DB} \cong \overline{BD}$	5. Reflexive property
6. $\triangle DAB \cong \triangle BCD$	6. ASA for $\cong \triangle$'s
7. $\therefore \overline{AB} \cong \overline{CD}$ and $\overline{AD} \cong \overline{CB}$	· 7. Corr. sides of $\cong \triangle$'s are $\cong$.

EXAMPLE 1 In $\square ABCD$, $m\angle A = 120$,
Find the measure of each
of the other angles.

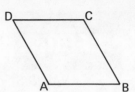

· Int. $\angle$'s on same side of transversal for
∥ lines are supplementary.
Sum $m\angle$'s of quad. = 360. ⟶

$m\angle D = 60$
$m\angle B = 60$
$m\angle C = 120$

Theorem 7.3

· Opposite angles of a parallelogram are congruent.

(See Exercise 16.)

EXAMPLE 2 $PQRS$ is a parallelogram.
$m\angle S = 4x - 60$
$m\angle Q = 30 - x$
, Find the measure of
each angle.

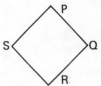

Oppos. $\angle$'s of a $\square$ are $\cong$. ⟶

$$m\angle S = m\angle Q$$
$$4x - 60 = 30 - x$$
$$5x = 90$$
$$x = 18$$

$4(18) - 60 = 12$ ⟶
$30 - 18 = 12$ ⟶
$\angle P$ and $\angle Q$ are supplements. ⟶
Opp. $\angle$'s of a $\square$ are $\cong$. ⟶

$m\angle S = 12$
$m\angle Q = 12$
$m\angle P = 168$
$m\angle R = 168$

EXAMPLE 3 $ABCD$ is a parallelogram.
$AC = 12$, $BD = 16$.
Find AO, OC, BO, and OD.

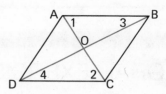

$\overline{AB} \parallel \overline{CD}$ ⟶
Opp. sides of a $\square$ are $\cong$. ⟶
$\overline{AB} \parallel \overline{CD}$ ⟶

$\left.\begin{array}{l} \angle 1 \cong \angle 2 \\ \overline{AB} \cong \overline{CD} \\ \angle 3 \cong \angle 4 \end{array}\right\} \rightarrow \triangle AOB \cong \triangle COD$

Corr. sides of $\cong \triangle$'s are $\cong$. ⟶

$$AO = OC \qquad BO = OD$$
$$\downarrow \qquad\qquad \downarrow$$

O is the midpoint of $\overline{AC}$. O is the midpoint of $\overline{BD}$.
Thus, $AO = 6$, $OC = 6$, $BO = 8$, and $OD = 8$.

Example 3 suggests the theorem on the next page.

Theorem 7.4

The diagonals of a parallelogram bisect each other.

ANALYSIS

Show △TNO ≅ △JXO.

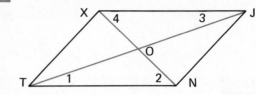

GIVEN
▱XTNJ, $\overline{XJ} \parallel \overline{TN}$,
$\overline{XT} \parallel \overline{JN}$
PROVE
$\overline{NO} \cong \overline{XO}$,
$\overline{TO} \cong \overline{JO}$

PROOF

STATEMENTS	REASONS
1. $\overline{TN} \cong \overline{JX}$	1. Opp. sides of a ▱ are ≅.
2. $\angle 1 \cong \angle 3$	2. Alt. int. ∠'s of ∥ lines are ≅.
3. $\angle 2 \cong \angle 4$	3. Same as 2.
4. △TNO ≅ △JXO	4. ASA for ≅ △'s
5. ∴ $\overline{NO} \cong \overline{XO}$ and $\overline{TO} \cong \overline{JO}$	5. Corr. sides of ≅ △'s are ≅.

Properties of a Parallelogram

Opposite sides
are parallel.

Opposite sides
are congruent.

Opposite angles
are congruent.

Diagonals bisect
each other.

ORAL EXERCISES

Which are parallelograms?

1.

2.

3.

4.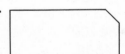

5.

6.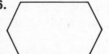

7.

8.

EXERCISES

1. In ▱*JKLM*, which sides are parallel?

3. In ▱*JKLM*, which angles are congruent?

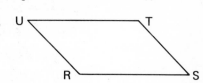

2. In ▱*JKLM*, which sides are congruent?

4. In ▱*JKLM*, which angles are supplements?

5. In ▱*RSTU* if $m \angle R = 130$, find the measure of each angle.

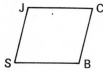

6. In ▱*RSTU* if $m \angle S = 47$, find the measure of each angle.

7. In ▱*SBCJ*, $m \angle B = 2m \angle S$. Find $m \angle S$ and $m \angle B$.

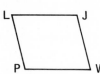

8. In ▱*SBCJ*, $m \angle S = 3x + 5$, $m \angle C = 4x - 25$. Find $m \angle S$ and $m \angle B$.

9. In ▱*PWJL*, $m \angle P = 7x - 12$, $m \angle W = 2x + 3$. Find $m \angle P$ and $m \angle W$.

10. In ▱*PWJL*, $PW = 5x - 3$, $LJ = 3x + 3$. Find *PW*.

LMNO is a parallelogram. Which of the following pairs of triangles are congruent? Why are they congruent?

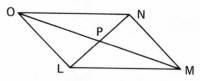

11. △*OPL* and △*MPN* ≅

12. △*OLM* and △*NML*

13. △*OMN* and △*MOL* ≅

14. Prove: A diagonal of a parallelogram determines two congruent triangles.

16. Prove Theorem 7.3.

15. Prove: Consective angles of a parallelogram are supplements.

17. In ▱*ABCD*, diagonals $\overline{AC}$ and $\overline{BD}$ intersect at *O*. Is *O* the midpoint of $\overline{XY}$? If so, prove it.

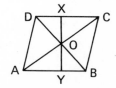

18. In ▱*XYZW*, *T* is the midpoint of $\overline{WZ}$, *U* is the midpoint of $\overline{XY}$. Is *O* the midpoint of $\overline{TU}$? Of $\overline{XZ}$? If so, prove it.

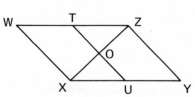

Proving Parallelograms

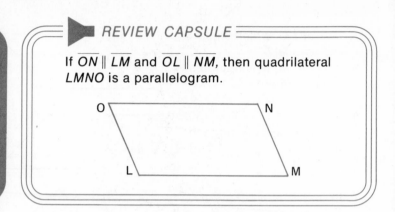

▶ REVIEW CAPSULE

If $\overline{ON} \parallel \overline{LM}$ and $\overline{OL} \parallel \overline{NM}$, then quadrilateral *LMNO* is a parallelogram.

EXAMPLE 1   In quadrilateral *ABCD*, what must be shown to prove that *ABCD* is a parallelogram?

Use the definition. ⟶   Show $\overline{AB} \parallel \overline{DC}$ and $\overline{AD} \parallel \overline{BC}$.

Theorem   7.5

If opposite sides of a quadrilateral are congruent, then the quadrilateral is a parallelogram.

ANALYSIS
Show $\overline{AB} \parallel \overline{DC}$ and $\overline{AD} \parallel \overline{BC}$.
Use ≅ △'s to show the
alt. int. ∠'s are ≅.

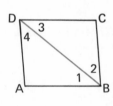

GIVEN
$\overline{AB} \cong \overline{CD}$, $\overline{AD} \cong \overline{BC}$
PROVE
ABCD is a parallelogram.

PROOF

STATEMENTS	REASONS
1. Draw diagonal $\overline{BD}$.	1. Two points are contained in exactly one line.
2. $\overline{AB} \cong \overline{CD}$	2. Given
3. $\overline{AD} \cong \overline{BC}$	3. Given
4. $\overline{BD} \cong \overline{BD}$	4. Reflexive property
5. $\triangle ABD \cong \triangle CDB$	5. SSS for ≅ △'s
6. $\angle 1 \cong \angle 3$ and $\angle 2 \cong \angle 4$	6. Corr. ∠'s of ≅ △'s are ≅.
7. $\overline{AB} \parallel \overline{DC}$ and $\overline{AD} \parallel \overline{BC}$	7. If alt. int. ∠'s are ≅, then lines are ∥.
8. ∴ *ABCD* is a ▱.	8. Def. of ▱

Theorem 7.6

If opposite angles of a quadrilateral are congruent, then the quadrilateral is a parallelogram.

(See Exercise 14.)

EXAMPLE 2

The converse of this statement was proved as a theorem.

ABCD is called a *kite*.

If a diagonal of a quadrilateral determines two congruent triangles, is the quadrilateral a parallelogram?

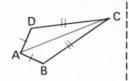

$\triangle ABC \cong \triangle ADC$
Not a parallelogram

$\triangle XYZ \cong \triangle ZWX$
Parallelogram

Thus, a quadrilateral is not necessarily a parallelogram if its diagonal determines two congruent triangles.

Theorem 7.7

If two sides of a quadrilateral are both parallel and congruent, then the quadrilateral is a parallelogram.

ANALYSIS

Show that $\overline{BC} \cong \overline{DA}$ by proving $\triangle ABC \cong \triangle CDA$. Then use Theorem 7.5.

GIVEN
$\overline{AB} \parallel \overline{CD}, \overline{AB} \cong \overline{CD}$
PROVE
ABCD is a parallelogram.

PROOF

STATEMENTS	REASONS
1. $\overline{AB} \cong \overline{CD}$	1. Given
2. $\overline{AB} \parallel \overline{CD}$	2. Given
3. $\angle 1 \cong \angle 2$	3. Alt. int. ∠'s of ∥ lines are ≅.
4. $\overline{AC} \cong \overline{CA}$	4. Reflexive property
5. $\triangle ABC \cong \triangle CDA$	5. SAS for ≅ △'s
6. $\overline{BC} \cong \overline{DA}$	6. Corr. sides of ≅ △'s are ≅.
7. ∴ ABCD is a ▱.	7. If opp. sides are ≅, then quad. is a ▱.

EXAMPLE 3

In quadrilateral ABCD, $AO = CO = 8$ and $BO = DO = 7$. Is ABCD a parallelogram?

$\overline{AO} \cong \overline{CO}, \angle AOB \cong \angle COD, \overline{BO} \cong \overline{OD} \longrightarrow$ $\triangle AOB \cong \triangle COD$
So, $\overline{AB} \cong \overline{CD}$ and $\angle 1 \cong \angle 2$
∴ $\overline{AB} \parallel \overline{CD}$

Use Th. 7.7 $\longrightarrow$ **Thus,** ABCD is a parallelogram.

<table>
<tr><td>**Theorem**</td><td>**7.8**</td><td>If the diagonals of a quadrilateral bisect each other, then the quadrilateral is a parallelogram.</td></tr>
</table>

(See Exercise 15.)

Ways to Prove That a Quadrilateral Is a Parallelogram

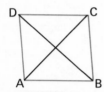

1. Show that both pairs of opposite sides are parallel.
2. Show that both pairs of opposite sides are congruent.
3. Show that both pairs of opposite angles are congruent.
4. Show that one pair of opposite sides is congruent and parallel.
5. Show that the diagonals bisect each other.

EXERCISES

PART A

1. Is *ABCD* a parallelogram?

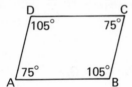

2. Is *XYZW* a parallelogram?

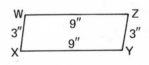

3. Is *JKLM* a parallelogram?

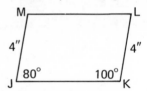

Is *ABCD* a parallelogram? Give a reason for your answer.

4. $\overline{AB} \parallel \overline{DC}$ and $\overline{AD} \parallel \overline{BC}$
6. $\overline{AB} \parallel \overline{DC}$ and $\overline{AD} \cong \overline{BC}$
8. $\triangle ABC \cong \triangle ADC$
10. $\angle ABC \cong \angle ADC$ and $\angle DAB \cong \angle DCD$
12. $\triangle AOB \cong \triangle COD$

5. $\overline{AB} \cong \overline{DC}$ and $\overline{AD} \cong \overline{BC}$
7. $\overline{DO} \cong \overline{BO}$ and $\overline{AO} \cong \overline{CO}$
9. $\angle 1 \cong \angle 2$ and $\angle 3 \cong \angle 4$
11. $\overline{AC} \cong \overline{BD}$
13. $\overline{AB} \cong \overline{DC}$ and $\angle 2 \cong \angle 1$

PART B

14. Prove Theorem 7.6.
16. If consecutive angles of a quadrilateral are supplementary, is the quadrilateral a parallelogram? Prove your answer.

15. Prove Theorem 7.8.
17. If the diagonals of a quadrilateral are perpendicular, is the quadrilateral a parallelogram? Prove your answer.

PART C

18. If the bisectors of a pair of opposite angles of a quadrilateral form a parallelogram, is the quadrilateral a parallelogram? Prove your answer.

19. If the segments joining the midpoints of consecutive sides of a quadrilateral form a parallelogram, is the quadrilateral a parallelogram? Prove your answer.

A Special Segment in a Triangle

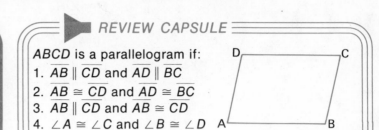

REVIEW CAPSULE

$ABCD$ is a parallelogram if:
1. $\overline{AB} \parallel \overline{CD}$ and $\overline{AD} \parallel \overline{BC}$
2. $\overline{AB} \cong \overline{CD}$ and $\overline{AD} \cong \overline{BC}$
3. $\overline{AB} \parallel \overline{CD}$ and $\overline{AB} \cong \overline{CD}$
4. $\angle A \cong \angle C$ and $\angle B \cong \angle D$

EXAMPLE 1

D is the midpoint of $\overline{AC}$, E is the midpoint of CB.
Using a ruler, find DE and AB.

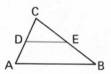

$\overline{DE}$ and $\overline{AB}$ seem to be $\parallel$. $DE = \frac{1}{2}AB$ ⟶ **Thus,** $DE = \frac{1}{2}$ in. and $AB = 1$ in.

Theorem 7.9

The segment joining the midpoints of two sides of a triangle is parallel to the third side and is half as long.

ANALYSIS

Extend $\overline{DE}$ its own length to F.
Show that $ABFD$ is a $\square$.
Use the properties of $\square$'s.

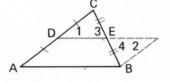

GIVEN
D is the midpoint of $\overline{AC}$,
E is the midpoint of $\overline{BC}$.
PROVE
$\overline{DE} \parallel \overline{AB}$ and $DE = \frac{1}{2}AB$

PROOF

STATEMENTS	REASONS
1. Draw $\overline{EF} \cong \overline{DE}$ and collinear with it.	1. Post. 5
2. Draw $\overline{BF}$.	2. Two points are contained in exactly one line.
3. $\triangle DEC \cong \triangle FEB$	3. SAS for $\cong \triangle$'s ($\overline{DE} \cong \overline{FE}$, $\angle 3 \cong \angle 4$, $\overline{CE} \cong \overline{BE}$)
4. $\angle 1 \cong \angle 2$ and $\overline{CD} \cong \overline{BF}$	4. Corr. parts of $\cong \triangle$'s are $\cong$.
5. $\overline{CD} \cong \overline{DA}$	5. Def. of midpoint
6. $\overline{BF} \cong \overline{DA}$	6. Substitution
7. $\overline{BF} \parallel \overline{DA}$	7. Lines are $\parallel$ if alt. int. $\angle$'s are $\cong$.
8. $ABFD$ is a $\square$.	8. Quad. is a $\square$ if two sides are $\parallel$ and $\cong$.
9. $\overline{DF} \parallel \overline{AB}$ and $\therefore$ $\overline{DE} \parallel \overline{AB}$	9. Opp. sides of a $\square$ are $\parallel$.
10. $\overline{DF} \cong \overline{AB}$ and $DF = AB$	10. Opp. sides of a $\square$ are $\cong$.
11. $DE = \frac{1}{2}DF$	11. Step 1
12. $\therefore$ $DE = \frac{1}{2}AB$	12. Substitution

EXAMPLE 2

$ST = \frac{1}{2}QR$ ⟶

S is the midpoint of $\overline{PQ}$ and T is the midpoint of $\overline{PR}$. $ST = 7$. Find QR.

$$7 = \frac{1}{2}(QR)$$

Thus, $QR = 14$.

EXAMPLE 3

$DE = \frac{1}{2}BC$

D and E are the midpoints of $\overline{AB}$ and $\overline{AC}$, respectively. $DE = x + 3$, $BC = 3x + 3$. Find DE and BC.

$$x + 3 = \frac{1}{2}(3x + 3)$$
$$2(x + 3) = 3x + 3$$
$$2x + 6 = 3x + 3$$
$$3 = x$$

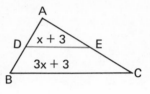

$DE = (3) + 3; BC = 3(3) + 3$

Thus, $DE = 6$ and $BC = 12$.

EXAMPLE 4

Prove: The segments joining the midpoints of consecutive sides of a quadrilateral form a parallelogram.

Draw a diagram.
Write the Given and Prove.

    ANALYSIS

    Draw diagonal $\overline{SH}$.
    Use Th. 7.9 to show
    $\overline{TN} \parallel \overline{LV}$ and $\overline{TN} \cong \overline{LV}$.

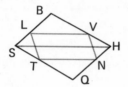

Given: L, T, N, and V are the midpoints of $\overline{SB}$, $\overline{SQ}$, $\overline{QH}$, and $\overline{HB}$, respectively.
Prove: $TNVL$ is a ▱.

$\overline{SH}$ forms $\triangle SHB$ and $\triangle SHQ$.

Theorem 7.9.   ⟶

Theorem 7.9   ⟶

Proof

Statements	Reasons
1. Draw diagonal $\overline{SH}$.	1. Two points are contained in exactly one line.
2. $\overline{TN} \parallel \overline{SH}$ and $\overline{LV} \parallel \overline{SH}$	2. Seg. joining midpts. of two sides of a $\triangle$ is $\parallel$ to third side.
3. $\overline{TN} \parallel \overline{LV}$	3. Two lines $\parallel$ to same line are $\parallel$.
4. $TN = \frac{1}{2}SH$ $\quad LV = \frac{1}{2}SH$	4. Seg. joining midpts. of 2 sides of a $\triangle$ is half as long as 3rd side.
5. $TN = LV$ and $\overline{TN} \cong \overline{LV}$	5. Substitution
6. $\therefore$ $TNVL$ is a ▱.	6. Quad. with a pair of opp. sides $\parallel$ and $\cong$.

ORAL EXERCISES

K is the midpoint of $\overline{AL}$.
Z is the midpoint of $\overline{AT}$.

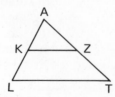

1. If $LT = 10$, then $KZ = ?$
2. If $LT = 3$, then $KZ = ?$
3. If $KZ = 6$, then $LT = ?$
4. If $KZ = 7$, then $LT = ?$

EXERCISES

PART A

B is the midpoint of $\overline{MQ}$.
W is the midpoint of $\overline{QH}$.
N is the midpoint of $\overline{HM}$.

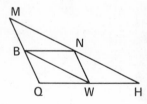

1. If $MH = 12$, then $BW = ?$
2. If $NW = t$, then $MQ = ?$
3. $\overline{BW} \parallel ?$
4. $\overline{QW} \parallel ?$
5. If $QW = 3$, then $BN = ?$
6. If $MB = \ell$, then $NW = ?$

7. *N* and *I* are the midpoints of $\overline{WL}$ and $\overline{DL}$ respectively. $WD = 4x - 6$, $NI = x - 1$. Find *NI*.

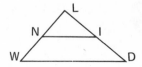

8. *N* and *I* are the midpoints of $\overline{WL}$ and $\overline{DL}$ respectively. $WD = 5n - 2$, $NI = 2n + 3$. Find *WD*.

9. Given: *I*, *W*, and *N* are the midpoints of $\overline{RY}$, $\overline{YQ}$, and $\overline{RQ}$ respectively.
Prove: *IWNR* is a $\square$.

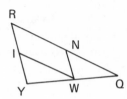

10. Given: *I*, *W*, and *N* are the midpoints of $\overline{RY}$, $\overline{YQ}$, and $\overline{RQ}$ respectively.
Prove: $\triangle IYW \cong \triangle NWQ$

PART B

11. Given: *W* and *X* are the midpoints of $\overline{VR}$ and $\overline{VL}$ respectively. $\overline{XT} \cong \overline{WX}$.
Prove: *VWLT* is a $\square$.

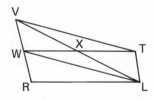

12. Given: *VWLT* is a $\square$ *W* is the midpoint of $\overline{VR}$.
Prove: *WRLT* is a $\square$.

13. Given: $\square MXVP$, $\overline{AT} \parallel \overline{PV}$
Prove: *MXTA* is a $\square$.

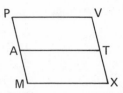

14. Given: $\square MXVP$, $\overline{AT} \parallel \overline{PV}$, *A* is the midpoint of $\overline{MP}$.
Prove: *T* is the midpoint of $\overline{XV}$.

Part C

15. Prove: The segments joining the midpoints of the opposite sides of a quadrilateral bisect each other.

16. Prove: The opposite angles of the quadrilateral formed by the bisectors of the angles of a convex quadrilateral are supplementary.

More About Parallel Lines

> ► REVIEW CAPSULE
>
> Given line ℓ. Construct a line through S parallel to ℓ.

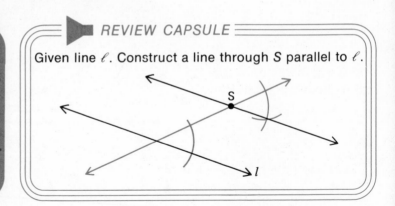

Theorem 7.10

If three parallel lines cut off congruent segments on one transversal, then they cut off congruent segments on any transversal.

ANALYSIS

Make ▱'s by drawing $\overline{TU} \parallel \overline{CB}$ and $\overline{SV} \parallel \overline{BA}$. Use the prop. of ▱'s and ∥ lines to show △TUS ≅ △SVR.

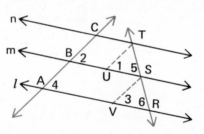

GIVEN
$\ell \parallel m \parallel n, \overline{CB} \cong \overline{BA}$
PROVE
$\overline{ST} \cong \overline{RS}$

PROOF

STATEMENTS	REASONS
1. Draw $\overline{TU} \parallel \overline{CB}$.	1. Through a given pt., there is exactly one line ∥ to a given line.
2. Draw $\overline{SV} \parallel \overline{BA}$.	2. Same as 1
3. $\ell \parallel m \parallel n$	3. Given
4. $AVSB$ and $BUTC$ are ▱'s.	4. Def. of ▱
5. $\overline{TU} \cong \overline{CB}$ and $\overline{SV} \cong \overline{BA}$	5. Opp. sides of a ▱ are ≅.
6. $\overline{CB} \cong \overline{BA}$	6. Given
7. $\overline{SV} \cong \overline{TU}$ (S)	7. Transitive property of ≅
8. ∠1 ≅ ∠2 and ∠3 ≅ ∠4	8. Corr. ∠'s of ∥ lines are ≅.
9. ∠2 ≅ ∠4	9. Same as 8
10. ∠1 ≅ ∠3 (A)	10. Transitive property of ≅
11. ∠5 ≅ ∠6 (A)	11. Same as 8
12. △TUS ≅ △SVR	12. AAS for ≅ △'s
13. ∴ $\overline{ST} \cong \overline{RS}$	13. Corr. sides of ≅ △'s are ≅.

EXAMPLE 1 $\overleftrightarrow{AD} \parallel \overleftrightarrow{BE} \parallel \overleftrightarrow{CF}$, $AB = 7$,
$BC = 7$, $DE = 6$.
Find DF.

Use Theorem 7.10. ──────────────────→ $EF = DE = 6$

Thus, $DF = 12$.

Theorem 7.10 can be extended to any number of lines.

Corollary

If any number of parallel lines cut off congruent segments on one transversal, then they cut off congruent segments on any transversal.

The corollary to Theorem 7.10 is the basis for the following construction.

---

construction

To divide $\overline{AB}$ into three congruent segments

STRATEGY		GIVEN

Apply the corollary to Theorem 7.10 by constructing parallel lines.

A ─────────────── B

GIVEN
$\overline{AB}$
CONSTRUCT
Points P and Q on $\overline{AB}$
so that $\overline{AP} \cong \overline{PQ} \cong \overline{QB}$

Draw $\overrightarrow{AX}$.

Set compass at any convenient radius. On $\overrightarrow{AX}$, mark off $\overline{AH} \cong \overline{HJ} \cong \overline{JK}$.

Draw $\overline{BK}$. Construct $\overline{HP} \parallel \overline{BK}$ and $\overline{JQ} \parallel \overline{BK}$.

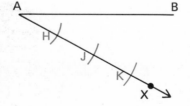

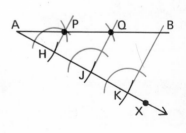

Conclusion: $\overline{AP} \cong \overline{PQ} \cong \overline{QB}$

Mark off $n \cong$ segments on $\overrightarrow{AX}$. ──────→

This same construction can be used to divide a line into any number of congruent parts.

The distance between two points is measured along the shortest path, a segment.

Postulate 18

The shortest curve joining two points is a segment.

The distance from a point to a line is measured along the perpendicular to the line.

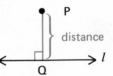

EXAMPLE 2

Given: $\ell \parallel m$, $\overline{PX} \perp m$, $\overline{QY} \perp m$
Prove: $\overline{PX} \cong \overline{QY}$

ANALYSIS

Opp. sides of a ▱ are ≅.

Segments in ∥ lines are ∥. ⟶

Proof

Statements	Reasons
1. $\overline{PQ} \parallel \overline{XY}$	1. $\ell \parallel m$
2. $\overline{PX} \parallel \overline{QY}$	2. Lines ⊥ to same line are ∥.
3. $PXYQ$ is a ▱.	3. Def. of ▱
4. ∴ $\overline{PX} \cong \overline{QY}$	4. Opp. sides of a ▱ are ≅.

P and Q are any two points on ℓ.

PX is the distance from P to m.
QY is the distance from Q to m.

Definition of *distance* between two parallel lines. ⟶

The *distance between two parallel lines* is the distance from a point on one line to the other.

Theorem 7.11

Parallel lines are equidistant at all points.

ORAL EXERCISES

$\ell \parallel m \parallel n$, $AD = 5$, $DG = 5$

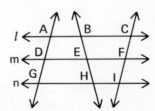

1. If $BE = 4$, then $EH = ?$
3. If $CF = 10$, then $CI = ?$
5. If $BH = 14$, then $BE = ?$
7. If $CF = 7$, then $FI = ?$

2. If $EH = 3$, then $BE = ?$
4. If $BH = 9$, then $EH = ?$
6. If $CI = 11$, then $CF = ?$
8. If $CI = 13$, then $FI = ?$

EXERCISES

PART A

$\ell \parallel m \parallel n \parallel r \parallel s \parallel t$, $\overline{AD} \cong \overline{DH} \cong \overline{HK} \cong \overline{KN} \cong \overline{NQ}$

1. If $AD = 5$, then $KN = ?$
2. If $CF = 7$, then $MP = ?$
3. If $BE = 4$, then $IL = ?$
4. If $CJ = 9$, then $CF = ?$
5. If $AQ = 30$, then $HN = ?$
6. If $CM = 32$, then $CS = ?$
7. If $BR = 40$, then $BL = ?$
8. If $DK = 3$, then $DN = ?$
9. If $CP = 10$, then $CS = ?$
10. If $AQ = 17$, then $DQ = ?$

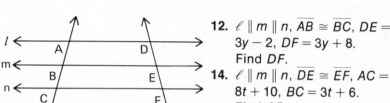

11. $\ell \parallel m \parallel n$, $\overline{AB} \cong \overline{BC}$, $DE = 3x + 4$, $EF = x + 8$.
Find DE.

13. $\ell \parallel m \parallel n$, $\overline{DE} \cong \overline{EF}$, $AB = 2n + 5$, $BC = 4n - 3$.
Find AC.

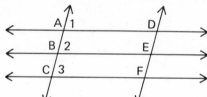

12. $\ell \parallel m \parallel n$, $\overline{AB} \cong \overline{BC}$, $DE = 3y - 2$, $DF = 3y + 8$.
Find DF.

14. $\ell \parallel m \parallel n$, $\overline{DE} \cong \overline{EF}$, $AC = 8t + 10$, $BC = 3t + 6$.
Find AB.

15. Draw a segment 3 inches long. Divide it into three congruent segments.

16. Draw a segment 4 inches long. Divide it into five congruent segments.

17. Draw a segment 7 cm long. Divide it into four congruent segments.

18. Given: $\angle 1 \cong \angle 2 \cong \angle 3$, $\overline{AB} \cong \overline{BC}$
Prove: $\overline{DE} \cong \overline{EF}$

19. Given: $\overline{AB} \parallel \overline{DE}$, $\overline{BE} \parallel \overline{CF}$, $\overline{AB} \cong \overline{DE}$, $\overline{AB} \cong \overline{BC}$
Prove: $\overline{DE} \cong \overline{EF}$

PART B

20. Draw a segment 4 inches long. Construct a segment two thirds as long.

21. Draw a segment 8 cm long. Construct a segment four fifths as long.

22. Draw a segment 5 inches long. Construct a segment four thirds as long.

PART C

True or false? If true, prove the statement as a theorem. If false, show a counterexample.

23. If three lines cut off congruent segments on each of two transversals, then the lines are parallel.

24. If a segment is parallel to one side of a triangle and bisects a second side, then it bisects the third side.

Constructing Regular Pentagons and Decagons

REGULAR PENTAGRAM

The pentagram was the symbol of the Pythagoreans, a society of mathematicians founded by Pythagoras, active during the sixth century B.C.

Use only a compass and straightedge.

1. Draw diameter $\overline{AB}$ in circle O.

2. Construct the perpendicular bisector of $\overline{AB}$. ($\overline{CO} \perp \overline{AB}$)

3. Bisect $\overline{OB}$. ($\overline{OD} \cong \overline{DB}$)

4. With D as a center, and CD as a radius, draw arc $\overparen{CE}$.

5. Chord $\overline{CE}$ is a side of a regular pentagon.
   Chord $\overline{EO}$ is a side of a regular decagon inscribed in circle O.

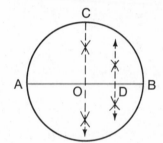

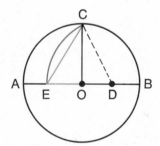

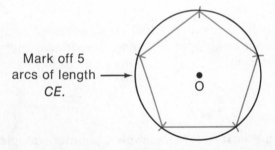

Mark off 5 arcs of length ⟶ CE.

REGULAR PENTAGON

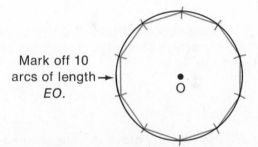

Mark off 10 arcs of length ⟶ EO.

REGULAR DECAGON

Trapezoids

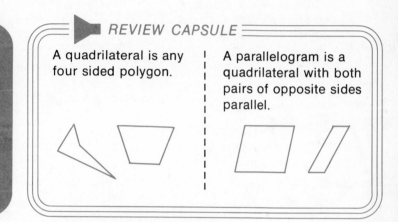

REVIEW CAPSULE

A quadrilateral is any four sided polygon.

A parallelogram is a quadrilateral with both pairs of opposite sides parallel.

Definition of trapezoid ⟶ A *trapezoid* is a quadrilateral with at least one pair of parallel sides.

EXAMPLE 1 Which of the following are trapezoids?

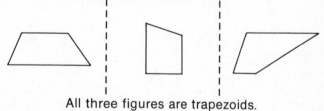

All three figures are trapezoids.

EXAMPLE 2 *ABCD* is a parallelogram. Is *ABCD* a trapezoid?

ABCD has *at least one* pair of parallel sides. ⟶ *ABCD* is a trapezoid.

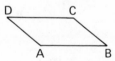

EXAMPLE 3 By careful drawings, determine whether or not the diagonals of a trapezoid are congruent.

$\overline{AC}$ and $\overline{BD}$ are the diagonals of *ABCD*. $\overline{RT}$ and $\overline{SU}$ are the diagonals of *RSTU*.

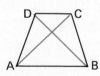 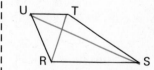

In trapezoid *ABCD*, $\overline{AC} \cong \overline{BD}$

In trapezoid *RSTU*, $\overline{RT} \not\cong \overline{SU}$

Measure with a ruler. ⟶

Thus, diagonals are not necessarily congruent.

EXAMPLE 4

ANALYSIS
Show △DEA ≅ △CFB.
Use corresponding angles of
congruent triangles

Given: Trapezoid *ABCD*
$\overline{DE} \perp \overline{AB}$, $\overline{CF} \perp \overline{AB}$, $\overline{AD} \cong \overline{BC}$
Prove: $\angle 1 \cong \angle 2$

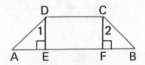

Proof

Statements	Reasons
1. $\overline{DC} \parallel \overline{AB}$	1. Def. of trapezoid
2. $\overline{DE} \cong \overline{CF}$ (L)	2. ∥ lines are equidistant at all points.
3. $\overline{AD} \cong \overline{BC}$ (H)	3. Given
4. △DEA and △CFB are rt. △'s	4. ⊥'s form rt. ∠'s.
Theorem 5.3 ⟶ 5. △DEA ≅ △CFB	5. HL for ≅ rt △'s
6. ∴ $\angle 1 \cong \angle 2$	6. Corr. ∠'s of ≅ △'s are ≅.

ORAL EXERCISES

Which of the following are trapezoids?

1.

2.

3.

4.

5.

6.

7.

8.

EXERCISES

PART A

Make careful drawings to determine each of the following.

1. Do any trapezoids have two congruent sides?

2. Do any trapezoids have two congruent angles?

3. Do any trapezoids have congruent diagonals?

4. Do any trapezoids have diagonals which bisect each other?

5. Do any trapezoids have two right angles?

6. Do any trapezoids have diagonals which are perpendicular?

7. Given: Trapezoid $ABCD$,
$\overline{AD} \cong \overline{BC}$, $\overline{DE} \perp \overline{AB}$, $\overline{CF} \perp$
$\overline{AB}$
Prove: $\angle A \cong \angle B$

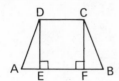

8. Given: Trapezoid $ABCD$,
$\angle A \cong \angle B$, $\overline{DE} \perp \overline{AB}$, $\overline{CF} \perp$
$\overline{AB}$
Prove: $\overline{AD} \cong \overline{BC}$

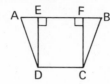

9. Given: D is midpoint of $\overline{AC}$,
E is midpoint of $\overline{BC}$.
Prove: $ABED$ is a
trapezoid.

PART B

For each of the following questions, make careful drawings. If the statement seems to be true, try to prove it. If not, show a counterexample.

10. Are the opposite angles of a trapezoid congruent?

11. Are the opposite angles of a trapezoid supplements?

12. Are adjacent angles of a trapezoid supplements?

13. Do the diagonals of a trapezoid bisect its angles?

14. Do the segments joining midpoints of adjacent sides of a trapezoid form a trapezoid?

15. Do the segments joining midpoints of opposite sides of a trapezoid bisect each other?

16. If the diagonals of a quadrilateral bisect each other, is the quadrilateral a trapezoid?

17. If the diagonals of a quadrilateral are congruent, is the quadrilateral a trapezoid?

Algebra Review

OBJECTIVE
■ To solve a proportion

If $\dfrac{a}{b} = \dfrac{c}{d}$, then $ad = bc$.

In a true proportion, the product of the extremes equals the product of the means.

EXAMPLE   Solve $\dfrac{5}{15} = \dfrac{x}{x+8}$.

Prod. of extremes = prod. of means.

$$5(x+8) = 15x$$
$$5x + 40 = 15x$$
$$40 = 10x$$
$$4 = x$$

Thus, the solution is 4.

Solve.

1. $\dfrac{5}{4} = \dfrac{a}{12}$

2. $\dfrac{x+10}{x} = \dfrac{18}{12}$

3. $\dfrac{3x+3}{3} = \dfrac{7x-1}{5}$

4. $\dfrac{y}{12-y} = \dfrac{10}{30}$

Medians and Altitudes of Trapezoids

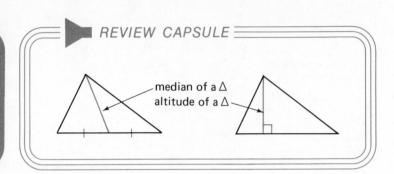

REVIEW CAPSULE

median of a △
altitude of a △

A ▱ is also a trapezoid. Either set of ∥ sides can be the bases.

The *bases* of a trapezoid are the two parallel sides.
The *legs* of a trapezoid are the other two sides.
The *median* of a trapezoid is the segment which joins the midpoints of the legs.

EXAMPLE 1

Which sides of the trapezoids are the bases?

IJKL is also a ▱.

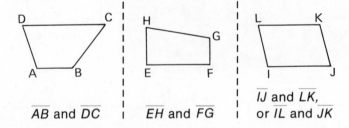

The bases are a pair of parallel sides.

$\overline{AB}$ and $\overline{DC}$ | $\overline{EH}$ and $\overline{FG}$ | $\overline{IJ}$ and $\overline{LK}$, or $\overline{IL}$ and $\overline{JK}$

EXAMPLE 2

Measure the bases and the median of trapezoid *ABCD*. Are the lengths related?

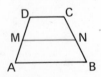

$$AB = 1.6 \text{ in.}, \quad DC = .8 \text{ in.}, \quad MN = 1.2 \text{ in.}$$
$$1.2 = \tfrac{1}{2}(1.6 + .8)$$

It is the average of the lengths of the bases.

The length of the median is half the sum of the lengths of the bases.

Theorem 7.12

The median of a trapezoid is parallel to its bases, and its length is half the sum of the lengths of the bases.

ANALYSIS

Draw $\overline{RS} \parallel \overline{CB}$ through X.
Show $RSBC$ is a $\square$.
Use the properties of $\square$'s.

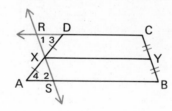

GIVEN

Trapezoid $ABCD$, $\overline{AB} \parallel \overline{DC}$,
X is the midpoint of $\overline{AD}$, Y
is the midpoint of $\overline{BC}$.

PROVE

$\overline{XY} \parallel \overline{DC} \parallel \overline{AB}$,
$XY = \frac{1}{2}(DC + AB)$

OUTLINE OF PROOF
(Reasons are omitted.)

I Prove $\overline{XY} \parallel \overline{DC} \parallel \overline{AB}$.
1. Draw $\overline{RS} \parallel \overline{CB}$ through X.
2. $\overline{SB} \parallel \overline{RC}$
3. $RSBC$ is a $\square$.
4. $\angle 1 \cong \angle 2$ and $\angle 3 \cong \angle 4$
5. $\triangle RXD \cong \triangle SXA$
6. $RX = SX$, or $RX = \frac{1}{2}(RS)$
7. $CY = \frac{1}{2}(CB)$
8. But, $RS = CB$
9. $\therefore RX = CY$
10. $RXYC$ is a $\square$.
11. $\overline{XY} \parallel \overline{DC}$
12. Similarly, $XYBS$ is a $\square$
   and $\overline{XY} \parallel \overline{DC} \parallel \overline{AB}$.

II Prove $XY = \frac{1}{2}(DC + AB)$.
13. $XY = RC$ ($RXCY$ is a $\square$.)
14. $RC = DC + RD$
15. $XY = DC + RD$
16. $RD = SA$
17. $XY = DC + SA$
18. $XY = SB$ ($XYBS$ is a $\square$.)
19. $XY + XY = DC + \underline{SA + SB}$,
   or $2(XY) = DC + AB$
20. $\therefore XY = \frac{1}{2}(DC + AB)$

EXAMPLE 3 $ABCD$ is a trapezoid. Find y.

$y = \frac{1}{2}(AB + CD)$ $\longrightarrow$

$$y = \frac{1}{2}(5 + 7)$$
Thus, $y = 6$

EXAMPLE 4 $ABCD$ is a trapezoid. E is the midpoint of $\overline{AD}$. F is the midpoint of $\overline{BC}$. $AB = 6$ cm, $EF = 4$ cm. Find CD.

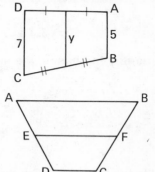

$$EF = \frac{1}{2}(AB + CD)$$
$$4 = \frac{1}{2}(6 + CD)$$

Multiply each side by 2. $\longrightarrow$
$$8 = 6 + CD$$
$$2 = CD$$

Thus, $CD = 2$ cm.

EXAMPLE 5　$\overline{XY}$ is the median of trapezoid $PQRS$. $PS = 2t + 2$, $XY = 3t$, $QR = 5t - 7$. Find XY.

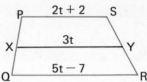

$XY = \frac{1}{2}(PS + QR)$ ⟶ $3t = \frac{1}{2}[(2t + 2) + (5t - 7)]$

Multiply each side by 2. ⟶ $6t = (2t + 2) + (5t - 7)$

$6t = 7t - 5$

$t = 5$

$XY = 3t = 3(5)$ ⟶ **Thus,** $XY = 15$.

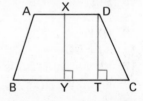

A trapezoid has many altitudes.

Definition of *altitude* of a trapezoid. ⟶

An *altitude* of a trapezoid is any segment from a point on one of the bases perpendicular to the line containing the other base.

EXAMPLE 6　Show that all altitudes of a trapezoid are congruent.

Let $\overline{XY}$ and $\overline{DT}$ be two altitudes.

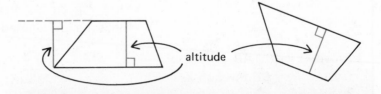

Def. of a trapezoid. ⟶ $\overline{AD} \parallel \overline{BC}$

$\parallel$ lines are equidistant. ⟶ **Thus,** $XY = DT$ and $\overline{XY} \cong \overline{DT}$.

ORAL EXERCISES

Identify the bases, the median, and an altitude.

1.
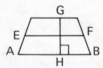

2.
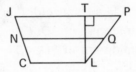

3.

4.

Find the length of the median.

5.
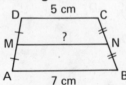

6.
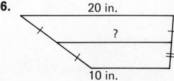

7.

EXERCISES

PART A

For each given trapezoid, find the length of the median $\overline{VW}$.

1. $UT = 6$, $RS = 8$, $VW = $?
3. $UT = 11$, $RS = 19$, $VW = $?
5. $UT = x + 3$, $RS = 3x - 5$,
    $VW = x + 7$

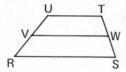

2. $UT = 9$, $RS = 3$, $VW = $?
4. $UT = 5$, $RS = 4$, $VW = $?
6. $UT = 2x - 1$, $RS = 5x + 1$,
    $VW = 3x + 2$

For each given trapezoid, find the length(s) of the unknown base(s). $\overline{GH}$ is the median.

7. $WZ = 6$, $GH = 8$, $XY = $?
9. $WZ = 5$, $GH = 13$, $XY = $?
11. $WZ = t + 5$, $GH = 3t - 7$,
    $XY = 3t - 1$

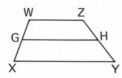

8. $WZ = $?, $GH = 7$, $XY = 8$
10. $WZ = $?, $GH = 9$, $XY = 14$
12. $WZ = t + 5$, $GH = 3t$,
    $XY = 4t - 3$

PART B

Give one conclusion which can be drawn from the given in each of the following.

13. Given: Trapezoid $ABCD$,
    median $\overline{MN}$, diagonal $\overline{DB}$

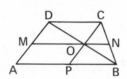

14. Given: Trapezoid $ABCD$, N
    is the midpoint of $\overline{BC}$, O is
    the midpoint of $\overline{PC}$.

15. Prove: The median of a
    trapezoid bisects both
    diagonals.

16. Prove: The altitudes of
    congruent trapezoids are
    congruent.

17. Prove: The medians of
    congruent trapezoids are
    congruent.

PART C

Prove the conclusion or disprove it by giving a counterexample.

18. Given: Trapezoid $RSTU$,
    median $\overline{VW}$, diagonal $\overline{RT}$
    intersecting both $\overline{VW}$ and
    $\overline{UP}$ at O.
    Prove or disprove: $PSTU$ is
    a $\square$.

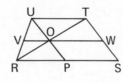

19. Given: Trapezoid $RSTU$,
    median $\overline{VW}$, diagonal $\overline{RT}$
    intersecting both $\overline{VW}$ and
    $\overline{UP}$ at O.
    Prove or disprove: $\triangle RPU$ is
    isosceles.

20. Is there any relationship between the
    lengths of the legs, bases, and altitudes
    of a trapezoid?

21. Is there any relationship between the
    length of the median of a trapezoid and
    the length of an altitude?

MEDIANS AND ALTITUDES OF TRAPEZOIDS   **223**

Symmetric Polygons

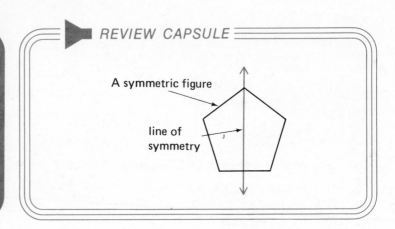

REVIEW CAPSULE

A symmetric figure

line of symmetry

A symmetric polygon is its own reflection about the line of symmetry.

Symmetric Polygons

EXAMPLE 1   Draw all the lines of symmetry of the symmetric polygon.

This symmetric polygon has two lines of symmetry. ⟶

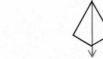

EXAMPLE 2 $\overleftrightarrow{PR}$ is a line of symmetry for quadrilateral *ABCD*. *X* and *Y* are corresponding points. How are $\overline{XY}$ and $\overleftrightarrow{PR}$ related?

X and *Y* are reflections of each other. ⟶

Check by measuring. ⟶ $\overleftrightarrow{PR}$ seems to be the perpendicular bisector of $\overline{XY}$.

Postulate 19

The line of symmetry of a symmetric figure is the perpendicular bisector of a segment joining two corresponding points.

EXAMPLE 3 In symmetric polygon
ABCDEF, with line of
symmetry $\overleftrightarrow{AD}$, name the pairs
of corresponding sides.

Corresponding sides are reflections of
each other about the line of symmetry. } ⟶

$\overline{AB} \leftrightarrow \overline{AF}, \overline{BC} \leftrightarrow \overline{FE},$
$\overline{CD} \leftrightarrow \overline{ED}$

Theorem 7.13

Corresponding sides of symmetric polygons are
congruent.

ANALYSIS
Use def. of ⊥ bisector
to show $\overline{AB} \cong \overline{AF}$ and $\overline{CD} \cong \overline{ED}$.
Then show quad. *BXYC* ≅ quad. *FXYE*
to get $\overline{BC} \cong \overline{FE}$.

PROOF

GIVEN
Polygon *ABCDEF*, with line
of symmetry $\overleftrightarrow{AD}$
PROVE
$\overline{AB} \cong \overline{AF}, \overline{BC} \cong \overline{FE}, \overline{CD} \cong \overline{ED}$

STATEMENTS		REASONS
1. $\overleftrightarrow{AD}$ is the ⊥ bisector of $\overline{BF}$. $\overleftrightarrow{AD}$ is the ⊥ bisector of $\overline{CE}$.		1. The line of symmetry of a symmetric figure is the ⊥ bis. of a seg. joining 2 corr. points.
2. ∴ $\overline{AB} \cong \overline{AF}$ and $\overline{CD} \cong \overline{ED}$		2. Point on ⊥ bis. of seg. is equidistant from the endpoints of the seg.
3. $\overline{BX} \cong \overline{FX}$	(S)	3. Def. of ⊥ bisector
4. ∠*BXY* ≅ ∠*FXY*	(A)	4. All right ∠'s are ≅.
5. $\overline{XY} \cong \overline{XY}$	(S)	5. Reflexive property
6. ∠*XYC* ≅ ∠*XYE*	(A)	6. Same as 4
7. $\overline{CY} \cong \overline{EY}$	(S)	7. Same as 3
8. quad *BXYC* ≅ quad *FXYE*		8. SASAS for ≅ quad.
9. ∴ $\overline{BC} \cong \overline{FE}$		9. Corr. sides of ≅ quad. are ≅.

Theorem 7.14

Corresponding angles of symmetric polygons are
congruent.

EXAMPLE 4 If polygon *ABCDEF* is symmetric
about $\overleftrightarrow{AD}$, which sides and angles
are congruent?

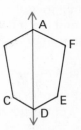

Corresponding sides are ≅. ⟶ $\overline{AB} \cong \overline{AF}, \overline{BC} \cong \overline{FE}, \overline{CD} \cong \overline{ED}$
Corresponding angles are ≅. ⟶ ∠*B* ≅ ∠*F*, ∠*C* ≅ ∠*E*

ORAL EXERCISES

Which of the following polygons are symmetric?

1.

2.

3.

4.

EXERCISES

PART A

Copy each figure. Draw all the lines of symmetry in each polygon.

1.

2.

3.

4.

Each polygon is symmetric about the axis of symmetry shown. Which sides and which angles are congruent?

5.

6.
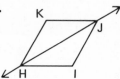

7.

8.

PART B

9. Is it possible for a triangle to have exactly one line of symmetry? Exactly two? Exactly three? More than three? Draw pictures to defend your answer.

10. Is it possible for a quadrilateral to have exactly one line of symmetry? Exactly two? Exactly three? Exactly four? More than four? Draw pictures to defend your answer.

11. Is there any relationship between the number of sides of a regular polygon and the number of lines of symmetry? If so, what is it?

12. Draw a pentagon with exactly one line of symmetry.

PART C

13. Prove Theorem 7.14.
14. If corresponding sides of a polygon are congruent, then is the polygon necessarily symmetric?

15. If corresponding angles of a polygon are congruent, then is the polygon necessarily symmetric?

Isosceles Trapezoids

OBJECTIVES

■ To identify isosceles trapezoids

■ To prove and apply theorems about isosceles trapezoids

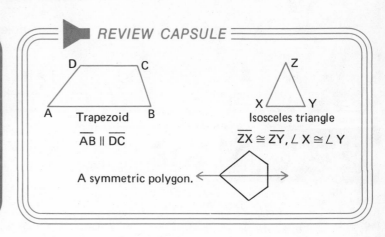

▶ REVIEW CAPSULE

Trapezoid
$\overline{AB} \parallel \overline{DC}$

Isosceles triangle
$\overline{ZX} \cong \overline{ZY}, \angle X \cong \angle Y$

A symmetric polygon.

EXAMPLE 1   Draw a symmetric trapezoid.

Definition of *isosceles trapezoid* ——————▶ An *isosceles trapezoid* is a trapezoid which is symmetric about a line through the midpoints of its bases.

EXAMPLE 2   Which of the following trapezoids are isosceles?

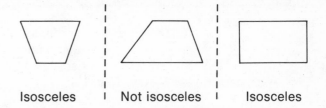

Isosceles | Not isosceles | Isosceles

EXAMPLE 3   *ABCD* is an isosceles trapezoid. Draw the line of symmetry. Which sides and angles are congruent?

Corr. sides are ≅. ——————▶ $\overline{AD} \cong \overline{BC}$

Corr. ∠'s are ≅. ——————▶ $\angle A \cong \angle B$
$\angle D \cong \angle C$

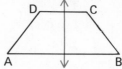

Since an isosceles trapezoid is a symmetric polygon, it has all the properties of a symmetric polygon.

Properties of Isosceles Trapezoids

Legs are congruent. Base angles are congruent.

Theorem 7.15

The diagonals of an isosceles trapezoid are congruent.

ANALYSIS

Show △URS ≅ △TSR.

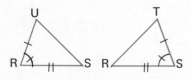

Corr. sides of ≅ △'s are ≅.

STATEMENTS

1. $\overline{UR} \cong \overline{TS}$
2. $\angle URS \cong \angle TSR$
3. $\overline{RS} \cong \overline{SR}$
4. $\triangle URS \cong \triangle TSR$
5. ∴ $\overline{US} \cong \overline{TR}$

GIVEN

Isosceles trapezoid RSTU

$\overline{UT} \parallel \overline{RS}$

PROVE

$\overline{US} \cong \overline{TR}$

PROOF

REASONS

1. Legs of an isos. trap. are ≅.
2. Base ∠'s of an isos. trap. are ≅.
3. Reflexive property
4. SAS for ≅ △'s
5. Corr. sides of ≅ △'s are ≅.

EXAMPLE 4 If a quadrilateral has congruent diagonals, is the quadrilateral an isosceles trapezoid?

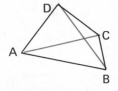

Not necessarily. *ABCD* is not even a trapezoid.

EXAMPLE 5 If the legs of a trapezoid are congruent, is the trapezoid necessarily isosceles?

A construction shows two possibilities.

$\overline{YX} \parallel \overline{ZW'}$

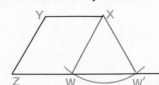

$\overline{XW} \cong \overline{YZ}$

$\overline{XW'} \cong \overline{YZ}$

Not necessarily. *XYZW* is a parallelogram but not an isosceles trapezoid. *XYZW'* is an isosceles trapezoid.

Theorem 7.16

If a trapezoid has a pair of congruent legs which are not parallel, then it is isosceles.

EXAMPLE 6 Trapezoid JKLM with $\overline{ML} \parallel \overline{JK}$.
Find $m\angle J$, $m\angle K$, $m\angle L$.

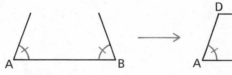

The legs are $\cong$. ⟶ JKLM is an isosceles trapezoid.

Base $\angle$'s of isos. trap. are $\cong$. ⟶ $\angle M \cong \angle L$ and $\angle J \cong \angle K$

Thus, $m\angle L = 110$,

$\angle J$ and $\angle M$ are supplements. ⟶ $\quad m\angle J = 70$, and $m\angle K = 70$.

EXAMPLE 7 If the base angles of a trapezoid are congruent, is the trapezoid isosceles?

Check this by construction. ⟶

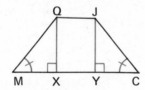

It can be proved that trapezoid ABCD is isosceles.

Theorem 7.17

If a trapezoid has at least one pair of congruent base angles, then it is isosceles.

ANALYSIS

Draw altitudes $\overline{QX}$ and $\overline{JY}$.
Show $\triangle QXM \cong \triangle JYC$.

GIVEN
Trapezoid MCJQ, $\overline{QJ} \parallel \overline{MC}$
$\angle M \cong \angle C$
PROVE
Trapezoid MCJQ is isosceles.

PROOF
(See Exercise 15.)

ORAL EXERCISES

Which of the following are isosceles trapezoids?

1.

2.

3.

4.

Which sides and which angles of the following isosceles trapezoids are congruent?

5.

6.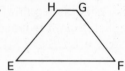

7.

8.

EXERCISES

PART A

Find the missing angle measures in each isosceles trapezoid.

1.

2.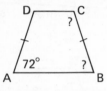

3.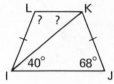

4.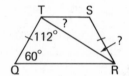

5.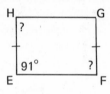

6.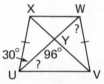

7. Given: $\overline{RC} \cong \overline{RL}$, $\overline{XT} \parallel \overline{CL}$
Prove: $XTLC$ is an isosceles trapezoid.

8. Given: $XTLC$ is an isosceles trapezoid.
Prove: $\triangle LRC$ is isosceles.

PART B

9. Given: Isos. trap. $ABCD$,
$\overline{DC} \parallel \overline{AB}$. Is $\triangle ABD \cong \triangle BAC$?
Why or why not?

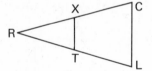

10. Given: Isos. trap. $ABCD$,
$\overline{DC} \parallel \overline{AB}$. Is $\triangle AED \cong \triangle BEC$?
Why or why not?

True or false? If true, prove. If false, give a counterexample.

11. If a trapezoid is isosceles, then opposite angles are supplements.

12. If the diagonals of a trapezoid are congruent, then the trapezoid is isosceles.

13. If opposite angles of a trapezoid are supplements, then the trapezoid is isosceles.

14. If the opposite angles of a quadrilateral are supplements, then the quadrilateral is an isosceles trapezoid.

PART C

15. Prove Theorem 7.17.

Rhombi, Rectangles, and Squares

OBJECTIVES
■ To identify rhombi, rectangles, and squares
■ To prove and apply properties of rhombi, rectangles, and squares

▶ REVIEW CAPSULE

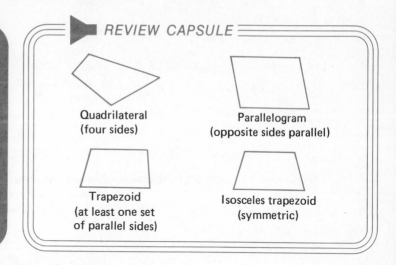

Quadrilateral
(four sides)

Parallelogram
(opposite sides parallel)

Trapezoid
(at least one set
of parallel sides)

Isosceles trapezoid
(symmetric)

Special Kinds of Parallelograms

RHOMBUS

A parallelogram with
two adjacent ≅ sides

RECTANGLE

A parallelogram with
at least one right angle

SQUARE

A rectangle with two
adjacent ≅ sides

EXAMPLE 1   True or false?

The plural of rhombus is rhombi. ──────▶

	Answers
All **squares** are rhombi.	True
All rhombi are parallelograms.	True
All squares are parallelograms.	True
All rhombi are rectangles.	False

A *Venn diagram* shows the relationships between rhombi, rectangles, and squares.

A square is both a rectangle and a rhombus.

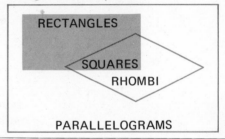

RECTANGLES

SQUARES

RHOMBI

PARALLELOGRAMS

EXAMPLE 2

Opp. sides of a ▱ are ≅.
∴ $\overline{AB} \cong \overline{DC}$, and $\overline{BC} \cong \overline{AD}$.
Since $\overline{AB} \cong \overline{AD}$, all sides are ≅. ──────→

True or false?
A rhombus has four congruent sides.

True

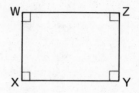

EXAMPLE 3

Opp. ∠'s of a ▱ are ≅.
∴ ∠X ≅ ∠Z and ∠W ≅ ∠Y
Adj. ∠'s are supplements.
∴ ∠X and ∠Y are rt. ∠'s, and all ∠'s are rt. ∠'s.

True or false?
A rectangle has four right angles.

True

EXAMPLE 4

The rectangle and the square are isosceles trapezoids. Diagonals of isosceles trapezoids are congruent.

Draw a rhombus, a rectangle, and a square. In which of these are the diagonals congruent?

not congruent   congruent   congruent

The diagonals of a rectangle and a square are congruent.

EXAMPLE 5

Diagonals of a rect. are ≅. ──────→

$AC = 4(3) + 1$ ──────────────→

ABCD is a rectangle. $AC = 4x + 1$, $BD = 6x - 5$. Find AC.

$$6x - 5 = 4x + 1$$
$$2x = 6$$
$$x = 3$$
$$AC = 13$$

EXAMPLE 6

ANALYSIS
Two points equidistant from ends of segment determine ⊥ bisector of segment.

Theorem 5.5 ──────────→

Given: Rhombus *LCGS*
Prove: $\overline{SC} \perp \overline{LG}$

Proof

Statements	Reasons
1. $\overline{SL} \cong \overline{SG}$, $\overline{CL} \cong \overline{CG}$	1. Adj. sides of rhombus are ≅.
2. ∴ $\overline{SC} \perp \overline{LG}$	2. Two points equidistant from ends of seg. determine ⊥ bis. of seg.

Example 6 proves that the diagonals of a rhombus are perpendicular.

ORAL EXERCISES

Identify each figure as a rhombus, a rectangle, a square, or none of these. Some figures may correctly be identified in more than one way.

1.   **2.**   **3.**   **4.**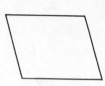

5.   **6.**   **7.**    **8.**

EXERCISES

PART A

For each given property, determine which of the following figures have that property: trapezoid, isosceles trapezoid, parallelogram, rhombus, rectangle, square.

1. Opposite sides are parallel.
3. Base angles are congruent.
5. Diagonals bisect each other.
7. Consecutive sides are congruent.
9. Opposite angles are supplements.

2. Opposite sides are congruent.
4. Opposite angles are congruent.
6. Diagonals are congruent.
8. Consecutive angles are congruent.
10. Adjacent angles are supplements.

True or false?

11. All squares are rectangles.
13. Some rectangles are rhombi.
15. Some trapezoids are rectangles.

12. All squares are trapezoids.
14. All rectangles are parallelograms.
16. All squares are quadrilaterals.

17. *ABCD* is a rhombus,
$m \angle A = 80$.
$m \angle B = ?, m \angle C = ?$

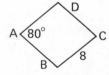

18. *ABCD* is a rhombus,
$BC = 8$.
$AB = ?, CD = ?$

PART B

19. Prove: A rhombus has four congruent sides.
21. Prove: A rectangle has four right angles.
22. Given: *T* is the midpoint of $\overline{XZ}$, *U* is the midpoint of $\overline{XY}$, *V* is the midpoint of $\overline{YZ}$. *TUVZ* is a rhombus.
Prove: $\triangle XYZ$ is isosceles.

20. Prove: The diagonals of a rhombus bisect the vertex angles.

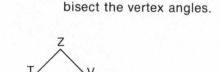

Proving Quadrilaterals

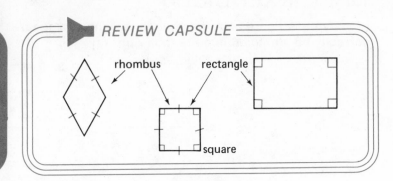

REVIEW CAPSULE

rhombus   rectangle

square

EXAMPLE 1

True or false? Draw a picture.
Any quadrilateral with congruent diagonals is a rectangle.

$\overline{AC} \cong \overline{BD}$, but ABCD is not a rectangle. ⟶ False

EXAMPLE 2

ANALYSIS
Show ∠PQR is a right ∠ by proving ∠PQR and ∠QPS are both ≅ and supplementary.

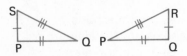

$m\angle PQR = m\angle QPS$
$m\angle PQR + m\angle QPS = 180$

$\therefore m\angle PQR = 90$

Prove: Any parallelogram with congruent diagonals is a rectangle.

Given: ▱PQRS, $\overline{PR} \cong \overline{SQ}$
Prove: PQRS is a rectangle.

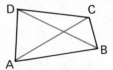

Proof

Statements		Reasons
1. $\overline{RQ} \cong \overline{SP}$ (S)		1. Opp. sides of ▱ are ≅.
2. $\overline{PR} \cong \overline{SQ}$ (S)		2. Given
3. $\overline{PQ} \cong \overline{QP}$ (S)		3. Seg. ≅ to itself
4. △PQR ≅ △QPS		4. SSS for ≅ △'s
5. ∠PQR ≅ ∠QPS		5. Corr. ∠'s of ≅ △'s are ≅.
6. ∠PQR and ∠QPS are suppl.		6. Adj. ∠'s of ▱ are suppl.
7. ∠PQR is a rt. ∠.		7. ≅ suppl. ∠'s are rt ∠'s.
8. ∴ PQRS is a rectangle.		8. ▱ with rt. ∠ is a rect.

EXAMPLE 3

True or false? Draw a picture.
Any quadrilateral with perpendicular diagonals is a rhombus.

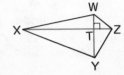

$\overline{WY} \perp \overline{XZ}$, but XYZW is not a rhombus. ⟶ False

EXAMPLE 4

Prove: Any parallelogram with perpendicular diagonals is a rhombus.

ANALYSIS
Prove adjacent sides $\overline{JM}$ and $\overline{JK}$ are $\cong$. (Show that $\triangle JNM \cong \triangle JNK$.)

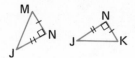

Given: $\square JKLM$, $\overline{LJ} \perp \overline{MK}$ at N
Prove: $JKLM$ is a rhombus.
Proof

Statements		Reasons
1. $MN \cong KN$	(S)	1. Diag. of $\square$ bisect each other.
2. $\angle MNJ \cong \angle KNJ$	(A)	2. $\perp$ forms $\cong$ rt. $\angle$'s
3. $JN \cong JN$	(S)	3. Reflexive property
4. $\triangle JNM \cong \triangle JNK$		4. SAS for $\cong \triangle$'s
5. $JM \cong JK$		5. Corr. sides of $\cong \triangle$'s are $\cong$.
6. $\therefore$ JKLM is a rhombus.		6. Def. of rhombus

SUMMARY

To show $\square ABCD$ is a rect., show it has a rt. $\angle$, or $\cong$ diag.

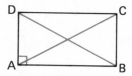

To show $\square ABCD$ is a rhombus, show two adj. sides are $\cong$, or the diag. are $\perp$.

To show $\square ABCD$ is a square show it is a rect. with two $\cong$ sides, or a rhombus with a rt. $\angle$.

EXAMPLE 5

In $\square ABCD$, $AB = x + 2$, $CD = 2x - 3$, $DA = 3x - 8$. What figure is $ABCD$?

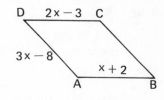

$\left.\begin{array}{l} ABCD \text{ is a } \square. \\ \overline{AB} \cong \overline{DC} \end{array}\right\}$ ⟶

$2x - 3 = x + 2$
$x = 5$

$AB = (5) + 2$
$DC = 2(5) - 3$
$DA = 3(5) - 8$
Use the definition. ⟶

$AB = 7$
$DC = 7$
$DA = 7$
Thus, $ABCD$ is a rhombus.

ORAL EXERCISES

Tell whether each figure is a parallelogram, a rectangle, a rhombus, a square, or cannot tell.

1.
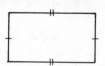

2.

3.

4.

5.   **6.** 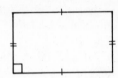 **7.**   **8.**

EXERCISES

PART A

List all quadrilaterals which have each of the given properties.

1. Diagonals are congruent.
2. Diagonals bisect each other.
3. Diagonals are perpendicular.
4. Diagonals bisect vertex angles.

For each given set of properties, tell whether quadrilateral _LCVQ_ is a rhombus, a rectangle, a square, or none of these.

5. $\square LCVQ$, $\overline{LV} \cong \overline{QC}$
7. $\square LCVQ$, $\overline{QM} \cong \overline{MC}$,
   $\overline{LM} \cong \overline{MV}$
9. $\overline{QM} \cong \overline{MC} \cong \overline{LM} \cong \overline{MV}$
11. $\square LCVQ$, $\overline{QL} \perp \overline{LC}$

6. $\square LCVQ$, $\overline{LV} \perp \overline{QC}$
8. $\square LCVQ$, $\overline{QM} \cong \overline{MC} \cong$
   $\overline{LM} \cong \overline{MV}$
10. $\square LCVQ$, $\overline{QL} \cong \overline{LC}$
12. $\overline{QL} \perp \overline{LC}$, $\overline{QV} \perp \overline{VC}$

13. Given: $\overline{HG} \cong \overline{EF}$, $\overline{HG} \parallel \overline{EF}$,
    $\overline{HF} \cong \overline{EG}$
    Prove: _EFGH_ is a rectangle.

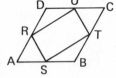

14. Given: $\overline{EF} \cong \overline{FG} \cong \overline{GH}$
    $\cong \overline{HE}$
    Prove: _EFGH_ is a rhombus.

PART B

15. Prove: If the diagonals of a rhombus are congruent, then the rhombus is a square.

16. Prove: If the diagonals of a rectangle are perpendicular, then the rectangle is a square.

17. Given: Rhombus _ABCD_; _R_, _S_, _T_, and _U_ are midpoints of $\overline{DA}$, $\overline{AB}$, $\overline{BC}$, and $\overline{CD}$ respectively.
    Prove: _RSTU_ is a rectangle.

18. Given: _R_, _S_, _T_, and _U_ are midpoints of $\overline{DA}$, $\overline{AB}$, $\overline{BC}$, and $\overline{CD}$ respectively. _RSTU_ is a rectangle. Is _ABCD_ a rhombus?

PART C

True or false? If true, prove the statement as a theorem. If false, show a counterexample.

19. If all sides of a quadrilateral are congruent, then the quadrilateral is a rhombus.

20. If all angles of a quadrilateral are congruent, then the quadrilateral is a rectangle.

21. If the diagonals of a quadrilateral bisect each other, then the quadrilateral is a rectangle.

22. If the diagonals of a quadrilateral are perpendicular bisectors of each other, then the quadrilateral is a rhombus.

Constructing Quadrilaterals

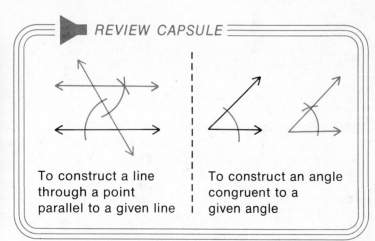

▶ *REVIEW CAPSULE*

To construct a line through a point parallel to a given line

To construct an angle congruent to a given angle

EXAMPLE 1 Construct a parallelogram with adjacent sides congruent to the given segments and the included angle congruent to the given angle.

Construct $\angle A \cong$ given $\angle$.
Construct $\overline{AB}$ with length a.
Construct $\overline{AD}$ with length b.

If opposite sides are $\cong$, quad. is a $\square$.

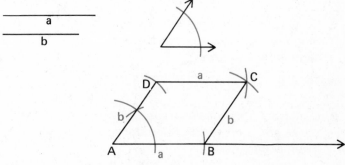

EXAMPLE 2 Construct a rhombus with diagonals congruent to two given segments.

If diagonals are $\perp$ bisectors of each other, then quadrilateral is a rhombus.

Bisect original segment with length b.
Construct $\overline{AB}$ with length a.
Construct $\perp$ bisector of $\overline{AB}$.
Construct endpoints of $\perp$ diagonal, each half with length $\frac{1}{2}b$.

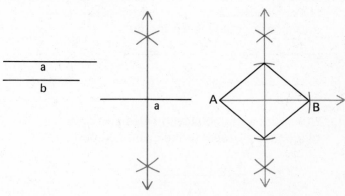

EXERCISES

PART A

1. Construct a square with sides congruent to the given segment.

$$\underline{\qquad\qquad}$$
s

2. Construct a rectangle with sides congruent to the given segments.

$$\underline{\qquad\qquad} \qquad \underline{\qquad\qquad\qquad}$$
a b

3. Construct a rhombus with sides congruent to the given segment and an angle congruent to the given angle.

s

4. Construct a parallelogram with sides congruent to the given segments and an angle congruent to the given angle.

a

b

5. Construct a rhombus with diagonals congruent to the given segments.

$$\underline{\qquad\qquad} \qquad \underline{\qquad\qquad}$$
d e

6. Construct a square with diagonals congruent to the given segment.

$$\underline{\qquad\qquad\qquad\qquad}$$
d

PART B

7. Construct a rectangle with a side and a diagonal congruent to the given segments.

$$\underline{\qquad\qquad} \qquad \underline{\qquad\qquad\qquad}$$
s d

8. Construct an isosceles trapezoid with bases and legs congruent to the given segments.

$$\underline{\qquad\qquad} \quad \underline{\qquad\qquad} \quad \underline{\qquad\qquad}$$
b b′ s

9. Construct an isosceles trapezoid with bases and a diagonal congruent to the given segments.

$$\underline{\qquad\qquad} \quad \underline{\qquad\qquad} \quad \underline{\qquad\qquad}$$
b b′ d

10. Construct a parallelogram with adjacent sides and one diagonal congruent to the given segments.

$$\underline{\qquad\qquad} \quad \underline{\qquad\qquad} \quad \underline{\qquad\qquad}$$
s s′ d

11. Construct a trapezoid with bases and a leg congruent to the given segments and a base angle measuring 60°.

$$\underline{\qquad\qquad} \qquad \underline{\qquad\qquad\qquad}$$
b b′

$$\underline{\qquad\qquad}$$
l

12. Construct a trapezoid with bases, one leg, and an altitude congruent to the given segments.

$$\underline{\qquad\qquad\qquad} \qquad \underline{\qquad\qquad}$$
b b′

$$\underline{\qquad\qquad} \qquad \underline{\qquad\qquad}$$
l h

13. Construct a rhombus with sides and one diagonal congruent to the given segment.

$$\underline{\qquad\qquad}$$
s

14. Construct an isosceles trapezoid with three sides of length s and diagonal of length d.

$$\underline{\qquad\qquad} \qquad \underline{\qquad\qquad\qquad}$$
s d

Reflections and Congruence

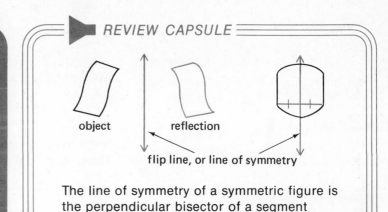

REVIEW CAPSULE

object   reflection

flip line, or line of symmetry

The line of symmetry of a symmetric figure is
the perpendicular bisector of a segment
joining two corresponding points.

EXAMPLE 1   Draw the reflection of the given figure about the given
line of symmetry.

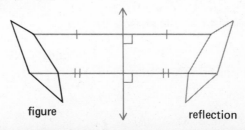

The line of symmetry is the ⊥ bisector of
segments joining corresponding points.

figure   reflection

Definition of *reflection*. ⟶

Two figures are *reflections* of each other if all
segments joining corresponding points have the
same perpendicular bisector.

EXAMPLE 2   Show that the two figures below are not reflections
of each other.

$\overline{PP'}$ and $\overline{QQ'}$ are two segments joining
corresponding points.

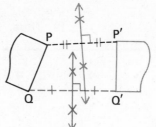

The ⊥ bisectors of $\overline{PP'}$ and $\overline{QQ'}$ are not
the same.

These are not reflections.

Fold the paper so that the two figures coincide.

The fold is the line of symmetry.

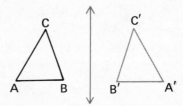

The line of symmetry of a pair of reflections can also be found by folding the sheet of paper on which they are drawn.

EXAMPLE 3

Trace the figures. Show by paper folding that they are ≅.

$\triangle ABC$ and $\triangle A'B'C'$ are reflections. $AB = 6$ cm. Find $A'B'$.

$\triangle ABC$ and $\triangle A'B'C'$ seem to be congruent.

$\overline{AB}$ and $\overline{A'B'}$ are corresponding sides. ⟶ **Thus,** $A'B' = 6$ cm.

Theorem 7.18

If two triangles are reflections, then they are congruent.

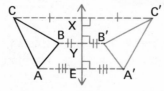

ANALYSIS

Show $\overline{CB} \cong \overline{C'B'}$ and $\overline{AB} \cong \overline{A'B'}$ by proving trapezoids ≅.
Then show $\overline{AC} \cong \overline{A'C'}$ by showing $AA'C'C$ is an isos. trap.

GIVEN
$\triangle A'B'C'$ is a reflection of $\triangle ABC$
Prove
$\triangle ABC \cong \triangle A'B'C'$

OUTLINE OF PROOF

I. Show trap. $CBYX \cong$ trap. $C'B'YX$.

1. $\overline{CX} \cong \overline{C'X}$ (S)
2. $\angle CXY \cong \angle C'XY$ (A)
3. $\overline{XY} \cong \overline{XY}$ (S)
4. $\angle XYB \cong \angle XYB'$ (A)
5. $\overline{BY} \cong \overline{B'Y}$ (S)
6. Trap. $CBYX \cong$ trap. $C'B'YX$
7. ∴ $\overline{CB} \cong \overline{C'B'}$

II. Show trap. $AEYB \cong$ trap. $A'EYB'$.

8. $\overline{BY} \cong \overline{B'Y'}$ (S)
9. $\angle B'YE \cong \angle BYE$ (A)
10. $\overline{YE} \cong \overline{YE}$ (S)
11. $\angle AEY \cong \angle A'EY$ (A)
12. $\overline{AE} \cong \overline{A'E}$ (S)
13. Trap. $AEYB \cong$ trap. $A'EYB'$
14. ∴ $\overline{AB} \cong \overline{A'B'}$

15. $\overline{AA'} \parallel \overline{CC'}$
16. $AA'C'C$ is a trapezoid.
17. $AA'C'C$ is an isosceles trapezoid.
18. ∴ $\overline{AC} \cong \overline{A'C'}$
19. **Thus,** $\triangle ABC \cong \triangle A'B'C'$

EXAMPLE 4

Are reflected quadrilaterals congruent?

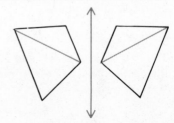

Segments form ≅ △'s. ⟶ Yes

EXERCISES

PART A

Copy the pictures. Determine by paper folding which are reflections.

1. 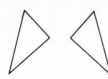 **2.** 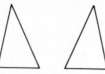 **3.**

Copy the pictures. Determine which are reflections by constructing the line of symmetry.

4.  **5.**  **6.**

In each pair of reflections, list the congruent segments and angles.

7.   **8.** 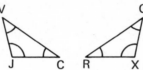 **9.**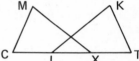

PART B

10. △ABC is a reflection of △DEF. Is △ABC ≅ △DEF? Why?

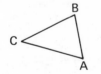

11. △ZXY is a reflection of △VTU. Describe the line of symmetry.

12. ℓ is the perpendicular bisector of $\overline{VR}$, $\overline{CH}$, $\overline{JX}$, and $\overline{LD}$. Is VCJL ≅ RHXD? Why?

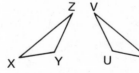

True of false?

13. Reflected triangles are congruent.

14. Reflected polygons are congruent.

15. Congruent triangles are reflections.

16. Congruent polygons are reflections.

PART C

17. Prove: Reflected quadrilaterals are congruent.

18. Describe a construction for finding the line of symmetry of reflections.

19. If a triangle is reflected about a line, and the image is then reflected about the same line, what is the result?

Chapter Seven Review

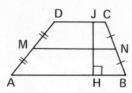

1. Which angles in trapezoid
   ABCD are opposite angles? [p. 195]
3. Which sides are consecutive sides?
   [p. 195]

2. Name an altitude in trapezoid
   ABCD. [p. 220]
4. Name a median. [p. 220]

Identify each figure as a quadrilateral, trapezoid, parallelogram, rhombus, rectangle, square, or none of these. Some figures may be identified correctly in more than one way.

[p. 202, 217, 231]

5.   6.   7.   8.   9.

True or false? Draw pictures to defend your answers.

10. Quadrilaterals can be proved congruent by an ASASA congruence correspondence. [p. 198]

11. Adjacent angles of parallelograms are supplements. [p. 202]

12. If opposite sides of a quadrilateral are both congruent and parallel, then the quadrilateral is a parallelogram. [p. 206]

13. The median of a triangle is half as long as the base and parallel to the base. [p. 209]

14. All segments cut off by parallel lines on transversals are congruent. [p. 212]

15. An isosceles trapezoid is a symmetric quadrilateral. [p. 227]

16. The median of an isosceles trapezoid is the same as its altitude to the base. [p. 220]

17. All congruent triangles are reflections of each other. [p. 239]

18. If all four angles of a quadrilateral are congruent, then the quadrilateral is a square. [p. 231]

19. If all four sides of a quadrilateral are congruent, then the quadrilateral is a rhombus. [p. 231]

20. A square is a rectangular rhombus. [p. 231]

21. Two sides of a trapezoid are congruent. [p. 217]

22. Given: $\overline{AD}$ and $\overline{NK}$ bisect each other. $\overline{PN} \parallel \overline{KL}$, $\overline{AP} \parallel \overline{LD}$.
    Prove: $JNPA \cong JKLD$ [p. 198]

23. Given: $\overline{VR} \cong \overline{VT}$; *S, U* and *W* are midpoints of $\overline{RT}$, $\overline{TV}$, and $\overline{VR}$.
    Prove: *WSUV* is a rhombus. [p. 234]

24. Given: isosceles trapezoid *NTCJ*, $\overline{NJ} \cong \overline{TC}$, $\overline{NT} \parallel \overline{JC}$
    Prove: $\triangle NTJ \cong \triangle TNC$ [p. 227]

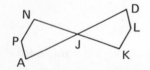   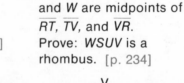   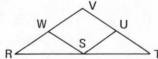

25. Draw a quadrilateral. Construct a quadrilateral congruent to it. [p. 237]

26. Copy the reflections. Construct their line of symmetry. [p. 239]

27. Draw a segment 9 cm long. Divide it into 4 congruent segments by construction. [p. 212]

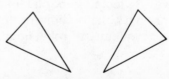

Chapter Seven Test

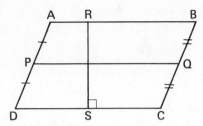

1. Which angles in quadrilateral *ABCD* are consecutive angles?
2. Name an altitude in quadrilateral *ABCD*.
3. Name a median in quadrilateral *ABCD*.

Identify each figure as a quadrilateral, trapezoid, parallelogram, rhombus, rectangle, square, or none of these. Some figures may be identified correctly in more than one way.

4.

5.

6.

True or false?

7. If two sides of a quadrilateral are both parallel and congruent, then the quadrilateral is a rectangle.
8. If the base angles of a trapezoid are congruent, then the trapezoid is isosceles.
9. The diagonals of a square are congruent.
10. The diagonals of a parallelogram are congruent.
11. The segments joining consecutive midpoints of the sides of a quadrilateral form a parallelogram.
12. If one angle of a parallelogram measures 90°, then the parallelogram is a rectangle.
13. The diagonals of a rhombus are never congruent.
14. Two quadrilaterals which are reflections are always congruent.

15. Given: *ABCD* is an isosceles trapezoid
    Prove: $\overline{AC} \cong \overline{BD}$

16. Given: $\square PQRS$
    $\overline{PF} \cong \overline{RE}$
    Prove: *FQES* is a $\square$

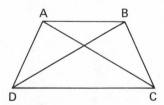

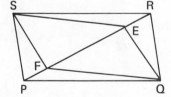

17. Copy $\overline{PQ}$.
    Divide $\overline{PQ}$ into 3 congruent segments by construction.

Mathematics in Surveying

Mathematics helps surveyors make accurate measurements of the earth. The woman surveyor is sighting through the transit.

The collected data is transferred to carefully constructed diagrams.

Surveying Problems

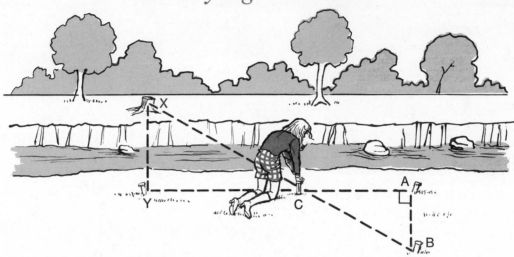

Laura needs to know the distance from a point *Y* on the bank of a river to a point *X* on the other side of the river. She drives a stake at *A* so that ∠*XYA* is a right angle, a stake at *B* so that ∠*YAB* is a right angle, and a stake at *C* where the line of sight from *B* to the tree stump intersects $\overline{YA}$. How does she determine the distance from *Y* to *X* without crossing the river?

John looked across the river to the point *X* and held out his hand until his finger tip was in the line of sight to the point. He then pivoted around with his hand at the same angle. He sighted across his finger to point *Z*. How does he find the distance from *Y* to *X* without crossing the river?

Shadows

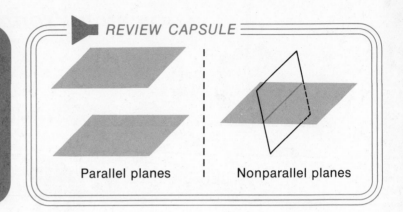

REVIEW CAPSULE

Parallel planes | Nonparallel planes

Shadows preserve certain gemetric patterns.

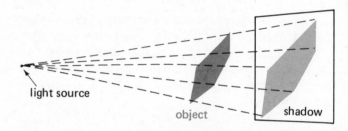

light source

object

shadow

There are four basic ways that shadows can be formed.

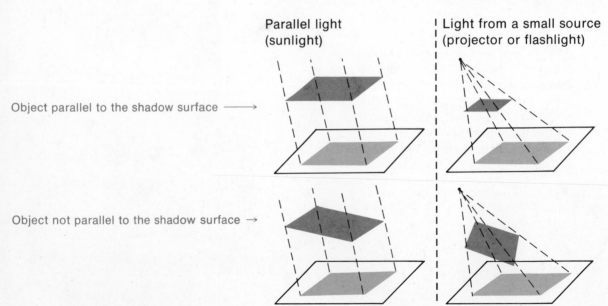

Parallel light (sunlight) | Light from a small source (projector or flashlight)

Object parallel to the shadow surface ⟶

Object not parallel to the shadow surface →

EXAMPLE 1 Tell whether each statement is always true, sometimes true, or never true.

The shadow of a line is a line or point.
Always true
If a point is between two other points, then its shadow is between the shadows of the other two.
Always true
The shadow of a figure is the same size as the figure.
Sometimes true
The shadow of a figure is the same shape as the figure.
Sometimes true

Check these answers by holding figures in sunlight and other light.

EXAMPLE 2 Draw a picture to show a shadow with the same size and shape as the original figure.

Sunlight can produce this kind of shadow. →

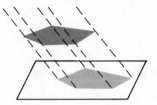

The light is parallel. The figure is parallel to its shadow.

EXAMPLE 3 The shadow pictured has the same shape as the object. The object is 5 feet from the light. The shadow is 10 feet from the light. If the edge of the object is 8 inches long, how long is the corresponding edge of the shadow?

The object is half way from the light to the shadow.

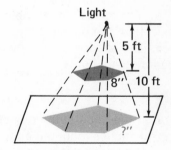

The edge of the shadow is twice as long as that of the object. ————————→ The edge of the shadow is 16 inches long.

EXAMPLE 4 On the shadow diagram below, show where to place the object so that the shadow is 3 times as tall as the object.

The shadow is three times as far from the light as the object is from the light.

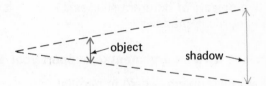

In the diagram, place the object $\frac{1}{3}$ the distance between the light and the shadow.

ORAL EXERCISES

Which of the pictures represent parallel light? Which represent objects parallel to the shadow surface?

1. 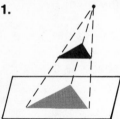 **2.** 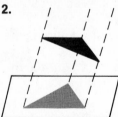 **3.** 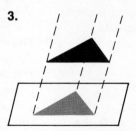 **4.**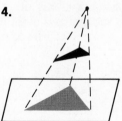

EXERCISES

PART A

Tell whether each statement is always true, sometimes true, or never true.

1. The shadow of parallel lines consists of parallel lines.

2. The shadow of perpendicular lines consists of perpendicular lines.

3. The shadow of an object is larger than the object.

4. The shadow of an object is smaller than the object.

5. The shadow of a convex figure is a convex figure.

6. The shadow of a parallelogram is a triangle.

PART B

7. If the edge of the object is 7 inches long, the edge of the shadow is 21 inches long, and the object is 5 feet from the light, how far is the shadow from the light?

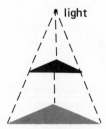

8. If the object is 4 inches from the light, the shadow is 12 inches from the object, and the edge of the shadow is 24 inches long, how long is the edge of the object?

PART C

9. Can two objects of different shapes have congruent shadows?

10. Can two objects of different sizes have congruent shadows?

True or false? Give an argument to support your answer.

11. If a triangular object is held in parallel light and parallel to the shadow surface, then the shadow is congruent to the object.

12. If a triangular object is held in projector light and parallel to the shadow surface, then the shadow is congruent to the object.

Ratio and Proportion

<table>
<tr><td>

OBJECTIVES

■ To write and solve
proportions
■ To find the geometric
mean of two numbers

</td></tr>
</table>

EXAMPLE 1   What is the ratio of the height of the stick to the
height of its shadow?

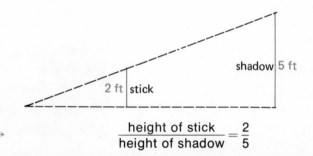

Both measures are in feet. ⟶ $\dfrac{\text{height of stick}}{\text{height of shadow}} = \dfrac{2}{5}$

Definition of *ratio* ⟶   The *ratio* of two numbers a and b is the number $\frac{a}{b}$,
$(b \neq 0)$.

EXAMPLE 2   Two numbers x and y have the ratio 2 to 7. Write a
mathematical sentence which states this.

$$\frac{x}{y} = \frac{2}{7}$$

Definition of *proportion* ⟶   A *proportion* is an equation of the form $\frac{a}{b} = \frac{c}{d}$,
$(b \neq 0, d \neq 0)$.

EXAMPLE 3   In the proportion $\frac{x}{y} = \frac{2}{7}$, find y if $x = 4$.

Substitute 4 for x. ─────────────→

$$\frac{4}{y} = \frac{2}{7}$$

Multiply by the LCD, $7y$. ─────────────→

$$(7y)\left(\frac{4}{y}\right) = (7y)\left(\frac{2}{7}\right)$$

$$28 = 2y$$

Divide each side by 2. ─────────────→

$$y = 14$$

Thus, y is 14 if $x = 4$.

In a proportion $\frac{a}{b} \bowtie \frac{c}{d}$

a and d are the *extremes*.
b and c are the *means*.

EXAMPLE 4   4, 6, 2, and x are in proportion. Write the proportion. Identify the means and extremes. Solve for x.

$$\frac{4}{6} = \frac{2}{x}$$

Means: 6 and 2
Extremes: 4 and x

Multiply by the LCD, $6x$. ─────────────→ $(6x)\left(\frac{4}{6}\right) = (6x)\left(\frac{2}{x}\right)$

$$4x = 12$$

$$x = 3$$

Example 4 suggests this. ─────────────→

In a true proportion, the product of the extremes equals the product of the means.

$\frac{4}{6} = \frac{2}{x}$
$4x = 6 \cdot 2$

If $\frac{a}{b} = \frac{c}{d}$, then $ad = bc$.

EXAMPLE 5   Is $\frac{5}{7} = \frac{7}{9}$ a true proportion?

No, $5 \cdot 9 \neq 7 \cdot 7$.

EXAMPLE 6   Solve the proportion $\frac{4}{m} = \frac{m}{16}$.

The product of the extremes equals the product of the means. ─────────────→

$$4 \cdot 16 = m^2$$

$$64 = m^2$$

$$m = 8, \text{ or } m = -8$$

Thus, the solutions are 8 and -8.

8 is called the *geometric mean* of 4 and 16.

Definition of *geometric mean* ──────────→ | The positive number *m* is the *geometric mean* of two positive numbers *a* and *b* if
$$\frac{a}{m} = \frac{m}{b}.$$

EXAMPLE 7 Find the geometric mean of 2 and 9.

Write the proportion. ──────────────→
$$\frac{2}{m} = \frac{m}{9}$$
$$m^2 = 18$$

Solve. ──────────────────────→
$$m = \sqrt{18}, \text{ or } m = -\sqrt{18}$$
Thus, $\sqrt{18}$ is the geometric mean of 2 and 9.

EXAMPLE 8 If $9x = 5 \cdot 90$, write three different proportions.

For each proportion, $9x = 5 \cdot 90$.

(The product of the extremes equals the product of the means.)

$$\frac{9}{5} = \frac{90}{x}, \text{ or } \frac{5}{9} = \frac{x}{90},$$
$$\text{or } \frac{x}{5} = \frac{90}{9}$$

ORAL EXERCISES

Which are ratios?

1. $\frac{2}{3}$ 　　　　　**2.** $3x$ 　　　　　**3.** $5 + 6$ 　　　　　**4.** $\frac{a}{b}$

In each proportion, identify the means and the extremes.

5. $\frac{2}{3} = \frac{4}{6}$ 　　　**6.** $\frac{8}{12} = \frac{12}{18}$ 　　　**7.** $\frac{14}{2} = \frac{49}{7}$ 　　　**8.** $\frac{n}{m} = \frac{x}{y}$

EXERCISES

PART A

Which are true proportions?

1. $\frac{3}{4} = \frac{6}{8}$ 　　**2.** $\frac{2}{3} = \frac{3}{4}$ 　　**3.** $\frac{6}{9} = \frac{4}{6}$ 　　**4.** $\frac{12}{16} = \frac{39}{52}$

5. $\frac{5}{6} = \frac{4 \cdot 5}{4 \cdot 6}$ 　　**6.** $\frac{3}{4} = \frac{3 + 3}{4 + 3}$ 　　**7.** $\frac{ab}{ac} = \frac{bd}{cd}$ 　　**8.** $\frac{a + b}{c + b} = \frac{a - b}{c - b}$

Find the value of x which makes each a true proportion.

9. $\frac{4}{6} = \frac{x}{15}$

10. $\frac{x}{9} = \frac{4}{12}$

11. $\frac{6}{x} = \frac{10}{15}$

12. $\frac{12}{8} = \frac{9}{x}$

Find the geometric mean of each pair of numbers.

13. 1 and 4

14. 9 and 16

15. 3 and 5

16. 6 and 8

Write three different proportions for each.

17. $3 \cdot 4 = 2 \cdot 6$

18. $5 \cdot 9 = 3 \cdot 15$

19. $4n = 7m$

20. $ab = cd$

What is the ratio of the height of the stick to the height of its shadow in each picture?

21.

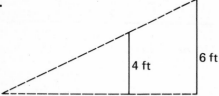

4 ft   6 ft

22.

2 ft   7 ft

PART B

Find the ratio of x to y.

23. $7x = 9y$

24. $13x = 12y$

25. $5y = 7x$

26. $rx = sy$

27. The measures of two complementary angles have the ratio 2 to 3. What is the measure of each angle?

28. The measures of two supplementary angles have the ratio 4 to 5. What is the measure of each angle?

29. The sum of the lengths of two segments is 121. The ratio of the lengths is 5 to 6. What is the length of each segment?

30. The difference of the lengths of two segments is 6. The ratio of the lengths is 3 to 5. What is the length of each segment?

PART C

True or false? If true, give an algebraic proof. If false, give a numerical counterexample.

31. If $\frac{a}{b} = \frac{c}{d}$, then $\frac{b}{a} = \frac{d}{c}$.

32. If $\frac{a}{b} = \frac{c}{d}$, then $\frac{a+n}{b+n} = \frac{c}{d}$.

33. If $\frac{a}{b} = \frac{c}{d}$, then $\frac{a+b}{b} = \frac{c+d}{d}$.

34. If $\frac{a}{b} = \frac{c}{d}$, then $\frac{a-b}{b} = \frac{c-d}{d}$.

35. If $\frac{a}{b} = \frac{c}{d}$, then $\frac{a}{a+b} = \frac{c}{c+d}$.

36. If $\frac{a}{b} = \frac{c}{d}$, then $\frac{a+b}{c+d} = \frac{a+d}{c+b}$.

37. If $\frac{a}{b} = \frac{c}{d}$, then $\frac{an}{bn} = \frac{cm}{dm}$.

38. If $\frac{a}{b} = \frac{c}{d}$, then $\frac{a^n}{b^n} = \frac{c^n}{d^n}$.

Similar Triangles

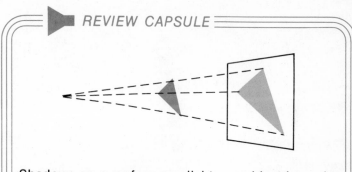

REVIEW CAPSULE

Shadows on a surface parallel to an object have the same shape as the object.

Congruent triangles | Similar triangles

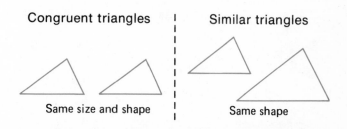

Same size and shape | Same shape

Two triangles are *similar* if they have the same shape.

EXAMPLE 1 Which of the triangles are similar?

Similar triangles have the same shape. ⟶

~ means is similar to. ⟶

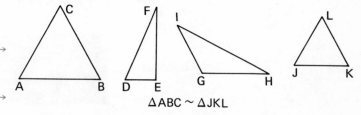

$\triangle ABC \sim \triangle JKL$

EXAMPLE 2 If $\triangle XCQ \sim \triangle TND$, which angles are congruent?

Angles determine shape. ⟶

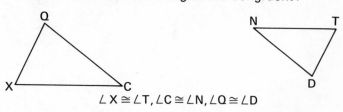

$\angle X \cong \angle T, \angle C \cong \angle N, \angle Q \cong \angle D$

Corresponding angles of similar triangles are congruent.

EXAMPLE 3 △*ENP* ~ △*JWT*. Find *PE*.

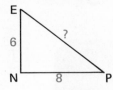

Each side of △*ENP* is twice as long as
the corresponding side of △*JWT*. ⟶

$EN = 2(JW)$, $NP = 2(WT)$
Thus, $PE = 2(TJ)$, or 10.

Lengths of corresponding sides have the
same ratio. ⟶

In △*ENP* and △*JWT*,
$$\frac{6}{3} = \frac{8}{4} = \frac{10}{5}, \text{ or } \frac{EN}{JW} = \frac{NP}{WT} = \frac{PE}{TJ}.$$

Two pairs of segments are proportional if their lengths
form a true proportion.

EXAMPLE 4 Which pairs of segments are proportional?

A 2 B   C 3 D   E   4   F

G   6   H

$$\frac{2}{3} = \frac{4}{6} \quad \text{or} \quad \frac{2}{4} = \frac{3}{6}$$

$$\frac{AB}{CD} = \frac{EF}{GH} \quad \text{or} \quad \frac{AB}{EF} = \frac{CD}{GH}$$

Thus, $\overline{AB}$ and $\overline{CD}$ are proportional to $\overline{EF}$ and $\overline{GH}$.
or $\overline{AB}$ and $\overline{EF}$ are proportional to $\overline{CD}$ and $\overline{GH}$.

Definition of *similar triangles* ⟶

> Two triangles are *similar* if corresponding angles
> are congruent and lengths of corresponding
> sides are proportional.

EXAMPLE 5 $\angle R \cong \angle J$, $\angle C \cong \angle S$, $\angle P \cong \angle A$,
$\frac{RC}{JS} = \frac{CP}{SA} = \frac{PR}{AJ}$. Are the triangles similar?

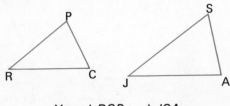

Use the definition. ⟶

Yes, △*RCP* ~ △*JSA*.

EXAMPLE 6 $\triangle PQR \sim \triangle JKL$.
Find KL, PR, and JL.

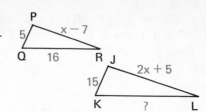

$$\frac{PQ}{JK} = \frac{QR}{KL} = \frac{PR}{JL} \longrightarrow$$

$$\frac{5}{15} = \frac{16}{KL}$$
$$5(KL) = 240$$
$$KL = 48$$

$$\frac{5}{15} = \frac{x-7}{2x+5}$$
$$5(2x+5) = 15(x-7)$$
$$10x + 25 = 15x - 105$$
$$-5x = -130$$
$$x = 26$$

$PR = x - 7$ or $26 - 7$
$JL = 2x + 5$ or $2(26) + 5$

Thus, $KL = 48$, $PR = 19$, and $JL = 57$.

ORAL EXERCISES

Which pairs of triangles appear to be similar?

1.   **2.**    **3.**    **4.**

Are the two pairs of segments proportional?

5.

5	15

8	24

6.

5	6

4	5

7.

4	12

6	18

EXERCISES

PART A

1. If $\triangle ABC \sim \triangle DEF$, which pairs of angles are congruent?

2. If $\triangle ABC \sim \triangle DEF$, which pairs of sides are proportional?

On the basis of the given information, can you conclude that the triangles are similar?

3. $\angle L \cong \angle W$, $\angle V \cong \angle N$,
$\dfrac{LV}{WN} = \dfrac{VQ}{NP} = \dfrac{QL}{PW}$

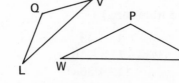

4. $LV = WN$, $VQ = NP$, $QL = PW$

5. $\triangle ABC \sim \triangle DEF$, $AB = 7$, $BC = 4$, $CA = 6$, $EF = 2$. Find DE and DF.

6. Isosceles $\triangle SLQ \sim \triangle PDM$, $SQ = LQ = 12$, $SL = 8$, $PM = 9$. Find PD and DM.

7. $\triangle RKC \sim \triangle NTW$, $m\angle R = 113$, $m\angle W = 42$. Find $m\angle C$, $m\angle T$, $m\angle N$.

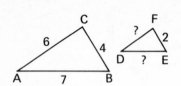
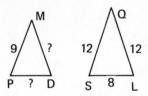
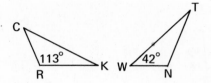

PART B

8. $\triangle RST \sim \triangle JKL$, $RT = 6$, $JL = 9$, $TS = 2x + 2$, $LK = 4x - 2$. Find TS and LK.

9. $\triangle NPQ \sim \triangle RVW$, $NQ = 9$, $NP = 12$, $RW = 2x + 1$, $RV = 3x - 1$. Find RW and RV.

10. $\triangle SXB \sim \triangle KTW$, $SX = 6$, $XB = 6$, $KT = x + 2$, $TW = 2x + 1$. Find KT and TW.

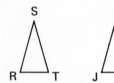
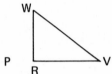

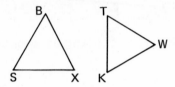

11. If two triangles are congruent, are they similar? Why or why not?

12. If two triangles are similar, are they congruent? Why or why not?

PART C

13. Using constructions, check whether two triangles are similar if the lengths of the three sides of one are double the corresponding lengths in the other.

14. Using constructions, check whether two triangles are similar if the 3 angles of one are congruent to the corresponding angles of the other.

Algebra Review

OBJECTIVE
■ To simplify radicals

To simplify a radical:
1. Factor.   2. Use $\sqrt{ab} = \sqrt{a} \cdot \sqrt{b}$.

EXAMPLE Simplify $\sqrt{128}$.

64 is a perfect square. ⟶ $\sqrt{64 \cdot 2} = \sqrt{64} \cdot \sqrt{2} = 8\sqrt{2}$

Simplify. (All variables represent positive numbers.)

1. $\sqrt{8}$	**2.** $\sqrt{20}$	**3.** $\sqrt{40}$	**4.** $\sqrt{98}$
5. $2\sqrt{45}$	**6.** $-5\sqrt{24}$	**7.** $3\sqrt{18}$	**8.** $-2\sqrt{108}$
9. $\sqrt{r^2 s}$	**10.** $\sqrt{20x^2}$	**11.** $\sqrt{36a^3}$	**12.** $\sqrt{12a^2 b^3}$

The Proportionality Assumption

OBJECTIVE
■ To write and solve proportions when a line is parallel to a side of a triangle

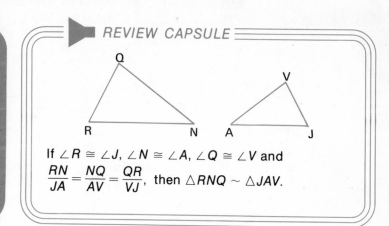

▶ REVIEW CAPSULE

If $\angle R \cong \angle J$, $\angle N \cong \angle A$, $\angle Q \cong \angle V$ and $\dfrac{RN}{JA} = \dfrac{NQ}{AV} = \dfrac{QR}{VJ}$, then $\triangle RNQ \sim \triangle JAV$.

EXAMPLE 1

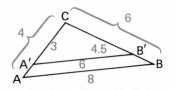

If $\overline{AB} \parallel \overline{A'B'}$, show that $\triangle ABC \sim \triangle A'B'C$.

Alt. int. $\angle$'s of $\parallel$ lines are $\cong$. ────────→ $\angle A \cong \angle A'$ and $\angle B \cong \angle B'$

$\dfrac{4}{3} = \dfrac{8}{6} = \dfrac{6}{4.5}$ ──────────── $\dfrac{AC}{A'C} = \dfrac{AB}{A'B'} = \dfrac{CB}{CB'}$

Use the definition. ────────→ **Thus,** $\triangle ABC \sim \triangle A'B'C$.

Postulate 20

In $\triangle ABC$, if $\overline{A'B'} \parallel \overline{AB}$, then $\dfrac{AB}{A'B'} = \dfrac{BC}{B'C} = \dfrac{CA}{CA'}$.

EXAMPLE 2 $\overline{QK} \parallel \overline{GA}$, $AK = 4$, $KW = 8$, $GQ = 5$. Find WQ.

Let $WQ = x$.

By Postulate 20 $\dfrac{WG}{WQ} = \dfrac{WA}{WK}$.

$$\frac{x + 5}{x} = \frac{8 + 4}{8}$$
$$8(x + 5) = 12x$$
$$8x + 40 = 12x$$
$$-4x = -40$$
$$x = 10$$

Thus, $WQ = 10$.

Theorem 8.1

A line parallel to one side of a triangle divides the other two sides proportionally.

ANALYSIS

Use Post. 20 to show $\dfrac{CA}{CA'} = \dfrac{CB}{CB'}$. Then use algebraic properties.

GIVEN
$\overline{A'B'} \parallel \overline{AB}$

PROVE
$\dfrac{AA'}{A'C} = \dfrac{BB'}{B'C}$

PROOF

STATEMENTS	REASONS
1. $\dfrac{CA}{CA'} = \dfrac{CB}{CB'}$	1. Postulate 20
2. $\dfrac{CA' + A'A}{CA'} = \dfrac{CB' + B'B}{CB'}$	2. Substitution
3. $1 + \dfrac{A'A}{CA'} = 1 + \dfrac{B'B}{CB'}$	3. $\dfrac{a+b}{c} = \dfrac{a}{c} + \dfrac{b}{c}$
4. $\therefore\ \dfrac{A'A}{CA'} = \dfrac{B'B}{CB'}$	4. Subtraction property for equations

Theorem 8.2

A line which divides two sides of a triangle proportionally is parallel to the third side.

EXAMPLE 3   Find x so that $\overline{DE} \parallel \overline{AB}$.

Apply Th. 8.2. ⟶

$$\frac{x}{9} = \frac{2}{6}$$
$$6x = 18$$
$$x = 3$$

Thus, if $x = 3$ then $\overline{DE} \parallel \overline{AB}$.

ORAL EXERCISES

Is the line intersecting the two sides parallel to the third?

1.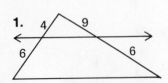

2.

3.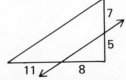

The line intersecting two of the sides of the triangle is parallel to the third side. Find the missing measurement.

4.

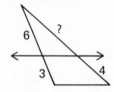

5.

6.

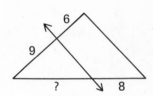

EXERCISES

PART A

In △ABE, $\overleftrightarrow{CD} \parallel \overline{AB}$.

1. $AC = 4$, $CE = 7$, $BD = 5$.
Find DE.

3. $AC = 9$, $AE = 13$, $DE = 8$.
Find BE.

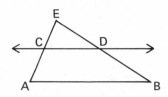

2. $AE = 6$, $CE = 4$, $BE = 9$.
Find BD.

4. $AC = 12$, $AE = 20$, $ED = 10$.
Find BD.

In △XTN, $\overleftrightarrow{CQ} \parallel \overline{XT}$. Complete each proportion.

5. $\dfrac{XC}{CN} = \dfrac{?}{QN}$

7. $\dfrac{NT}{NQ} = ?$

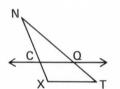

6. $\dfrac{NC}{NX} = \dfrac{CQ}{?}$

8. $\dfrac{CQ}{XT} = \dfrac{NC}{?}$

PART B

Find x so that $\overleftrightarrow{TM} \parallel \overline{BK}$.

9. $RT = 4$, $TB = 8$, $RK = 18$
$MK = x$.

11. $TM = 3\sqrt{3}$, $BK = 7\sqrt{5}$,
$MK = 3$, $RM = x$.

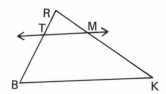

10. $RT = 3\sqrt{3}$, $RM = 2\sqrt{2}$,
$TB = 4$, $MK = x$.

12. $RT = 2$, $RM = 2\sqrt{3}$,
$TM = 3$, $MK = 4$, $BK = x$.

13. Given: $\dfrac{RH}{HJ} = \dfrac{NQ}{QJ}$, $\angle 1 \cong \angle 2$
Prove: $\angle R \cong \angle N$

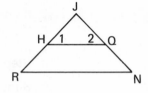

14. Given: $\angle R \cong \angle N$, $\angle 1 \cong \angle 2$
Prove: $\dfrac{RJ}{HJ} = \dfrac{NJ}{QJ}$

15. Given: $\square STBW$, $\overline{MN} \parallel \overline{BT}$,
$\overline{WX} \cong \overline{XT}$
Prove: $\dfrac{WM}{MB} = \dfrac{SN}{NT}$

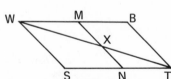

16. Given: $\dfrac{WM}{WB} = \dfrac{WX}{WT}$
$\triangle WMX \sim \triangle TNX$
Prove: $NTBM$ is a $\square$.

Angle-Angle Similarity

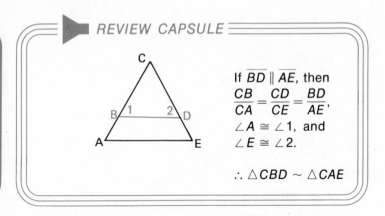

REVIEW CAPSULE

If $\overline{BD} \parallel \overline{AE}$, then
$$\frac{CB}{CA} = \frac{CD}{CE} = \frac{BD}{AE},$$
$\angle A \cong \angle 1$, and
$\angle E \cong \angle 2.$

$\therefore \triangle CBD \sim \triangle CAE$

Theorem 8.3

(AA for $\sim \triangle$'s)

If two angles of a triangle are congruent to two angles of a second triangle, then the two triangles are similar.

ANALYSIS
Construct a $\triangle D'E'C \cong \triangle DEF$. Show $\overline{D'E'} \parallel AB$. Use Post. 20 to show corr. sides in proportion.

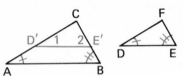

GIVEN
$\angle A \cong \angle D$, $\angle B \cong \angle E$
PROVE
$\triangle ABC \sim \triangle DEF$

PROOF

STATEMENTS	REASONS
1. $\angle A \cong \angle D$ and $\angle B \cong \angle E$	1. Given
2. $\angle C \cong \angle F$	2. Third $\angle$'s are $\cong$ if other $\angle$'s are $\cong$.
3. Draw $\overline{CD'} \cong \overline{FD}$ on $\overline{CA}$ and $\overline{CE'} \cong \overline{FE}$ on $\overline{CB}$.	3. There is a seg. $\cong$ to a given seg. (Post. 5)
4. $\triangle D'E'C \cong \triangle DEF$	4. SAS for $\cong \triangle$'s
5. $\angle 1 \cong \angle D$ and $\angle 2 \cong \angle E$	5. Corr. $\angle$'s of $\cong \triangle$'s are $\cong$.
6. $\angle 1 \cong \angle A$ and $\angle 2 \cong \angle B$	6. Substitution property
7. $\overline{D'E'} \parallel AB$	7. If corr. $\angle$'s are $\cong$, then the lines are $\parallel$.
8. $\dfrac{CD'}{CA} = \dfrac{CE'}{CB}$	8. If a line is $\parallel$ to side of a $\triangle$, then a proportion is formed. (Post. 20)
9. $\overline{FD} \cong \overline{CD'}$ and $\overline{FE} \cong \overline{CE'}$	9. Step 3
10. $\dfrac{FD}{CA} = \dfrac{FE}{CB}$	10. Substitution property

11. In a similar manner, it can be shown that $\dfrac{FE}{CB} = \dfrac{DE}{AB}$.

12. $\therefore \triangle ABC \sim \triangle DEF$ 12. Def. of $\sim \triangle$'s

EXAMPLE 1 Are the two triangles similar?

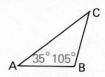

$m\angle C = 180 - (35 + 105)$ ⟶

AA for ~ △'s ⟶

$m\angle C = 40$

Thus, $\triangle ABC \sim \triangle EDF$.

EXAMPLE 2 If $\overline{AB} \parallel \overline{DE}$, is $\triangle ABC \sim \triangle EDC$

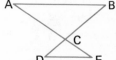

Alt. int. $\angle$'s of $\parallel$ lines are $\cong$. ⟶

AA for ~ △'s ⟶

$\angle A \cong \angle E,\ \angle B \cong \angle D$

Thus, $\triangle ABC \sim \triangle EDC$.

EXAMPLE 3 Find AD.

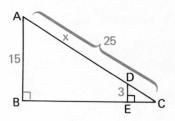

$\perp$'s form $\cong$ rt. $\angle$'s. ⟶

$\angle C$ is in both $\triangle ABC$ and $\triangle DEC$ ⟶

AA for ~ △'s ⟶

$\dfrac{AB}{DE} = \dfrac{AC}{DC}$ ⟶

$\angle B \cong \angle DEC$

$\angle C \cong \angle C$

$\triangle ABC \sim \triangle DEC$

$\dfrac{15}{3} = \dfrac{25}{25 - x}$

$15(25 - x) = 25 \cdot 3$

$375 - 15x = 75$

$-15x = -300$

$x = 20$

Thus, $AD = 20$.

EXAMPLE 4

ANALYSIS
Show that the △'s
are ~ by AA for ~ △'s.

Given: $\overline{PQ} \cong \overline{PR}$,
$\overline{PX}$ bisects $\angle QPR$.
Prove: $\triangle QPX \sim \triangle RPX$

Proof

Statements	Reasons
1. $\overline{PQ} \cong \overline{PR}$	1. Given
2. $\angle Q \cong \angle R$	2. $\angle$'s opp. $\cong$ sides of a △ are $\cong$.
3. $\angle QPX \cong \angle RPX$	3. Def. of $\angle$ bis.
4. $\therefore \triangle QPX \sim \triangle RPX$	4. AA for ~ △'s

ORAL EXERCISES

For which sets of angle measures is $\triangle RNQ$ similar to $\triangle VBX$?

1. $m\angle R = 62,\ m\angle N = 73,$
   $m\angle V = 62,\ m\angle B = 73.$
3. $m\angle R = 71,\ m\angle N = 69,$
   $m\angle V = 71,\ m\angle X = 40.$

 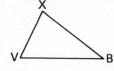

2. $m\angle Q = 80,\ m\angle R = 71,$
   $m\angle V = 71,\ m\angle X = 70$
4. $m\angle Q = 79,\ m\angle N = 56,$
   $m\angle V = 35,\ m\angle X = 79$

EXERCISES

1. Given: $\angle T \cong \angle NGV$
Prove: $\triangle NGV \sim \triangle NTX$

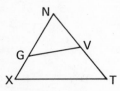

2. Given: $\angle R \cong \angle W$
Prove: $\triangle JYW \sim \triangle JMR$

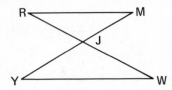

3. Given: $\overline{LK} \parallel \overline{CB}$
Prove: $\triangle LKM \sim \triangle BCM$

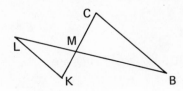

4. $\overline{NK} \perp \overline{JL}$, $\overline{ML} \perp \overline{JL}$, $NK = 4$,
$LM = 6$, $JM = 15$.
Find JN.

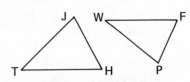

$\overline{NK} \perp \overline{JL}$, $\overline{ML} \perp \overline{JL}$, $JK = 9$,
$KL = 6$, $NK = 6$.
Find ML.

PART B

Based on the information given, is $\triangle THJ \sim \triangle WFP$?

6. $m \angle T = 47$, $m \angle H = 85$,
$m \angle W = x + 4$, $m \angle F = 2x - 1$, $m \angle P = x + 5$.

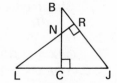

7. $m \angle T = 55$, $m \angle J = 75$,
$m \angle W = 2x + 3$, $m \angle P = 3x - 1$, $m \angle F = x + 22$.

8. Given: $\overline{CF} \perp \overline{AB}$, $\overline{BD} \perp \overline{AC}$
Prove: $\triangle FBE \sim \triangle DCE$

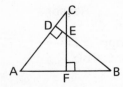

9. Given: $\overline{LR} \perp \overline{BJ}$, $\overline{BC} \perp \overline{LJ}$
Prove: $\triangle CBJ \sim \triangle RLJ$

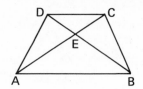

10. Given: $\overline{AB} \parallel \overline{DC}$
Prove: $\triangle ABE \sim \triangle CDE$

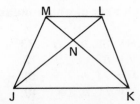

PART C

11. Given: $\overline{CM} \perp \overline{TX}$, $\overline{PQ} \perp \overline{TN}$,
$\overline{JL} \perp \overline{XN}$
Prove: $\triangle JCP \sim \triangle XTN$

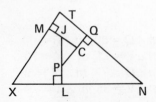

12. Given: $\overline{WZ} \cong \overline{XY}$, $\overline{WX} \cong \overline{ZY}$
Prove: $\triangle WTZ \sim \triangle VWX$

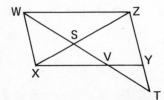

13. Given: $\overline{ML} \parallel \overline{JK}$
Prove: $\dfrac{MN}{NK} = \dfrac{LN}{NJ}$

SAS and SSS Similarity

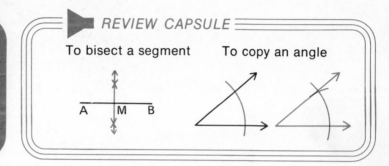

REVIEW CAPSULE

To bisect a segment   To copy an angle

EXAMPLE 1   Construct $\triangle A'B'C'$, with $\angle A' \cong \angle A$, $A'C' = \frac{3}{2} AC$,
and $A'B' = \frac{3}{2} AB$.

Construct $\angle A' \cong \angle A$.
Bisect $\overline{AC}$ and $\overline{AB}$.
Mark off these segments three times.

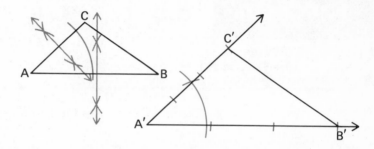

Example 1 suggests this. $\triangle A'B'C'$ seems to be similar to $\triangle ABC$.

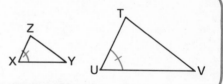

Theorem 8.4

(SAS for ~ △'s)
(See Exercise 24.)

If $\angle X \cong \angle U$ and
$\dfrac{XZ}{UT} = \dfrac{XY}{UV}$,
then $\triangle XYZ \sim \triangle UVT$.

EXAMPLE 2   Are the two given triangles similar?

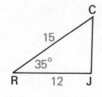

$$\frac{15}{10} = \frac{12}{8} \quad \therefore \quad \frac{RC}{BL} = \frac{RJ}{BQ}$$
$$\angle R \cong \angle B$$

SAS for ~ △'s ———————→ **Thus,** $\triangle CRJ \sim \triangle LBQ$.

EXAMPLE 3   Construct △*X'Y'Z'* with each side twice as long as the corresponding side of △*XYZ*.

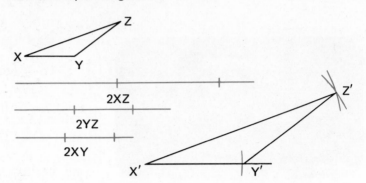

Construct segments with twice the given lengths.

Construct a triangle given three sides.

Example 3 suggests this. →

△*X'Y'Z'* seems to be similar to △*XYZ*.

Theorem   8.5

(SSS for ~ △'s)
(See Exercise 25.)

If $\dfrac{XY}{TU} = \dfrac{YZ}{UV} = \dfrac{ZX}{VT}$, then △*XYZ* ~ △*TUV*.

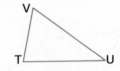

EXAMPLE 4   Are the two given triangles similar?

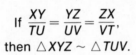

Pairs of corresponding sides are proportional. ⟶

SSS for ~ △'s ⟶

$$\dfrac{18}{12} = \dfrac{15}{10} = \dfrac{12}{8}$$

∴ $\dfrac{TM}{CX} = \dfrac{MQ}{XJ} = \dfrac{QT}{JC}$.

Thus, △*TMQ* ~ △*CXJ*

ORAL EXERCISES

Which pairs of triangles are similar? Why?

1.

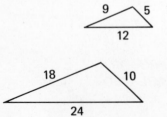

2.

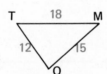

3.

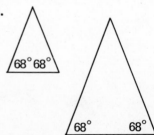

EXERCISES

PART A

Which pairs of triangles are similar? Why?

1.

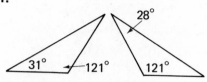

2.

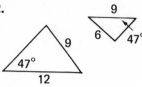

3.

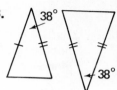

Which of the following are lengths of sides of similar triangles?

4. 3, 4, 5 and 6, 8, 10

7. $\frac{3}{4}$, 1, $\frac{5}{4}$ and $\frac{4}{5}$, 1, $\frac{6}{5}$

5. 9, 15, 18 and 6, 10, 12

8. 3.6, 12, 12.6 and 3, 10, 10.5

6. $\frac{4}{5}$, $\frac{6}{5}$, $\frac{8}{5}$ and $\frac{2}{7}$, $\frac{3}{7}$, $\frac{4}{7}$

9. 3.5, 4.6, 5.7 and 2.1, 3.3, 4.6

In which cases is $\triangle ABC \sim \triangle DEF$?

10. $\frac{AB}{DE} = \frac{BC}{EF} = \frac{CA}{FD}$

12. $\frac{AB}{DE} = \frac{BC}{EF}$, $\angle C \cong \angle F$

14. $\frac{BC}{EF} = \frac{AC}{DF}$, $\angle B \cong \angle D$

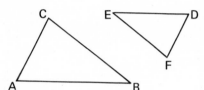

11. $\frac{AB}{BC} = \frac{DE}{EF}$, $\angle B \cong \angle E$

13. $\angle A \cong \angle D$, $\angle C \cong \angle E$

15. $\frac{AB}{BC} = \frac{BC}{DE} = \frac{DE}{EF}$

In which cases is $\triangle ABC \sim \triangle A'B'C$?

16. $\overline{AB} \parallel \overline{A'B'}$

18. $\frac{AC}{A'C} = \frac{BC}{B'C}$

20. $\frac{AA'}{A'C} = \frac{BB'}{B'C}$

17. $\angle A \cong \angle A'$

19. $\frac{AC}{A'C} = \frac{AB}{A'B}$

21. $\frac{AA'}{A'C} = \frac{A'B'}{AB}$

PART B

22. Prove: Two isosceles triangles are similar if their vertex angles are congruent.

23. Prove: Two isosceles triangles are similar if a base angle of one is congruent to a base angle of the other.

PART C

24. Prove Theorem 8.4.

       ANALYSIS

   Construct $\triangle D'E'C'$
so that $\overline{CD'} \cong \overline{FD}$ and $\overline{CE'} \cong \overline{FE}$.
Show $\triangle DEF \sim \triangle ABC$ by AA for $\sim \triangle$'s.

Given: $\triangle ABC$ and $\triangle DEF$

$\frac{DF}{AC} = \frac{EF}{BC}$

$\angle C \cong \angle F$

Prove: $\triangle ABC \sim \triangle DEF$

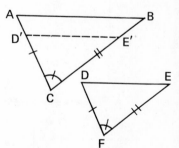

25. Prove Theorem 8.5.

Which Pocket?

Here is a scale drawing of a 3 ft by 4 ft pool table. A ball is shot from corner A along a 45° path.

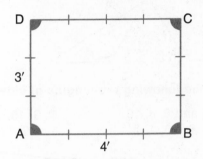

1. At what angle will it meet side $\overline{DC}$? (Use the angle-sum theorem for triangles.)

2. How far from D will the ball strike cushion $\overline{DC}$?

3. At what angle will the ball rebound?

4. If the path of the ball continues, which pocket will it eventually drop into?

Here are some different size pool tables. Assume that a ball is shot from corner A along a 45° path. Which pocket will it eventually drop into?

Suppose the ball is shot from corner B along a 45° path. Which pocket will it eventually drop into?

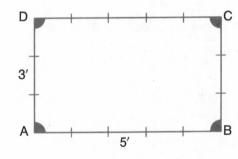

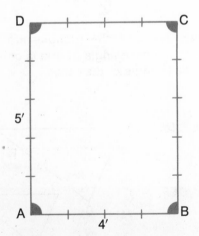

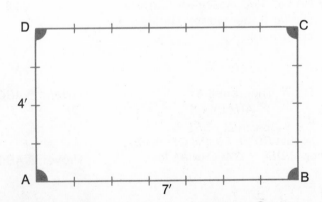

Similar Polygons

▶ REVIEW CAPSULE

Shadows on a surface parallel to an object have the same shape as the object.

$$\triangle XYZ \sim \triangle LMN \leftrightarrow \begin{cases} \angle X \cong \angle L,\ \angle Y \cong \angle M,\ \angle Z \cong \angle N \\ \dfrac{XY}{LM} = \dfrac{YZ}{MN} = \dfrac{ZX}{NL} \end{cases}$$

Congruent polygons ┊ Similar polygons

Similar polygons have the same shape. ⟶

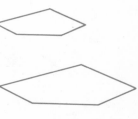

Same size and shape ┊ Same shape

EXAMPLE 1   Which of the polygons are similar?

III and V have the same shape.
IV and VI have the same shape.

III and V are similar. IV and VI are similar.

Definition of similar polygons ⟶

Two polygons are similar if corresponding angles are congruent and pairs of corresponding sides are proportional.

EXAMPLE 2   Trapezoid *ABCD* ~ trapezoid *EFGH.*
Which angles are congruent?

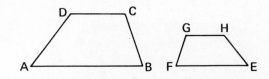

Corr. ∠'s are ≅. ──────────────⟶   ∠*A* ≅ ∠*E*, ∠*B* ≅ ∠*F*, ∠*C* ≅ ∠*G*, ∠*D* ≅ ∠*H*

EXAMPLE 3   Polygon *SJCNP* ~ polygon *BZHKR.*
Which pairs of sides are proportional?

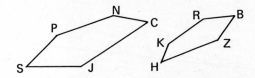

Corr. sides are proportional. ──────⟶ $\dfrac{SJ}{BZ} = \dfrac{JC}{ZH} = \dfrac{CN}{HK} = \dfrac{NP}{KR} = \dfrac{PS}{RB}$

EXAMPLE 4   Quad. *XMTV* ~ quad. *QRAJ.* Find *RA, AJ,* and *JQ.*

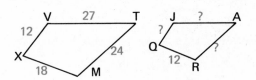

Corr. sides are proportional. ──────⟶ $\dfrac{XM}{QR} = \dfrac{MT}{RA} = \dfrac{TV}{AJ} = \dfrac{VX}{JQ}$

Write proportions using the given
lengths.

$\dfrac{3}{2} = \dfrac{24}{RA}$ $\dfrac{3}{2} = \dfrac{27}{AJ}$ $\dfrac{3}{2} = \dfrac{12}{JQ}$

Solve the proportions. ──────────⟶   *RA* = 16   *AJ* = 18   *JQ* = 8

EXAMPLE 5   Are two quadrilaterals similar if the four angles of one
are congruent to the four angles of the other?

Not necessarily.

Draw a counterexample. ──────────⟶

≁ means is not similar to. ────⟶   **Thus,** *ABCD* ≁ *EFGH* although the four angles of
rectangle *ABCD* are congruent to the four angles of
rectangle *EFGH.*

ORAL EXERCISES

Which of the following pairs of polygons appear to be similar?

1.

2.

3.

4.

5.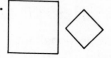

6.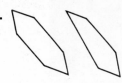

7.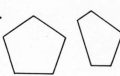

8.

EXERCISES

PART A

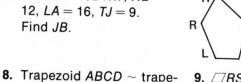

1. If $JQCVN \sim PRDTL$, which pairs of angles are congruent?

2. If $JQCVN \sim PRDTL$, which pairs of sides are proportional?

3. $XCVN \sim TQRG$, $m\angle X = 47$, $m\angle C = 39$, $m\angle V = 112$. Find $m\angle Q$ and $m\angle G$.

4. $GPLCV \sim RSWTA$. $m\angle G = 68$, $m\angle P = 110$, $m\angle L = 91$, $m\angle C = 94$. Find $m\angle W$, $m\angle R$, and $m\angle A$.

5. $\square XCNQ \sim \square TMPL$, $m\angle X = 70$. Find $m\angle M$ and $m\angle L$.

6. $LANHR \sim JBVXT$, $RL = 12$, $LA = 16$, $TJ = 9$. Find JB.

7. $LANHR \sim JBVXT$, $RL = 13$, $LA = 12$, $AN = 8$, $NH = 9$, $HR = 7$, $JB = 8$. Find VX and TJ.

8. Trapezoid $ABCD \sim$ trapezoid $LMNO$, $AB = 4$, $BC = 6$, $CD = 4$, $DA = 2$, $LM = 2$. Find NO and OL.

9. $\square RSTU \sim \square HJKL$, $RS = 12$, $UR = 8$, $JK = 6$. Find HJ and KL.

10. Rhombus $LCPT \sim$ rhombus $RAWZ$, $LC = 8$, $AW = 12$. Find CP and WZ.

PART B

11. Draw a parallelogram. Construct a second parallelogram similar to the first. How many sides and angles had to be constructed to guarantee similarity?

12. Draw a quadrilateral which is not a trapezoid. Construct a second similar to the first. How many sides and angles had to be constructed to guarantee similarity?

13. Prove: All squares are similar.

Proving Triangles Similar

<table>
<tr><td>

OBJECTIVE

■ To prove triangles similar using the basic similarity patterns

</td><td>

◣ **REVIEW CAPSULE**

Patterns for proving △'s similar:
AA (2 ∠'s ≅)
SAS (2 sides proportional and
      the included ∠'s ≅)
SSS (3 sides proportional)

</td></tr>
</table>

EXAMPLE 1

ANALYSIS
△'s can be proved
~ by AA for ~ △'s.

Given: $\overline{AC} \perp \overline{BC}$, $\overline{CD} \perp \overline{AB}$
Prove: △ADC ~ △CDB

Proof

Statements	Reasons
1. ∠1 ≅ ∠4	1. ⊥'s form ≅ rt. ∠'s.
2. ∠2 and ∠3 are complements.	2. ∠ACB is a rt. ∠.
3. ∠2 and ∠A are complements.	3. Acute ∠'s of a rt. △.
4. ∠A ≅ ∠3	4. Compl. of ≅ ∠'s are ≅.
5. ∴ △ADC ~ △CDB	5. AA for ~ △'s

EXAMPLE 2

ANALYSIS
△'s can be proved
~ by SAS for ~ △'s.

$LJ = \frac{2}{3}LC$
$WT = \frac{2}{3}WV$ }──────→

△LCP ~ △WVD ──────→

Given: △LCP ~ △WVD
$LJ = \frac{2}{3}LC$, $WT = \frac{2}{3}WV$
Prove: △LJP ~ △WTD

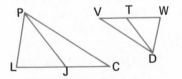

Proof

Statements	Reasons
1. ∠L ≅ ∠W	1. Corr. ∠'s of ~ △'s are ≅.
2. $\dfrac{LJ}{WT} = \dfrac{LC}{WV}$	2. Division property for equations
3. $\dfrac{LP}{WD} = \dfrac{LC}{WV}$	3. Corresponding sides of ~ △'s are proportional.
4. $\dfrac{LJ}{WT} = \dfrac{LP}{WD}$	4. Substitution
5. ∴ △LJP ~ △WTD	5. SAS for ~ △'s

EXAMPLE 3

Write the "given" and "prove." Draw a diagram.
Any two isosceles triangles with congruent vertex angles are similar.

Given: $\overline{AB} \cong \overline{AC}$, $\overline{DE} \cong \overline{D}$
      ∠A ≅ ∠D
Prove: △ABC ~ △DEF

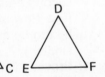

EXERCISES

PART A

1. Given: $\triangle TZS \sim \triangle XTR$
Prove: $\triangle TZS \sim \triangle XZY$

2. Given: $TSYR$ is a $\square$
Prove: $\triangle XRT \sim \triangle TSZ$

3. Given: $\overline{LT} \perp \overline{GJ}$, $\overline{JM} \perp \overline{LG}$
Prove: $\triangle LMQ \sim \triangle JTQ$

5. Given: $\overline{LT}$ and $\overline{JM}$ are altitudes of $\triangle LGJ$.
Prove: $\triangle LGT \sim \triangle JGM$

4. Given: $\overline{LT} \perp \overline{GJ}$, $\overline{JM} \perp \overline{LG}$
Prove: $\triangle JQT \sim \triangle JGM$

6. Given: $\overline{LT} \perp \overline{JG}$,
$\angle LJT \cong \angle LGT$
Prove: $\triangle LGT \sim \triangle LJT$

7. Given: $\square ABCD$
Prove: $\triangle BCE \sim \triangle FAB$

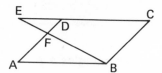

8. Given: $\overline{RT} \parallel \overline{QJ}$, $\overline{LT} \parallel \overline{NJ}$
Prove: $\triangle QNJ \sim \triangle RLT$

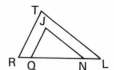

9. Given: $\overline{AT} \cong \overline{TN}$, $\overline{AJ} \cong \overline{JC}$
Prove: $\triangle AJT \sim \triangle ACN$

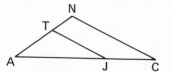

10. Given: $\triangle NTE \sim \triangle QRS$. $\overline{EM}$ bisects $\angle NET$, $\overline{SP}$ bisects $\angle QSR$.
Prove: $\triangle NEM \sim \triangle QSP$

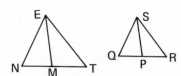

11. Given: $\triangle NTE \sim \triangle QRS$. M is the midpoint of $\overline{NT}$, P is the midpoint of $\overline{QR}$.
Prove: $\triangle MET \sim \triangle PSR$

PART B

12. Given: $\overline{CQ} \cong \overline{CV}$, $\overline{CT} \perp \overline{RV}$, $\overline{RJ} \perp \overline{CV}$
Prove: $\triangle QTC \sim \triangle VJR$

13. Given: $\triangle RCM \cong \triangle LTM$
Prove: $\triangle RLM \sim \triangle TCM$

14. Given: $\angle 1 \cong \angle Z$, $\dfrac{XZ}{VZ} = \dfrac{TZ}{XN}$
Prove: $\triangle NZV \sim \triangle TZX$

15. Draw a diagram. Write the "given" and "prove." Any two equilateral triangles are similar.

16. Prove the statement in Exercise 15.

PART C

For each of the following, draw pictures. Which triangles are similar? Congruent? State and prove appropriate theorems.

17. Connect the midpoints of the sides of a triangle.

18. A triangle whose sides are perpendicular to the sides of another triangle.

Proportional Segments

▶ **REVIEW CAPSULE**

Corresponding sides of similar triangles are proportional.

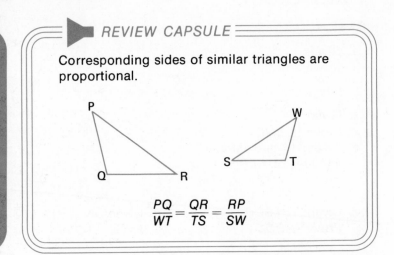

$$\frac{PQ}{WT} = \frac{QR}{TS} = \frac{RP}{SW}$$

Theorem 8.6

Corresponding medians of similar triangles are proportional to corresponding sides,

ANALYSIS
Show $\triangle CDB \sim \triangle GHF$.
Corresponding sides of $\sim \triangle$'s are proportional.

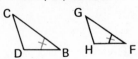

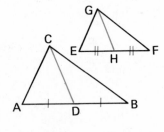

GIVEN
$\triangle ABC \sim \triangle EFG$, $\overline{CD}$ is a median to $\overline{AB}$, GH is a median to $\overline{EF}$.

PROVE
$$\frac{CD}{GH} = \frac{CB}{GF}$$

PROOF

STATEMENTS	REASONS
1. $\angle B \cong \angle F$	1. Corr. $\angle$'s of $\sim \triangle$'s are $\cong$.
2. $\dfrac{AB}{EF} = \dfrac{CB}{GF}$	2. Corr. sides of $\sim \triangle$'s are proportional.
3. $DB = \frac{1}{2}AB$ and $HF = \frac{1}{2}EF$	3. Def. of midpoint
4. $\dfrac{DB}{HF} = \dfrac{AB}{EF}$	4. Division property of equations
5. $\dfrac{DB}{HF} = \dfrac{CB}{GF}$	5. Substitution
6. $\triangle CDB \sim \triangle GHF$	6. SAS for $\sim \triangle$'s
7. $\therefore \dfrac{CD}{GH} = \dfrac{CB}{GF}$	7. Corr. sides of $\sim \triangle$'s are proportional.

EXAMPLE 1

$\triangle SLP \sim \triangle TJC.$ $\overline{SK}$ and $\overline{TR}$ are medians. Find TR.

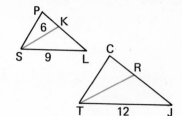

Apply Theorem 8.6.

$$\left.\frac{TR}{SK} = \frac{TJ}{SL}\right\}$$

$$\frac{TR}{6} = \frac{12}{9}$$
$$9(TR) = 72$$
$$TR = 8$$

EXAMPLE 2

$\triangle$'s must have $\overline{ZW}$, $\overline{ZX}$, $\overline{TU}$ and $\overline{TR}$ as sides.

Which pair of triangles must be proved similar to show that $\dfrac{ZW}{ZX} = \dfrac{TU}{TR}$?

Show that $\triangle ZXW \sim \triangle TRU$.

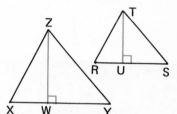

Theorem 8.7

Corresponding altitudes of similar triangles are proportional to corresponding sides.

Theorem 8.8

The bisector of an angle of a triangle divides the opposite side into segments proportional to the other sides of the triangle.

ANALYSIS
Draw $\overleftrightarrow{BF} \parallel \overline{DC}$. Extend $\overrightarrow{AC}$ to meet $\overleftrightarrow{BF}$ at E. $\overline{CD}$ is $\parallel$ to $\overline{BE}$ in $\triangle ABE$. Use Th. 8.1 to write a proportion. Then show $BC = CE$ and make a substitution in the proportion.

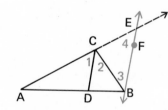

GIVEN
$\angle 1 \cong \angle 2$
PROVE
$\dfrac{AD}{DB} = \dfrac{AC}{BC}$

PROOF

STATEMENTS

1. Draw $\overleftrightarrow{BF} \parallel \overline{DC}$ through B.
2. Draw $\overrightarrow{AC}$ intersecting $\overleftrightarrow{BF}$ at E.
3. $\dfrac{AD}{DB} = \dfrac{AC}{CE}$
4. $\angle 2 \cong \angle 3$
5. $\angle 1 \cong \angle 4$
6. $\angle 1 \cong \angle 2$
7. $\angle 3 \cong \angle 4$
8. $BC = CE$
9. $\therefore \dfrac{AD}{DB} = \dfrac{AC}{BC}$

REASONS

1. There is only 1 line $\parallel$ to a given line through a pt.
2. A ray extends infinitely far.
3. A line $\parallel$ to one side of a $\triangle$ divides the other 2 sides proportionally.
4. Alt. int. $\angle$'s of $\parallel$ lines are $\cong$.
5. Corr. $\angle$'s of $\parallel$ lines are $\cong$.
6. Given
7. Substitution
8. Sides opp. $\cong$ $\angle$'s of a $\triangle$ are $\cong$.
9. Substitution

EXAMPLE 3 $\angle y \cong \angle z$, $RT = 9$,
$QT = 12$, $RQ = 14$.
Find RN and NQ.

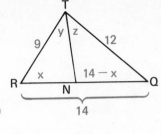

Apply Theorem 8.8.

$\left.\begin{array}{l} \dfrac{RN}{NQ} = \dfrac{RT}{TQ} \\[2mm] \text{Let } RN = x. \end{array}\right\}$ ⟶

$$\frac{x}{14 - x} = \frac{9}{12}$$
$$12x = 9(14 - x)$$
$$12x = 126 - 9x$$
$$21x = 126$$
$$x = 6$$

$RN + NQ = 14$ ⟶ **Thus,** $RN = 6$ and $NQ = 8$.

---

construction

To divide $\overline{AB}$ into two segments whose lengths have the ratio $\frac{2}{3}$.

STRATEGY
Apply Th. 8.8. Construct
$\triangle ABC$ so that $\dfrac{AC}{BC} = \dfrac{2}{3}$.

A ——————————— B

GIVEN
Segment $\overline{AB}$
CONSTRUCT
P on $\overline{AB}$ so that $\dfrac{AP}{PB} = \dfrac{2}{3}$

Draw a segment $\overline{XY}$. Construct segments with length $2(XY)$ and $3(XY)$.

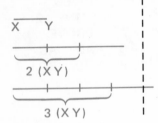

$2(XY)$

$3(XY)$

Construct $\triangle ABC$ so that $AC = 2(XY)$ and $BC = 3(XY)$.

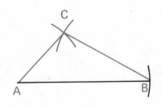

Bisect $\angle ACB$. Draw bisector intersecting $\overline{AB}$ at P.

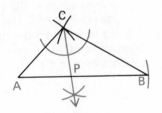

Conclusion: $\dfrac{AP}{PB} = \dfrac{AC}{CB} = \dfrac{2}{3}$

ORAL EXERCISES

In $\triangle RNQ$, $\overline{QJ}$ bisects $\angle NQR$.

1. If $\dfrac{RQ}{NQ} = \dfrac{3}{4}$, then $\dfrac{RJ}{JN} = ?$

3. If $\dfrac{RQ}{NQ} = \dfrac{4}{5}$, then $\dfrac{RJ}{JN} = ?$

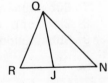

2. If $\dfrac{RJ}{JN} = \dfrac{3}{4}$, then $\dfrac{RQ}{NQ} = ?$

4. If $\dfrac{RJ}{JN} = \dfrac{1}{3}$, then $\dfrac{RQ}{NQ} = ?$

EXERCISES

PART A

1. $\overline{VC}$ bisects $\angle AVL$, $AV = 6$, $LV = 10$, $AL = 12$. Find AC and CL. ↘

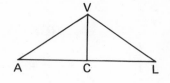

2. $\overline{VC}$ bisects $\angle AVL$, $AV = 5$, $LV = 10$, $AL = 12$. Find AC and CL.

3. $\overline{TW} \parallel \overline{XY}$, $\dfrac{ZT}{ZX} = \dfrac{3}{7}$, $ZW = 21$. Find ZY.

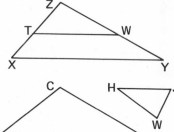

4. $\overline{TW} \parallel \overline{XY}$, $ZW = 10$, $ZY = 18$, $XY = 27$. Find TW.

5. $\triangle LQC \sim \triangle JHW$, $HW = 5$, $WJ = 3$, $LC = 2x + 1$, $CQ = 4x - 5$. Find LC and CQ.

6. $\triangle LQC \sim \triangle JHW$, $LQ = 15$, $CQ = 10$, $HJ = 2x + 2$, $HW = x + 3$. Find HJ and HW.

7. If $\triangle XTC \sim \triangle LPQ$, which sides are proportional?

PART B

8. Given: $\overline{EC} \perp \overline{AB}$, $\overline{BD} \perp \overline{AC}$

   Prove: $\dfrac{CA}{AB} = \dfrac{CE}{DB}$

9. Given: $\overline{AE}$ and $\overline{CD}$ are altitudes of $\triangle ABC$.

   Prove: $\dfrac{AD}{CE} = \dfrac{DF}{EF}$

10. Given: Rt. $\triangle ACB$, $\overline{CD} \perp \overline{AB}$

    Prove: $\dfrac{AD}{CD} = \dfrac{CD}{DB}$

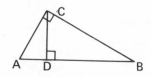

11. Given: $\overline{WX} \parallel \overline{YZ}$

    Prove: $\dfrac{XT}{YT} = \dfrac{WT}{ZT}$

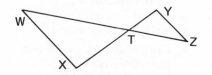

12. Given: $\overline{CQ} \parallel \overline{WD}$

    Prove: $\dfrac{WX}{XQ} = \dfrac{WD}{CQ}$

13. Given: $\overline{RA} \perp \overline{HN}$, $\overline{NM} \perp \overline{RH}$

    Prove: $\dfrac{AB}{MB} = \dfrac{NB}{RB}$

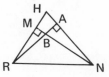

14. Draw $\overline{AB}$. Construct P so that $\dfrac{AP}{PB} = \dfrac{3}{4}$.

15. Draw $\overline{XY}$. Construct Q so that $\dfrac{XQ}{QY} = \dfrac{2}{5}$.

PART C

16. Prove: The diagonals of a trapezoid divide each other into proportional segments.

17. Prove: If two triangles are similar, then corresponding altitudes are proportional to corresponding medians.

Products of Lengths

REVIEW CAPSULE

$$\frac{6}{x} = \frac{3}{y} \qquad\qquad \frac{AB}{CD} = \frac{EF}{GH}$$
$$6y = 3x \qquad\qquad AB \cdot GH = CD \cdot EF$$

In a true proportion, the product of the extremes equals the product of the means.

EXAMPLE 1 △SQP ~ △HTM, SP = 11, HT = 7.
Find SQ · HM.

$$\frac{SQ}{HT} = \frac{SP}{HM}$$
SQ · HM = HT · SP

HT = 7 and SP = 11 ⟶ SQ · HM = 7 · 11, or 77

EXAMPLE 2 Write two proportions that give this product.
PQ · QR = FE · EG

Make one pair of factors the means; the other pair, the extremes.

$$\frac{PQ}{EG} = \frac{FE}{QR} \ \text{ or } \ \frac{FE}{PQ} = \frac{QR}{EG}$$

EXAMPLE 3

ANALYSIS

Show $\frac{AG}{CG} = \frac{FG}{EG}$
by proving △AGF ~ △CGE.

Given: ▱ABCD
Prove: AG · EG = FG · CG

Proof

Statements	Reasons
1. $\overline{AB} \parallel \overline{CD}$	1. Opp. sides of a ▱ are ∥.
2. ∠1 ≅ ∠2, ∠3 ≅ ∠4	2. Alt. int. ∠'s of ∥ lines are ≅.
3. △AGF ~ △CGE	3. AA for ~ △'s
4. $\frac{AG}{CG} = \frac{FG}{EG}$	4. Corr. sides of ~ △'s are proportional.
5. ∴ AG · EG = FG · CG	5. Prod. of extremes = prod. of means.

EXAMPLE 4 In Example 3, if AG = 7 and EG = 4, find FG · CG.

$$FG \cdot CG = AG \cdot EG$$
$$FG \cdot CG = 7 \cdot 4$$
$$FG \cdot CG = 28$$

EXAMPLE 5

ANALYSIS

Show $\dfrac{PB}{BY} = \dfrac{BY}{BC}$

by proving $\triangle PBY \sim \triangle YBC$.

Given: $\overline{PY} \perp \overline{CY}$, altitude $\overline{BY}$
Prove: $PB \cdot BC = (BY)^2$

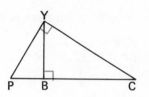

Proof

Statements	Reasons
1. $\angle 2 \cong \angle 3$	1. Def. of altitude
2. $\angle 1$ is a compl. of $\angle P$.	2. Acute $\angle$'s of rt. $\triangle$'s are compl.
3. $\angle C$ is a compl. of $\angle P$.	3. Same as 2
4. $\angle 1 \cong \angle C$	4. Compl. of same $\angle$ are $\cong$.
5. $\triangle PBY \sim \triangle YBC$	5. AA for $\sim \triangle$'s

BY is the geometric mean of PB and BC. $\longrightarrow$

6. $\dfrac{PB}{BY} = \dfrac{BY}{BC}$	6. Corr. sides of $\sim \triangle$'s are proportional.
7. $\therefore PB \cdot BC = (BY)^2$	7. Product. of extremes = prod. of means.

EXAMPLE 6 $\overline{PY} \perp CY$, altitude $\overline{BY}$
$PB = 4$, $BC = 9$.
Find BY.

See Example 5. $\longrightarrow$

$(BY)^2 = PB \cdot BC$
$(BY)^2 = 4 \cdot 9$, or 36
Thus, $BY = 6$.

ORAL EXERCISES

Give two proportions for each pair of products.

1. $XY \cdot ZW = AB \cdot CD$

2. $RJ \cdot TK = SP \cdot AD$

3. $(RP)^2 = AJ \cdot WF$

Find $AB \cdot CD$.

4. $\dfrac{AB}{4} = \dfrac{8}{CD}$

5. $\dfrac{3}{AB} = \dfrac{CD}{12}$

6. $\dfrac{AB}{6} = \dfrac{6}{CD}$

EXERCISES

PART A

1. $\triangle JQT \sim \triangle CPK$, $CP = 8$,
$QT = 12$.
Find $JQ \cdot PK$.

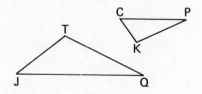

2. $\triangle JQT \sim \triangle CPK$, $JQ = 31$,
$PK = 18$.
Find $CP \cdot QT$.

3. Given: $\overline{GP} \perp \overline{PR}$, $\overline{WL} \perp \overline{RG}$
Prove: $WG \cdot RP = WL \cdot RG$

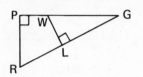

4. Given: $\overline{MG} \parallel \overline{KD}$
Prove: $GQ \cdot DQ = MQ \cdot KQ$

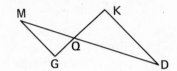

5. Given: $\overline{DS} \perp \overline{SF}$, $\overline{DP} \perp \overline{PF}$
Prove: $SJ \cdot FJ = PJ \cdot DJ$

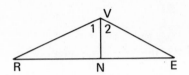

6. Given: $\overline{LR} \parallel \overline{ZE}$
Prove: $ZG \cdot LR = GR \cdot ZE$

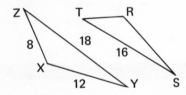

7. Given: $\overline{PT} \perp \overline{TX}$, $\overline{XO} \perp \overline{PO}$
Prove: $WT \cdot WX = WO \cdot WP$

8. Given: $\angle 1 \cong \angle 2$
Prove: $RN \cdot VE = NE \cdot RV$

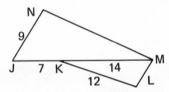

PART B

More data is given than is needed in each problem. Use only the necessary information.

9. $\triangle XYZ \sim \triangle RST$.
Find $RT \cdot YZ$.

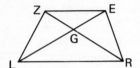

10. $\overline{FD} \perp \overline{CD}$, $\overline{EB} \perp \overline{FC}$.
Find $FB \cdot FC$.

11. $\triangle JNM \sim \triangle MLK$.
Find $ML \cdot NM$.

12. Given: $\overline{TX} \perp \overrightarrow{PQ}$, $\angle 1 \cong \angle 4$
Prove: $NT \cdot XC = NX \cdot TC$

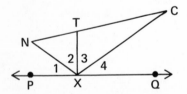

13. Given: $\square RQXZ$
Prove: $ZF \cdot FR = FP \cdot FX$

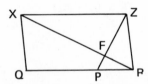

14. Given: $\angle 1 \cong \angle 2$, $\overline{JK} \parallel \overline{YZ}$
Prove: $XK \cdot JK = KZ \cdot XJ$

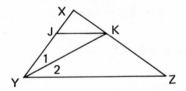

PART C

15. Given: $\square RQXZ$, $\angle 1 \cong \angle 2$
Prove: $FX \cdot RZ = RF \cdot ZX$

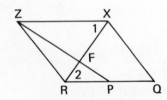

16. Given: $\overline{GC} \parallel \overline{TS}$, $\angle 1 \cong \angle 2$
Prove: $WT \cdot SC = TG \cdot WN$

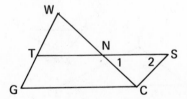

17. Given: $\angle 1 \cong \angle 4$, $\angle 5 \cong \angle J$
Prove: $BQ \cdot TQ = BT \cdot QJ$

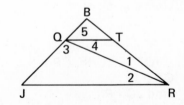

Similarity in Space

▶ REVIEW CAPSULE

Two planes are parallel it they do not intersect.

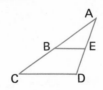

If $\overline{BE} \parallel \overline{CD}$, then
$\dfrac{AB}{BC} = \dfrac{AE}{ED}$ and $\dfrac{AB}{AC} = \dfrac{AE}{AD}$.

EXAMPLE 1

Use Theorem 8.1.

$\ell \parallel m \parallel n.$
Find x.

$\dfrac{5}{9} = \dfrac{a}{b}$ and $\dfrac{a}{b} = \dfrac{x}{12}$

$\dfrac{5}{9} = \dfrac{x}{12}$ and $9x = 60$

Thus, $x = 6\frac{2}{3}$.

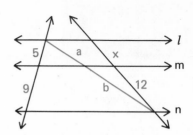

EXAMPLE 2

ANALYSIS

A line $\parallel$ to a side of a $\triangle$ divides the other 2 sides proportionally.

Prove: If two lines are intersected by three parallel planes, then their corresponding segments are proportional.

Given: Lines t and q, intersected by planes ℓ, m, and n at A, C, F and B, E, G. $\ell \parallel m \parallel n$.

Prove: $\dfrac{AC}{CF} = \dfrac{BE}{EG}$

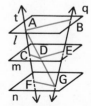

Proof

Statements	Reasons
1. Draw $\overline{AG}$ intersecting m at D.	1. Two points are contained in exactly one line.
2. Draw $\overline{AB}, \overline{FG}, \overline{CD}, \overline{DE}$.	2. Same as 1

$\overline{AB}$ and $\overline{DE}$ are coplanar and do not intersect. ⟶

Use $\triangle AGB$. ⟶

3. $\overline{AB} \parallel \overline{DE}$	3. Def. of $\parallel$ lines
4. $\dfrac{AD}{DG} = \dfrac{BE}{EG}$	4. A line $\parallel$ to a side of a $\triangle$ divides other 2 sides proportionally
5. $\overline{CD} \parallel \overline{FG}$	5. Same as 3

Use $\triangle AGF$. ⟶

6. $\dfrac{AC}{CF} = \dfrac{AD}{DG}$	6. Same as 4
7. $\therefore \dfrac{AC}{CF} = \dfrac{BE}{EG}$	7. Substitution

EXAMPLE 3 $r \parallel p \parallel q$, $AB = 9$, $BC = 12$, $DE = 8$.
Find EF.

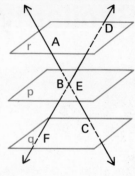

Apply Example 2. ──────────────→

$$\frac{AB}{BC} = \frac{DE}{EF}$$

$$\frac{9}{12} = \frac{8}{EF}$$

$$9(EF) = 96$$

Thus, $EF = 10\frac{2}{3}$.

A tetrahedron is a solid figure.

$ABCD$ is a *tetrahedron*.
$\triangle ABC$ is its *base*.
$\triangle ABD$, $\triangle BCD$, and $\triangle CAD$
are its *faces*.

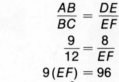

Theorem   8.9

If a tetraheadron is cut by a plane parallel to its base,
then the triangle formed by the intersection is
similar to the base.

ANALYSIS

Sides of similar $\triangle$'s are
proportional. Each face
contains $\sim$ $\triangle$'s.

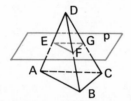

GIVEN
Tetrahedron $ABCD$ inter-
sected by plane p in $\triangle EFG$.
$p \parallel \triangle ABC$.
PROVE
$\triangle EFG \sim \triangle ABC$

OUTLINE OF PROOF

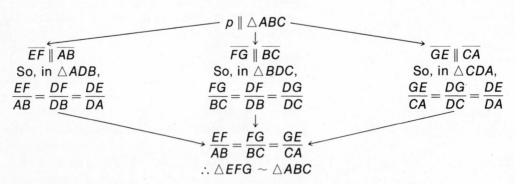

$$p \parallel \triangle ABC$$

$\overline{EF} \parallel \overline{AB}$	$\overline{FG} \parallel \overline{BC}$	$\overline{GE} \parallel \overline{CA}$
So, in $\triangle ADB$,	So, in $\triangle BDC$,	So, in $\triangle CDA$,
$\dfrac{EF}{AB} = \dfrac{DF}{DB} = \dfrac{DE}{DA}$	$\dfrac{FG}{BC} = \dfrac{DF}{DB} = \dfrac{DG}{DC}$	$\dfrac{GE}{CA} = \dfrac{DG}{DC} = \dfrac{DE}{DA}$

$$\frac{EF}{AB} = \frac{FG}{BC} = \frac{GE}{CA}$$
$$\therefore \triangle EFG \sim \triangle ABC$$

EXAMPLE 4 $p \parallel \triangle ABC$.
Find XY.

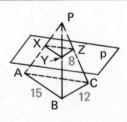

$\triangle XYZ \sim \triangle ABC$ ──────────────→

$$\frac{XY}{15} = \frac{8}{12}$$

$$12(XY) = 120$$

$$XY = 10$$

A shadow and the original object are similar if they are parallel. This can be proved using Theorem 8.9.

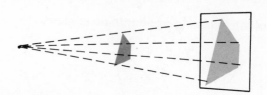

EXERCISES

PART A

1. $p \parallel q \parallel r$, $AB = 7$, $BC = 9$, $DE = 8$.
Find EF.

3. $p \parallel q \parallel r$, $AB = 6$, $BC = 9$, $DE = 2x + 1$, $EF = 4x - 1$.
Find DE and EF.

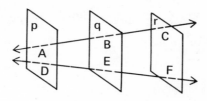

2. $p \parallel q \parallel r$, $AB = 8$, $AC = 18$, $DE = 10$.
Find EF.

4. $p \parallel q \parallel r$, $AB = 6$, $AC = 14$, $DE = 3x + 1$, $EF = 5x - 2$.
Find DE and EF.

5. $q \parallel \triangle PCV$, distance from L to $\triangle PCV = 8$, $\dfrac{VP}{NR} = \dfrac{2}{3}$.
Find distance from L to q.

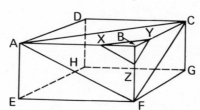

6. $q \parallel \triangle PCV$, distance from q to $\triangle VCP = 2x + 6$, distance from L to $\triangle VCP = 4x - 2$, $\dfrac{VC}{NT} = \dfrac{3}{5}$
Find distance from L to q.

PART B

7. Given: $\triangle XBZ \sim \triangle ABF$, $\triangle YBZ \sim \triangle CBF$
Prove: $\triangle XBY \sim \triangle ABC$

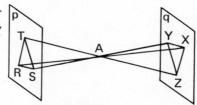

8. Given: $\triangle XBZ \sim \triangle YBZ$, $\triangle ABF \sim \triangle CBF$
Prove: $\triangle XBY \sim \triangle ABC$

9. Given: $p \parallel q$, $\dfrac{AR}{AX} = \dfrac{AS}{AY} = \dfrac{AT}{AZ}$
Prove: $\triangle ATS \sim \triangle AZY$

10. Given: $p \parallel q$, $\dfrac{AR}{AX} = \dfrac{AS}{AY} = \dfrac{AT}{AZ}$
Prove: $\triangle RST \cong \triangle XYZ$

11. Given: $\overline{RN} \parallel \overline{QT}$, $\overline{AN} \parallel \overline{CT}$
Prove: $\dfrac{RQ}{QW} = \dfrac{AC}{CW}$

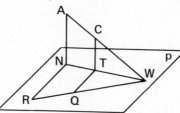

12. Give a complete proof of Theorem 8.9.

Chapter Eight Review

Which of the following appear to be similar? [p. 253]

1.

2.

3.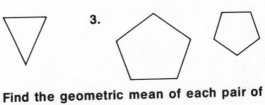

Find the value of x which makes each a true proportion. [p. 249]

4. $\dfrac{8}{12} = \dfrac{x}{15}$

5. $\dfrac{x}{9} = \dfrac{5}{4}$

Find the geometric mean of each pair of numbers. [p. 249]

6. 9 and 16

7. 2 and 5

In which of the following are the triangles similar? Why? [p. 260, 263]

8.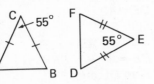

9.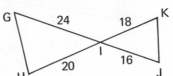

10.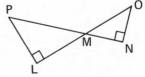

Is the statement always true, sometimes true, or never true? [p. 246]

11. Shadows parallel to the object are similar to the object.

12. Shadows produced in sunlight are congruent to the object.

13. $\overline{NQ} \parallel \overline{PV}$, $RN = 8$, $NP = 12$, $RV = 15$.
Find QV. [p. 257]

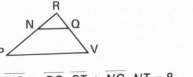

14. $\overline{JW}$ bisects $\angle LJP$, $LW = 4$, $WP = 6$, $LJ = 12$.
Find JP. [p. 272]

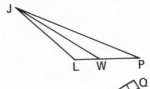

15. $\overline{RJ} \parallel \overline{CK}$, $RS = 8$, $SC = 10$.
Find $JS \cdot SK$. [p. 276]

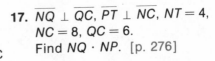

16. $\overline{NQ} \perp \overline{QC}$, $\overline{PT} \perp \overline{NC}$, $NT = 8$, $NQ = 12$, $NP = 3x - 1$, $NC = 4x + 2$.
Find NP and NC. [p. 276]

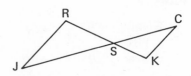

17. $\overline{NQ} \perp \overline{QC}$, $\overline{PT} \perp \overline{NC}$, $NT = 4$, $NC = 8$, $QC = 6$.
Find $NQ \cdot NP$. [p. 276]

18. Given: $\overline{LC} \perp \overline{JQ}$, $\overline{JR} \perp \overline{LQ}$
Prove: $\triangle LPR \sim \triangle LQC$
[p. 260]

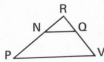

19. Given: $\overline{BN} \parallel \overline{JT}$, $\overline{BJ} \cong \overline{NT}$
Prove: $\dfrac{BJ}{NT} = \dfrac{BT}{NJ}$ [p. 272]

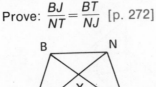

20. Given: Rhombus $ADMR$
Prove: $RP \cdot MT = RM \cdot PT$
[p. 272, 276]

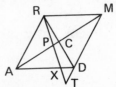

Chapter Eight Test

Which of the following appear to be similar?

1.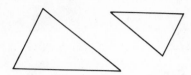

2.

3.

4. Find the value of *x* which makes this a true proportion.

$$\frac{12}{x} = \frac{16}{20}$$

5. Find the geometric mean of 9 and 36.

In which of the following are the triangles similar? Why?

6.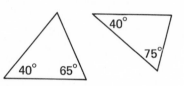

7.

8.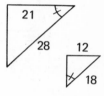

9. $\triangle JTL \sim \triangle CPQ$, $JL = 6$, $CQ = 4$, $CP = 10$. Find *JT*.

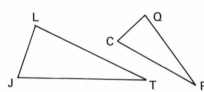

10. $\triangle JTL \sim \triangle CPQ$, $JT = 15$, $JL = 12$, $CP = 2x - 4$, $CQ = x + 1$. Find *CP*.

11. Given: $\overline{ED} \parallel \overline{AB}$
Prove: $\triangle ABG \sim \triangle DEG$

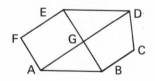

12. Given: *A, C, F*, and *H* are the midpoints of $\overline{IB}$, $\overline{BE}$, $\overline{EG}$, and $\overline{GI}$.

Prove: $\dfrac{GH}{GJ} = \dfrac{GF}{GD}$

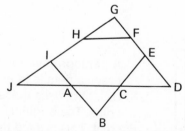

13. Given: *ABDE* is a square.
Prove: $AE \cdot CF = CE \cdot AF$

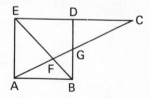

Is the statement always true, sometimes true, or never true?

14. Shadows produced in sunlight are similar to the object.

15. Shadows parallel to the object are congruent to the object.

USING SIMILAR TRIANGLES

The Pantograph

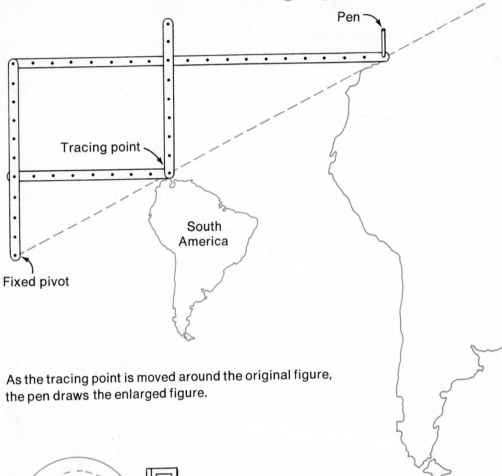

Pen

Tracing point

Fixed pivot

South America

As the tracing point is moved around the original figure, the pen draws the enlarged figure.

A pantographic die cutter, reproduces precise details in exact proportions. The U.S. Mint uses these machines to make coins. The original model is copied in soft steel. This is used to make a negative impression on a cylinder, or die. After hardening, this die is used to make the coins.

Similarity in Right Triangles

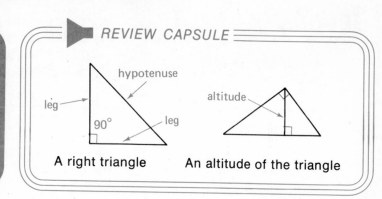

REVIEW CAPSULE

hypotenuse

leg

90°

leg

A right triangle

altitude

An altitude of the triangle

EXAMPLE 1 If $\overline{CD}$ is an altitude of rt. $\triangle ABC$, which triangles formed are similar?

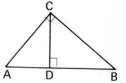

AA for ~ $\triangle$'s ——————————→
AA for ~ $\triangle$'s ——————————→
Both are ~ to $\triangle ABC$. ——————————→
Example 1 suggests Th. 9.1. ⌐

$\triangle ABC \sim \triangle ACD$
$\triangle ABC \sim \triangle CBD$
$\triangle ACD \sim \triangle CBD$
Thus, $\triangle ABC \sim \triangle ACD \sim \triangle CBD$.

Theorem 9.1

(See Exercise 19.)

In a right triangle, the altitude to the hypotenuse forms two triangles, each similar to the original triangle, and each similar to the other.

EXAMPLE 2 $\overline{HT} \perp \overline{NX}$, $\overline{NH} \perp \overline{HX}$, $NT = 8$, $HT = 6$. Find TX.

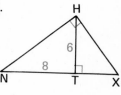

$\dfrac{NT}{HT} = \dfrac{HT}{TX}$ ——————————→

$\triangle NTH \sim \triangle HTX$
$\dfrac{8}{6} = \dfrac{6}{TX}$
$8(TX) = 36$
$TX = \dfrac{36}{8}$, or $4\frac{1}{2}$

EXAMPLE 3 $\overline{RH} \perp \overline{JQ}$, $\overline{JR} \perp \overline{RQ}$, $JH = 6$, $QH = 9$. Find RH.

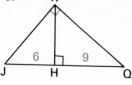

$\dfrac{JH}{RH} = \dfrac{RH}{QH}$ ——————————→

$\triangle RJH \sim \triangle QRH$
$\dfrac{6}{RH} = \dfrac{RH}{9}$
$(RH)^2 = 54$
$RH = \sqrt{54}$, or $3\sqrt{6}$

RH is the geometric mean of JH and QH.

Example 3 suggests a corollary of Theorem 9.1.

Corollary 1

(See Exercise 20.)

In a right triangle, the length of the altitude to the hypotenuse is the geometric mean of the lengths of the segments of the hypotenuse.

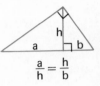

$$\frac{a}{h} = \frac{h}{b}$$

EXAMPLE 4

Rt. $\triangle RJT$, altitude $\overline{JC}$, $RC = 12$, $CT = 6$. Find JC.

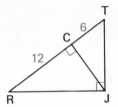

Apply Corollary 1.

$$\frac{RC}{JC} = \frac{JC}{CT}$$

$$\frac{12}{JC} = \frac{JC}{6}$$

$$(JC)^2 = 72$$

$\sqrt{72} = \sqrt{36 \cdot 2} = 6\sqrt{2}$ ⟶ $JC = \sqrt{72}$, or $6\sqrt{2}$

EXAMPLE 5

Draw rt. $\triangle ABC$, with hypotenuse $\overline{AB}$ and altitude $\overline{CD}$. If $AB = 16$ and $DB = 4$, find CD.

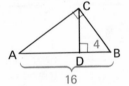

Apply Corollary 1.

$AD = AB - DB$ ⟶

CD is the geometric mean of AD and DB. ⟶

$$\frac{4}{CD} = \frac{CD}{12}$$

$$(CD)^2 = 48$$

$$CD = \sqrt{48}, \text{ or } 4\sqrt{3}$$

EXAMPLE 6

Rt. $\triangle CAB$, altitude $\overline{CD}$, $CA = 5$, $BA = 7$. Find DA.

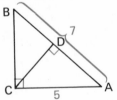

$$\triangle CAB \sim \triangle DAC$$

$$\frac{7}{5} = \frac{5}{DA}$$

$\dfrac{BA}{CA} = \dfrac{CA}{DA}$ ⟶

$$7(DA) = 25$$

$$DA = \tfrac{25}{7}, \text{ or } 3\tfrac{4}{7}$$

Example 6 suggests Corollary 2. ⟶

Corollary 2

(See Exercise 20.)

In a right triangle, the length of either leg is the geometric mean of the lengths of the hypotenuse and the segment of the hypotenuse bounded by the altitude and that leg.

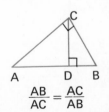

$$\frac{AB}{AC} = \frac{AC}{AB}$$

EXERCISES

PART A

1. $\angle RDC$ is a right angle. $\overline{DJ}$ is an altitude. Which triangles formed are similar?

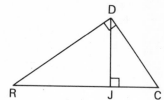

2. $\angle RDC$ is a right angle. $\overline{DJ}$ is an altitude. List three different true proportions of lengths of segments.

$\angle REW$ is a right angle. $\overline{EJ}$ is an altitude. Find the missing lengths.

3. $RJ = 8$, $JE = 4$, $JW = ?$
5. $RJ = 27$, $JE = ?$, $JW = 3$
7. $RJ = ?$, $JE = 2$, $JW = 1$
9. $RJ = 12$, $JE = 6$, $JW = ?$

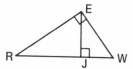

4. $RW = 32$, $RE = 24$, $RJ = ?$
6. $RW = ?$, $JW = 4$, $EW = 6$
8. $RW = 16$, $RJ = 8$, $RE = ?$
10. $RW = 25$, $JW = 5$, $EW = ?$

$\angle CKV$ is a right angle. $\overline{KM}$ is an altitude. Find the missing lengths.

11. $CV = 20$, $MV = 4$, $KM = ?$
13. $CV = ?$, $CM = 4$, $CK = 6$
15. $CV = 16$, $MV = 8$, $KV = ?$
17. $CV = 25$, $CM = 5$, $KM = ?$

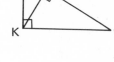

12. $CV = 18$, $KV = 12$, $MV = ?$
14. $CV = 8$, $CK = ?$, $CM = 2$
16. $CV = ?$, $CK = 24$, $CM = 18$
18. $CV = 20$, $KV = ?$, $MV = 15$

PART B

19. Prove Theorem 9.1.

20. Prove Corollaries 1 and 2.

21. Given: $\overline{SL} \perp \overline{LC}$, $\overline{LV} \perp \overline{SC}$
$\overline{VT} \perp \overline{LC}$
Prove: $\triangle SVL \sim \triangle LTV$

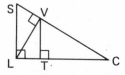

22. Given: $\overline{SL} \perp \overline{LC}$, $\overline{LV} \perp \overline{SC}$,
$\overline{VT} \perp \overline{LC}$
Prove: $SV \cdot CT = VT \cdot LV$

$\angle XZY$ is a right angle, $\overline{ZH} \perp \overline{XY}$, $\overline{HM} \perp \overline{XZ}$. Can the length of each unknown segment be found by methods in this lesson? If so, find the length.

23. $HY = 4$, $XH = 16$,
Find ZH and XZ.
25. $XH = 9$, $ZH = 6$
Find HY and ZY.

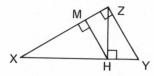

24. $XM = 16$, $MZ = 4$
Find MH and ZH.
26. $XZ = 9$, $XY = 12$
Find XH and MH.

27. Prove or disprove: In a right triangle, the product of the lengths of the hypotenuse and the altitude to the hypotenuse is equal to the product of of the lengths of the legs.

28. Prove or disprove: In a right triangle, the ratios of the length of each leg to the length of the segment of the hypotenuse determined by the altitude and adjacent to that same leg are equal.

The Pythagorean Theorem

OBJECTIVE

■ To apply the Pythagorean theorem to finding lengths of segments of right triangles and quadrilaterals

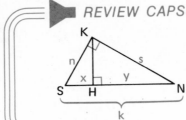

▶ REVIEW CAPSULE

If $\triangle SNK$ is a right triangle, and $\overline{KH}$ is an altitude, then
$$\frac{k}{n} = \frac{n}{x} \text{ and } \frac{k}{s} = \frac{s}{y}.$$

Lengths of Sides of Triangles

Acute and obtuse triangles

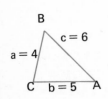

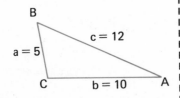

$a = 4, b = 5, c = 6$
$a^2 = 16, b^2 = 25, c^2 = 36, 16 + 25 \neq 36$

$a = 5, b = 10, c = 12$
$a^2 = 25, b^2 = 100, c^2 = 144, 25 + 100 \neq 144$

No obvious pattern

Right triangles

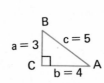

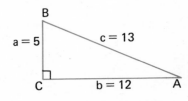

$a = 3, b = 4, c = 5$
$a^2 = 9, b^2 = 16, c^2 = 25, 9 + 16 = 25$

$a = 5, b = 12, c = 13$
$a^2 = 25, b^2 = 144, c^2 = 169, 25 + 144 = 169$
$a^2 + b^2 = c^2$

Theorem 9.2

PYTHAGOREAN THEOREM

If a triangle is a right triangle, then the square of the length of the hypotenuse is equal to the sum of the squares of the lengths of the two legs.

ANALYSIS

Use Theorem 9.1 and its corollaries to write proportions. Then use algebra.

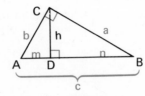

GIVEN
Rt. $\triangle ABC$, rt. $\angle ACB$, lengths of segments as marked

PROVE
$a^2 + b^2 = c^2$

OUTLINE OF PROOF

1. $\dfrac{c}{a} = \dfrac{a}{n}$ and $\dfrac{c}{b} = \dfrac{b}{m}$
2. $a^2 = cn$ and $b^2 = cm$
3. $a^2 + b^2 = cn + cm$
4. $a^2 + b^2 = c(n + m)$
5. But, $m + n = c$
6. $\therefore a^2 + b^2 = c \cdot c$, or $a^2 + b^2 = c^2$

EXAMPLE 1

Rt. $\angle C$, $AC = 40$, $BC = 9$
Find AB.

$c^2 = a^2 + b^2$ ⟶

$c^2 = 9^2 + 40^2$
$c^2 = 81 + 1,600$
$c^2 = 1,681$
$c = \sqrt{1,681}$, or 41

The hypotenuse is longer than either leg. ⟶

Thus, $AB = 41$.

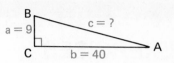

EXAMPLE 2

Can 4, 5, and 6 be the lengths of the sides of a right triangle?

$a^2 + b^2$	c^2
$4^2 + 5^2$	6^2
16 + 25	36
41	36

$a^2 + b^2 \neq c^2$ ⟶

Thus, 4, 5, and 6 are not the lengths of the sides of a right triangle.

EXAMPLE 3

The diagonals of a rhombus are 10 cm and 18 cm long. Find the measure of a side.

Draw a figure.
The diagonals are ⊥ bisectors of each other.

$s^2 = 5^2 + 9^2$
$s^2 = 25 + 81$
$s^2 = 106$
$s = \sqrt{106}$

The answer may be left in radical form. ⟶ **Thus,** a side measures $\sqrt{106}$ cm.

EXAMPLE 4

Find the length of a rectangle with a width of 8 inches and a diagonal 17 inches long.

Draw a figure.

Right triangles are formed.

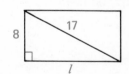

$\ell^2 + 8^2 = 17^2$
$\ell^2 = 289 - 64$
$\ell^2 = 225$
$\ell = 15$

Thus, the length is 15 inches.

EXAMPLE 5

Find the length of the altitude to the hypotenuse of a right triangle if the lengths of the legs are 9 and 12.

Draw a figure.

Find c.
Use $\sim \triangle$'s to find h.

$c^2 = 9^2 + 12^2$ $\triangle ACD \sim \triangle ABC$
$c^2 = 81 + 144$ $\dfrac{AC}{AB} = \dfrac{CD}{BC}$
$c^2 = 225$
$c = 15$ ⟶ $\dfrac{9}{15} = \dfrac{h}{12}$

Thus, $h = 7\frac{1}{5}$

$15h = 108$

EXERCISES

Which of the following sets of numbers cannot be the lengths of sides of right triangles?

1. 6, 8, 10   **2.** 1, 2, 3   **3.** 15, 36, 39   **4.** 8, 15, 17

5. 3, 6, 8   **6.** 10, 24, 26   **7.** 2, 2.1, 2.9   **8.** 0.5, 1.2, 1.3

9. 0.9, 4, 4.1   **10.** $\frac{8}{3}$, 5, $\frac{17}{3}$ **11.** $\frac{2}{5}$, $\frac{3}{5}$, 1   **12.** $\frac{20}{7}$, 3, $\frac{29}{7}$

13. $\sqrt{3}$, $\sqrt{4}$, $\sqrt{5}$ **14.** $\sqrt{2}$, $\sqrt{3}$, $\sqrt{5}$ **15.** $\sqrt{2}$, $\sqrt{2}$, 2   **16.** $\sqrt{3}$, $\sqrt{3}$, 3

For each right triangle, find the missing length.

17.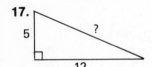

18.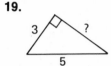

19.   **20.**

In each of the following sets of numbers, the first two are the lengths of legs of a right triangle and the third is the length of a hypotenuse. Find the missing numbers.

21. 3, 4, _____   **22.** 5, _____, 13   **23.** _____, 40, 41   **24.** 4, 5, _____

25. 2, _____, 3   **26.** 4, 4, _____   **27.** $\sqrt{3}$, _____, $\sqrt{5}$ **28.** $\sqrt{7}$, _____, 7

29. Find the length of each side of a rhombus with diagonals 12 and 16 inches long.

30. A diagonal of a rhombus is 20 inches long. A side is 26 inches long. Find the length of the other diagonal.

31. Find the length of a rectangle if the width is 15 cm and a diagonal is 36 cm long.

32. Find the length of a diagonal of a square if a side is 5 cm long.

PART B

33. If the length of one leg of an isosceles right triangle is *s*, what is the length of the hypotenuse?

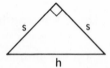

34. If the length of the hypotenuse of an isosceles right triangle is *h*, what is the length of a leg?

35. Find the length of the altitude to the hypotenuse of a right triangle if the lengths of the legs are 10 and 24.

36. Find the length of the altitude to the hypotenuse of a right triangle if the lengths of the legs are 8 and 15.

37. Find the length of the hypotenuse of a right triangle if the length of the altitude to the hypotenuse is 5 and the length of a leg is 13.

38. Find the length of a leg of a right triangle if the length of the other leg is 5 and the length of the altitude to the hypotenuse is 4.

39. Given: $\overline{JH} \perp \overline{XB}$
Prove: $(XJ)^2 + (HB)^2 =$
$(XH)^2 + (JB)^2$

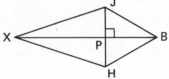

40. Given: $\overline{TC} \perp \overline{CN}, \overline{TC} \perp \overline{TQ}$
Prove: $(TN)^2 - (CN)^2 =$
$(CQ)^2 - (TQ)^2$

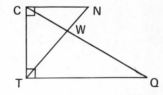

41. Given: $\overline{TZ} \perp \overline{ZS}$
Prove: $(MB)^2 + (TS)^2 =$
$(MS)^2 + (TB)^2$

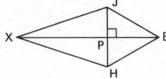

EXAMPLE

The solid is called a rectangular solid.

Each face of the solid is a rectangle. The lengths of the edges are *a*, *b*, and *c*. Find the length *d* of the diagonal $\overline{DF}$.

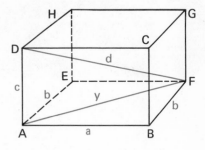

In rt. $\triangle AFD$ ⟶
In rt. $\triangle ABF$ ⟶

$d^2 = c^2 + y^2$
$y^2 = a^2 + b^2$
$d^2 = a^2 + b^2 + c^2$
Thus, $d = \sqrt{a^2 + b^2 + c^2}$.

42. If the edges of a rectangular solid are 3 cm, 4 cm, and 12 cm long, find the length of the diagonal of the solid.

43. A cube is a rectangular solid with congruent edges. Find the length of a diagonal of a cube if the length of an edge is 5.

44. Find a formula for the length of a diagonal of a cube if the length of each edge is *s*.

EXAMPLE Find the length of altitude $\overline{QB}$.

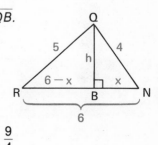

In rt. $\triangle NBQ$ ⟶
In rt. $\triangle RBQ$ ⟶

$x^2 + h^2 = 16$

In rt. $\triangle NBQ$ ⟶

$x^2 + h^2 = 16$
$(6 - x)^2 + h^2 = 25$
$36 - 12x + x^2 + h^2 = 25$
$36 - 12x + 16 = 25$
$-12x = -27$
$x = \dfrac{27}{12}, \text{ or } \dfrac{9}{4}$
$h^2 + x^2 = 4^2$
$h^2 = 16 - \left(\dfrac{9}{4}\right)^2$

$h^2 = 16 - \left(\dfrac{9}{4}\right)^2 = \dfrac{256}{16} - \dfrac{81}{16}$ ⟶ **Thus,** $QB = \sqrt{\dfrac{175}{16}}, \text{ or } \dfrac{5\sqrt{7}}{4}$.

45. $AB = 5, BC = 4, CA = 3$.
Find CD.

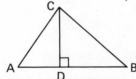

46. $AB = 9, BC = 6, AC = 4$.
Find CD.

Converse of the Pythagorean Theorem

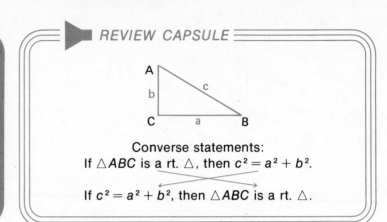

REVIEW CAPSULE

Converse statements:
If $\triangle ABC$ is a rt. $\triangle$, then $c^2 = a^2 + b^2$.

If $c^2 = a^2 + b^2$, then $\triangle ABC$ is a rt. $\triangle$.

EXAMPLE 1

In $\triangle ABC$, $AB = 5$, $BC = 3$, $AC = 4$.
Show that $\triangle ABC$ is a right triangle.

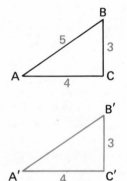

There is a right $\triangle A'B'C'$
with $A'C' = 4$ and $B'C' = 3$.

In $\triangle A'B'C'$ ⟶

$$(A'B')^2 = 3^2 + 4^2$$
$$(A'B')^2 = 9 + 16$$
$$(A'B')^2 = 25$$
$$A'B' = 5$$

SSS for $\cong$ $\triangle$'s ⟶ $\triangle ABC \cong \triangle A'B'C'$

$m \angle C = m \angle C' = 90$ ⟶ **Thus,** $\triangle ABC$ is a right triangle.

Example 1 suggests that the converse of the Pythagorean theorem is true.

Theorem 9.3

If the sum of the squares of the lengths of two sides of a triangle is equal to the square of the length of the third side, then the triangle is a right triangle.

ANALYSIS
Construct $\triangle A'B'C'$ with rt.
$\angle C'$, $A'C' = b$, $B'C' = a$. Show
$\triangle ABC \cong \triangle A'B'C'$.

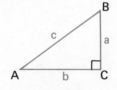

GIVEN
$\triangle ABC$ with lengths as marked,
$a^2 + b^2 = c^2$.
PROVE
$\triangle ABC$ is a rt. $\triangle$.

PROOF

(See Exercise 26.)

EXAMPLE 2 Is a triangle whose sides are 20 cm, 21 cm, and 29 cm long a right triangle?

Use the longest length for *c*.
Apply Theorem 9.3. ⟶

$a^2 + b^2$	c^2
$(20)^2 + (21)^2$	$(29)^2$
$400 + 441$	841
841	

Thus, the triangle is a right triangle.

EXAMPLE 3 In Example 2, which is the right angle?

The right angle is opposite the hypotenuse.

The longest side is the hypotenuse. ⟶ **Thus,** the angle opposite the 29 cm side is the right angle.

EXAMPLE 4 Show that quadrilateral *ABCD* is a rhombus.

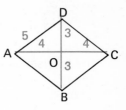

$$3^2 + 4^2 = 5^2$$
$\triangle AOD$ is a right triangle.
Therefore, $\overline{DB}$ and $\overline{AC}$ are perpendicular bisectors of each other.

If diagonals are ⊥ bisectors, the quadrilateral is a rhombus. ⟶ **Thus,** *ABCD* is a rhombus.

EXERCISES

PART A

Which of the triangles are right triangles?

1.
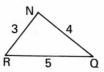

2.

3.

4.

Which of the following are lengths of sides of right triangles? Which angle of each right triangle is the right angle?

5. $AB = 3$, $BC = 4$, $CA = 5$

6. $XC = 0.5$, $CP = 1.2$, $PX = 1.3$

7. $RT = 4$, $TQ = 7$, $QR = 9$

8. $PC = \sqrt{3}$, $CM = \sqrt{4}$, $MP = \sqrt{5}$

9. $RB = \sqrt{3}$, $BC = \sqrt{3}$, $CR = \sqrt{6}$

10. $MD = 3$, $DQ = 5$, $QM = \sqrt{34}$

Determine whether the quadrilateral is a rhombus.

11.
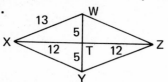

12.
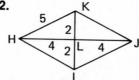

13.
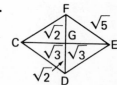

CONVERSE OF THE PYTHAGOREAN THEOREM **293**

PART B

14. Given: $\dfrac{1}{v^2} + \dfrac{1}{g^2} = \dfrac{p^2}{v^2 g^2}$

Prove: $\triangle GPV$ is a rt. $\triangle$.

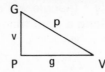

15. Given: $v^2 = (p - g)(p + g)$

Prove: $\triangle GPV$ is a rt. $\triangle$.

Which of the following are lengths of sides of right triangles?

16. $3x, 4x, 5x$

17. $n, n, 2n$

18. $5y^2, 12y^2, 13y^2$

19. $n, m, n + m$

20. $s, \sqrt{t^2 - s^2}, t$

21. $\dfrac{1}{a}, \dfrac{1}{b}, \dfrac{1}{\sqrt{a^2 + b^2}}$

PART C

22. Given: $\overline{CD} \perp \overline{AB}$, CD is the geometric mean of AD and DB.

Prove: $\triangle ABC$ is a rt. $\triangle$.

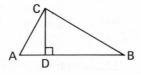

23. Given: $\overline{CD} \perp \overline{AB}$, AC is the geometric mean of AD and AB.

Prove: $\triangle ABC$ is a rt. $\triangle$.

24. Given: $a^2 + b^2 \neq c^2$. ($\overline{AB}$ is the longest side.)

Prove: $\triangle ABC$ is not a right $\triangle$.

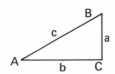

25. Given: $\triangle ABC$ is not a right triangle.

Prove: $a^2 + b^2 \neq c^2$

26. Prove Theorem 9.3.

Algebra Review

OBJECTIVE
■ To perform operations with radicals

To add or subtract radicals:
1. Simplify each radical.   2. Combine like terms.

To multiply: Use
$$\sqrt{a} \cdot \sqrt{b} = \sqrt{ab}.$$

To divide: Use
$$\dfrac{\sqrt{a}}{\sqrt{b}} = \sqrt{\dfrac{a}{b}}.$$

EXAMPLE Simplify

$5\sqrt{3} + 4\sqrt{12} - 2\sqrt{75}$
$5\sqrt{3} + 4\sqrt{4 \cdot 3} - 2\sqrt{25 \cdot 3}$
$5\sqrt{3} + 8\sqrt{3} - 10\sqrt{3}$

$3\sqrt{3}$

$3\sqrt{2} \cdot \sqrt{2}$
$3\sqrt{2 \cdot 2}$
$3 \cdot 2$

6

$\dfrac{12\sqrt{75}}{4\sqrt{3}}$
$\dfrac{12}{4} \cdot \sqrt{\dfrac{75}{3}}$
$3\sqrt{25} = 15$

Simplify.

1. $8\sqrt{2} + 7\sqrt{2}$

2. $\sqrt{2} + \sqrt{50}$

3. $\sqrt{27} + \sqrt{75}$

4. $\sqrt{72} - \sqrt{50}$

5. $\sqrt{80} - \sqrt{5}$

6. $7\sqrt{2} - \sqrt{2}$

7. $\sqrt{5} + \sqrt{45} + \sqrt{80}$

8. $\sqrt{12} - \sqrt{48} + \sqrt{3}$

9. $\sqrt{98} - 4\sqrt{8} + 3\sqrt{128}$

10. $\sqrt{5} \cdot \sqrt{5}$

11. $\sqrt{32} \cdot \sqrt{2}$

12. $5\sqrt{8} \cdot 7\sqrt{3}$

13. $\dfrac{12\sqrt{20}}{3\sqrt{5}}$

14. $\dfrac{4\sqrt{48}}{8\sqrt{3}}$

15. $\dfrac{14\sqrt{150}}{7\sqrt{2}}$

Proving the Pythagorean Theorem

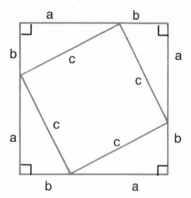

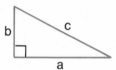

Cut out four identical right triangles.

Arrange them as shown. Verify that the figure in the center is a square.

The area of the big square can be found in two ways.

$$\begin{pmatrix} \text{Area of} \\ \text{Big Square} \end{pmatrix} = \begin{pmatrix} \text{length} \\ \text{of side} \end{pmatrix} \times \begin{pmatrix} \text{length} \\ \text{of side} \end{pmatrix}$$

$$= (a + b)\ \ (a + b)$$
$$= a^2 + 2ab + b^2$$

$$\begin{pmatrix} \text{Area of} \\ \text{Big Square} \end{pmatrix} = \begin{pmatrix} \text{4 times area} \\ \text{of triangle} \end{pmatrix} + \begin{pmatrix} \text{area of} \\ \text{small square} \end{pmatrix}$$

$$= \quad 4(\tfrac{1}{2}ab) \quad + \quad c^2$$

$$= \quad 2ab + c^2$$

These are equal.

Thus, $a^2 + 2ab + b^2 = 2ab + c^2$

or $\qquad a^2 + b^2 = c^2$

Another proof depends on a similar arrangement.

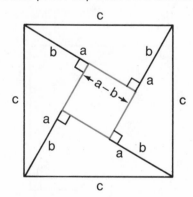

Make the arrangement. Can you prove the Pythagorean theorem from it.

[Hint: Find the area of the big square two ways.]

President Garfield discovered another proof.

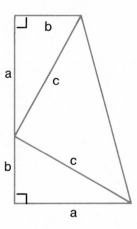

Verify that the figure in the center is a right triangle.

Verify that the large figure is a trapezoid with:
a and b the lengths of the bases
(a + b) the length of the altitude.

Find the area of the trapezoid in two ways and complete the proof.

Can you find a fourth proof?

Each of these two large squares can be made from four right triangles. Use the two squares to prove the Pythagorean Theorem.

[Hint: Suppose the four triangles are removed from the squares.]

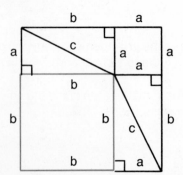

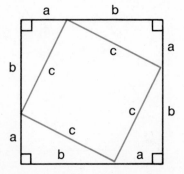

Special Right Triangles

▶ REVIEW CAPSULE

Each angle of an equilateral triangle has a measure of 60°.

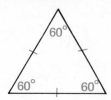

The altitude to the base of an isosceles triangle bisects the base and the vertex angle.

EXAMPLE 1 $\overline{AC} \cong \overline{BC}$, rt. $\angle C$, $AB = 10$
Find AC.

Use the Pythagorean theorem. ──────▶

$$x^2 + x^2 = 10^2$$
$$2x^2 = 100$$
$$x^2 = 50$$
$$x = \sqrt{50}, \text{ or } 5\sqrt{2}$$

Example 1 suggests a proof of a more general theorem.

Theorem 9.4

(See Exercise 17.)

In an isosceles right triangle, the length ℓ of a leg is $\dfrac{\text{hyp.}}{2}\sqrt{2}$.

$$\ell = \frac{\text{hyp.}}{2}\sqrt{2}$$

EXAMPLE 2 $\triangle ABC$ is a 45°-45° rt. triangle, the length of a leg is 15.
Find the length of the hypotenuse.

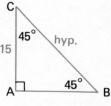

Sides opp. $\cong \angle$'s are $\cong$. ──────▶

$\triangle ABC$ is isosceles.
$$15 = \frac{\text{hyp.}}{2}\sqrt{2}$$
$$30 = \text{hyp.} \sqrt{2}$$
$$\text{hyp.} = \frac{30}{\sqrt{2}}, \text{ or } 15\sqrt{2}$$

$\dfrac{30}{\sqrt{2}} = \dfrac{30}{\sqrt{2}} \cdot \dfrac{\sqrt{2}}{\sqrt{2}} = \dfrac{30\sqrt{2}}{2}$ ──────

EXAMPLE 3   Find a formula for the length of an altitude of an equilateral triangle with sides of length *s*.

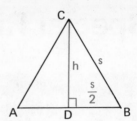

Alt. is also median in isos. △. ──────→

$$DB = \frac{s}{2}$$

△*DBC* is a rt △. ──────→

$$s^2 = h^2 + \left(\frac{s}{2}\right)^2$$

$$s^2 - \frac{s^2}{4} = h^2$$

$$s^2 - \frac{s^2}{4} = \frac{4s^2}{4} - \frac{s^2}{4}$$ ──────

$$\frac{3s^2}{4} = h^2$$

$$\sqrt{\frac{3s^2}{4}} = \frac{s\sqrt{3}}{2}$$ ──────→

$$h = \sqrt{\frac{3s^2}{4}}, \text{ or } h = \frac{s}{2}\sqrt{3}$$

EXAMPLE 4   If an altitude of an equilateral triangle is 10 cm long, how long is a side?

Apply Example 3. ──────→

$$10 = \frac{s}{2}\sqrt{3}$$

$$20 = s\sqrt{3}$$

$$\frac{20}{\sqrt{3}} = \frac{20}{\sqrt{3}} \cdot \frac{\sqrt{3}}{\sqrt{3}} = \frac{20\sqrt{3}}{3}$$ ──────

$$s = \frac{20}{\sqrt{3}}, \text{ or } \frac{20\sqrt{3}}{3}$$

Thus, a side is $\frac{20\sqrt{3}}{3}$ cm long.

Theorem 9.5

(See Exercise 18.)

In a 30°-60° rt. triangle, the length ℓ of the leg opposite the 30° angle is $\frac{\text{hyp.}}{2}$.

$$\ell = \frac{\text{hyp.}}{2}$$

The length ℓ' of the leg opposite the 60° angle is $\frac{\text{hyp.}}{2}\sqrt{3}$.

$$\ell' = \frac{\text{hyp.}}{2}\sqrt{3}$$

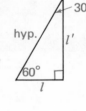

EXAMPLE 5   *ABCD* is a rhombus, $m\angle DBC = 60$, $BC = 8$.
Find the length of each diagonal.

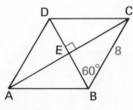

Diagonals of a rhombus are ⊥ bisectors of each other. ──────→

△*BCE* is a 30°-60° rt. triangle.

$BE = \frac{1}{2}BC$ ──────→ $BE = 4$

$CE = \frac{\sqrt{3}}{2}BC$ ──────→ $CE = 4\sqrt{3}$

Thus, $DB = 8$ and $AC = 8\sqrt{3}$.

ORAL EXERCISES

How long is each side of each right triangle?

1.

2.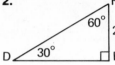

3.

4.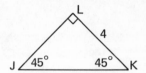

EXERCISES

PART A

△*ABC* is a 30°-60° rt. triangle. Find the missing lengths of sides.

1. $AB = 36$, $BC = ?$, $CA = ?$
3. $AB = ?$, $BC = 9$, $CA = ?$
5. $AB = ?$, $BC = ?$, $CA = 6\sqrt{3}$

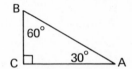

2. $AB = 27$, $BC = ?$, $CA = ?$
4. $AB = ?$, $BC = 4\sqrt{3}$, $CA = ?$
6. $AB = ?$, $BC = ?$, $CA = 10$

△*XYZ* is a 45°-45° rt. triangle. Find the missing lengths of sides.

7. $XY = 12$, $XZ = ?$, $YZ = ?$
9. $XY = ?$ $XZ = 3\sqrt{2}$, $YZ = ?$
11. $XY = ?$, $XZ = ?$, $YZ = 4$

8. $XY = 27$, $XZ = ?$, $YZ = ?$
10. $XY = ?$, $XZ = ?$, $YZ = 9\sqrt{2}$
12. $XY = 8\sqrt{2}$, $XZ = ?$, $YZ = ?$

13. △*RST* is equilateral. $\overline{TV}$ is an altitude. $RT = 20$. Find *TV*.

14. △*RST* is equilateral. $\overline{TV}$ is an altitude. $TV = 8$. Find *RT*.

15. Isosceles right △*JKL*. $\overline{LM}$ is the altitude to the hypotenuse. $JL = 12$. Find *LM* and *JK*.

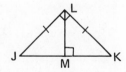

16. Isosceles right △*JKL*. $\overline{LM}$ is the altitude to the hypotenuse. $LM = 6$. Find *JL* and *JK*.

PART B

17. Prove Theorem 9.4.
19. Prove or disprove.
Given: Rhombus *RSTU*,
$m\angle URS = 60$.
$$\frac{RS + ST + TU + UR}{(RT)(SU)} = \frac{1}{2\sqrt{3}}$$

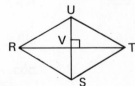

18. Prove Theorem 9.5.

20. Prove or disprove.
Given: Rhombus *RSTU*,
$m\angle URS = 60$.
Prove: $(RT)(SU) = \sqrt{3}\,(RS)(UT)$

Trigonometric Ratios

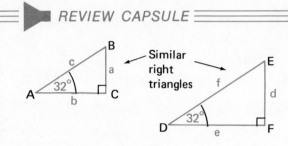

REVIEW CAPSULE

Right triangles with one pair of congruent acute angles are similar.

$$\triangle ABC \sim \triangle DEF$$

Thus, $\dfrac{a}{b} = \dfrac{d}{e}$ $\dfrac{a}{c} = \dfrac{d}{f}$ $\dfrac{b}{c} = \dfrac{e}{f}$.

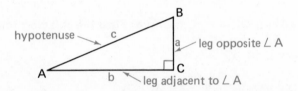

Terms associated with right triangles ⟶

Any two right triangles with congruent acute angles are similar.

Thus:

The ratio $\frac{a}{b}$ is the same for all $\sim \triangle$'s.

The ratio $\frac{a}{c}$ is the same for all $\sim \triangle$'s.

The ratio $\frac{b}{c}$ is the same for all $\sim \triangle$'s.

TRIGONOMETRIC RATIOS FOR RIGHT TRIANGLES	
Ratio	*Abbreviation*
tangent of $m\angle A = \dfrac{\text{measure of opposite leg}}{\text{measure of adjacent leg}}$	$\tan A = \dfrac{a}{b}$
sine of $m\angle A = \dfrac{\text{measure of opposite leg}}{\text{measure of hypotenuse}}$	$\sin A = \dfrac{a}{c}$
cosine of $m\angle A = \dfrac{\text{measure of adjacent leg}}{\text{measure of hypotenuse}}$	$\cos A = \dfrac{b}{c}$

EXAMPLE 1   For $\triangle ABC$, find $\tan A$, $\sin A$, and $\cos A$.

$\tan = \dfrac{\text{opp.}}{\text{adj.}}$ ⟶ $\tan A = \dfrac{4}{3}$, or 1.333

$\sin = \dfrac{\text{opp.}}{\text{hyp.}}$ ⟶ $\sin A = \dfrac{4}{5}$, or .8

$\cos = \dfrac{\text{adj.}}{\text{hyp.}}$ ⟶ $\cos A = \dfrac{3}{5}$, or .6

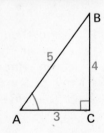

EXAMPLE 2 For △ABC, find tan B, sin B, and cos B, to three decimal places.

$\tan = \dfrac{\text{opp.}}{\text{adj.}}$ ——————————→ $\tan B = \dfrac{15}{8} = 1.875$

$\sin = \dfrac{\text{opp.}}{\text{hyp.}}$ ——————————→ $\sin B = \dfrac{15}{17} = .882$

$\cos = \dfrac{\text{adj.}}{\text{hyp.}}$ ——————————→ $\cos B = \dfrac{8}{17} = .471$

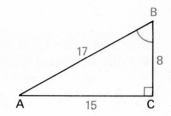

EXAMPLE 3 All right triangles with a 30° angle are similar. Use each triangle below to find sin 30°.

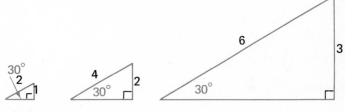

The result is the same in all three cases. ——→ $\sin 30° = \dfrac{1}{2}$ $\sin 30° = \dfrac{2}{4} = \dfrac{1}{2}$ $\sin 30° = \dfrac{3}{6} = \dfrac{1}{2}$

Thus, $\sin 30° = \dfrac{1}{2}$, or .500.

EXAMPLE 4 Use △ABC to find cos 30° and tan 30°.

$\doteq$ means approximately =.

$\cos 30° = \dfrac{\sqrt{3}}{2} \doteq \dfrac{1.732}{2}$
$\qquad\qquad \doteq .866$

$\tan 30° = \dfrac{1}{\sqrt{3}} = \dfrac{1}{\sqrt{3}} \cdot \dfrac{\sqrt{3}}{\sqrt{3}}$
$\qquad\qquad = \dfrac{\sqrt{3}}{3} \doteq \dfrac{1.732}{3} \doteq .577$

ORAL EXERCISES

1. Name the leg adjacent to ∠R.
3. Name the hypotenuse.
5. Name the leg adjacent to ∠S.
7. What is cos S ?
9. What is sin S?
11. What is cos R ?

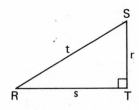

2. Name the leg opposite ∠S.
4. Name the leg opposite ∠R.
6. What is sin R ?
8. What is tan S ?
10. What is tan R ?

EXERCISES

PART A

For each triangle, find tan A, sin A, cos A, tan B, sin B, and cos B, to three decimal places. (Use the Table of Square Roots in the back of the book.)

1.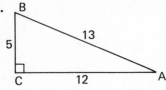

2.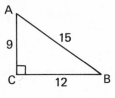

3.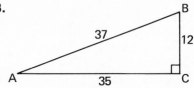

4.

5.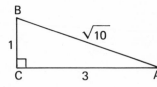

6.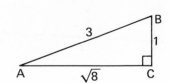

Find each value to three decimal places. Use the triangle shown.

7. tan 60°
8. sin 60°
9. cos 60°

10. tan 45°
11. sin 45°
12. cos 45°

PART B

For each triangle, find tan A, sin A, cos A, tan B, sin B, and cos B, to three decimal places. [**HINT:** Use the Pythagorean theorem first.]

13.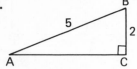

14.

15.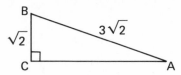

PART C

Show that each statement is true. Use the figure below.

16. $\sin B = \cos A$

18. $\tan B = \dfrac{1}{\tan A}$

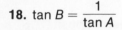

17. $\cos B = \sin A$
19. $(\sin B)^2 = 1 - (\cos B)^2$
[Hint: Use the Pythagorean theorem.]

20. The tangent of an acute angle is equal to the reciprocal of the tangent of its complement.

21. The sine of an acute angle is equal to the cosine of its complement.

Tables of Trigonometric Ratios

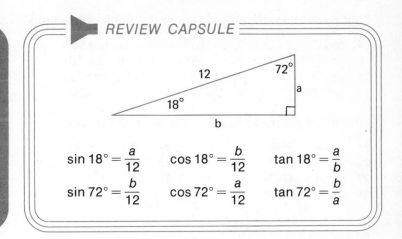

REVIEW CAPSULE

$$\sin 18° = \frac{a}{12} \qquad \cos 18° = \frac{b}{12} \qquad \tan 18° = \frac{a}{b}$$

$$\sin 72° = \frac{b}{12} \qquad \cos 72° = \frac{a}{12} \qquad \tan 72° = \frac{b}{a}$$

Tables have been constructed to give trigonometric ratios.

A portion of the table is shown.

The ratios are approximated.

Angle Meas.	Sin	Cos	Tan	Angle Meas.	Sin	Cos	Tan
21°	.3584	.9336	.3839	67°	.9205	.3907	2.356
22°	.3746	.9272	.4040	68°	.9272	.3746	2.475
23°	.3907	.9205	.4245	69°	.9336	.3584	2.605
24°	.4067	.9135	.4452	70°	.9397	.3420	2.747
25°	.4226	.9063	.4663	71°	.9455	.3256	2.904
26°	.4384	.8988	.4877	72°	.9511	.3090	3.077
27°	.4540	.8910	.5095	73°	.9563	.2924	3.270
28°	.4695	.8829	.5317	74°	.9613	.2756	3.487
29°	.4848	.8746	.5543	75°	.9659	.2588	3.732
30°	.5000	.8660	.5774	76°	.9703	.2419	4.010

EXAMPLE 1   Use the table to find sin 24°, cos 24°, and tan 24°.

Look in the appropriate column next
to 24°. ──────────────→   sin 24° = .4067   cos 24° = .9135   tan 24° = .4452

EXAMPLE 2   Find $m \angle A$ if cos A = .3090.

Find .3090 in the Cos column. ──────→   cos 72° = .3090.
Thus, $m \angle A = 72$.

EXAMPLE 3   Find $m \angle B$ to the nearest degree, if tan B = .5403.

Find the closest value to .5403 in the
Tan column. ──────────────→   tan 28° = .5317.
Thus, $m \angle B = 28$ to the nearest degree.

ORAL EXERCISES

Find each ratio. (Use the table in the back of the book.)

1. $\cos 5°$	**2.** $\sin 76°$	**3.** $\tan 15°$	**4.** $\sin 41°$	**5.** $\tan 47°$
6. $\cos 85°$	**7.** $\sin 56°$	**8.** $\cos 38°$	**9.** $\tan 52°$	**10.** $\tan 30°$
11. $\sin 12°$	**12.** $\tan 81°$	**13.** $\cos 73°$	**14.** $\sin 29°$	**15.** $\cos 59°$
16. $\tan 35°$	**17.** $\cos 74°$	**18.** $\sin 55°$	**19.** $\cos 21°$	**20.** $\sin 61°$

Find $m \angle A$. (Use the table in the back of the book.)

21. $\cos A = .9659$	**22.** $\sin A = .9945$	**23.** $\tan A = 1.111$
24. $\sin A = .4067$	**25.** $\tan A = 3.487$	**26.** $\cos A = .4695$
27. $\tan A = .4245$	**28.** $\cos A = .1736$	**29.** $\sin A = .7986$
30. $\sin A = .6428$	**31.** $\tan A = .8693$	**32.** $\cos A = .7771$

EXERCISES

PART A

Find $m \angle B$ to the nearest degree. (Use the table in the back of the book.)

1. $\sin B = .2593$	**2.** $\tan B = .4439$	**3.** $\sin B = .9927$
4. $\cos B = .9931$	**5.** $\cos B = .8516$	**6.** $\tan B = 12.57$
7. $\cos B = .4259$	**8.** $\tan B = .8721$	**9.** $\sin B = .8392$
10. $\tan B = 1.352$	**11.** $\sin B = .5036$	**12.** $\cos B = .1196$

PART B

True or false? Use the figure at the right.

13. $\sin A = \cos B$ **14.** $\tan A = \dfrac{b}{a}$ **15.** $\sin B = \dfrac{b}{c}$

16. $\tan B = \dfrac{1}{\tan A}$ **17.** $\cos A = \cos B$ **18.** $\cos A = \dfrac{a}{b}$

19. $\sin A + \cos A = \dfrac{a+b}{c}$ **20.** $(\tan A)(\tan B) = 1$ **21.** $a^2 = c^2 - b^2$

22. $\angle A$ and $\angle B$ are supplementary.

23. $m \angle A + m \angle B = m \angle C$

24. If $m \angle A < m \angle B$, then $\cos A > \cos B$.

25. If $m \angle A < m \angle B$, then $\tan A < \tan B$.

26. If $\sin A > \sin B$, then $m \angle A < m \angle B$.

27. $(\sin A)^2 + (\sin B)^2 = 1$

PART C

28. Explain why $\sin A$ cannot be greater than 1.

29. Explain why $\cos A$ decreases as $m \angle A$ increases.

30. Show that $\tan A = \dfrac{\sin A}{\cos A}$.

31. Explain why $\tan A$ gets infinitely large as $m \angle A$ increases.

Finding Measures in Right Triangles

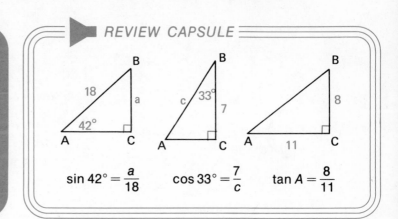

▶ *REVIEW CAPSULE*

$$\sin 42° = \frac{a}{18} \qquad \cos 33° = \frac{7}{c} \qquad \tan A = \frac{8}{11}$$

EXAMPLE 1   If $m \angle A = 52$ and $c = 12$, find b to the nearest tenth.

Use cos A, since we are working with b and c. ⟶

$$\cos A = \frac{b}{c}$$

$m \angle A = 52$, $c = 12$ ⟶

$$\cos 52° = \frac{b}{12}$$

Use table. cos 52° $\doteq$ .6157 ⟶

$$.6157 \doteq \frac{b}{12}$$

Multiply each side by 12. ⟶ $(.6157)(12) \doteq b$

$$7.3884 \doteq b$$

Round to the nearest tenth. ⟶ $7.4 \doteq b$

Thus, b is 7.4 to the nearest tenth.

EXAMPLE 2   If $m \angle B = 73$ and $b = 8$, find c to the nearest tenth.

$$\sin B = \frac{b}{c}$$

$m \angle B = 73$, $b = 8$ ⟶ $\sin 73° = \dfrac{8}{c}$

Use table. sin 73° $\doteq$ .9563 ⟶ $.9563 \doteq \dfrac{8}{c}$

Multiply each side by c. ⟶ $.9563c \doteq 8$

Divide each side by .9563. ⟶ $c \doteq \dfrac{8}{.9563}$

$$c \doteq 8.36$$

Thus, c is 8.4 to the nearest tenth.

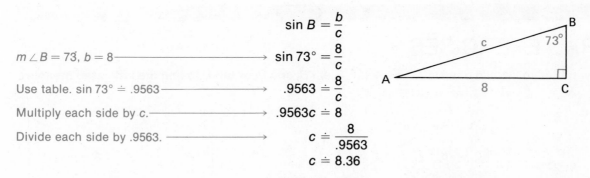

EXAMPLE 3   If $m \angle A = 23$ and $a = 15$, find b to the nearest tenth.

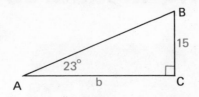

Use either
    tan A or tan B.

$\tan A = \dfrac{15}{b}$ $\tan B = \dfrac{b}{15}$

First Way	Second Way
$\tan A = \dfrac{a}{b}$	$m \angle B = 90 - 23 = 67$
$\tan 23° = \dfrac{15}{b}$	$\tan B = \dfrac{b}{15}$
$.4245 \doteq \dfrac{15}{b}$	$\tan 67° = \dfrac{b}{15}$
$.4245b \doteq 15$	$2.356 \doteq \dfrac{b}{15}$
$b \doteq \dfrac{15}{.4245}$	$(2.356)(15) \doteq b$
$b \doteq 35.3$	$35.340 \doteq b$
	$35.3 \doteq b$

Note: In the second way, we multiply rather than divide.

Thus, b is 35.3 to the nearest tenth.

EXAMPLE 4   If $a = 4$ and $c = 12$, find $m \angle B$ to the nearest degree.

$a = 4$
$c = 12$

Use the Cos column.
Find the nearest entry to .3333.
$\cos 71° \doteq .3256$

$\cos B = \dfrac{a}{c}$

$\cos B = \dfrac{4}{12}$

$\cos B = \dfrac{1}{3}$

$\cos B \doteq .3333$

$m \angle B \doteq 71$

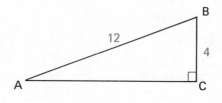

Thus, $m \angle B$ is 71 to the nearest degree.

ORAL EXERCISES

Tell whether you would use sin A, cos A, tan A, sin B, cos B, or tan B to find the indicated measure.

1.
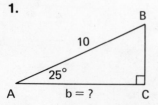

2.
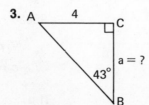

3.

4.
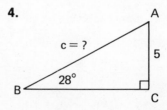

EXERCISES

PART A

Find the indicated measures (sides to the nearest tenth and angles to the nearest degree).

1.

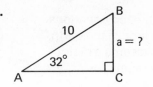

2.

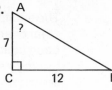

3.

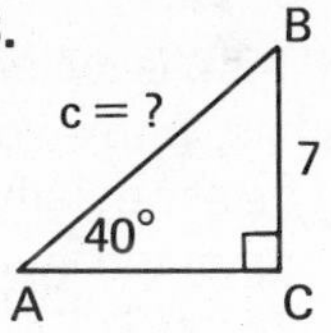

4.

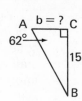

5.

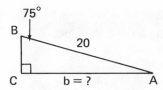

6.

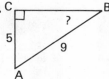

7.

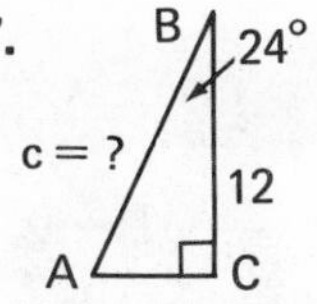

8.

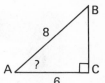

Find the indicated measures (sides to the nearest tenth and angles to the nearest degree).

Use the figure at the right.

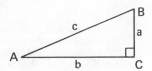

9. If $a = 6$ and $m\angle B = 18$, find b.
10. If $a = 12$ and $c = 19$, find $m\angle B$.
11. If $b = 9$ and $c = 15$, find $m\angle B$.
12. If $b = 21$ and $m\angle B = 76$, find a.
13. If $b = 15$ and $c = 20$, find $m\angle A$.
14. If $c = 28$ and $m\angle A = 31$, find a.
15. If $c = 18$ and $m\angle B = 40$, find a.
16. If $a = 9$ and $b = 13$, find $m\angle B$.
17. If $b = 17$ and $m\angle B = 49$, find c.
18. If $c = 26$ and $m\angle B = 62$, find a.
19. If $c = 10$ and $m\angle A = 38$, find a.
20. If $b = 16$ and $m\angle A = 12$, find c.
21. If $a = 3$ and $c = 5$, find $m\angle A$.
22. If $b = 18$ and $m\angle B = 38$, find a.
23. If $a = 14$ and $b = 17$, find $m\angle A$.
24. If $a = 16$ and $m\angle B = 8$, find c.

PART B

Find all the missing measures (sides to the nearest tenth and angles to the nearest degree).

25.

26.

27.

28.

29.

30.

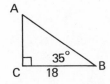

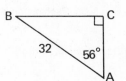

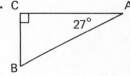

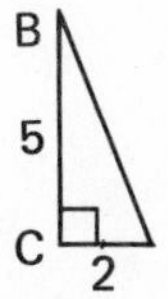

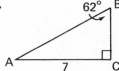

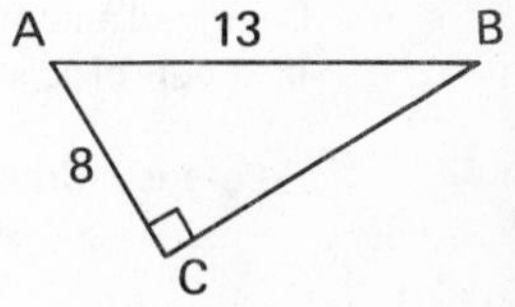

Fun for Philatelists

A *philatelist* (fi lat' l-ist) is a stamp collector. Philatelists, who also like mathematics, will be especially interested in a group of ten stamps issued by Nicaragua in 1971.

The stamps show the ten equations "that changed the face of the earth." Each equation represents a major turning point in mathematics or science.

$$E = m c^2$$

$$f = \frac{Gm_1 m_2}{r^2}$$

This famous equation, associated with Albert Einstein, equates energy with mass and the speed of light. From a small amount of matter much energy can be created. Nuclear energy can be used in reactors to supply energy for generating heat and electricity.

This equation of the famous mathematician, Isaac Newton, shows that all bodies attract one another by gravitational forces. It helps to explain the force that holds the planets in orbit around the sun or the moon around the earth. The equation also shows that a force depends upon the masses of the bodies involved.

Designed and printed by Thos. De La Rue & Co. Each stamp is 48 x 32 mm. in sheets of 50 stamps.

Reference: *Crown Agents Stamp and Coin Bulletin,* April 1971.

Applications of Trigonometry

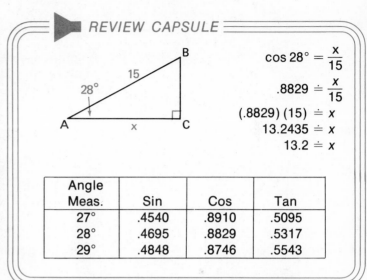

◤ *REVIEW CAPSULE*

$$\cos 28° = \frac{x}{15}$$

$$.8829 \doteq \frac{x}{15}$$

$$(.8829)(15) \doteq x$$

$$13.2435 \doteq x$$

$$13.2 \doteq x$$

Angle Meas.	Sin	Cos	Tan
27°	.4540	.8910	.5095
28°	.4695	.8829	.5317
29°	.4848	.8746	.5543

EXAMPLE 1 Find the height of the tower to the nearest tenth of a foot.

$\tan = \dfrac{\text{opp.}}{\text{adj.}}$

$$\tan 38° = \frac{x}{30}$$

Use table. $\tan 38° \doteq .7813$ ⟶

$$.7813 \doteq \frac{x}{30}$$

Multiply each side by 30. ⟶
$$(.7813)(30) \doteq x$$
$$23.4390 \doteq x$$
$$23.4 \doteq x$$

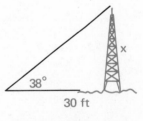

To the nearest foot ⟶ **Thus,** the height of the tower is 23 ft.

EXAMPLE 2 A 3-inch diagonal of a rectangle makes an angle of 67° with a side of the rectangle. Find the dimensions of the rectangle to the nearest tenth of an inch.

$\sin = \dfrac{\text{opp.}}{\text{hyp.}} \quad \cos = \dfrac{\text{adj.}}{\text{hyp.}}$ ⟶

$$\sin 67° = \frac{\ell}{3} \qquad \cos 67° = \frac{w}{3}$$

Use the table. ⟶

$$.9205 \doteq \frac{\ell}{3} \qquad .3907 \doteq \frac{w}{3}$$

Multiply each side by 3. ⟶
$$(.9205)(3) \doteq \ell \qquad (.3907)(3) \doteq w$$
$$2.7615 \doteq \ell \qquad 1.1721 \doteq w$$
$$2.8 \doteq \ell \qquad 1.2 \doteq w$$

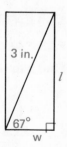

To the nearest tenth ⟶ **Thus,** the length is 2.8 in. and the width is 1.2 in.

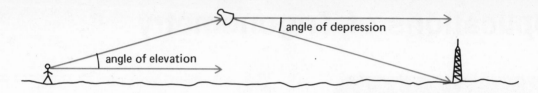

angle of depression

angle of elevation

EXAMPLE 3   A lighthouse casts an 80-foot shadow when the angle of elevation of the sun measures 36°. How tall is the lighthouse?

$\tan = \dfrac{\text{opp.}}{\text{adj.}}$ ⟶

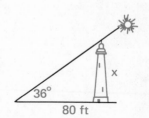

$$\tan 36° = \frac{x}{80}$$

$$.7265 \doteq \frac{x}{80}$$

$$(.7265)(80) \doteq x$$

$$58.1200 \doteq x$$

$$58.1 \doteq x$$

To the nearest tenth ⟶ **Thus,** the lighthouse is about 58.1 feet tall.

EXAMPLE 4   From her treehouse, Joan can look directly into her bedroom window. The angle of depression from the treehouse to the base of her house is 42°. The tree is 35 feet from the base of the house. How far is the treehouse from the base of the house?

$\cos = \dfrac{\text{adj.}}{\text{hyp.}}$ ⟶

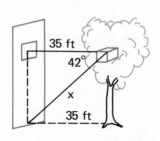

$$\cos 42° = \frac{35}{x}$$

$$.7431 \doteq \frac{35}{x}$$

$$.7431x \doteq 35$$

$$x \doteq \frac{35}{.7431}$$

$$x \doteq 47.1$$

Thus, the treehouse is about 47.1 ft from the base of the house.

EXERCISES

PART A

Find x to the nearest tenth.

1.

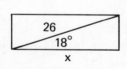

100 ft   25°   x

2.

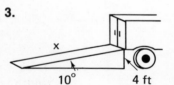

26   18°   x

3.

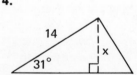

x   10°   4 ft

4.

14   31°   x

Find lengths to the nearest tenth and angle measures to the nearest degree.

5. The leg opposite the 50° angle in a right triangle measures 8 meters. Find the length of the hypotenuse.

6. The angle of elevation from a ship to the top of a 70-foot lighthouse on the coast measures 26°. How far from the coast is the lighthouse?

7. A ramp is 60 feet long. It rises a vertical distance of 8 feet. Find the measure of the angle of elevation.

8. The diagonal of a rectangle is 6 inches long. It makes an angle of 55° with a side of the rectangle. Find the dimensions of the rectangle.

9. A cliff is 90 feet above the sea. From the cliff, the angle of depression of a boat measures 46°. How far is the boat from the base of the cliff?

10. Two sides of a triangle measure 8 inches and 11 inches. The included angle measures 34°. Find the measure of the altitude to the 11-inch side.

11. A tree casts a 50-foot shadow while the angle of elevation of the sun is 48°. How tall is the tree?

12. A kite is flying at the end of a 150-foot string (straight). The string makes an angle of 75° with the ground. How high above the ground is the kite?

PART B

Find lengths to the nearest tenth and angle measures to the nearest degree.

13. In the trapezoid below, $\overline{AB} \parallel \overline{CD}$ and $\overline{DA} \perp \overline{AB}$. $DC = 12$, $CB = 9$, and $m\angle B = 52$. Find AB. [Hint: Draw $\overline{CE} \perp \overline{AB}$.]

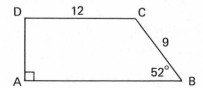

14. The diagonals of the rhombus below measure 10 and 20. Find the measure of each angle of the rhombus.

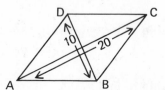

PART C

Find lengths to the nearest tenth and angle measures to the nearest degree.

15. The sides of an isosceles triangle measure 7, 7, and 9. Find the measure of each angle of the triangle.

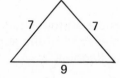

16. An angle of a rhombus measures 70° and the diagonal opposite that angle measures 15. Find the measure of the other diagonal.

Chapter Nine Review

1. Right $\triangle RJB$, altitude $\overline{RT}$. Which triangles formed are similar? [p. 285]

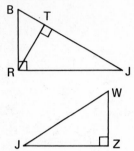

2. $\overline{BR} \perp \overline{RJ}$, $\overline{RT} \perp \overline{BJ}$, $BT = 3$, $TJ = 27$. Find RT and RJ. [p. 285]

3. Right $\triangle JZW$, $JZ = 8$, $WZ = 5$. Find JW. [p. 288]

4. Right $\triangle JZW$, $JW = 9$, $WZ = 4$. Find JZ. [p. 288]

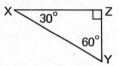

For which lengths of sides is $\triangle ABC$ a right triangle? [p. 292]

5. $AB = 9$, $BC = 12$, $CA = 15$

6. $AB = 6$, $BC = 8$, $CA = 12$

7. $AB = \sqrt{5}$, $BC = \sqrt{6}$, $CA = \sqrt{11}$

8. $\triangle XYZ$ is a 30°-60° rt. triangle, $XY = 4$. Find YZ and XZ. [p. 297]

9. $\triangle XYZ$ is a 30°-60° rt. triangle, $XZ = 4$. Find XY and YZ. [p. 297]

10. $\triangle RST$ is a 45°-45° rt. triangle, $RT = 6$. Find RS and TS. [p. 297]

11. $\triangle RST$ is a 45°-45° rt. triangle, $RS = 6$. Find RT and TS. [p. 297]

12. Right $\triangle XYZ$, $XY = 4$, $YZ = 3$, $XZ = 5$. Find $\tan X$. [p. 300]

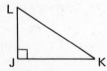

13. Right $\triangle XYZ$, $XY = 4$, $YZ = 3$, $XZ = 5$. Find $\sin Z$. [p. 300]

Use the table of trigonometric ratios to find each of the following. [p. 303]

14. $\sin 32°$

15. $\cos 84°$

16. $\tan 57°$

Use the table to find $m \angle A$. [p. 303]

17. $\tan A = .5317$

18. $\sin A = .9781$

19. $\cos A = .6691$

20. $\tan K = .5543$, $JK = 10$, Find LJ. [p. 305]

21. $\sin K = .6947$, $JK = 10$ Find LK. [p. 305]

Find the lengths to the nearest tenth. [p. 309]

22. A ladder leaning against a house makes an angle of 65° with the ground. If the ladder is 20 feet long, how far up on the house does it reach?

23. A flagpole casts a 50-foot shadow while the angle of elevation of the sun is 42°. How tall is the flagpole?

Chapter Nine Test

1. Right $\triangle XBP$, altitude $\overline{PH}$. Which triangles formed are similar?

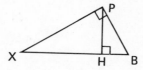

2. Right $\triangle XBP$, altitude $\overline{PH}$, $XB = 36$, $HB = 9$. Find PB.

3. Right $\triangle HJK$, $HK = 4$, $KJ = 7$. Find HJ.

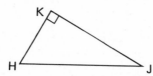

4. Right $\triangle HJK$, $HJ = 9$, $KJ = 7$. Find HK.

Which of the following could be the lengths of sides of a right triangle?

5. 5, 12, 13

6. 2, 3, 5

7. $\sqrt{3}$, $\sqrt{3}$, 3

8. $\triangle JTL$ is a 30°-60° rt. triangle. $LT = 12$. Find JT and LJ.

9. $\triangle BGW$ is a 45°-45° rt. triangle. $WG = 6$. Find BG.

Use the diagram at the right.

10. Find cos S.
11. Find tan E.

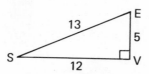

Use the table of trigonometric ratios below for items 12–17.

Angle Measure	Sin	Cos	Tan		Angle Measure	Sin	Cos	Tan
28°	.4695	.8829	.5317		60°	.8660	.5000	1.732
29°	.4848	.8746	.5543		61°	.8746	.4848	1.804
30°	.5000	.8660	.5774		62°	.8829	.4695	1.881

12. Find cos 62°.

13. If tan $A = 1.804$, find $m\angle A$.

14. Right $\triangle LZV$, $m\angle L = 29$, $VZ = 10$. Find LZ.

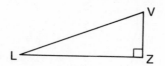

15. Right $\triangle LZV$, $m\angle V = 62$, $LV = 10$. Find VZ.

Find the lengths to the nearest tenth.

16. A wire brace is needed to brace a 40-foot vertical pole. The brace is to make an angle of 60° with the ground. How long a wire is needed?

17. The angle of depression from the top of a 200-foot tower to a lake is 28°. How far from the base of the tower is the lake?

Map Coloring

How many colors does it take to
color a map?

Rule
　Two states with a common boundary
　cannot be the same color.

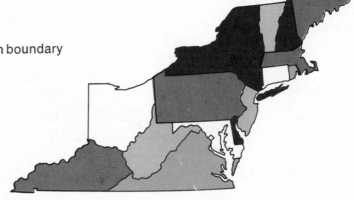

For this map four colors are enough.
Can the map below be colored
with four colors?

Are four colors enough for a map on a sphere?
Are four colors enough for a map on a doughnut?

Circles, Segments, and Lines

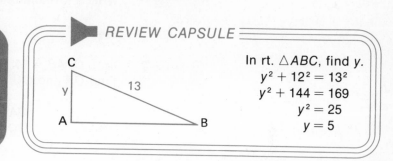

REVIEW CAPSULE

In rt. $\triangle ABC$, find y.
$$y^2 + 12^2 = 13^2$$
$$y^2 + 144 = 169$$
$$y^2 = 25$$
$$y = 5$$

A *radius* of a circle is a segment joining the center and any point on the circle. The plural of *radius* is *radii*.

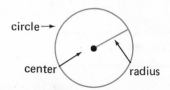

circle →
center
radius

Definition of *circle* ⎯⎯⎯⎯⎯⎯→ A *circle* is the set of all points in a plane a given distance from a fixed point.

Segments and Lines Related to Circles

A segment joining any two points on the circle

A chord passing through the center of the circle

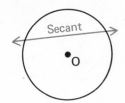

A line intersecting the circle at two points

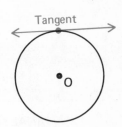

A line coplanar with the circle intersecting at exactly one point.

EXAMPLE 1

⊙ O (read circle O) is a circle with center O.

Identify a radius, a diameter, a chord, a secant, and a tangent of ⊙ O.

Radius: $\overline{OB}$, $\overline{OC}$, or $\overline{OD}$
Diameter: $\overline{BD}$
Chord: $\overline{EA}$, or $\overline{BD}$
Secant: $\overleftrightarrow{EA}$
Tangent: $\overleftrightarrow{FA}$

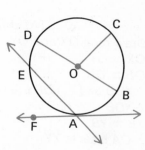

EXAMPLE 2   If *r* is the length of a radius, and *d* is the length of a diameter, write a formula relating *r* and *d*.

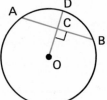

Each diameter is twice as long as a radius. ⟶ $d = 2r$

EXAMPLE 3   In ⊙ *O*, *AB* = 14.
Find *OA* and *OC*.

$\overline{AB}$ is a diameter.
$\overline{OA}$ is a radius.
$d = 2r$

$OA = 7$
$OC = 7$

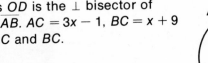

Theorem 10.1   Any two radii of a circle are congruent.

(See Exercise 9.)

EXAMPLE 4   Radius $\overline{OD}$ is the ⊥ bisector of chord $\overline{AB}$. *AC* = 3*x* − 1, *BC* = *x* + 9
Find *AC* and *BC*.

segments.
Bisector forms ≅ segments. ⟶ $3x - 1 = x + 9$
$2x = 10$
$x = 5$

$AC = 3(5) - 1$
$BC = 5 + 9$

Thus, *AC* = 14 and *BC* = 14.

Theorem 10.2   In a circle, a radius perpendicular to a chord bisects the chord.

ANALYSIS
Draw radii $\overline{OX}$ and $\overline{OY}$.
Show △*OBX* ≅ △*OBY*.

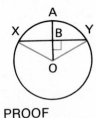

GIVEN
⊙ *O*, radius $\overline{OA}$ ⊥ chord $\overline{XY}$
PROVE
$\overline{OA}$ bisects $\overline{XY}$.

PROOF

STATEMENTS	REASONS
1. Draw radii $\overline{OX}$ and $\overline{OY}$.	1. Two points are contained in exactly one line.
2. $\overline{OX} \cong \overline{OY}$ (H)	2. Any two radii of a ⊙ are ≅.
3. $\overline{OB} \cong \overline{OB}$ (L)	3. Reflexive property
4. △*XOB* and △*YOB* are rt. △'s.	4. ⊥ forms rt. ∠'s.
5. △*XOB* ≅ △*YOB*	5. HL for ≅ rt. △'s
6. $\overline{XB} \cong \overline{YB}$	6. Corr. sides of ≅ △'s are ≅.
7. ∴ $\overline{OA}$ bisects $\overline{XY}$.	7. Def. of bisector

EXAMPLE 5 A circle with a radius 5 in. long has a chord 3 in. from the center. How long is the chord?

Draw a figure.
Distance is measured along ⊥.
△AOD is a rt. △.

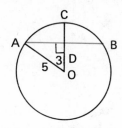

$$\overline{OD} \perp \overline{AB}$$
$$(AO)^2 = (OD)^2 + (AD)^2$$
$$5^2 = 3^2 + (AD)^2$$
$$25 = 9 + (AD)^2$$
$$16 = (AD)^2$$
$$AD = 4$$

D is midpoint of $\overline{AB}$. ⟶ **Thus,** $AB = 8$ inches.

ORAL EXERCISES

Name all radii and diameters.

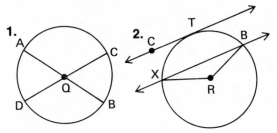

Name all secants, chords, and tangents.

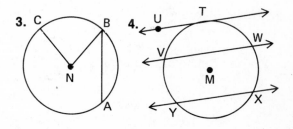

True or false?

5. A circle is a regular polygon.
7. A circle is a closed figure.
9. A chord can be part of a secant.
11. A diameter is a chord.
13. A diameter of a circle is twice as long as a radius of the same circle.

6. A circle is a polygon.
8. A circle has exactly two radii.
10. A chord can be part of a tangent.
12. A radius can be part of a diameter.
14. The union of any two radii of a circle is a diameter of the circle.

EXERCISES

PART A

Which triangles are congruent?

1. $\overline{BD}$ is a diameter of ⊙ O, $\overline{AB} \cong \overline{CB}$.

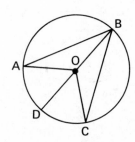

2. $\overline{BD}$ is a diameter of ⊙ O, $\angle AOB \cong \angle COB$.

3. The distance from O to $\overline{AB}$ is 4 in. The length of a radius is 5 in. Find AB.

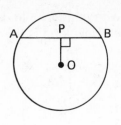

4. $AB = 10$ cm. A radius is 8 cm long. Find the distance from O to $\overline{AB}$.

5. Radius $\overline{OZ} \perp$ chord $\overline{XY}$. $XP = 3x + 4$, $PY = 5x - 2$. Find XY.

6. Radii $\overline{OX}$ and $\overline{OY}$. $OX = x + 8$, $OY = 2x - 1$. Find OX and OY.

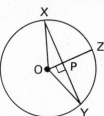

7. Given: Radii $\overline{OA}$ and $\overline{OB}$
   Prove: $\angle OAB \cong \angle OBA$

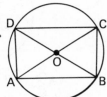

8. Given: $\angle AOC \cong \angle BOC$, $\overline{OA}$ and $\overline{OB}$ are radii.
   Prove: $\overline{OC}$ is the $\perp$ bisector of $\overline{AB}$.

PART B

9. Prove Theorem 10.1.

10. Prove: A radius of a circle which bisects a chord is perpendicular to the chord.

11. Given: Diameters $\overline{AC}$ and $\overline{BD}$ of $\odot O$
    Prove: $\overline{AD} \cong \overline{BC}$

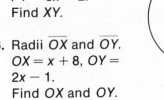

12. Given: Diameters $\overline{AC}$ and $\overline{BD}$ of $\odot O$
    Prove: $ABCD$ is a rectangle.

13. Given: Diameter $\overline{XY}$ of $\odot O$, chord $\overline{RS} \parallel$ chord $\overline{TU}$, $\overline{XY}$ bisects $\overline{RS}$ at M.
    Prove: N is the midpoint of $\overline{TU}$.

14. Given: $\overline{LM}$ is a diameter of $\odot O$. $\overline{LM} \perp$ chord $\overline{JQ}$.
    Prove: $\overline{JL} \cong \overline{QL}$

15. Given: Diameter $\overline{FC}$ bisects chords $\overline{TH}$ and $\overline{BV}$.
    Prove: $\overline{TH} \parallel \overline{BV}$

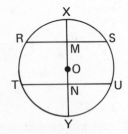

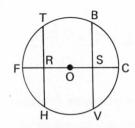

PART C

16. A chord is as long as its distance from the center of the circle. A second chord of the same circle is twice as long. How far is the second chord from the center?

17. Prove: The perpendicular bisector of a chord of a circle in the same plane as the circle goes through the center of the circle.

Congruent Circles

REVIEW CAPSULE

Congruent figures have the same size and shape.

$\overline{OA} \cong \overline{PB}$ —————————→

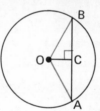

Circle O is congruent to circle P. —————→

$\odot O \cong \odot P$

Definition of *congruent circles* —————→ | *Congruent circles* are circles with congruent radii.

EXAMPLE 1

Given: $\odot O \cong \odot P$
$\overline{OC} \perp \overline{AB}$,
$\overline{PF} \perp \overline{DE}$,
$\overline{AB} \cong \overline{DE}$
Prove: $\overline{OC} \cong \overline{PF}$

ANALYSIS

Show $\triangle AOB \cong \triangle DPE$.
Then $\overline{OC}$ and $\overline{PF}$ are altitudes of $\cong \triangle$'s.

Proof

Statements	Reasons
1. $\overline{OA} \cong \overline{PE}$, $\overline{OB} \cong \overline{PD}$	1. Radii of $\cong \odot$'s are $\cong$.
2. $\overline{AB} \cong \overline{DE}$	2. Given
3. $\triangle AOB \cong \triangle DPE$	3. SSS for $\cong \triangle$'s
4. $\overline{OC} \cong \overline{PF}$	4. Alt. of $\cong \triangle$'s are $\cong$.

$\overline{OC}$ is an altitude of $\triangle AOB$. ⎤
$\overline{PF}$ is an altitude of $\triangle DPE$. ⎦ —————→

In Example 1, OC and PF are the distances from the centers to chords $\overline{AB}$ and $\overline{DE}$.

Theorem 10.3

(See Exercise 18.)

If chords of a circle (or congruent circles) are congruent, then they are equidistant from the center(s).

EXAMPLE 2

$JK = 12$, $MS = 6$, $\overline{CS} \perp \overline{MN}$, $\overline{CR} \perp \overline{JK}$, $CR = 3$.
Find CS.

If $MS = 6$, then $MN = 12$.
$\therefore \overline{MN} \cong \overline{JK}$.

Use Theorem 10.3. ⟶ **Thus, $\overline{CS} \cong \overline{CR}$ and $CS = 3$.**

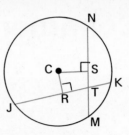

EXAMPLE 3

State the converse of Theorem 10.3. Draw a picture and state what is given and what is to be proved. Write an analysis for the proof.

If chords of a circle (or congruent circles) are equidistant from the center(s), then the chords are congruent.

Given: $\odot O \cong \odot P$,
$OC = PF$,
Distance is measured along $\perp$'s. ⟶ $\overline{OC} \perp \overline{AB}$, $\overline{PF} \perp \overline{DE}$
Prove: $\overline{AB} \cong \overline{DE}$

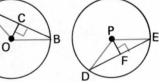

Analysis: Show $\triangle OCB \cong \triangle PFE$. So, $\angle B \cong \angle E$.
Similarly, show $\triangle OCA \cong \triangle PFD$ and $\angle A \cong \angle D$. Then,
$\triangle OAB \cong \triangle PDE$ by AAS and $\overline{AB} \cong \overline{DE}$.

Theorem 10.4

(See Exercise 19.)

If chords of a circle (or congruent circles) are equidistant from the center(s), then the chords are congruent.

EXERCISES

PART A

In each case, determine whether $\odot O \cong \odot O'$.

1. $AO = 5$ in., $A'O' = 5$ in.
3. $OB = 4$ cm, $A'B' = 4$ cm
5. $AB = 3$ yd, $A'B' = 3$ ft
7. $OA = 8$ in., $A'B' = 1.5$ ft

2. $AO = 8$ cm, $B'O' = 8$ cm
4. $AB = 10$ cm, $A'O' = 5$ cm
6. $AO = 12$ in. $A'B' = 2$ ft
8. $OB = \frac{2}{3}$ ft, $A'B' = 16$ in.

9. $\overline{OJ} \perp \overline{RS}$, $\overline{OM} \perp \overline{TU}$, $OJ = 9$, $RS = 16$, $OM = 9$
Find TU.

10. $\overline{OJ} \perp \overline{RS}$, $\overline{OM} \perp \overline{TU}$, $RS = 16$, $TM = 8$, $OM = 4$
Find OJ.

On the basis of the given information, which segments can you conclude are congruent?

11. $\odot A \cong \odot B$, $\overline{RS} \cong \overline{TU}$, $\overline{AM} \perp \overline{RS}$, $\overline{BN} \perp \overline{UT}$

12. In $\odot H$, $\overline{HQ} \cong \overline{HP}$

13. Radii $\overline{NA} \cong \overline{ND} \cong \overline{QX} \cong \overline{OZ}$, $\overline{NT} \perp \overline{AD}$, $\overline{QS} \perp \overline{XZ}$

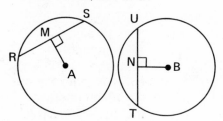

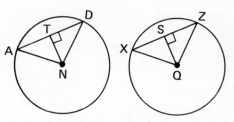

14. Diameter $\overline{XY}$ of $\odot O$, $\overline{OY}$ bisects $\angle ROS$, $OR = 12$, $m \angle ROS = 120$, $\overline{TU} \cong \overline{RS}$. Find WX.

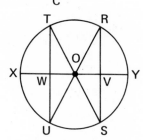

15. Diameter $\overline{XY}$ of $\odot O$, $\overline{OY}$ $\perp \overline{RS}$ at V, $OV = 12$, $OS = 16$, $\overline{TU} \cong \overline{RS}$, $\overline{OX} \perp \overline{TU}$ at W. Find OW.

PART B

16. Given: Radii $\overline{OW}$, $\overline{OX}$, $\overline{OY}$, $\overline{OZ}$ of $\odot O$. $\overline{OT} \perp \overline{XY}$, $\overline{OU} \perp \overline{WZ}$, $\overline{OT} \cong \overline{OU}$
Prove: $\triangle XOY \cong \triangle ZOW$

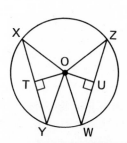

17. Given: Radii $\overline{OW}$, $\overline{OX}$, $\overline{OY}$, $\overline{OZ}$ of $\odot O$. $\overline{OT} \perp \overline{XY}$, $\overline{OU}$ $\perp \overline{WZ}$, $\angle XOY \cong \angle ZOW$
Prove: $\overline{OT} \cong \overline{OU}$

18. Prove Theorem 10.3.

19. Prove Theorem 10.4.

Definition of *inscribed polygon* ⟶ An *inscribed polygon* is a polygon whose sides are chords of a circle.

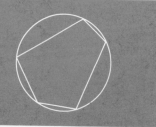

Draw a picture for each of the following. State what is given and what is to be proved. Write an analysis for the proof.

20. If congruent chords are equidistant from the centers of circles, then the circles are congruent.

21. If the center of a circle is equidistant from the sides of an inscribed triangle, then the triangle is equilateral.

22. If the center of a circle is equidistant from the sides of an inscribed quadrilateral, then the quadrilateral is a square.

Tangents to Circles

▶ REVIEW CAPSULE

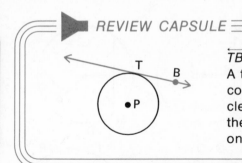

$\overleftrightarrow{TB}$ is tangent to ⊙ P. A tangent is a line coplanar with the circle which intersects the circle in exactly one point.

EXAMPLE 1 Draw a circle and a radius. Construct a line perpendicular to the radius at its endpoint on the circle.

Use the construction for a ⊥ to a line through a point on the line.

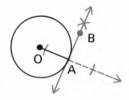

$\overleftrightarrow{BA} \perp \overline{OA}$. $\overleftrightarrow{BA}$ is also tangent to ⊙ O at A.

Theorem	**10.5**	If a line is perpendicular to a radius at its endpoint on the circle, then it is tangent to the circle.

↗ means is not ⊥.

Tangent ℓ ⊥ radius $\overline{OP}$.   Secant ℓ ↗ radius $\overline{OP}$.

Theorem	**10.6**	If a line is tangent to a circle, then it is perpendicular to a radius which ends at the point of tangency.

EXAMPLE 2 $\overleftrightarrow{TQ}$ is tangent to ⊙ O at J. Find $m \angle OJT$.

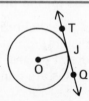

Apply Theorem 10.6. ────────────▶ Since $\overline{OJ} \perp \overline{TQ}$, $m \angle OJT = 90$.

EXAMPLE 3 $\overline{PT}$ tangent to $\odot O$. $\overline{OT}$ is a radius. $OT = 5$, $PO = 11$. Find PT.

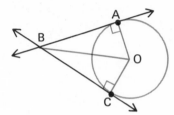

$\overleftrightarrow{PT}$ is on tangent $\overrightarrow{PT}$.

$\overline{OT} \perp \overline{PT}$ by Th. 10.6. ⟶ $\triangle OPT$ is a right $\triangle$.

Pythagorean Theorem ⟶
$$11^2 = 5^2 + x^2$$
$$121 = 25 + x^2$$
$$96 = x^2$$
$$x = \sqrt{96}, \text{ or } 4\sqrt{6}$$

A tangent segment joins the point of tangency with another point on the tangent. ⟶ $\overline{PT}$, in Example 3, is called a *tangent segment*.

Thus, $PT = 4\sqrt{6}$.

Theorem   10.7

Tangent segments to a circle from the same point are congruent.

ANALYSIS
Draw radii $\overline{OA}$ and $\overline{OC}$. Draw $\overline{OB}$.
Show $\triangle OAB \cong \triangle OCB$.

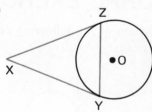

GIVEN
$\overleftrightarrow{BA}$ and $\overleftrightarrow{BC}$ tangents to $\odot O$
PROVE
$\overline{BA} \cong \overline{BC}$

PROOF

STATEMENTS

1. Draw radii $\overline{OA}$ and $\overline{OC}$.
2. $\overline{OA} \perp \overline{BA}$ and $\overline{OC} \perp \overline{BC}$
3. Draw $\overline{OB}$, forming rt. $\triangle$'s AOB and COB.
4. $\overline{BO} \cong \overline{BO}$ (H)
5. $\overline{OA} \cong \overline{OC}$ (L)
6. $\triangle AOB \cong \triangle COB$
7. $\therefore \overline{BA} \cong \overline{BC}$

REASONS

1. Two points are contained in exactly one line.
2. Radii are $\perp$ to tangents.
3. Same as 1
4. Reflexive property
5. All radii of a $\odot$ are $\cong$.
6. *HL* for $\cong$ rt. $\triangle$'s
7. Corr. sides of $\cong$ $\triangle$'s are $\cong$.

EXAMPLE 4 $\overline{XY}$ and $\overline{XZ}$ are tangent to $\odot O$ at Y and Z. $m\angle Y = 6t - 2$, $m\angle Z = 4t + 22$. Find $m\angle X$.

$\overline{XZ} \cong \overline{XY}$

$\angle$'s opp. $\cong$ sides of $\triangle$ are $\cong$. ⟶
$$\angle Y = \angle Z$$
$$6t - 2 = 4t + 22$$
$$2t = 24$$
$$t = 12$$

$m\angle Y = 6(12) - 2$
$m\angle Z = 4(12) + 22$ ⟶ $m\angle Y = 70$, $m\angle Z = 70$
$m\angle X + 70 + 70 = 180$. ⟶ **Thus,** $m\angle X = 40$.

Definition of *tangent circles* ──────→ Two circles are *tangent* if they are coplanar and
tangent to the same line at the same point.

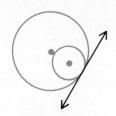

Externally tangent circles   Internally tangent circles

EXAMPLE 5   Given: ⊙O ≅ ⊙P. ⊙O and
⊙P are externally tangent
to $\overleftrightarrow{ST}$.

ANALYSIS   Prove: $\overline{OS} \cong \overline{PS}$
Show that △OTS ≅ △PTS.

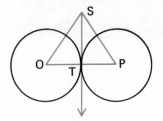

Proof

Statements	Reasons
1. $\overline{OT} \perp \overrightarrow{ST}$	1. A radius is ⊥ to tangent.
2. $\overline{PT} \perp \overrightarrow{ST}$	2. Same as 1
3. ∠OTS ≅ ∠PTS (A)	3. ⊥'s form ≅ rt. ∠'s.
4. $\overline{OT} \cong \overline{PT}$ (S)	4. Radii of ≅ ⊙'s are ≅.
5. $\overline{ST} \cong \overline{ST}$ (S)	5. Reflexive property
6. △OTS ≅ △PTS	6. SAS for ≅ △'s
7. ∴ $\overline{OS} \cong \overline{PS}$	7. Corr. sides of ≅ △'s are ≅.

ORAL EXERCISES

Which of the following pairs of circles are tangent internally? Which are tangent externally?

1.

2.

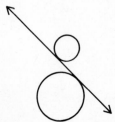

3.

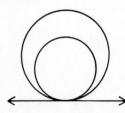

4.

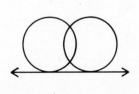

EXERCISES

PART A

1. Tangents $\overrightarrow{XT}$, $\overrightarrow{XN}$, and $\overrightarrow{XC}$, $XC = 8$. Find XT.

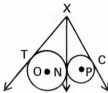

2. Tangents $\overline{AB}$, $\overline{BC}$, and $\overline{CA}$, $AD = 4$, $DB = 6$, $CE = 2$. Find $AB + BC + CA$.

3. Tangents $\overrightarrow{PH}$ and $\overrightarrow{PX}$. $HN = 5$, $NP = 8$. Find XP.

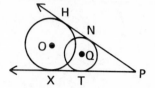

4. Radii $\overline{OA}$ and $\overline{OC}$, tangents $\overrightarrow{AP}$ and $\overrightarrow{CP}$, $m\angle AOC = 140$. Find $m\angle APC$.

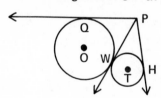

5. Tangents $\overline{AC}$, $\overline{CE}$, $\overline{EG}$ and $\overline{GA}$, $AB = 5$, $CD = 4$, $DE = 3$, $FG = 2$. Find $AC + CE + EG + GA$.

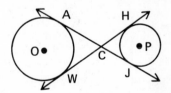

6. Diameter $\overline{XY}$, tangent $\overleftrightarrow{WZ}$, $XY = 10$, $WZ = 12$. Find YZ.

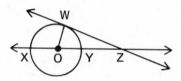

Which segments are congruent? Which angles are congruent?

7. $\overrightarrow{PQ}$ tangent to $\odot O$ at Q, $\overrightarrow{PW}$ tangent to $\odot O$ and $\odot T$ at W, $\overrightarrow{PH}$ tangent to $\odot T$ at H.

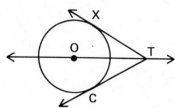

8. $\overleftrightarrow{AJ}$ tangent to $\odot O$ at A and $\odot P$ at J, $\overleftrightarrow{WH}$ tangent to $\odot O$ at W and $\odot P$ at H.

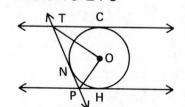

9. $\overline{TQ}$ is a diameter of $\odot O$, $\overleftrightarrow{XN}$ tangent to $\odot O$ at T, $\overleftrightarrow{CV}$ tangent to $\odot O$ at Q.

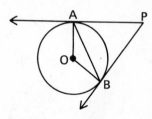

PART B

10. Given: $\overleftrightarrow{TX}$ tangent to $\odot O$ at X, $\overleftrightarrow{TC}$ tangent to $\odot O$ at C. Prove: $\overrightarrow{TO}$ bisects $\angle XTC$.

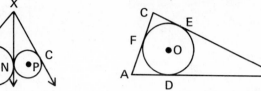

11. Given: $\overleftrightarrow{TC}$ tangent to $\odot O$ at C, $\overleftrightarrow{PH}$ tangent to $\odot O$ at N, $\overleftrightarrow{TC} \parallel \overleftrightarrow{PH}$ Prove: $\overline{TO} \perp \overline{PO}$

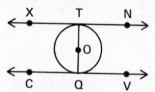

12. Given: $\overrightarrow{PA}$ tangent to $\odot O$ at A, $\overrightarrow{PB}$ tangent to $\odot O$ at B. Prove: $m\angle P = 2\, m\angle OAB$

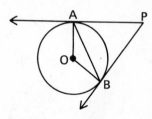

13. Given: $\overrightarrow{JX}$ tangent to $\odot O$ at J, $\overrightarrow{VT}$ tangent to $\odot O$ at V, $\overleftrightarrow{XT}$ tangent to $\odot O$ at M, $\overline{XO} \perp \overline{TO}$
Prove: $\overrightarrow{JX} \parallel \overrightarrow{VT}$

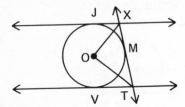

14. Given: Two circles with same center O, chord $\overline{AB}$ of outer circle tangent to inner circle at X
Prove: $\overline{AX} \cong \overline{BX}$

15. Given: Radius $\overline{OA} \perp$ radius $\overline{OB}$ of $\odot O$, chord $\overline{AD}$, $\overrightarrow{DE}$ tangent at D, radius $\overline{OD}$
Prove: $\angle ECD \cong \angle EDC$

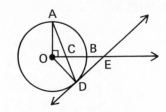

PART C

16. $\overrightarrow{XY}$ tangent to $\odot O$ and $\odot P$, $OX = 16$, $PY = 6$, $OP = 26$. Find XY.

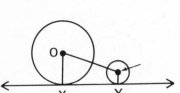

17. Tangents $\overline{XY}$, $\overline{YZ}$, and $\overline{ZX}$, $XY = 7$, $YZ = 8$, $ZX = 5$. Find AX, BY, and CZ.

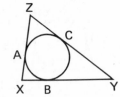

18. Tangents $\overline{ZN}$, $\overline{NQ}$, $\overline{QC}$, and $\overline{CZ}$, $ZC = 21$, $ZN = 24$, $NQ = 30$. Find CQ.

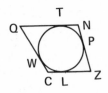

Algebra Review

To solve a radical equation:
1. Get the radical alone on one side of $=$.
2. Square each side.
3. Solve the new equation.
4. Check.

EXAMPLE Solve $\sqrt{2x + 1} - 1 = 4$

Get the radical alone. ⟶ $\sqrt{2x + 1} = 5$

Square each side. ⟶ $2x + 1 = 25$

$2x = 24$

$x = 12$

Check.

$$\begin{array}{c|c} \sqrt{2x + 1} - 1 & 4 \\ \hline \sqrt{2(12) + 1} - 1 & 4 \\ \sqrt{25} - 1 & \\ 4 & \end{array}$$

Thus, the solution is 12.

Solve.

1. $\sqrt{x} = 5$

2. $\sqrt{y + 1} = 4$

3. $\sqrt{3b + 3} = 6$

4. $3\sqrt{x} - 2 = 10$

5. $\sqrt{5a - 1} - 3 = 0$

6. $\sqrt{2t + 7} = 8$

7. $\sqrt{3x - 8} = \sqrt{x}$

8. $\sqrt{5y} - \sqrt{2y + 6} = 0$

9. $\sqrt{4m - 3} = \sqrt{3m + 4}$

Arcs and Central Angles

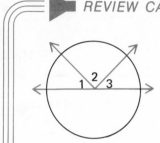

REVIEW CAPSULE

$$m \angle 1 + m \angle 2 + m \angle 3 = 180$$

The sum of the measures of the angles with the same vertex on one side of a line is 180°.

EXAMPLE 1 $\overleftrightarrow{PA}$ and $\overleftrightarrow{PB}$ are tangents.
$m \angle APB = 60$.
Find $m \angle AOB$.

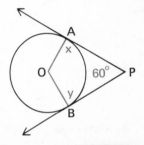

Radii are ⊥ to tangents.
Sum of the angle measures of a quadrilateral is 360°.

$m \angle x = m \angle y = 90$
$m \angle AOB = 360 - (90 + 90 + 60)$
Thus, $m \angle AOB = 120$.

Definition of *central angle*

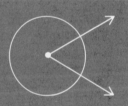

A *central angle* of a circle is an angle whose vertex is the center of the circle.

Central angles are used to measure arcs.

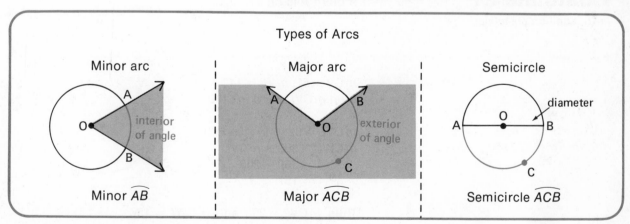

Types of Arcs

Minor arc	Major arc	Semicircle
interior of angle	exterior of angle	diameter
Minor $\overarc{AB}$	Major $\overarc{ACB}$	Semicircle $\overarc{ACB}$

EXAMPLE 2 Identify each arc as a minor arc, major arc, or semicircle.

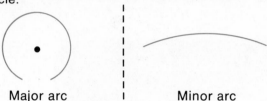

Major arc   Minor arc

Degree Measures of Arcs

Minor arc	Major arc	Semicircle

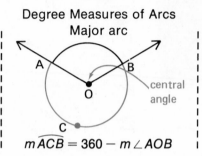

$m\widehat{AB} = m\angle AOB$ $m\widehat{ACB} = 360 - m\angle AOB$ $m\widehat{ACB} = 180$

EXAMPLE 3 Find the measure of each given arc.

Three points are usually used to name a major arc.

$m\angle AOB = 60.$ $m\angle QOL = 60.$ $m\angle SOA = 120.$
Find $m\widehat{AB}.$ Find $m\widehat{QL}.$ Find $m\widehat{SCA}.$

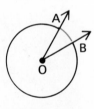
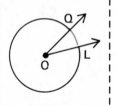
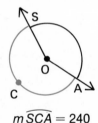

Arcs from circles of different sizes can have equal degree measures.

$m\widehat{AB} = 60$ $m\widehat{QL} = 60$ $m\widehat{SCA} = 240$

Postulate 21
(Arc addition postulate)

If point P is on $\widehat{AB}$, then
$$m\widehat{AP} + m\widehat{PB} = m\widehat{AB}.$$

EXAMPLE 4 $m\widehat{CV} = 62,\ m\widehat{VL} = 141.$
Find $m\widehat{CVL}.$ Find $m\widehat{CWL}.$

V is on $\widehat{CVL}.$
$m\widehat{CVL} = m\widehat{CV} + m\widehat{VL}$ ⟶ $m\widehat{CVL} = 62 + 141,$ or 203
$m\widehat{CWL} + m\widehat{CVL} = 360$ ⟶ $m\widehat{CWL} = 360 - m\widehat{CVL}$
$= 360 - 203$
$= 157$

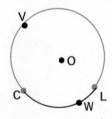

Thus, $m\widehat{CVL} = 203$ and $m\widehat{CWL} = 157.$

EXAMPLE 5 Find the contradictory information.
Diameter $\overline{AD}$, $m\widehat{AC} = 72$,
$m\widehat{CD} = 118$, $m\widehat{DB} = 62$.

Contradiction. ————————→ If $\overline{AD}$ is a diameter, then $m\widehat{ACD} = 180$.
————————→ But, $m\widehat{ACD} = m\widehat{AC} + m\widehat{CD} = 72 + 118$, or 190.
Thus, for the given arc measures, $\overline{AD}$ cannot be a
diameter.

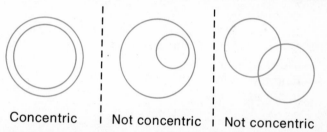

common center

Concentric circles

Definition of *concentric circles* ————————→ | *Concentric circles* are circles with a common center.

EXAMPLE 6 Which of the following appear to be concentric circles?

Concentric circles must have the same
center.

Concentric | Not concentric | Not concentric

ORAL EXERCISES

Give the measure of each arc.

1.

$m\widehat{AB} = ?$

2.

$m\widehat{CED} = ?$

3.

$m\widehat{FG} = ?$

4.

$m\widehat{HKJ} = ?$

Which of the following are concentric circles?

5.

6.

7.

8.

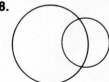

EXERCISES

PART A

Find the measure of each arc by measuring the central angle with a protractor.

1.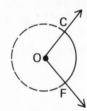

2.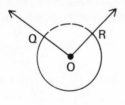

3.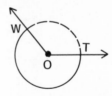

4.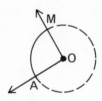

BD is a diameter.

5. Identify all minor arcs of ⊙O.

6. Identify all major arcs of ⊙O.

7. Identify all semicircles of ⊙O.

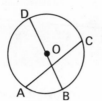

8. $\overline{UX}$ is a diameter of ⊙O. $m\,\widehat{UV} = 62$, $m\,\widehat{WX} = 42$. Find $m\,\widehat{VW}$. 76

9. $m\,\widehat{TU} = 72$, $m\,\widehat{UV} = 48$, $m\,\widehat{VW} = 60$, $m\,\widehat{WX} = 72$, $m\,\widehat{XY} = 56$, $m\,\widehat{YT} = 52$. Which chords (if any) are diameters?

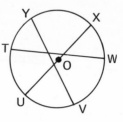

10. $\overline{LC}$ and $\overline{QV}$ are diameters of ⊙O, $m\angle VOC = 56$. Find the measure of each minor arc.

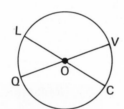

11. $\overline{LC}$ and $\overline{QV}$ are diameters of ⊙O, $m\,\widehat{VC} = 63$. Find the measure of each major arc.

AC and BD are diameters of ⊙O, $m\,\widehat{DC} = 79$.

12. Find $m\angle AOD$.
13. Find $m\angle AOB$.
14. Find $m\,\widehat{ADC}$.
15. Find $m\,\widehat{BC}$.

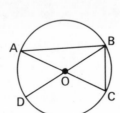

AC and BD are diameters of ⊙O, $m\angle AOB = 123$.

16. Find $m\angle BOC$.
17. Find $m\,\widehat{AB}$.
18. Find $m\,\widehat{BCD}$.
19. Find $m\,\widehat{CAB}$.

PART B

In each of the following, determine whether contradictory information is given. If so, which information contradicts which?

20. $\overline{GJ}$ and $\overline{HK}$ are diameters. $m\,\widehat{GL} = 84$, $m\,\widehat{LK} = 34$, $m\,\widehat{KJ} = 62$, $m\,\widehat{JI} = 27$, $m\,\widehat{IH} = 79$, $m\,\widehat{HG} = 74$.

21. $\overline{GJ}$ is a diameter, $m\,\widehat{GK} = 110$ $m\,\widehat{LK} = 72$, $m\,\widehat{LJ} = 142$, $m\,\widehat{GI} = 113$, $m\,\widehat{HI} = 44$, $m\,\widehat{IJ} = 77$.

Arcs and Chords

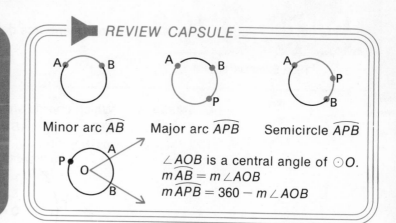

REVIEW CAPSULE

Minor arc $\overset{\frown}{AB}$ Major arc $\overset{\frown}{APB}$ Semicircle $\overset{\frown}{APB}$

$\angle AOB$ is a central angle of $\odot O$.
$m\overset{\frown}{AB} = m\angle AOB$
$m\overset{\frown}{APB} = 360 - m\angle AOB$

Some arcs with the same measure are congruent.

≢ is read is not congruent to ⟶

$\odot O \not\cong \odot Q$
$m\overset{\frown}{AB} = m\overset{\frown}{CD},\ \overset{\frown}{AB} \not\cong \overset{\frown}{CD}$

$\odot O \cong \odot Q$
$m\overset{\frown}{AB} = m\overset{\frown}{CD},\ \overset{\frown}{AB} \cong \overset{\frown}{CD}$

Definition of congruent arcs ⟶

Congruent arcs are arcs of the same (or congruent circles) with the same degree measure.

EXAMPLE 1   Based on the information given, which arcs are congruent?
$m\overset{\frown}{AB} = 48$, $m\overset{\frown}{AC} = 124$,
$m\overset{\frown}{ABD} = 208$, $m\overset{\frown}{ABE} = 312$

$m\overset{\frown}{EA} = 360 - m\overset{\frown}{ABE}$ ⟶ $m\overset{\frown}{EA} = 48$ $m\overset{\frown}{AB} = 48$
Thus, $\overset{\frown}{AB} \cong \overset{\frown}{EA}$.

EXAMPLE 2 $\odot O \cong \odot P$, $m\overset{\frown}{AB} = 120$, $m\overset{\frown}{CD} = 120$,
$OA = 5$, $PC = 5$.
Find AB and CD.

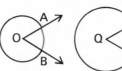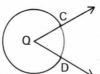

⊥ bis. of base of isos. rt. △ bisects vertex ∠. ⟶ $\triangle AOG$ is a 30°-60° rt. △.
$AG = \frac{5}{2}\sqrt{3}$
$AB = 5\sqrt{3}$

$\overline{AB}$ and $\overline{CD}$ are ≅ chords. ⟶ $\triangle DPH$ is a 30°-60° rt. △.
$CH = \frac{5}{2}\sqrt{3}$
$CD = 5\sqrt{3}$

In Example 2, $\overarc{AB}$ determines $\overline{AB}$ and $\overline{AB}$ determines $\overarc{AB}$.

| **Theorem** | **10.8** | Congruent arcs determine congruent chords. |

(See Exercise 17.)

EXAMPLE 3 Which chords are congruent?
$\odot O \cong \odot P$, $m\overarc{AB} = 118$, $m\overarc{CD} = 133$, $m\overarc{EF} = 129$, $m\overarc{GH} = 118$.

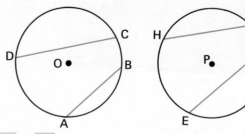

$\overarc{AB} \cong \overarc{GH}$ ⟶ **Thus,** $\overline{AB} \cong \overline{GH}$

EXAMPLE 4 Prove or disprove: Congruent chords determine congruent arcs.

A counterexample will disprove the statement.

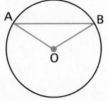

The chords are ≅ but the arcs they determine are not.

But $m\overarc{AB} = 82$ and $m\overarc{CD} = 103$. $\overarc{AB} \not\cong \overarc{CD}$

| **Theorem** | **10.9** | Congruent chords of the same circle (or congruent circles) determine congruent minor arcs. |

(See Exercise 18.)

ANALYSIS
Show $\angle AOB \cong \angle A'O'B'$ by proving $\triangle OAB \cong \triangle O'A'B'$.

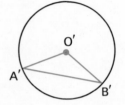

GIVEN
$\odot O \cong \odot O'$
$\overline{AB} \cong \overline{A'B'}$
PROVE
$\overarc{AB} \cong \overarc{A'B'}$

OUTLINE OF PROOF

1. $\overline{AB} \cong \overline{A'B'}$
2. $\overline{OA} \cong \overline{O'A'}$ and $\overline{OB} \cong \overline{O'B'}$
3. $\triangle OAB \cong \triangle O'A'B'$

4. $\angle AOB \cong \angle A'O'B'$
5. $m\overarc{AB} = m\angle AOB$ and $m\overarc{A'B'} = m\angle A'O'B'$
6. $\therefore \overarc{AB} \cong \overarc{A'B'}$

EXAMPLE 5 Prove: A radius perpendicular to a chord bisects the arc determined by the chord.

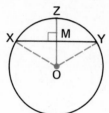

ANALYSIS
Draw radii $\overline{OX}$ and $\overline{OY}$.
Show $\angle XOM \cong \angle YOM$ by proving $\triangle$'s $\cong$.

Given: Radius $\overline{OZ} \perp$ chord $\overline{XY}$
Prove: $\widehat{XZ} \cong \widehat{ZY}$

Proof

Statements	Reasons
1. $\overline{XM} \cong \overline{MY}$	1. Radius $\perp$ chord bisects chord
2. $\overline{OX} \cong \overline{OY}$	2. Radii of a $\odot$ are $\cong$.
3. $\overline{OM} \cong \overline{OM}$	3. Reflexive property
4. $\triangle XOM \cong \triangle YOM$	4. SSS for $\cong \triangle$'s
5. $\angle XOM \cong \angle YOM$	5. Corr. $\angle$'s of $\cong \triangle$'s are $\cong$.
6. $\therefore \widehat{XZ} \cong \widehat{ZY}$	6. Def. of $\cong$ arcs.

$\left. \begin{array}{l} m\widehat{XZ} = m\angle XOM \\ m\widehat{ZY} = m\angle YOM \end{array} \right\}$

EXAMPLE 6 $\overline{XW} \cong \overline{YZ}$, $m\widehat{XW} = 10t + 5$, $m\widehat{YZ} = 12t - 21$
Find $m\widehat{XW}$.

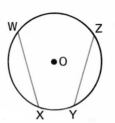

$\overline{XW} \cong \overline{YZ}$ ⟶
$\widehat{XW} \cong \widehat{YZ}$
$10t + 5 = 12t - 21$
$-2t = -26$
$t = 13$

$m\widehat{XW} = 10(13) + 5$ ⟶ **Thus, $m\widehat{XW} = 135$.**

ORAL EXERCISES

Which arcs are congruent?

1. $AB = 7$, $BC = 8$, $CD = 9$, $DA = 8$
2. $\overline{AB} \cong \overline{CB}$

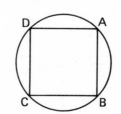

Which chords are congruent?

3. $m\widehat{AB} = 150$, $m\widehat{BC} = 80$ $m\widehat{CD} = 50$, $m\widehat{DA} = 80$
4. $\widehat{AB} \cong \widehat{CD}$, $\widehat{DA} \cong \widehat{CB}$

EXERCISES

PART A

In which cases can you conclude that chord $\overline{WX} \cong$ chord $\overline{ST}$?

1. $\overline{OW} \cong \overline{PS}$
2. $\widehat{WX} \cong \widehat{ST}$
3. $m\widehat{WYX} = m\widehat{SUT}$

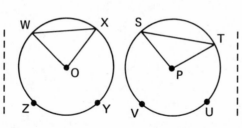

Which arcs are congruent if $\odot O \cong \odot P$?

4. $m\widehat{XY} = 85$ $m\widehat{ST} = 95$
   $m\widehat{XYZ} = 190$ $m\widehat{STU} = 180$
   $m\widehat{XZW} = 300$ $m\widehat{STV} = 240$

On the basis of the given information, which arcs (if any) are congruent?

5. $\overline{CD} \cong \overline{PQ}$

6. Radius $\overline{OC} \cong$ radius $\overline{PT}$, $\overline{CL} \cong \overline{TM}$

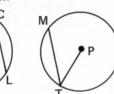

7. $\angle TOV \cong \angle WCB$

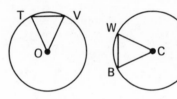

Which arcs are congruent to $\widehat{AB}$ **? to** $\widehat{BC}$ **? to** $\widehat{DF}$ **?**

8. $m\widehat{AB} = 35$, $m\widehat{AC} = 75$, $m\widehat{AD} = 110$
$m\widehat{AE} = 160$, $m\widehat{ABF} = 180$, $m\widehat{ADG} = 215$
$m\widehat{ADH} = 240$, $m\widehat{ADI} = 280$, $m\widehat{ADJ} = 305$

9. Given: $\widehat{RY} \cong \widehat{RL}$
Prove: $\triangle RLY$ is isosceles.

10. Given: $\angle Y \cong \angle L$
Prove: $\widehat{RY} \cong \widehat{RL}$

11. $\overline{AB} \cong \overline{CD}$, $m\widehat{AB} = 3x + 18$,
$m\widehat{CD} = 4x - 12$.
Find $m\widehat{AB}$.

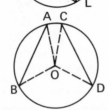

12. $\angle AOB \cong \angle COD$, $m\widehat{AB} = 10x + 18$, $m\widehat{CD} = 12x - 6$.
Find $m\widehat{AB}$.

13. Given: $\overline{OX}, \overline{OY}, \overline{OZ}$ are radii
of $\odot O$, $\angle ZXY \cong \angle ZYX$.
Prove: $\angle XOZ \cong \angle YOZ$

14. Given: $\overline{OX}, \overline{OY}, \overline{OZ}$ are radii
of $\odot O$, $\triangle XOZ \cong \triangle YOZ$.
Prove: $\widehat{XZ} \cong \widehat{YZ}$

PART B

15. Given: $\overline{NL}$ is a diameter
of $\odot O$, $\widehat{KL} = \widehat{ML}$.
Prove: $\angle KNL \cong \angle MNL$

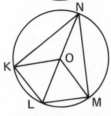

16. Given: $\overline{NL}$ is a diameter of
$\odot O$, $\angle KNL \cong \angle MNL$.
Prove: $\widehat{KL} \cong \widehat{ML}$

17. Prove Theorem 10.8.

18. Prove Theorem 10.9.

19. Given: Radii $\overline{OB}$ and $\overline{OV}$,
$\overline{NH} \perp \overline{OB}$, $\overline{NJ} \perp \overline{OV}$, $\widehat{NB} \cong \widehat{NV}$
Prove: $\overline{NH} \cong \overline{NJ}$.

20. Given: Radii $\overline{OB}$ and $\overline{OV}$,
$\overline{NH} \perp \overline{OB}$, $\overline{NJ} \perp \overline{OV}$,
$\overline{NH} \cong \overline{NJ}$
Prove: $\widehat{NB} \cong \widehat{NV}$

A Square Circle?

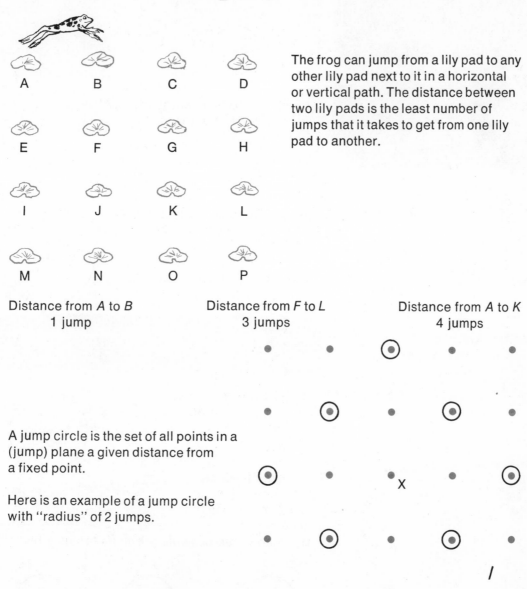

The frog can jump from a lily pad to any other lily pad next to it in a horizontal or vertical path. The distance between two lily pads is the least number of jumps that it takes to get from one lily pad to another.

A B C D

E F G H

I J K L

M N O P

Distance from *A* to *B*
1 jump

Distance from *F* to *L*
3 jumps

Distance from *A* to *K*
4 jumps

A jump circle is the set of all points in a (jump) plane a given distance from a fixed point.

Here is an example of a jump circle with "radius" of 2 jumps.

A jump circle is a square!

What would a jump circle with a "radius" of 3 jumps look like?

Inscribed Angles

REVIEW CAPSULE

 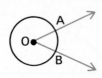

If ∠AOB is a central angle of ⊙O, then $m\angle AOB = m\widehat{AB}$.

$m\widehat{AP} + m\widehat{PB} + m\widehat{BA} = 360$

EXAMPLE 1 Use a protractor to measure ∠XTR and ∠XOR. Are the measures related?

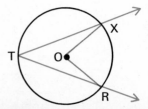

∠XOR is a central angle. ⟶ $m\angle XTR = 40$, $m\angle XOR = 80$
$m\angle XOR = 2m\angle XTR$

Definition of *inscribed angle* ⟶
In Example 1, ∠XTR is an inscribed angle.

An *inscribed angle* is formed by two secants intersecting on the circle.

EXAMPLE 2 In ⊙O $\overline{BC}$ is a diameter and $\overline{OA}$ is a radius. $m\widehat{AC} = 30$. Find $m\angle y$.

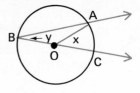

∠x is an exterior ∠ of △ABO. ⟶
$\overline{OB} \cong \overline{OA}$ in △ABO ⟶
$m\angle x = 2m\angle y$ ⟶
$m\angle x = 30$ ⟶

$m\angle x = m\angle y + m\angle A$
$m\angle y = m\angle A$
$m\angle y = \frac{1}{2}m\angle x$
Thus, $m\angle y = 15$.

There are three possible positions for inscribed angles.

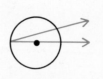   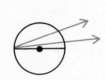

Case I
A side contains a diameter.

Case II
The diameter is inside the angle.

Case III
The diameter is outside the angle.

EXAMPLE 3

An inscribed angle intercepts an arc.
Which arc is intercepted by $\angle XNT$?
$\angle XNT$ intercepts $\overset{\frown}{XT}$.

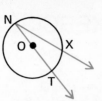

Theorem 10.10

The measure of an inscribed angle is one half the measure of its intercepted arc.

CASE I: A side of the angle contains a diameter.

ANALYSIS

$\angle y$ is an exterior $\angle$ of $\triangle AOB$.
Show $m\angle P = \frac{1}{2}m\angle y$.
Then use $m\angle y = m\overset{\frown}{AB}$.

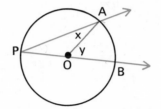

GIVEN

Inscribed $\angle APB$, diameter $\overline{PB}$
PROVE
$m\angle P = \frac{1}{2}m\overset{\frown}{AB}$

PROOF

STATEMENTS	REASONS
1. $\overline{OA} \cong \overline{OP}$	1. Radii of a $\odot$ are $\cong$.
2. $m\angle x = m\angle P$	2. $\angle$'s opp. $\cong$ sides of a $\triangle$ are $\cong$.
3. $m\angle y = m\angle x + m\angle P$	3. Meas. of ext. $\angle$ = sum of meas. of opp. int. $\angle$'s.
4. $m\angle y = 2m\angle P$	4. Substitution property
5. $m\angle P = \frac{1}{2}m\angle y$	5. Multiplication property of =
6. $m\angle y = m\overset{\frown}{AB}$	6. Meas. of arc = meas. of central $\angle$.
7. $\therefore m\angle P = \frac{1}{2}m\overset{\frown}{AB}$	7. Substitution

CASE II and CASE III can be proved by adding or subtracting measures of angles of the type in CASE I.

EXAMPLE 4 $m\angle ABC = 62$, $m\overset{\frown}{BC} = 110$.
Find $m\angle A$ and $m\overset{\frown}{AB}$.

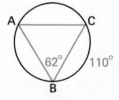

$m\angle A = \frac{1}{2}m\overset{\frown}{BC}$ ⟶ $m\angle A = 55$
$m\angle C = 180 - (62 + 55)$ ⟶ $m\angle C = 63$
$m\angle C = \frac{1}{2}m\overset{\frown}{AB}$ ⟶ $m\overset{\frown}{AB} = 126$

ORAL EXERCISES

Find $m\angle AXB$.

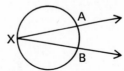

1. $m\overset{\frown}{AB} = 72$ 2. $m\overset{\frown}{AB} = 84$
3. $m\overset{\frown}{AB} = 110$ 4. $m\overset{\frown}{AB} = 44$

Find $m\overset{\frown}{AB}$.

5. $m\angle AXB = 25$ 6. $m\angle AXB = 40$
7. $m\angle AXB = 63$ 8. $m\angle AXB = 18$

EXERCISES

PART A

1. $m\widehat{LC} = 86$.
Find $m \angle LXC$.

2. $m \angle RNQ = 81$.
Find $m\widehat{RQ}$.

3. $m \angle RBS = 33$.
Find $m \angle ROS$.

4. $m\widehat{SQC} = 156$.
Find $m \angle W$ and
$m \angle Q$.

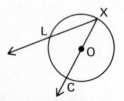

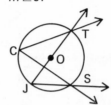

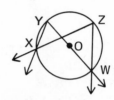

5. $\overline{CN}$ is a diameter.
Find $m \angle CPN$.

6. $\overline{RD} \cong \overline{KD}$, $m\widehat{RD} = 110$.
Find $m \angle RDK$.

7. $m\widehat{TS} = 112$.
Find $m \angle C$ and
$m \angle J$.

8. $m \angle Y = 63$.
Find $m\widehat{XW}$ and
$m \angle Z$.

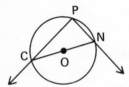

PART B

9. $\overline{RM} \parallel \overline{KW}$, $m\widehat{RK} = 108$.
Find $m \angle K$ and $m \angle KTW$.

10. $\angle TNO \cong \angle TZO$, $m\widehat{NZ} = 65$.
Find $m \angle TNO$ and
$m \angle ONZ$.

11. Diameter $\overline{CJ}$, $m\widehat{RC} = 50$,
$m\widehat{CT} = 30$.
Find $m \angle RCJ$ and $m \angle JTC$.

12. Prove Case II of Theorem 10.10. (Sides
of the inscribed angle are on opposite
sides of a diameter.)

13. Prove Case III of Theorem 10.10. (Sides
of the inscribed angle are on the same
side of a diameter.)

PART C

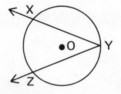

$\angle$ **XYZ is inscribed in** $\widehat{XYZ}$.

14. Prove or disprove: An angle inscribed in
a major arc is acute.

15. Prove or disprove: An angle inscribed in
a minor arc is acute.

Using Inscribed Angles

 REVIEW CAPSULE

OBJECTIVE

■ To apply measurement properties of inscribed angles

Central angle
$m \angle AOB = m\widehat{AB}$

Inscribed angle
$m \angle ACB = \frac{1}{2}\, m\widehat{AB}$

EXAMPLE 1 $m \angle TCP = 3x + 3$, $m\widehat{TP} = 7x - 7$.
Find $m \angle TCP$.

$m \angle TCP = \frac{1}{2}m\widehat{TP}$ ⟶
Multiply each side by 2. ⟶

$$3x + 3 = \frac{1}{2}(7x - 7)$$
$$2(3x + 3) = 7x - 7$$
$$6x + 6 = 7x - 7$$
$$-x = -13$$
$$x = 13$$

$m \angle TCP = 3(13) + 3$ ⟶   **Thus,** $m \angle TCP = 42$.

EXAMPLE 2   Prove: If two arcs are determined by parallel lines, then they are congruent.

ANALYSIS
Draw chord $\overline{RP}$.
Use $\angle x \cong \angle y$ to show $\widehat{CR} \cong \widehat{PM}$.

Given: $\overleftrightarrow{RM} \parallel \overleftrightarrow{CP}$
Prove: $\widehat{CR} \cong \widehat{PM}$

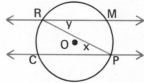

Proof

Statements	Reasons
1. Draw chord $\overline{RP}$.	1. Two points are contained in exactly one line.
2. $m \angle x = m \angle y$	2. Alt. int. $\angle$'s of $\parallel$ lines are $\cong$.
3. $m \angle x = \frac{1}{2}m\widehat{CR}$ $m \angle y = \frac{1}{2}m\widehat{PM}$	3. Meas. of inscribed $\angle = \frac{1}{2}$ meas. of intercepted arc.
4. $\frac{1}{2}m\widehat{CR} = \frac{1}{2}m\widehat{PM}$	4. Substitution property
5. $m\widehat{CR} = m\widehat{PM}$	5. Multiplication property
6. $\therefore \widehat{CR} \cong \widehat{PM}$	6. Def. of $\cong$ arcs

Multiply each side by 2. ⟶

EXAMPLE 3 $\overleftrightarrow{KR} \parallel \overleftrightarrow{JS}$, $m \angle KOJ = 51$.
Find $m\widehat{RS}$.

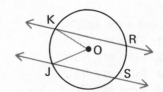

$m\widehat{KJ} = m \angle KOJ$ ⟶
$\parallel$ lines determine $\cong$ arcs. ⟶

$$m\widehat{KJ} = 51$$
Thus, $m\widehat{RS} = 51$.

EXAMPLE 4

ANALYSIS

Show that the intercepted arc measures 180°. Then use Theorem 10.10.

Prove: An angle inscribed in a semicircle is a right angle.

Given: $\overline{XQ}$ is a diameter of $\odot O$.
Prove: $\angle XTQ$ is a right angle.

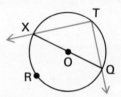

Proof

Statements	Reasons
1. $m\angle XTQ = \frac{1}{2}m\widehat{XRQ}$	1. Meas. of inscribed $\angle = \frac{1}{2}$ meas. of intercepted arc.
2. $m\widehat{XRQ} = 180$	2. Meas. of a semicircle = 180°.
3. $m\angle XTQ = 90$	3. Substitution
4. $\therefore \angle XTQ$ is a rt. $\angle$.	4. Def. of rt. $\angle$

Diameter $\overline{XQ}$ forms semicircle. ⟶ (statement 2)
$\frac{1}{2}(180) = 90$ ⟶ (statement 3)

EXAMPLE 5

ANALYSIS

Express measures of opposite angles in terms of arcs. Show that the sum of the measures of opposite angles is 180°.

Prove: Opposite angles of a quadrilateral inscribed in a circle are supplementary.

Given: Chords $\overline{LM}, \overline{MN}, \overline{NK}, \overline{KL}$
Prove: $\angle K$ and $\angle M$ are supplements.
$\angle L$ and $\angle N$ are supplements.

Proof

Statements	Reasons
1. $m\angle K = \frac{1}{2}m\widehat{LMN}$ $m\angle M = \frac{1}{2}m\widehat{LKN}$	1. Meas. of inscribed $\angle = \frac{1}{2}$ meas. of intercepted arc.
2. $m\angle K + m\angle M = \frac{1}{2}m\widehat{LMN} + \frac{1}{2}m\widehat{LKN}$	2. Addition postulate
3. $m\angle K + m\angle M = \frac{1}{2}(m\widehat{LMN} + m\widehat{LKN})$	3. Distributive property
4. $m\widehat{LMN} + m\widehat{LKN} = 360$	4. Sum of meas. of arcs = 360°.
5. $m\angle K + m\angle M = 180$	5. Substitution
6. $\therefore \angle K$ and $\angle M$ are supplements.	6. Def. of supplements
7. Similarly, $\angle L$ and $\angle N$ are supplements.	7. Steps 1–6.

$\frac{1}{2}(m\widehat{LMN} = m\widehat{LKN}) = \frac{1}{2}(360)$ ⟶ (statement 5)

EXERCISES

PART A

$m\widehat{RM} = 86, \, m\widehat{SD} = 62$

1. Find $m\angle SRD$.
2. Find $m\angle RSM$.
3. Find $m\angle RSQ$.
4. Find $m\angle RQM$.

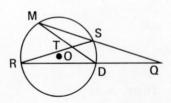

$m\angle R = 36, \, m\angle Q = 42$

5. Find $m\angle RSM$.
6. Find $m\widehat{RM}$.
7. Find $m\widehat{SD}$.
8. Find $m\angle MTS$.

9. $m\angle L = 86$, $m\angle W = 113$.
Find $m\angle J$ and $m\angle B$.

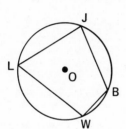

10. $\overline{NR}$ is a diameter of $\odot O$,
$m\widehat{QR} = 84$.
Find $m\angle NQR$ and $m\angle QRN$.

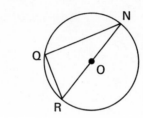

11. Diameter $\overline{AC} \parallel \overline{PV}$,
$m\widehat{PA} = 64$.
Find $m\angle AVC$ and $m\widehat{VC}$.

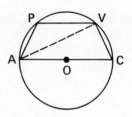

$\overleftrightarrow{TL} \parallel$ **tangent** $\overleftrightarrow{PN}$, $m\angle LTC = 61$.

12. Find $m\widehat{LC}$.
13. Find $m\widehat{TC}$.
14. Find $m\angle TLC$.
15. Find $m\widehat{TL}$.

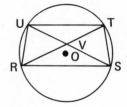

$\overleftrightarrow{TL} \parallel$ **tangent** $\overleftrightarrow{PN}$, $m\widehat{TC} = 142$,
$TC = 8$.

16. Find $m\widehat{LC}$.
17. Find $m\angle TLC$.
18. Find LC.

PART B

19. Given: Diameters $\overline{UT}$ and $\overline{NQ}$
Prove: $\angle UTQ \cong \angle NQT$

20. Given: Diameter $\overline{DX}$,
$m\angle AXD = \frac{1}{2}m\angle DOW$
Prove: $\widehat{AD} \cong \widehat{WD}$

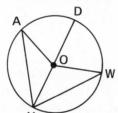

21. Given: $\overline{RS} \parallel \overline{UT}$
Prove: $\overline{RT} \cong \overline{SU}$

22. Given: Diameter $\overline{BX}$,
$\overline{LD} \perp \overline{BX}$
Prove: $\triangle BDL \sim \triangle BLX$

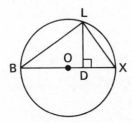

23. Given: Diameter $\overline{BX}$,
$\overline{LD} \perp \overline{BX}$
Prove: $BD \cdot LX = BL \cdot LD$

PART C

Prove or disprove.

24. Two triangles inscribed in congruent circles are congruent if two angles of one are congruent to two angles of the other.

25. If two arcs of a circle intercepted by two secants are congruent, then the secants are parallel.

26. If two consecutive angles of an inscribed quadrilateral are congruent, then the quadrilateral is an isosceles trapezoid.

27. Two triangles inscribed in congruent circles are congruent if a side and an angle of one are congruent to a side and angle of the other.

Secants and Angles

OBJECTIVE

■ To apply formulas for measuring angles formed by two secants

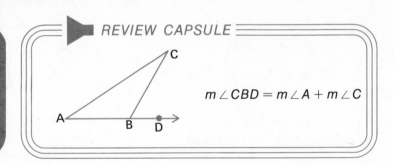

▶ *REVIEW CAPSULE*

$$m \angle CBD = m \angle A + m \angle C$$

Angles are formed by secants.

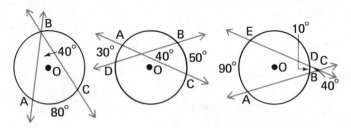

Theorem 10.11

The measure of an angle formed by two secants intersecting in the interior of a circle is one half the sum of the measures of the arcs intercepted by the angle and its vertical angle.

ANALYSIS
Draw $\overleftrightarrow{AC}$. $m \angle APD = m \angle 1 + m \angle 2$.
Express $m \angle 1$ and $m \angle 2$ in terms of their intercepted arcs.

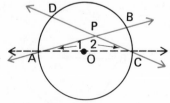

GIVEN
Secants $\overleftrightarrow{AB}$ and $\overleftrightarrow{CD}$ intersecting at P in $\odot O$
PROVE
$m \angle APD = \frac{1}{2}(m\widehat{BC} + m\widehat{AD})$

PROOF

STATEMENTS	REASONS
1. Draw secant $\overleftrightarrow{AC}$	1. Two pts. are contained in exactly one line.
2. $m \angle APD = m \angle 1 + m \angle 2$	2. Meas. of ext. $\angle$ of $\triangle$ = sum of meas. of opp. int. $\angle$'s.
3. $m \angle 1 = \frac{1}{2}m\widehat{BC}$	3. Meas. of inscribed $\angle = \frac{1}{2}$ meas. of intercepted arc.
4. $m \angle 2 = \frac{1}{2}m\widehat{AD}$	4. Same as 3
5. $m \angle APD = \frac{1}{2}m\widehat{BC} + \frac{1}{2}m\widehat{AD}$	5. Substitution property
6. $\therefore m \angle APD = \frac{1}{2}(m\widehat{BC} + m\widehat{AD})$	6. Distributive property

EXAMPLE 1 $m\widehat{RS} = 62$, $m\widehat{TU} = 40$.
Find $m\angle RWS$.

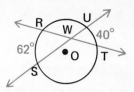

$m\angle RWS = \frac{1}{2}(m\widehat{RS} + m\widehat{TU})$ ⟶ $m\angle RWS = \frac{1}{2}(62 + 40)$, or $\frac{1}{2}(102)$
$m\angle RWS = 51$

EXAMPLE 2 $m\angle AEB = 75$, $m\widehat{CD} = 50$.
Find $m\widehat{AB}$.

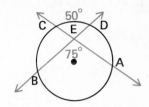

$m\angle AEB = \frac{1}{2}(m\widehat{CD} + m\widehat{AB})$

$75 = \frac{1}{2}(50 + m\widehat{AB})$
$150 = 50 + m\widehat{AB}$
$m\widehat{AB} = 100$

EXAMPLE 3 $m\widehat{ZM} = 102$, $m\widehat{KT} = 38$
Find $m\angle ZBM$.

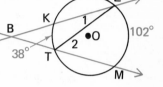

$m\angle 2 = m\angle 1 + m\angle ZBM$
$m\angle 2 = 51$
$m\angle 2 = \frac{1}{2}m\widehat{ZM}$ $m\angle 1 = 19$
$m\angle 1 = \frac{1}{2}m\widehat{KT}$ $m\angle ZBM = 51 - 19$, or 32
$m\angle ZBM = m\angle 2 - m\angle 1$

Theorem 10.12

(See Exercise 14.)

The measure of an angle formed by two secants intersecting in the exterior of a circle is one half the difference of the measures of the intercepted arcs.

EXAMPLE 4 $m\widehat{AB} = y$, $m\widehat{BC} = 2y$,
$m\widehat{CD} = y$, $m\widehat{DA} = 5y$.
Find $m\angle APD$.

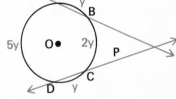

Sum of meas. of arcs = 360. ⟶ $y + 2y + y + 5y = 360$
$9y = 360$
$y = 40$
$m\widehat{DA} = 5(40)$, $m\widehat{BC} = 2(40)$ ⟶ $m\widehat{DA} = 200$ and $m\widehat{BC} = 80$
Use Theorem 10.12. ⟶ $m\angle APD = \frac{1}{2}(200 - 80)$, or 60

ORAL EXERCISES

1. $m\widehat{RS} = 60$, $m\widehat{UT} = 40$.
Find $m\angle RPS$.

3. $m\widehat{RS} = 20$, $m\widehat{UT} = 100$.
Find $m\angle UPT$.

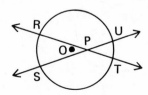

2. $m\widehat{RU} = 100$, $m\widehat{ST} = 80$.
Find $m\angle RPU$.

4. $m\widehat{RU} = 90$, $m\widehat{ST} = 110$
Find $m\angle TPS$.

5. $m\widehat{MJ} = 140$, $m\widehat{LK} = 40$.
Find $m\angle MPJ$.

7. $m\widehat{MJ} = 90$, $m\widehat{LK} = 30$.
Find $m\angle MPJ$.

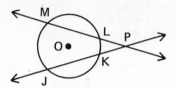

6. $m\widehat{MJ} = 200$, $m\widehat{LK} = 100$.
Find $m\angle MPJ$.

8. $m\widehat{MJ} = 120$, $m\widehat{LK} = 60$.
Find $m\angle MPJ$.

EXERCISES

PART A

1. $m\widehat{AB} = 115$, $m\angle ATB = 63$.
Find $m\widehat{DC}$.

3. $m\widehat{AB} = 6x$, $m\widehat{BC} = 6x$,
$m\widehat{CD} = x$, $m\widehat{DA} = 2x$.
Find $m\angle ATB$.

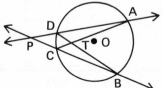

2. $m\angle APC = 27$, $m\widehat{DC} = 27$.
Find $m\widehat{AB}$.

4. $m\widehat{AB} = 4x$, $m\widehat{BC} = 3x$,
$m\widehat{CD} = 2x$, $m\widehat{DA} = 3x$.
Find $m\angle APB$.

5. $m\angle G = 103$, $m\angle GRK = 71$,
$\overline{RT} \parallel \overline{GC}$.
Find $m\angle KRT$ and $m\angle C$.

6. Diameter $\overline{QN}$, $m\widehat{WN} = 41$,
$m\widehat{QC} = 53$.
Find $m\angle Q$ and $m\angle NXW$.

7. $\overrightarrow{QK} \parallel \overrightarrow{ET}$, $m\widehat{KT} = 62$,
$m\angle QET = 104$.
Find $m\angle QOE$ and $m\angle EQT$.

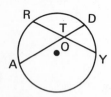

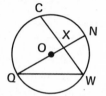

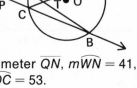

PART B

8. $m\widehat{AR} = 2x + 1$, $m\widehat{RD} = 3x - 2$, $m\widehat{DY} = 4x - 5$, $m\widehat{YA} = x - 4$.
Find $m\angle RTA$.

9. $m\widehat{AB} = 7x + 3$, $m\widehat{BC} = 2x + 10$, $m\widehat{CD} = 6x$, $m\widehat{DA} = 6x - 10$.
Find $m\angle DPA$.

10. $m\angle KTZ = 42$, $m\angle KPZ = 18$.
Find $m\widehat{KZ}$ and $m\widehat{BF}$.

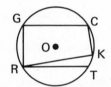

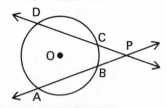

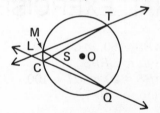

11. Given: $\overline{LC} \perp \overline{JV}$ at T
Prove: $m\widehat{LJ} + m\widehat{CV} = 180$

12. Given: $\overline{RT} \cong \overline{US}$
Prove: $\overline{UR} \cong \overline{TS}$

13. Given: Secants $\overleftrightarrow{LT}$ and $\overleftrightarrow{LQ}$
Prove: $\triangle LQM \sim \triangle LTC$

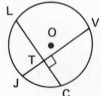

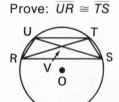

14. Prove Theorem 10.12.

Secants, Tangents, and Angles

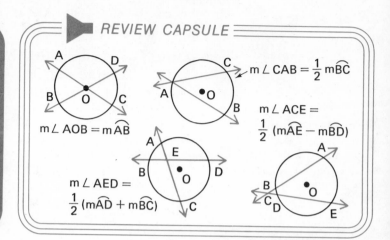

▶ REVIEW CAPSULE

$m\angle AOB = m\widehat{AB}$

$m\angle CAB = \frac{1}{2}m\widehat{BC}$

$m\angle ACE = \frac{1}{2}(m\widehat{AE} - m\widehat{BD})$

$m\angle AED = \frac{1}{2}(m\widehat{AD} + m\widehat{BC})$

Angles are formed by a secant and a tangent or by two tangents.

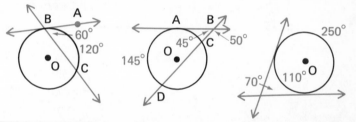

Theorem 10.13

The measure of an angle formed by a secant and a tangent intersecting at the point of tangency is one half the measure of the intercepted arc.

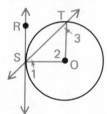

ANALYSIS
Draw radii $\overline{OS}$ and $\overline{OT}$.
$m\angle TSR + m\angle 1 = 90$.
Express $m\angle 1$ in terms of $m\angle 2$.
Then use $m\angle 2 = m\widehat{ST}$.

GIVEN
Secant $\overleftrightarrow{TS}$, tangent $\overleftrightarrow{RS}$
PROVE
$m\angle TSR = \frac{1}{2}m\widehat{ST}$

OUTLINE OF PROOF

1. $m\angle TSR + m\angle 1 = 90$
2. $m\angle TSR = 90 - m\angle 1$
3. $m\angle 1 + m\angle 2 + m\angle 3 = 180$
4. $m\angle 3 = m\angle 1$
5. $m\angle 2 = m\widehat{ST}$

6. $m\angle 1 + m\widehat{ST} + m\angle 1 = 180$
7. $m\angle 1 = \frac{1}{2}(180 - m\widehat{ST})$
8. $m\angle 1 = 90 - \frac{1}{2}m\widehat{ST}$
9. $m\angle TSR = 90 - (90 - \frac{1}{2}m\widehat{ST})$
10. $\therefore m\angle TSR = \frac{1}{2}m\widehat{ST}$

EXAMPLE 1

Tangent $\overrightarrow{YZ}$, $m\widehat{XY} = 112$
Find $m\angle XYZ$.

$m\angle XYZ = \frac{1}{2}m\widehat{XY}$ ⟶ $m\angle XYZ = \frac{1}{2}(112)$
Thus, $m\angle XYZ = 56$.

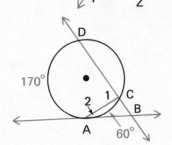

EXAMPLE 2

Tangent $\overleftrightarrow{AB}$, $m\widehat{AD} = 170$,
$m\widehat{AC} = 60$
Find $m\angle ABD$

$m\angle ACD = \frac{1}{2}m\widehat{AD}$ ⟶ $m\angle 1 = 85$
$m\angle CAB = \frac{1}{2}m\widehat{AC}$ ⟶ $m\angle 2 = 30$
$\angle 1$ is ext. $\angle$ of $\triangle ABC$ ⟶ $m\angle ABD + 30 = 85$
$m\angle ABD = \frac{1}{2}(m\widehat{AD} - m\widehat{AC})$ **Thus, $m\angle ABD = 55$.**

Example 2 suggests a proof of Theorem 10.14.

Theorem 10.14

(See Exercise 18.)

The measure of an angle formed by a secant and a tangent intersecting outside the circle is one half the difference of the measures of the intercepted arcs.

EXAMPLE 3

Tangent $\overleftrightarrow{PW}$, $m\widehat{TW} = 165$,
$m\widehat{JW} = 57$.
Find $m\angle JPW$.

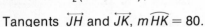

$m\angle JPW = \frac{1}{2}(m\widehat{TW} - m\widehat{JW})$ $m\angle JPW = \frac{1}{2}(165 - 57)$, or 54

EXAMPLE 4

Tangents $\overleftrightarrow{JH}$ and $\overleftrightarrow{JK}$, $m\widehat{HK} = 80$.
Find $m\angle HJK$.

$m\angle HJK + m\angle 1 + m\angle 2 = 180$
$m\angle 1 = 40$

$m\angle 1 = \frac{1}{2}m\widehat{HK}$ ⟶
$m\angle 2 = \frac{1}{2}m\widehat{HK}$ ⟶ $m\angle 2 = 40$
$m\angle HJK = 180 - m\widehat{HK}$ **Thus, $m\angle HJK = 180 - 40 - 40$, or 100.**

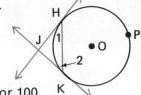

Using Example 4, we can express $m\angle HJK$ in terms of arcs.
$m\widehat{HK} = 80$ So, $m\widehat{HPK} = 280$
$100 = \frac{1}{2}(280 - 80)$
This suggests Theorem 10.15. ⟶ $m\angle HJK = \frac{1}{2}(m\widehat{HPK} - m\widehat{HK})$

Theorem 10.15

(See Exercise 19.)

The measure of an angle formed by two intersecting tangents is one half the difference of the measures of the intercepted arcs.

EXAMPLE 5 $m \angle TNP = 46.$
Find $m\widehat{TP}$ and $m\widehat{TQP}$.

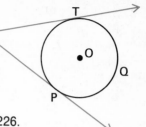

$m \angle TNP = \frac{1}{2}(m\widehat{TQP} - m\widehat{TP})$
$m\widehat{TQP} = 360 - m\widehat{TP}$ ⟶
Multiply each side by 2. ⟶

$46 = \frac{1}{2}(m\widehat{TQP} - m\widehat{TP})$
$46 = \frac{1}{2}[(360 - m\widehat{TP}) - m\widehat{TP}]$
$92 = 360 - 2m\widehat{TP}$
$2m\widehat{TP} = 268$

$m\widehat{TQP} = 360 - m\widehat{TP}$

Thus, $m\widehat{TP} = 134$ and $m\widehat{TQP} = 226.$

Angles Formed by Secants or Tangents

If the intersection of two secants is inside the circle, then the measure of the angle is one half the sum of the measures of the intercepted arcs.

If the intersection of a secant and a tangent is on the circle, then the measure of the angle is one half the measure of the intercepted arc.

If the intersection of two secants or tangents is outside the circle, then the measure of the angle is one half the difference of the measures of the intercepted arcs.

ORAL EXERCISES

Which arcs are the intercepted arcs of each angle?

1.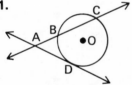

2.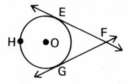

3.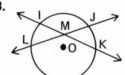

4.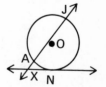

EXERCISES

PART A

1. $m\widehat{PA} = 104.$
   Find $m \angle PTA.$
2. $m \angle PTA = 71.$
   Find $m\widehat{PA}.$

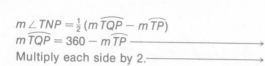

3. $m\widehat{AN} = 42, m\widehat{NJ} = 138.$
   Find $m \angle JXN.$
4. $m \angle JXN = 46, m\widehat{JN} = 121.$
   Find $m\widehat{AN}.$

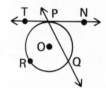

5. $m\widehat{HT} = 142.$
   Find $m \angle HTJ.$
6. $m \angle HTJ = 61.$
   Find $m\widehat{HQT}.$

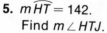
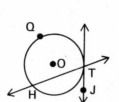

7. $m\widehat{TC} = 40, m\widehat{WR} = 70.$
   Find $m \angle WPR.$
8. $m \angle TPW = 151, m\widehat{TC} = 30.$
   Find $m\widehat{WR}.$

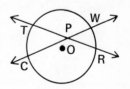

9. $m\widehat{XVZ} = 212$.
   Find $m\angle XYZ$.
10. $m\widehat{XW} = 47$, $m\angle XYV = 47$.
    Find $m\widehat{XV}$.
11. $m\widehat{XVZ} = 3m\widehat{XZ}$
    Find $m\angle XYZ$.

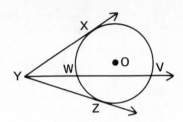

12. $m\widehat{NK} = 162$.
    Find $m\angle JKN$.
13. $m\widehat{KGN} = \frac{3}{2}m\widehat{KMN}$.
    Find $m\angle NKL$.
14. $m\widehat{MK} = 3m\widehat{GK}$, $m\widehat{GM} = 160$.
    Find $m\angle MJL$.

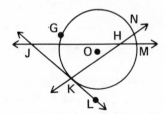

PART B

15. Diameter $\overline{AC}$, $\overline{AD} \cong \overline{AO}$.
    Find $m\angle CAD$ and $m\angle DBA$.
16. $m\widehat{AD} = 92$, $m\widehat{CD} = 103$, $m\widehat{BC} = 41$, tangent $\overleftrightarrow{AF}$.
    Find $m\angle CQD$ and $m\angle ECA$.
17. $m\widehat{AB} = 43$, $\overline{AC} \cong \overline{BC}$, tangent $\overleftrightarrow{DE}$.
    Find $m\angle CAO$ and $m\angle DAC$.

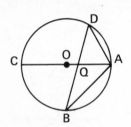

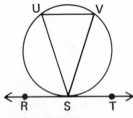

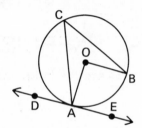

18. Prove Theorem 10.14.

19. Prove Theorem 10.15.

20. Given: $\overline{US} \cong \overline{VS}$, tangent $\overleftrightarrow{RT}$
    Prove: $\overline{UV} \parallel \overleftrightarrow{RT}$

21. Given: Tangent $\overleftrightarrow{RT} \parallel \overline{UV}$
    Prove: $\overline{US} \cong \overline{VS}$

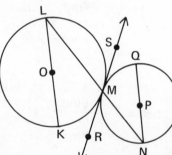

22. Given: $\overleftrightarrow{RS}$ tangent to $\odot O$ and $\odot P$, diameter $\overline{KL}$, diameter $\overline{QN}$
    Prove: $m\widehat{LM} = m\widehat{NM}$

23. Given: $\overleftrightarrow{RS}$ tangent to $\odot O$ and $\odot P$, diameter $\overline{KL}$, diameter $\overline{QN}$
    Prove: $\overline{KL} \parallel \overline{QN}$

Ratios and Products of Lengths

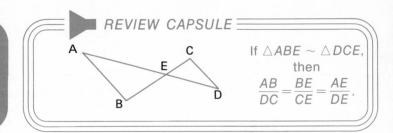

REVIEW CAPSULE

If △ABE ~ △DCE, then

$$\frac{AB}{DC} = \frac{BE}{CE} = \frac{AE}{DE}.$$

EXAMPLE 1

Find the relationship between the lengths of the segments of chords $\overline{AB}$ and $\overline{CD}$.

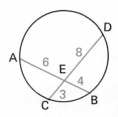

In $\overline{AB}$, $AE = 6$ and $EB = 4$
In $\overline{CD}$, $CE = 3$ and $ED = 8$
$$6 \cdot 4 = 3 \cdot 8$$
Thus, $AE \cdot EB = CE \cdot ED$.

Theorem 10.16

If two chords of a circle intersect, then the product of the lengths of the segments of one equals the product of the lengths of the segments of the other.

ANALYSIS

Show $\dfrac{JV}{QV} = \dfrac{VT}{VC}$ by

proving $\triangle JTV \sim \triangle QCV$.

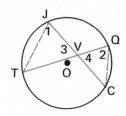

GIVEN
Chords $\overline{TQ}$ and $\overline{JC}$ intersect at V.
PROVE
$JV \cdot VC = QV \cdot VT$

PROOF

STATEMENTS

1. Draw chords $\overline{TJ}$ and $\overline{CQ}$.
2. $m\angle 1 = \frac{1}{2}\widehat{TC}$
3. $m\angle 2 = \frac{1}{2}\widehat{TC}$
4. $m\angle 1 = m\angle 2$
5. $\angle 1 \cong \angle 2$
6. $\angle 3 \cong \angle 4$
7. $\triangle JTV \sim \triangle QCV$
8. $\dfrac{JV}{QV} = \dfrac{VT}{VC}$
9. $\therefore JV \cdot VC = QV \cdot VT$

REASONS

1. Two points are contained in exactly one line.
2. Meas. of inscribed $\angle = \frac{1}{2}$ meas. of intercepted arc.
3. Same as 2
4. Substitution
5. Def. of $\cong$ $\angle$'s
6. Vertical $\angle$'s are $\cong$.
7. AA for $\sim$ $\triangle$'s
8. Corr. sides of $\sim$ $\triangle$'s are proportional.
9. Prod. of extremes = prod. of means.

EXAMPLE 2 $NC = 4$, $CK = 8$, $AC = 6$.
Find CT.

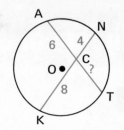

$AC \cdot CT = NC \cdot CK$ ─────────────────→

$$6 \cdot CT = 4 \cdot 8$$
$$6\ CT = 32$$
$$CT = \tfrac{32}{6} \text{ or } 5\tfrac{1}{3}$$

EXAMPLE 3 Find the relationship between the lengths of the secant segments of secants $\overrightarrow{EA}$ and $\overrightarrow{EC}$.

$\overline{EA}$ is a *secant segment.*
$\overline{EB}$ is its *external secant segment.*

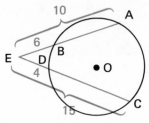

In $\overleftrightarrow{AE}$, $AE = 10$ and $EB = 6$.
In $\overleftrightarrow{CE}$, $CE = 15$ and $ED = 4$.
$$10 \cdot 6 = 15 \cdot 4$$
Thus, $AE \cdot EB = CE \cdot ED$.

Theorem 10.17

If two secants intersect outside a circle, then the product of the lengths of one secant segment and its external secant segment equals the product of the lengths of the other secant segment and its external secant segment.

ANALYSIS
Draw $\overline{CQ}$ and $\overline{JT}$

Show $\dfrac{JV}{QV} = \dfrac{VT}{VC}$

by proving $\triangle JVT \sim \triangle QVC$.

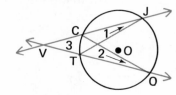

GIVEN
Secants $\overrightarrow{TQ}$ and $\overrightarrow{JC}$ intersect at V.
PROVE $JV \cdot VC = QV \cdot VT$

PROOF
(See Exercise 14.)

EXAMPLE 4 $KT = 10$, $TX = 6$, $NX = 8$
Find AN.

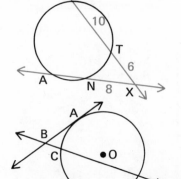

$AX \cdot NX = KX \cdot TX$ ─────────────────→

$$8 \cdot AX = (10 + 6) \cdot 6$$
$$8 \cdot AX = 96$$
$$AX = 12$$

$AN = AX - NX$ **Thus,** $AN = 4$.

$\overline{AB}$ is a tangent segment. ─────────────→ Tangents and secants can intersect.

Theorem 10.18

If a tangent and a secant intersect outside a circle, then the square of the length of the tangent segment equals the product of the lengths of the secant segment and its external secant segment.

ANALYSIS

Draw $\overline{JT}$ and $\overline{CT}$.

Show $\dfrac{JV}{VT} = \dfrac{VT}{VC}$

by proving $\triangle JVT \sim \triangle TVC$.

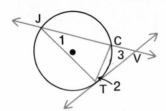

GIVEN

Tangent $\overrightarrow{VT}$, secant $\overrightarrow{JV}$

PROVE

$(VT)^2 = JV \cdot VC$

PROOF

(See Exercise 15.)

EXAMPLE 5 $AC = 2$, $AL = 8$.
Find AT.

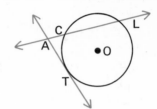

$(AT)^2 = AL \cdot AC$ $\longrightarrow$ $(AT)^2 = 8 \cdot 2$
$(AT)^2 = 16$
Thus, $AT = 4$.

EXAMPLE 6   A tangent and a secant intersect outside the circle. The tangent segment is 10 cm long and the secant segment is 25 cm long. Find the length of the external secant segment.

Draw a labeled picture.
$ZY \cdot WY = (XY)^2$

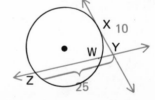

$25 \cdot WY = (10)^2$
$25 \cdot WY = 100$
$WY = 4$

Thus, WY is 4 cm long.

EXERCISES

PART A

1. $AP = 12$, $PC = 9$, $PD = 4$.
   Find PB.
2. $AP = 9$, $AB = 17$, $CP = 12$.
   Find CD.
3. $AP = 4x$, $PB = x$, $CP = 6$,
   $PD = 6$.
   Find AP.

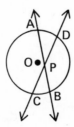

4. $AP = 12$, $PC = 8$, $PB = 4$.
   Find PD.
5. $AP = 18$, $BP = 3$, $CP = 9$.
   Find CD.
6. $AP = 9x$, $BP = 4x$,
   $CP = 16$, $DP = 9$.
   Find BP.

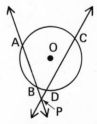

7. $PB = 3$, $PA = 12$.
Find PC.

9. $PA = 4x$, $PB = x$, $PC = 6$.
Find PA.

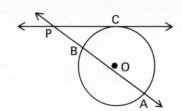

8. $PA = 16$, $PC = 8$.
Find PB.

10. $PA = 7$, $PB = 3$.
Find PC.

PART B

11. $RX = 16$, $RS = 5$, $RN = 6$.
Find RW and SX.

12. $PW + WG = 12$, $PQ = 3$.
Find $\dfrac{PW}{PF}$.

13. $CR = 20$, $XR = 4$, $WR = 6$.
Find YW and CY.

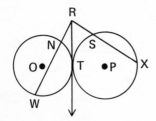

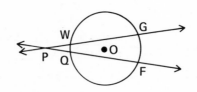

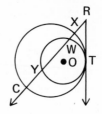

14. Prove Theorem 10.17.

15. Prove Theorem 10.18.

16. $LW = 2x$, $WP = 6$, $SP = 2x - 1$,
$MP = 8$
Find LP and SP.

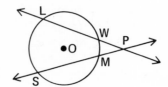

17. $LW = 8$, $SM = 2$, $MP = 6$
Find LP.

PART C

18. Given: Tangent $\overrightarrow{TX}$
Prove: $XT \cdot XL = XZ \cdot LT$

19. Given: Diameter $\overline{CH}$,
tangent $\overleftrightarrow{JH}$
Prove: $IH = \sqrt{IJ \cdot IC}$

20. Given: Secants $\overrightarrow{TK}$ and $\overrightarrow{TN}$
Prove: $KW \cdot RT = NR \cdot WT$

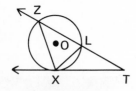

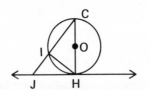

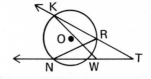

21. Given: Tangent $\overleftrightarrow{TM}$
Prove: $MC \cdot MG$
$= MB \cdot MF$

22. Given: Secants $\overleftrightarrow{IM}$ and $\overleftrightarrow{IJ}$
Prove: $\dfrac{IQ}{IM} = \dfrac{IX}{IJ}$

23. Given: $\overarc{RJ} \cong \overarc{TJ}$, $\overarc{ER} \cong \overarc{YT}$
Prove: $EJ \cdot QJ = YJ \cdot LJ$

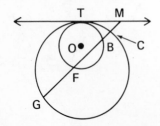

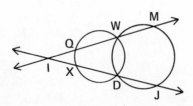

Constructions

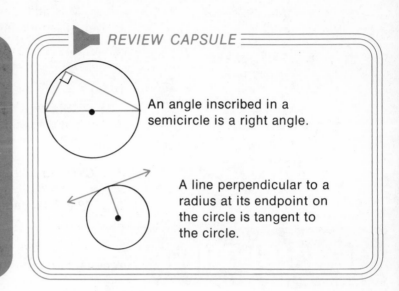

An angle inscribed in a semicircle is a right angle.

A line perpendicular to a radius at its endpoint on the circle is tangent to the circle.

construction

The tangents to a circle from a point outside the circle.

STRATEGY
Construct a ⊙ with $\overline{OP}$ as its diameter. Apply Th. 10.5.

GIVEN
⊙O and a point P
CONSTRUCT
Two tangents to ⊙O from P

Draw $\overline{OP}$. Construct M, the midpoint of $\overline{OP}$.

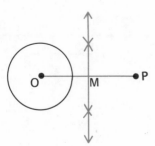

Construct ⊙M with radius $\overline{MO}$.

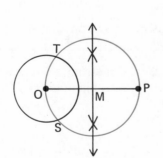

Draw $\overleftrightarrow{PT}$ and $\overleftrightarrow{PS}$.

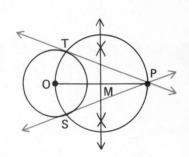

Conclusion: $\overleftrightarrow{PT}$ and $\overleftrightarrow{PS}$ are the desired tangents.

EXAMPLE 1

Prove the construction for a tangent to a circle.

Given: *M* is midpoint of $\overline{OP}$.
Prove: $\overrightarrow{PT}$ is tangent to $\odot O$.

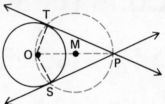

ANALYSIS
Show that radius
$\overline{OT} \perp \overleftrightarrow{PT}$. Then use
Theorem 10.5.

Proof

Statements	Reasons
1. $\overline{OP}$ is a diameter of $\odot M$.	1. Def. of diameter
2. Draw $\overline{OT}$.	2. Two points are contained in exactly one line.
3. $\angle OTP$ is a rt. $\angle$.	3. $\angle$ inscribed in semicircle
4. $\overline{OT}$ is a radius.	4. Def. of radius
5. $\therefore \overleftrightarrow{TP}$ is a tangent.	5. Theorem 10.5

construction

A circle through three noncollinear points

STRATEGY
Construct the $\perp$ bisectors of
$\overline{AC}$ and $\overline{BC}$. They intersect
at the center of the $\odot$.

A•   •B

•C

GIVEN
Noncollinear points *A*, *B*, and *C*
CONSTRUCT
A circle containing *A*, *B*, and *C*

Draw $\overline{AC}$. Construct its $\perp$ bisector.

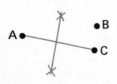

Draw $\overline{BC}$. Construct its $\perp$ bisector. The $\perp$ bisectors intersect at *O*.

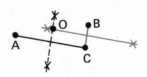

Draw a $\odot$ with center *O* and radius $\overline{OA}$.

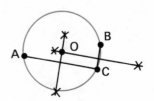

Conclusion: $\odot O$ contains *A*, *B*, and *C*.

EXAMPLE 2

Construct a circle with $\overline{AB}$ as a diameter.

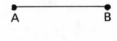

Construct *M*, the midpoint of $\overline{AB}$.
M is the center of the $\odot$.

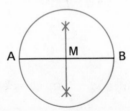

$\odot M$ is the desired circle.

EXERCISES

PART A

1. Draw a segment 1 inch long. Construct a circle with a radius congruent to this segment.

2. Draw a segment 5 cm long. Construct a circle with a diameter congruent to this segment.

3. Draw a circle with a diameter approximately 2 inches long. From a point outside this circle, construct two tangents to the circle.

4. Draw a circle with a diameter approximately 6 cm long. Mark a point on the circle. Construct a tangent to the circle at this point.

5. Draw a segment 1 inch long and a line. Mark a point on the line. At that point, construct a circle tangent to the line with a radius congruent to the given segment.

6. Draw three noncollinear points. Construct a circle which contains these points.

7. Draw a triangle. Construct a circle which contains the three vertices of the triangle.

PART B

8. Draw two segments. Construct a right triangle with the hypotenuse congruent to the longer segment and the altitude to the hypotenuse congruent to the shorter segment. [Hint: An angle inscribed in a semicircle is a right angle.]

9. Draw a circle and a point outside the circle. Construct two tangents to the circle from this point. Construct a second circle tangent both to the given circle and to the two tangents.

10. Prove the construction for a circle through 3 noncollinear points.

PART C

11. Inscribe a circle in a given square.

12. Inscribe a square in a given circle.

13. Inscribe a square in a semicircle.
[Hint: Use the figure as a guide.]

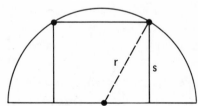

14. Draw two segments with lengths a and b. Construct a segment of length x such that $\frac{a}{x} = \frac{x}{b}$. [Hint: See Th. 9.1, Corollary 1]

Draw two segments with lengths a and b. Construct segments with each of the following lengths.

15. $\sqrt{ab}$

16. $\sqrt{2ab}$

17. $2\sqrt{ab}$

18. $\sqrt{\frac{1}{2}ab}$

19. $\sqrt{\frac{a^2}{2}}$

20. $\sqrt{a^2 + b^2}$

Chapter Ten Review

[p. 315]

1. Name all radii of ⊙*O*. [p. 315]
2. Name all chords of ⊙*O*.
3. Name a secant of ⊙*O*. [p. 315]
4. Name a tangent of ⊙*O*.
5. Name a diameter of ⊙*O*. [p. 315]
6. Name a minor arc of ⊙*O*.

[p. 327]

In which cases can you conclude that chord $\overline{AB}$ ≅ chord $\overline{CD}$? [p. 319, 331]

7. $\overline{OA} \cong \overline{PD}$
8. ⊙*O* ≅ ⊙*P*, $\overline{OR} \cong \overline{PS}$
9. $\widehat{AB} \cong \widehat{CD}$
10. ∠*AOB* ≅ ∠*CPD*

In which cases can you conclude that $\widehat{AB} \cong \widehat{CD}$? [p. 331, 336]

11. $\overline{AB} \cong \overline{CD}$
12. ∠*AXB* ≅ ∠*CYD*
13. $\widehat{AXB} \cong \widehat{CYD}$
14. $\overline{OA} \cong \overline{PC}$, ∠*AXB* ≅ ∠*CYD*

15. In ⊙*O*, $m\widehat{AB} = 82$.
    Find *m*∠*AOB*. [p. 327]
16. In ⊙*O*, *m*∠*ACB* = 32.
    Find $m\widehat{AB}$. [p. 336]

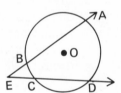

17. $m\widehat{AD} = 84$, $m\widehat{BC} = 62$.
    Find *m*∠*AED*. [p. 342]
18. $m\widehat{AC} = 91$, *m*∠*AEC* = 97.
    Find $m\widehat{BD}$. [p. 342]

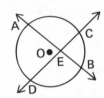

19. $m\widehat{AD} = 113$, $m\widehat{BC} = 48$.
    Find *m*∠*AED*. [p. 342]
20. $m\widehat{BC} = 21$, *m*∠*AED* = 47.
    Find $m\widehat{AD}$. [p. 342]

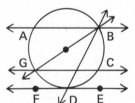

21. $\widehat{AC} = 115$.
    Find *m*∠*AEC*. [p. 345]
22. Diameter $\overline{BD}$, $m\widehat{BC} = 50$.
    Find *m*∠*DEC*. [p. 345]

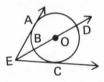

23. $\overleftrightarrow{AB} \parallel \overleftrightarrow{GC} \parallel$ tangent $\overleftrightarrow{FE}$,
    $\overline{AB} \cong \overline{GC}$, $m\widehat{BD} = 122$,
    $m\widehat{AB} = 80$.
    Find *m*∠*FDB* and
    m∠*BGC*. [p. 339, 345]

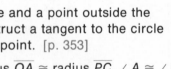

24. *AB* = 14.
    Find *BD*. [p. 322]
25. *AB* = 12, *BC* = 9.
    Find *BE*. [p. 349]

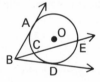

26. Draw a circle and a point outside the circle. Construct a tangent to the circle through the point. [p. 353]

27. Draw three noncollinear points. Construct a circle containing them.
    [p. 353]

28. Given: Radius $\overline{OA}$ ≅ radius $\overline{PC}$, ∠*A* ≅ ∠*C*
    Prove: $\widehat{AB} \cong \widehat{CD}$ [p. 327, 331]

29. Given: $\widehat{AD} \cong \widehat{CD}$, $\widehat{AB} \cong \widehat{CB}$
    Prove: ∠*C* ≅ ∠*A* [p. 331]

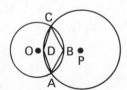

Chapter Ten Test

1. Name a diameter of ⊙ O.
2. Which circle does not have a secant?
3. Name a tangent of ⊙ P.
4. Name a semicircle of ⊙ O.
5. Name a minor arc of ⊙ P.

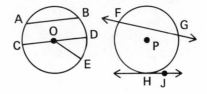

In which cases can you conclude that chord $\overline{QR}$ ≅ chord $\overline{ST}$?

6. $\overline{OV} \cong \overline{OW}$
7. $\overline{OQ} \cong \overline{OS}$
8. $\overarc{QR} \cong \overarc{ST}$

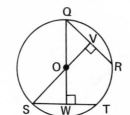

In which cases can you conclude that $\overline{EF} \cong \overline{GH}$?

9. $\overline{EF} \cong \overline{EG}$
10. $\overarc{EF} \cong \overarc{GH}$
11. ∠ EPF ≅ ∠ GPH

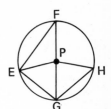

12. $m\overarc{SRT} = 200$.
    Find $m \angle SOT$.

13. $m\overarc{RS} = 71$, $m\overarc{UT} = 43$.
    Find $m \angle RNS$.

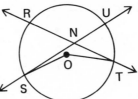

14. $\overleftrightarrow{AB} \parallel \overleftrightarrow{CD}$,
    $m \angle RCD = 80$.
    Find $m\overarc{RC}$.

15. $\overleftrightarrow{AB}$ tangent to ⊙ O,
    $\overleftrightarrow{AB} \parallel \overleftrightarrow{CD}$, $m\overarc{CD} = 140$.
    Find $m \angle CRB$.

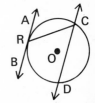

16. $\overline{FH}$ is a diameter, $m\overarc{FJ} = 100$, $m\overarc{GF} = 120$.
    Find $m \angle FMJ$.

17. $WS = 9$, $WR = 4$.
    Find WT.

18. Given a circle and a point P outside the circle. Construct the tangents to the circle from point P.

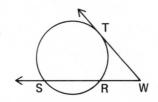

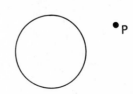

19. Given: Diameter $\overline{PJ}$, $\overarc{CJ} \cong \overarc{PT}$
    Prove: PTJC is a rectangle.

20. Given: $\overleftrightarrow{XY}$ tangent to ⊙ O and ⊙ P,
    $\overleftrightarrow{ZT}$ tangent to ⊙ O and ⊙ P,
    $\overline{XT} \cong \overline{YT}$.
    Prove: $\overleftrightarrow{TZ} \perp \overleftrightarrow{XY}$

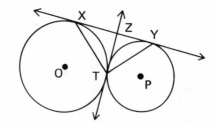

The Nine Point Circle

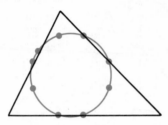

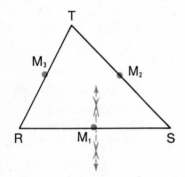

Start with a triangle.
Mark the midpoints of
$\overline{RS}$, $\overline{ST}$, and $\overline{RT}$.

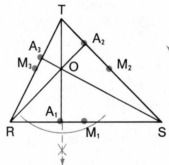

Construct the altitudes.

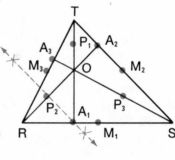

Find the midpoints of
$\overline{TO}$, $\overline{RO}$, and $\overline{SO}$.

Construct the perpendicular bisectors of
$\overline{A_1 P_2}$ and $\overline{A_1 P_3}$. The center of the circle
will be where they meet.

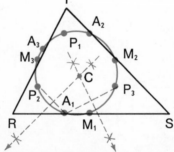

1. Draw a large isosceles triangle.
   Construct a nine-point circle in it.

2. Construct nine-point circles in other
   kinds of triangles.

Area of a Rectangle

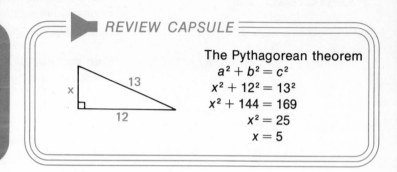

REVIEW CAPSULE

The Pythagorean theorem
$$a^2 + b^2 = c^2$$
$$x^2 + 12^2 = 13^2$$
$$x^2 + 144 = 169$$
$$x^2 = 25$$
$$x = 5$$

EXAMPLE 1 Which figure has the greater area?

If one figure can fit inside another, the outer figure is larger. ⟶

A tracing shows that the pentagon has the greater area.

EXAMPLE 2 If the small square is the unit of area, how many units are contained in the rectangle?

$3 \times 5 = 15$

There are 3 rows of 5 squares.
The rectangle contains 15 square units.

EXAMPLE 3 If the small square is the unit of area, how many units are contained in the rectangle?

$1\frac{1}{2} \times 4 = 6$

There is one row of four squares and a row of four half squares. The rectangle contains 6 square units.

Examples 2 and 3 suggest a formula for the area of a rectangle.

Postulate 22

The area of a rectangle is the product of the lengths of two consecutive sides.

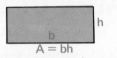

$A = bh$

EXAMPLE 4 Find the area of a rectangle with a base length of 12 in. and a diagonal with a length of 13 in.

Use the Pythagorean theorem. ⟶
If the lengths are in inches, the area is in square inches.

$h^2 + 12^2 = 13^2$
$h^2 + 144 = 169$
$\quad h^2 = 25$, or $h = 5$

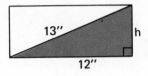

$A = bh$

$A = 12 \cdot 5$, or 60 square inches

EXAMPLE 5 Find the area of a square with a side 7 ft long.

Consecutive sides of a sq. are ≅. ⟶ $A = 7 \cdot 7$, or 49 square feet

Corollary

The area of a square is the square of the length of a side.

$A = s^2$

EXAMPLE 6 Each angle of the polygon is a right angle. Find the area by breaking it down into rectangles.

Dimensions of each rectangle are determined from the total length and width.

Area of rectangle I = 6 × 4, or 24 sq in.
Area of rectangle II = 12 × 2, or 24 sq in.
Area of rectangle III = 4 × 2, or 8 sq in.
Total area = 56 sq in.

Postulate 23

If a region is the union of two or more nonoverlapping regions, then its area is the sum of the areas of these nonoverlapping regions.

EXAMPLE 7 Find the length of a rectangle with an area of 360 square inches and a height of 9 inches.

$A = bh$ ⟶

$360 = 9h$
$\ 40 = h$

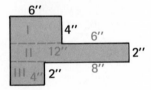

Thus, the length is 40 inches.

ORAL EXERCISES

If the sides of a rectangle are measured in the following units, what is the corresponding unit for the area?

1. feet   **2.** centimeters   **3.** yards   **4.** meters

Find the area of each of the following rectangles. State the unit of measurement.

5. $b = 3$ cm, $h = 2$ cm   **6.** $b = 8$ yd, $h = 4$ yd   **7.** $b = 7$ mi, $h = 9$ mi
8. $b = 10$ ft, $h = 6$ ft   **9.** $b = 9$ in., $h = 3$ in.   **10.** $b = 6$ m, $h = 5$ m

Find the missing length.

11. $A = 12$ sq in., $b = 4$ in., $h = ?$ **12.** $A = 63$ sq yd, $b = ?$, $h = 7$ yd
13. $A = 72$ sq cm, $b = ?$, $h = 8$ cm   **14.** $A = 120$ sq m, $b = 10$ m, $h = ?$

Find the area of each square.

15. $s = 3$ in.   **16.** $s = 9$ cm   **17.** $s = 30$ ft

EXERCISES

PART A

Trace each pair of figures. By direct comparison determine which is larger.

1.    **2.**

Find the area of each rectangle. State the unit of measure, if possible.

3. $b = 7.5$ yd, $h = 2.5$ yd   **4.** $b = 4.27$ in., $h = 3.94$ in.   **5.** $b = 5\frac{2}{3}$ cm, $h = 4\frac{1}{4}$ cm
6. $b = 3.5$ m, $h = 2\frac{1}{4}$ m   **7.** $b = \sqrt{5}$ ft, $h = \sqrt{7}$ ft   **8.** $b = 5$ mi, $h = \sqrt{7}$ mi
9. Square with $s = 6$ yd   **10.** Square with $s = \sqrt{6}$ cm   **11.** Square with $s = (x - y)$
12. $b = (x - y)$, $h = (x + y)$ **13.** $b = (x + y)$, $h = (x + y)$ **14.** $b = (2x + 3)$, $h = (3x - 5)$

Find b if A and h are given.

15. $A = 69$ sq cm, $h = 1.5$ cm   **16.** $A = 9.86$ sq mi, $h = 3.4$ mi   **17.** $A = 5$ sq yd, $h = \sqrt{5}$ yd
18. $A = x^2 + 2x + 1$, $h = x + 1$ **19.** $A = x^2 - 3x - 4$, $h = x - 4$ **20.** $A = 2x^2 - 5x - 12$, $h = x - 4$

PART B

Find the area of each rectangle with the given lengths.

21. $b = 4$, length of diagonal $= 5$ **22.** $h = 40$, length of diagonal $= 41$
23. $b = 3$, length of diagonal $= 7$ **24.** $h = \sqrt{2}$, length of diagonal $= \sqrt{3}$

Find the area of each polygonal region. Each angle is a right angle.

25.

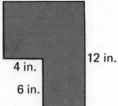
9 in.
4 in.
12 in.
6 in.

26.

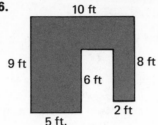
10 ft
9 ft
8 ft
6 ft
5 ft.
2 ft

27.

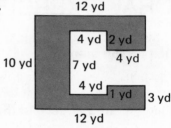
12 yd
4 yd 2 yd
10 yd 7 yd 4 yd
4 yd 1 yd 3 yd
12 yd

PART C

28. Find the area of a square inscribed in a circle with a radius 8 inches long.

29. A circle with a radius 8 inches long is inscribed in a square. Find the area of the square.

30. Prove or disprove: The ratio of the areas of two rectangles is equal to the ratio of the products of the lengths of their bases and altitudes.

31. Prove or disprove: The ratio of the areas of two rectangles with congruent altitudes is equal to the ratio of the lengths of their bases.

$$\frac{A}{A'} = \frac{bh}{b'h'}$$

A h
b

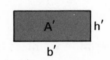
A' h'
b'

$$\frac{A}{A'} = \frac{b}{b'}$$

A h
b

A' h'
b'

Algebra Review

OBJECTIVE

■ To solve an equation like $ax + bx = 6c$ for one of its variables

To solve $bx = ax + c$ for x:

$$bx = ax + c$$

Add $-ax$ to each side. ⟶ $bx - ax = c$

Distributive property ⟶ $(b - a)x = c$

Divide each side by $b - a$. ⟶ $x = \dfrac{c}{b - a}$

EXAMPLE

Add $-3x$ to each side. ⟶

Divide each side by 2. ⟶

Solve $3x + 2y = 7$ for y.

$$2y = -3x + 7$$
$$y = -\tfrac{3}{2}x + \tfrac{7}{2}$$

Solve each equation for the indicated variable.

1. $5x = b$; x

2. $4 + x = k$; x

3. $rx + s = t$; x

4. $9y - 24a = 6a + 4y$; y

5. $5t + 2b = t + 6b$; t

6. $rsx - 2s = 3$; s

7. $x + y = 3$; y

8. $2x + y = 8$; y

9. $3x - y = 12$; y

Area of a Triangle

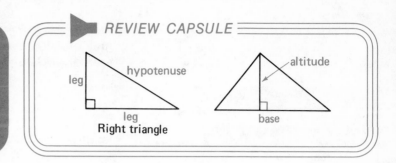

▶ *REVIEW CAPSULE*

Right triangle

base

EXAMPLE 1 △ABC ≅ △DEF.
Compare their areas.

≅ △'s have the same size and shape. ——→ The areas are equal.

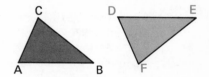

Postulate 24

Congruent figures have the same area.

EXAMPLE 2 Find the area of right △ABC.

$A = bh$ ——————————→ Area of rectangle ABCD = 8 · 5,
or 40 sq cm

Diag. forms 2 ≅ △'s. ——————→ Area △ABC = area △CDA
Area △ABC = $\frac{1}{2}$ area rect. ABCD

$\frac{1}{2} \times 40 = 20$ ——————————→ **Thus,** the area of right △ABC is 20 sq cm.

Example 2 suggests a proof of the following.

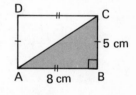

5 cm

8 cm

Theorem 11.1

(Area of rt. △ = $\frac{1}{2}bh$)

The area of a right triangle is
one half the product of the lengths
of the two legs.

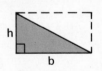

h

b

EXAMPLE 3 Find the area of a right triangle
whose legs are 7 inches and 9
inches long.

Area of rt. △ = $\frac{1}{2}bh$ ——————→ Area of rt. △XYZ = $\frac{1}{2}$ (9) (7)

$= \frac{1}{2} \cdot 63$

$= 31\frac{1}{2}$

Thus, the area of the right triangle is $31\frac{1}{2}$ sq in.

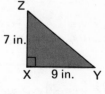

7 in.

9 in.

EXAMPLE 4 Find the area of *ABCDE*.

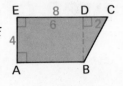

Postulate 23 ⟶ Area of *ABCDE* = Area of rect. *ABDE*
+ Area of △*BCD*

△*BCD* is a rt △. ⟶ Area of *ABCDE* = (4 · 6) + ($\frac{1}{2}$ · 2 · 4)
Area of *ABCDE* = 24 + 4
Area of *ABCDE* = 28 sq units

Theorem 11.2

The area of any triangle is one half the product of the lengths of a base and the corresponding altitude.

(Area$_△$ = $\frac{1}{2}bh$)

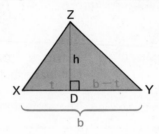

ANALYSIS
Area of △*XYZ* = area of
rt. △*ZDY* + area of rt. △*DZX*.
Use the formula for the area of a
right △.

GIVEN
△*XYZ*, length of base $\overline{XY} = b$,
length of altitude $\overline{ZD} = h$.
PROVE
Area of △*XYZ* = $\frac{1}{2}bh$

PROOF

STATEMENTS

1. △*ZDY* and △*DZX* are rt. △'s.
2. Area of △*ZDY* = $\frac{1}{2}(b - t)h$
   Area of △*DZX* = $\frac{1}{2}th$
3. Area of △*XYZ* = area of △*ZDY* +
   area of △*DZX*
4. Area of △*XYZ* = $\frac{1}{2}(b - t)h + \frac{1}{2}th$
5. Area of △*XYZ* = $\frac{1}{2}h(b - t + t)$
6. ∴ Area of △*XYZ* = $\frac{1}{2}bh$

REASONS

1. Altitude is ⊥ to base.
2. Area of rt. △ = $\frac{1}{2}bh$.

3. Area of a region = sum of areas of
   nonoverlapping regions.
4. Substitution
5. Distributive property
6. $b - t + t = b + 0 = b$

EXAMPLE 5 Find the areas of △*ABC* and △*XYZ*.

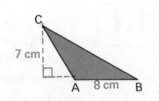

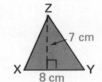

△*ABC* ≇ △*XYZ*, but area
of △*ABC* = area of △*XYZ*.

Area of △*ABC* = (7 · 8),
or 28 sq cm

Area of △*XYZ* = $\frac{1}{2}$(7 · 8)
or 28 sq cm

Corollary

Triangles with congruent bases and congruent
corresponding altitudes have the same area.

EXAMPLE 6   Find the area of an equilateral triangle if each side is 9 cm long.

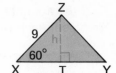

Altitude of an equilateral $\triangle$ is $\frac{s}{2}\sqrt{3}$. ———→ $h = \frac{9}{2}\sqrt{3}$

Area of $\triangle XYZ = \frac{1}{2}(9)\left(\frac{9}{2}\sqrt{3}\right)$

Thus, Area $\triangle XYZ = \frac{81}{4}\sqrt{3}$ sq cm

EXAMPLE 7 $AB = 8$, $CD = 4$, $BC = 6$
Find AE.

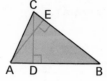

Area of $\triangle ABC = \frac{1}{2}(AB)(CD)$ ———→ Area of $\triangle ABC = \frac{1}{2}(8)(4)$ or 16

Area of $\triangle ABC = \frac{1}{2}(BC)(AE)$ ———→ $16 = \frac{1}{2}(6)(AE)$

$32 = 6(AE)$

Thus, $AE = \frac{32}{6}$, or $5\frac{1}{3}$.

EXERCISES

PART A

Find the area of each triangle.

1.

3 in.
4 in.

2.

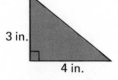

4 ft
6 ft

3.

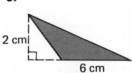

2 cm
6 cm

4.

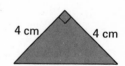

4 cm   4 cm

5.

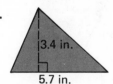

3.4 in.
5.7 in.

6.

$5\frac{1}{4}$ ft $3\frac{1}{2}$ ft

7.

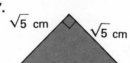

$\sqrt{5}$ cm $\sqrt{5}$ cm

8.

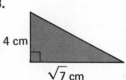

4 cm
$\sqrt{7}$ cm

Supply the missing information for each triangle.

	Length of Base b	Length of Altitude h	Area
9.	9 cm	?	72 sq cm
10.	?	$\sqrt{5}$ in.	5 sq in.
11.	7 ft	?	63 sq ft
12.	?	.7 yd	.56 sq yd
13.	$\frac{2}{3}$ in.	?	$\frac{3}{4}$ sq in.
14.	$x - 3$	$2x + 6$	?
15.	?	$x - 1$	$x^2 + 3x - 4$
16.	$x + 2$	?	$2x^2 + 8x + 8$

PART B

17. Find the area of an equilateral triangle if each side is 8 ft long.

18. Find the area of an equilateral triangle if each side is 12 cm long.

19. $XY = 12$, $ZT = 8$, $YZ = 16$. Find XW.

21. $XW = 4$, $YZ = 7$, $ZT = 6$. Find XY.

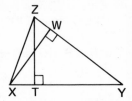

20. $XY = 15$, $ZT = 9$, $XW = 12$. Find YZ.

22. $XY = 22$, $YZ = 33$, $XW = 12$. Find ZT.

PART C

This formula can be used to find the area of a △ if the lengths of the sides are known.

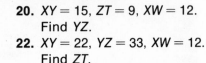

HERO'S FORMULA
Area of a triangle $= \sqrt{s(s-a)(s-b)(s-c)}$, where a, b, and c are the lengths of the three sides and $s = \frac{1}{2}(a+b+c)$.

EXAMPLE

Find the area of a triangle whose sides are 3 in., 4 in., and 5 in. long.

$$s = \tfrac{1}{2}(3+4+5), \text{ or } 6$$
$$\text{Area} = \sqrt{6(6-3)(6-4)(6-5)}$$
$$\text{Area} = \sqrt{6 \cdot 3 \cdot 2 \cdot 1}, \text{ or } \sqrt{36}$$
$$\text{Area} = 6 \text{ sq in.}$$

Find the area of each triangle.

23.

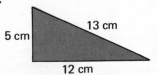

24.

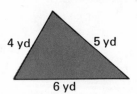

25.

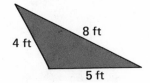

Prove or disprove each of the following.

26. The ratio of the areas of two similar triangles is equal to the ratio of the lengths of the corresponding altitudes.

28. The ratio of the areas of two triangles with congruent bases is equal to the ratio of the lengths of their altitudes.

30. Any median of a triangle separates the region into two regions with equal areas.

27. The areas of two similar triangles have the same ratio as the squares of the lengths of any two corresponding sides.

29. If two triangles have equal areas, then the ratio of the lengths of their bases is equal to the ratios of the lengths of their altitudes.

31. Any angle bisector of a triangle separates the region into two regions with equal areas.

Area of a Parallelogram

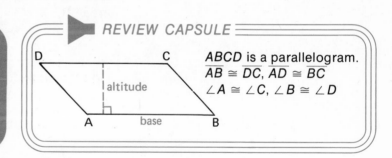

REVIEW CAPSULE

ABCD is a parallelogram.
$\overline{AB} \cong \overline{DC}$, $\overline{AD} \cong \overline{BC}$
$\angle A \cong \angle C$, $\angle B \cong \angle D$

EXAMPLE 1   Cut a parallelogram shaped piece of paper. Show that it can be cut and rearranged into a rectangular shape with the same base and altitude lengths.

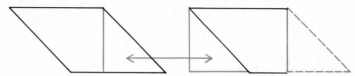

Example 1 suggests a proof of Theorem 11.3. ⌐→

Theorem 11.3

The area of a parallelogram is the product of the length of a base and the length of its corresponding altitude.

ANALYSIS
Area of ▱ABCD = area of rectangle FECD if △FAD ≅ △EBC. Show △FAD ≅ △EBC.

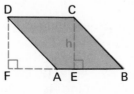

GIVEN
▱ABCD, length of base $\overline{AB}$ = b, length of altitude $\overline{CE}$ = h.
PROVE
Area of ▱ABCD = bh.

PROOF

STATEMENTS

1. Draw $\overleftrightarrow{CE} \perp \overleftrightarrow{AB}$ and $\overleftrightarrow{DF} \perp \overleftrightarrow{AB}$.
2. $\overline{DC} \parallel \overleftrightarrow{AB}$
3. $\overline{DF} \cong \overline{CE}$ (L)
4. $\overline{AD} \cong \overline{BC}$ (H)
5. △FAD ≅ △EBC
6. Area of △FAD = area of △EBC
7. Area of AECD + area of △FAD = area of AECD + area of △EBC
8. Area of ▱ABCD = area of rect. FECD
9. Area of rect. FECD = bh
10. ∴ Area of ▱ABCD = bh

REASONS

1. There is exactly one ⊥ from a pt to a line.
2. Opp. sides of a ▱ are ∥.
3. ∥ lines are everywhere equidistant.
4. Opp. sides of a ▱ are ≅.
5. HL for ≅ rt. △'s
6. ≅ △'s have the same area.
7. Area of region = sum of areas of nonoverlapping regions.
8. Substitution
9. Area of rect. = base × height
10. Substitution

EXAMPLE 2   Find the area of $\square XTNZ$.

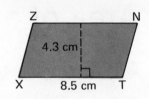

Area of $\square = bh$ ⟶ Area of $\square XTNZ = (8.5)\,(4.3)$
Area of $\square XTNZ = 36.55$ sq cm.

EXAMPLE 3   Find the area of each parallelogram.

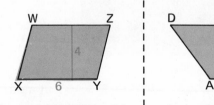

$\square XYZW \not\cong \square ABCD$, but area of
$\square XYZW$ = area of $\square ABCD$. ⟶

Area of $\square XYZW = 24$ Area of $\square ABCD = 24$

Corollary

Parallelograms with congruent bases and congruent corresponding altitudes have the same area.

EXAMPLE 4   In $\square JKLM$, which measures are used to find the area?

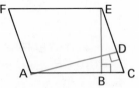

JM is not the length of an altitude ⟶ JK and HK are used.

EXAMPLE 5 $AC = 12$, $BE = 6$, $CE = 8$
Find AD.

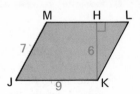

Area of $\square ACEF = AC \cdot BE$ ⟶ Area of $\square ACEF = 12 \cdot 6$, or 72
Area of $\square ACEF = CE \cdot AD$ ⟶ $72 = 8 \cdot (AD)$
                 $AD = 9$

EXAMPLE 6   The lengths of two adjacent sides of a parallelogram are 8 and 10 inches. The included angle measures 30°. Find the area of the parallelogram.

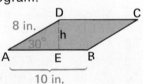

$\triangle AED$ is a 30°-60° rt. $\triangle$. ⟶

Area of $\square ABCD = 10 \cdot h$
      and $h = 4$
Area of $\square ABCD = 10 \cdot 4$
                 or 40
Thus, the area of $\square ABCD$ is 40 sq in.

EXERCISES

PART A

Find the area of each parallelogram.

1.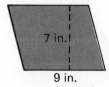
7 in.
9 in.

2.
5.7 cm
$4\frac{1}{3}$ cm

3.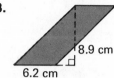
8.9 cm
6.2 cm

4.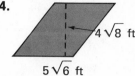
$4\sqrt{8}$ ft
$5\sqrt{6}$ ft

Supply the missing information for each parallelogram.

	Length of Base b	Length of Altitude h	Area
5.	8 cm	?	64 sq cm
6.	?	9 in.	.72 sq in.
7.	$\frac{3}{4}$ ft	?	$\frac{2}{3}$ sq ft
8.	?	$\sqrt{7}$ yd	7 sq yd
9.	$x + 2$	$3x - 1$	?
10.	?	$2x - 1$	$6x^2 + 5x - 4$
11.	$3x - 2$	?	$12x^2 - 11x + 2$

PART B

12. $AC = 18$, $BF = 6$, $CE = 12$.
Find DG.

14. $AC = 35$, $CE = 24$, $DG = 21$.
Find BF.

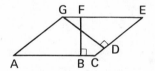

13. $AC = 24$, $BF = 8$, $DG = 12$.
Find CE.

15. $GE = \sqrt{8}$, $DG = 9$,
$BF = \sqrt{6}$.
Find AC.

In which cases is enough information given to find the area of the parallelogram?

16.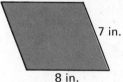
7 in.
8 in.

17.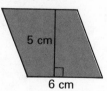
5 cm
6 cm

18.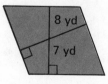
8 yd
7 yd

19.
6 yd
8 yd

PART C

The area of a parallelogram can
be found by the formula
Area $= ab \sin A$.

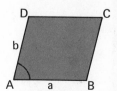

Find each area.

20. $a = 8$, $b = 5$, $m \angle A = 30$

21. $a = 5$, $b = 6$, $m \angle A = 60$

Standard Beans

Triangular Beans

Quadrilateral Beans

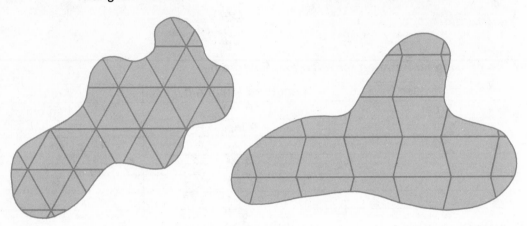

Fancy Beans

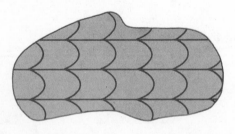

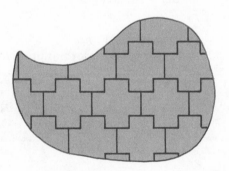

Standard beans are shapes that cover
a region but do not overlap.

Circles or discs cannot be used as standard beans. Why not?

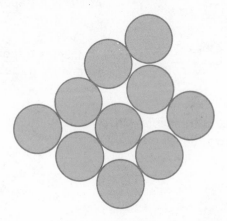
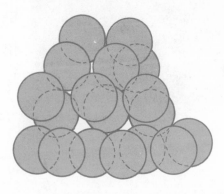

How can a standard bean be used to compare areas?

Make a set of standard beans. Use them to compare these regions.

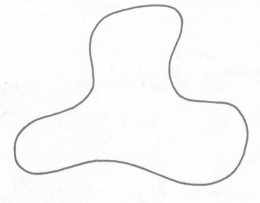

Which region is larger?

Area of a Trapezoid

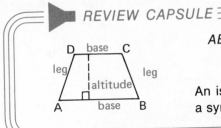
EXAMPLE 1 Find the area of trapezoid $ABCD$ by dividing the region into two triangular regions.

$\triangle ABD$ and $\triangle DBC$ have congruent altitudes.

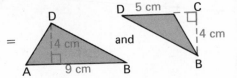

Area of trap. $ABCD$ = area of $\triangle ABD$ + area of $\triangle DBC$
$= \frac{1}{2}(4)(9) + \frac{1}{2}(4)(5)$
$= \frac{1}{2}(4)[9 + 5]$
$= (2)(14)$, or 28 sq cm

Example 1 suggests a proof of Theorem 11.4. ⌐

Theorem 11.4

(See Exercise 15)

The area of a trapezoid is one half the product of the length of an altitude and the sum of the lengths of the two bases.

ANALYSIS
Area of trap. $ABCD$ = area of $\triangle ABD$ + area of $\triangle DBC$

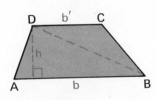

GIVEN
Trap. $ABCD$, length of base $\overline{AB} = b$, length of base $\overline{DC} = b'$, length of an altitude $= h$
PROVE
Area of trap. $ABCD = \frac{1}{2}h(b + b')$

EXAMPLE 2 Find the area of trapezoid $XYZW$

Apply Theorem 11.4. ⟶ Area of trap. $XYZW = \frac{1}{2}(14)(9 + 15)$
$= (7)(24)$, or 168
Thus, area of trap. $XYZW = 168$ sq in.

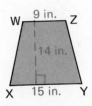

EXAMPLE 3   In trapezoid $AJTC$, $CT = 6$, $CW = 4$, Area of $AJTC = 32$. Find AJ.

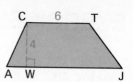

Area $= \frac{1}{2}h(b + b')$

$$32 = \frac{1}{2}(4)(6 + AJ)$$
$$32 = 2(6 + AJ)$$
$$32 = 12 + 2(AJ)$$
$$20 = 2(AJ)$$

Thus, $AJ = 10$.

EXAMPLE 4   The area of a trapezoid is 168 sq in. The altitude is 8 in. long. If the longer base is 12 in. greater than twice the shorter, find the length of each base.

Let $x =$ length of shorter base
$2x + 12 =$ length of longer base

Area of trap. $= \frac{1}{2}h(b + b')$ ⟶

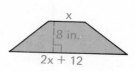

$$168 = \frac{1}{2} \cdot 8 \cdot [x + (2x + 12)]$$
$$168 = 4(3x + 12)$$

Solve the equation. ⟶

$$10 = x$$
$$32 = 2x + 12$$

Thus, the lengths of the bases are 10 in. and 32 in.

EXAMPLE 5   In trapezoid $TPCH$, $TP = 10$, $HC = 6$, $TH = 6$, $m\angle A = 60$. Find the area of trap. $TPCH$.

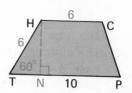

$\triangle TNH$ is a 30°-60° rt. $\triangle$
So, $HN = \frac{6}{2}\sqrt{3}$, or $3\sqrt{3}$

Area of trap. $= \frac{1}{2}(h)(b + b')$ ⟶

Area of trap. $TPCH = \frac{1}{2}(3\sqrt{3})(10 + 6)$
$= \frac{1}{2}(3\sqrt{3})(16)$
$= \frac{1}{2}(48\sqrt{3})$, or $24\sqrt{3}$

Thus, the area of trap. $TPCH$ is $24\sqrt{3}$.

ORAL EXERCISES

In which cases is enough information given to find the area of the trapezoid?

1.

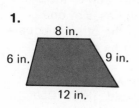

2.

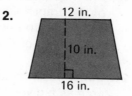

3.

4.

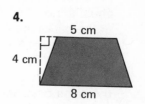

EXERCISES

PART A

Find the area of each trapezoid.

1.
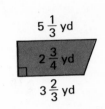
6 in.
4 in.
8 in.

2.
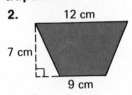
12 cm
7 cm
9 cm

3.
$5\frac{1}{3}$ yd
$2\frac{3}{4}$ yd
$3\frac{2}{3}$ yd

4.
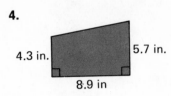
4.3 in.
5.7 in.
8.9 in

Supply the missing information for each trapezoid.

	Length of Base b	Length of Base b'	Length of Altitude h	Area
5.	12 ft	11 ft	9 ft	?
6.	9 cm	15 cm	?	72 sq cm
7.	8 in.	?	10 in.	55 sq in.
8.	$x + 2$	$3x - 6$	$2x + 1$	?
9.	$3x - 1$	$5x + 7$	?	$4x^2 - 13x - 12$
10.	?	$2x + 3$	$2x + 1$	$4x^2 + 4x + 1$

PART B

11. The area of a trapezoid is 136 sq cm. The altitude is 8 cm long. If the longer base is 4 cm greater than the shorter, find the length of each base.

12. The area of a trapezoid is 234 sq yd. The altitude is 12 yd long. If the longer base is 9 yd less than twice the shorter, find the length of each base.

13. In trapezoid $ABCD$, the lengths of bases $\overline{AB}$ and $\overline{CD}$ are 30 and 20. The length of side $\overline{AD}$ is 8. If $m\angle A = 60$, find the area of trapezoid $ABCD$.

14. In trapezoid $XYZW$, the lengths of bases $\overline{XY}$ and $\overline{WZ}$ are 15 and 3. The length of side $\overline{XW}$ is 8. If $m\angle x = 45$, find the area of trapezoid $XYZW$.

PART C

15. Prove Theorem 11.4.

16. In trapezoid $ABCD$, the lengths of bases $\overline{AB}$ and $\overline{CD}$ are 17 and 13. The length of side $\overline{AD}$ is 4. If $m\angle A = 37$, find the area of trapezoid $ABCD$ to the nearest tenth.

17. In trapezoid $XYZW$, the lengths of bases $\overline{XY}$ and $\overline{WZ}$ are 9 and 4. The length of side $\overline{XW}$ is 3. If $m\angle x = 72$, find the area of trapezoid $XYZW$ to the nearest tenth.

18. Prove or disprove: If two trapezoids have equal areas, then the sums of the lengths of the bases are inversely proportional to the lengths of the corresponding altitudes.

19. Prove or disprove: The ratio of the areas of two trapezoids with bases of one congruent to bases of the other is equal to the ratio of the lengths of their altitudes.

20. Construct an isosceles trapezoid with the same base and area as a given nonisosceles trapezoid.

21. Construct a rectangle with the same area as a given trapezoid. [Hint: Use the median of the trapezoid.]

Similar Triangles: Areas and Perimeters

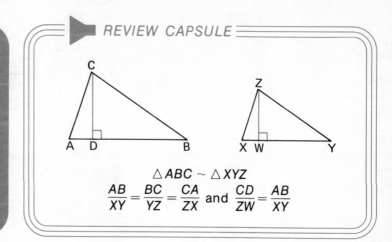

▶ REVIEW CAPSULE

$\triangle ABC \sim \triangle XYZ$

$$\frac{AB}{XY} = \frac{BC}{YZ} = \frac{CA}{ZX} \text{ and } \frac{CD}{ZW} = \frac{AB}{XY}$$

EXAMPLE 1

$\triangle RST \sim \triangle LMN$, $RS = 4$, $LM = 12$, $NP = 6$.
Find the ratio of the areas of $\triangle RST$ and $\triangle LMN$.

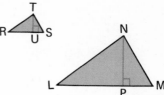

First, find the alt. of $\triangle RST$.

$$\frac{TU}{NP} = \frac{RS}{LM}$$

$$\frac{TU}{6} = \frac{4}{12}$$
$$12(TU) = 24$$
$$TU = 2$$

Area of $\triangle RST = \frac{1}{2}(4)(2)$, or 4
Area of $\triangle LMN = \frac{1}{2}(12)(6)$, or 36

Thus, $\dfrac{\text{Area of } \triangle RST}{\text{Area of } \triangle LMN} = \dfrac{4}{36}$, or $\dfrac{1}{9}$.

In Example 1 the ratio of the lengths of a pair of corresponding sides is $\frac{1}{3}$. The ratio of the areas is $\frac{1}{9}$.

Theorem 11.5

(See Exercise 12)

The ratio of the areas of two similar triangles is the square of the ratio of the lengths of two corresponding sides.

EXAMPLE 2

If the ratio of the lengths of two corresponding sides is $\frac{2}{3}$, find the ratio of their areas.

$$\frac{\text{Area of 1st } \triangle}{\text{Area of 2nd } \triangle} = \left(\frac{2}{3}\right)^2, \text{ or } \frac{4}{9}$$

EXAMPLE 3

The ratio of the areas of
$\triangle ABC$ and $\triangle XYZ$ is $\frac{9}{16}$.
$BC = 6$.
Find YZ.

$\dfrac{\text{Area of } \triangle ABC}{\text{Area of } \triangle XYZ} = \left(\dfrac{BC}{YZ}\right)^2$

$$\frac{9}{16} = \left(\frac{6}{YZ}\right)^2$$
$$\frac{9}{16} = \frac{36}{(YZ)^2}$$
$$9(YZ)^2 = 16 \cdot 36$$
$$(YZ)^2 = 64$$

Thus, $YZ = 8$.

Definition of *perimeter* ⟶ The *perimeter* of a polygon is the sum of the lengths of its sides.

EXAMPLE 4

Find the perimeter of $\triangle ABC$ and $\square\, SRQP$.

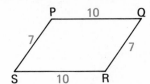

To find the perimeter, add the lengths
of the sides. ⟶ Perimeter of $\triangle ABC = 3 + 4 + 6$, or 13.
Perimeter of $\square\, SRQP = 10 + 7 + 10 + 7$, or 34

EXAMPLE 5

$\triangle ABC \sim \triangle XYZ$. Find the
ratio of their perimeters.

$\dfrac{XY}{AB} = \dfrac{YZ}{BC} = \dfrac{XZ}{AC}$

$\dfrac{XZ}{12} = \dfrac{12}{8}$ $\dfrac{YZ}{14} = \dfrac{12}{8}$

$8(XZ) = 144$ $8(YZ) = 168$

Find lengths of $\overline{YZ}$ and $\overline{XZ}$. ⟶ $XZ = 18$ $YZ = 21$

Perimeter of $\triangle ABC = 8 + 14 + 12$, or 34.
Perimeter of $\triangle XYZ = 12 + 21 + 18$, or 51.

Thus, $\dfrac{\text{perimeter of } \triangle ABC}{\text{perimeter of } \triangle XYZ} = \dfrac{34}{51}$, or $\dfrac{2}{3}$.

In Example 5, the ratio of lengths of sides is also $\frac{2}{3}$.

Theorem   11.6

(See Exercise 13.)

The ratio of the perimeters of two similar polygons is the same as the ratio of the lengths of two corresponding sides.

EXAMPLE 6

Prove or disprove: The ratio of the perimeters of two rectangles is the same as the ratio of the areas.

A counterexample disproves the statement. ————————————→

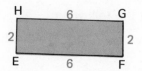
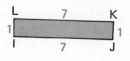

Perimeter of $EFGH = 6 + 2 + 6 + 2$, or 16.
Perimeter of $IJKL = 7 + 1 + 7 + 1$, or 16.
The ratio of the perimeters is $\frac{16}{16}$, or $\frac{1}{1}$.
Area of $EFGH = 6 \cdot 2$, or 12.
Area of $IJKL = 7 \cdot 1$, or 7.
The ratio $\dfrac{\text{area of } EFGH}{\text{area of } IJKL} = \dfrac{12}{7}$.

$\frac{12}{7} \neq \frac{1}{1}$ ————————————→ **Thus,** the ratios are not the same.

EXAMPLE 7

The ratio of the lengths of corresponding sides of similar triangles is $\frac{2}{5}$. If the perimeter of the larger triangle is 10 in., find the perimeter of the smaller.

Apply Theorem 11.6. ————————————→

$$\frac{p}{10} = \frac{2}{5}$$
$$5p = 2 \cdot 10$$
$$5p = 20$$
$$p = 4$$

Thus, the perimeter of the smaller is 4 in.

ORAL EXERCISES

What is the perimeter of each polygon?

1.

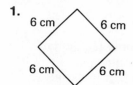

6 cm, 6 cm, 6 cm, 6 cm

2.

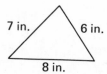

7 in., 6 in., 8 in.

3.

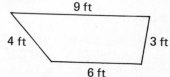

9 ft, 4 ft, 3 ft, 6 ft

Find the ratio of the areas and the ratio of the perimeters for each pair of similar triangles.

4.

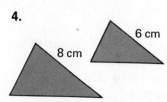

8 cm, 6 cm

5.

6 in., 5 in.

6.

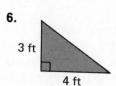

3 ft, 4 ft, 4 ft

EXERCISES

PART A

Find the perimeter of each of the following.

1. Equilateral $\triangle RNQ$,
$RN = 7$

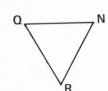

2. $\square ACLZ$, $AC = 5.1$ in.,
$CL = 3.4$ in.

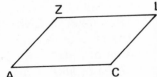
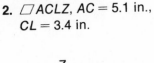

3. Isosceles trapezoid $NTWH$
$NT = \frac{3}{4}$ cm, $TW = \frac{2}{3}$ cm,
$WH = \frac{1}{2}$ cm

4. Square $MTZB$,
$MT = 2x + 1$

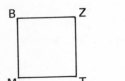

5. $\square STPB$, $ST = 3x^2 + 2x$,
$BS = 4x - 5$

6. Isosceles trapezoid $RJKC$,
$RJ = x^3 + 2x$, $JK = 2x - 4$,
$KC = x^2 + 3x$

Find the ratio of the areas and ratio of the perimeters.

7. $\triangle LDC \sim \triangle WFP$, $\overline{LD} \cong$
$\overline{DC}$, $LC = 6$, $\overline{DJ} \perp \overline{LC}$,
$JD = 8$, $PW = 4$

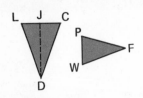

8. Right $\triangle TCN \sim \triangle AJP$,
$TC = 12$, $CN = 5$, $AP = 6.5$

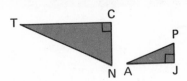

9. Equilateral $\triangle XTP \sim \triangle QKM$
$XT = 12$, $QK = 6$

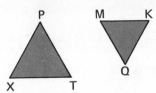

PART B

10. In two similar triangles, corresponding sides are 4 in. and 2 in. long. If the area of the smaller is 18 sq in. less than the area of the larger, find the area of the larger.

11. The area of one triangle is 9 sq cm. The area of a similar triangle is 4 sq cm. If the perimeter of the first is $5x - 3$ and the perimeter of the second is $2x + 2$, what is the perimeter of each?

PART C

12. Prove Theorem 11.5.

14. Prove: The ratio of the areas of two similar polygons is the square of the ratio of the lengths of a pair of corresponding sides.

13. Prove Theorem 11.6.

15. Prove: The ratio of the perimeters of two similar polygons is the same as the ratio of the lengths of a pair of corresponding sides.

Area of a Regular Polygon

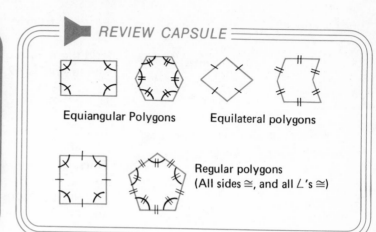

▶ REVIEW CAPSULE

Equiangular Polygons   Equilateral polygons

Regular polygons
(All sides ≅, and all ∠'s ≅)

EXAMPLE 1   △ABC is equilateral, BC = 5.
Find the area of △ABC.

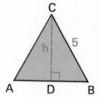

△DBC is a 30°-60° rt. △. ⟶

△ABC is equilateral ⟶

$$h = \frac{5}{2}\sqrt{3}$$
$$AB = 5$$

Area of a △ = $\frac{1}{2}bh$ ⟶

Area of △ABC = $\frac{1}{2}(5)\left(\frac{5}{2}\sqrt{3}\right)$, or $\frac{25}{4}\sqrt{3}$

Theorem 11.7

The area of an equilateral triangle having sides of length s is $\frac{s^2}{4}\sqrt{3}$.

ANALYSIS

Area of △ = $\frac{1}{2}bh$. In equilateral △, alt. forms 30°-60° rt. △. $h = \frac{s}{2}\sqrt{3}$

PROOF

GIVEN
Equilateral △ABC, s is the length of each side
PROVE
Area of △ABC = $\frac{s^2}{4}\sqrt{3}$

STATEMENTS

1. Draw altitude $\overline{CD} \perp \overline{AB}$ with length h.
2. △CDB is a 30°-60° rt. △.
3. $h = \frac{s}{2}\sqrt{3}$
4. ∴ Area of △ABC = $\frac{1}{2}(s)\left(\frac{s}{2}\sqrt{3}\right)$ or $\frac{s^2}{4}\sqrt{3}$.

REASONS

1. There is exactly one ⊥ from a pt. to a line.
2. Each ∠ of equilateral △ is a 60° ∠.
3. Theorem 9.5
4. Area of a △ = $\frac{1}{2}bh$

EXAMPLE 2 Find the area of an equilateral triangle whose sides are 2.3 cm long.

Apply Theorem 11.7. ————→ $\text{Area} = \dfrac{(2.3)^2}{4}\sqrt{3}$ or $\dfrac{5.29\sqrt{3}}{4}$ sq cm.

EXAMPLE 3 Find the length of a side of an equilateral triangle whose area is $12\sqrt{3}$ sq cm.

$\text{Area} = \dfrac{s^2}{4}\sqrt{3}$

$12\sqrt{3} = \dfrac{s^2}{4}\sqrt{3}$

Multiply each side by 4. ————→ $48\sqrt{3} = s^2\sqrt{3}$

Divide each side by $\sqrt{3}$. ————→ $s^2 = 48$

Thus, $s = \sqrt{48}$, or $4\sqrt{3}$ cm.

Regular polygons can be inscribed in or circumscribed around circles.

A circle can be inscribed in or circumscribed around a regular polygon.

a is the *apothem* of the polygon.

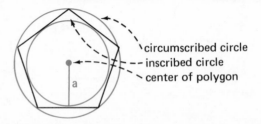

circumscribed circle
inscribed circle
center of polygon

The apothem is the distance from the center to a side.

Definition of apothem ————→ The *apothem* of a regular polygon is the length of a radius of the inscribed circle.

EXAMPLE 4 Find the area of a regular hexagon if the length of each side is 8 cm and the apothem is $4\sqrt{3}$ cm.

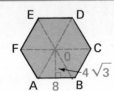

Divide the hexagon into 6 ≅ △'s

Area of a △ $= \frac{1}{2}bh$ ————→

6 △'s were formed ————→

Area of $\triangle ABO = \frac{1}{2}(8)(4\sqrt{3})$ or $16\sqrt{3}$.

Area of $ABCDEF = 6(16\sqrt{3})$.

Thus, area $= 96\sqrt{3}$ sq cm.

The method in Example 4 suggests a proof of the following theorem.

Theorem 11.8

(See Exercise 33)

The area of a regular polygon is one half the product of the apothem and the perimeter.

EXAMPLE 5 Find the area of a regular octagon
if the length of each side is 1 yd
and the apothem is 1.2 yd.

Perimeter is the sum of the lengths of
the sides. ————————————→ Perimeter = 8 · 1, or 8 yd.
Apply Theorem 11.8. ——————→ Area = $\frac{1}{2}$ (8) (1.2), or 4.8 sq yd.

EXAMPLE 6 A regular hexagon is inscribed in a circle. If the
length of the radius is 7, find the area of the
hexagon.

$\frac{(n-2)(180)}{n}$ ————————————→ $m \angle FAB = 120$

$\overline{OA}$ bisects $\angle FAB$. ——————→ $m \angle OAB = 60$

$\triangle AXO$ is a 30°-60° rt. $\triangle$ ————→ $a = \frac{7}{2}\sqrt{3}$

$\triangle ABO$ is equilateral. ——————→ $AB = 7$

Perimeter = 6 · 7, or 42.

Apply Theorem 11.8.   Area of $ABCDEF = \frac{1}{2}(\frac{7}{2}\sqrt{3})(42)$.

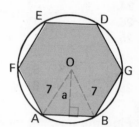

Thus, the area of the hexagon is $\frac{147\sqrt{3}}{2}$.

EXERCISES

PART A

Find the area of an equilateral triangle with sides of the given length.

1. 5 cm   **2.** 6.7 yd   **3.** $5\sqrt{2}$ ft   **4.** $(2x-1)$

Find the area of a square with sides of the given length.

5. 8.9 ft   **6.** $\frac{4}{5}$ cm   **7.** $3\sqrt{5}$ yd   **8.** $(x+3)$

Find the area of each of the following regular polygons.

	Number of Sides	Length of Side	Apothem	Area
9.	3	6	$\sqrt{3}$	?
10.	3	2	$\frac{\sqrt{3}}{3}$	?
11.	3	$16\sqrt{3}$	8	?
12.	4	10	5	?
13.	4	$\sqrt{3}$	$\frac{\sqrt{3}}{2}$	?
14.	5	2	1.4	?
15.	5	1.4	1	?
16.	6	12	$6\sqrt{3}$	?
17.	6	$\frac{2\sqrt{3}}{3}$	1	?
18.	8	10	12.1	?
19.	8	.5	.6	?

Find the length of each side of an equilateral triangle with the given area.

20. $\dfrac{9\sqrt{3}}{4}$ sq cm   **21.** $4\sqrt{3}$ sq ft   **22.** $5\sqrt{3}$ sq yd   **23.** $9\sqrt{3}$ sq cm

Find the area of each regular polygon inscribed in a circle.

	Number of Sides	Length of Radius of Circle	Apothem	Area
24.	3	10	?	?
25.	3	?	$6\sqrt{3}$	?
26.	4	4	?	?
27.	4	?	4	?
28.	6	8	?	?
29.	6	?	$4\sqrt{3}$	?

Find the missing measures of each regular polygon inscribed in a circle.

	Number of Sides	Length of Radius of Circle	Apothem	Area	Length of Side
30.	3	?	?	$12\sqrt{3}$	?
31.	4	?	?	25	?
32.	6	?	?	$8\sqrt{3}$	?

33. Prove Theorem 11.8.

Prove or disprove each of the following.

34. The ratio of the areas of two similar regular polygons is equal to the ratio of their perimeters.

35. The ratio of the areas of two similar regular polygons is equal to the ratio of their apothems.

Using the appropriate trigonometric ratios find the missing measures to the nearest hundredth of each regular polygon inscribed in a circle.

	Number of Sides	Length of Radius of Circle	Apothem	Area
36.	5	4	?	?
37.	5	?	4	?
38.	5	?	?	4
39.	9	6	?	?
40.	9	?	10	?
41.	9	?	?	12
42.	10	8	?	?
43.	10	?	6	?
44.	10	?	?	10

Circumference of a Circle

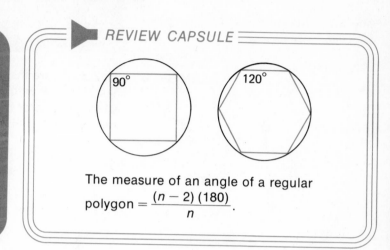
EXAMPLE 1

Show how an approximate length of the curve below can be found by measuring segments.

Choose any number of points. Connect them. Measure each segment.

P_1 is read P sub one.
$\doteq$ means is approximately equal to.

The length $\doteq PP_1 + P_1P_2 + P_2P_3 + P_3P_4 + P_4P_5 + P_5P_6 + P_6P_7 + P_7P_8 + P_8Q$.

Using more points would give a better approximation.

EXAMPLE 2

Find the perimeter of each regular polygon. Which is the best approximation of the "distance around" the circle?

The octagon has more points on the circle.

Perimeter $\doteq$ 4(1.41), or 5.64 in.

Perimeter $\doteq$ 5(1.18), or 5.90 in.

Perimeter $\doteq$ 8(.76), or 6.08 in.

The distance around a circle is called the circumference.

The perimeter of the octagon is the best approximation of the "distance around" the circle.

Definition of *circumference*

The limit is the number that the perimeters get closer and closer to.

> The *circumference* of a circle is the limit of the perimeters of inscribed regular polygons of the circle as the number of sides of the polygons increases indefinitely.

EXAMPLE 3   Hexagons are inscribed in ⊙O with a radius of length s and in ⊙P with a radius of length t. Find the ratio of the perimeter of the hexagon to the length of the diameter for each circle.

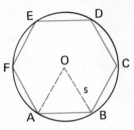
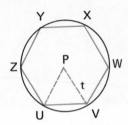

In hexagon *ABCDEF*, △*AOB* is equilateral. ────────→

A diameter contains two radii. ────────→

The ratios are equal. ────────→

$AB = s$	$UV = t$
perimeter = $6s$	perimeter = $6t$
length of diameter = $2s$	length of diameter = $2t$
$\dfrac{\text{perimeter}}{\text{length of diam.}} = \dfrac{6s}{2s}$	$\dfrac{\text{perimeter}}{\text{length of diam.}} = \dfrac{6t}{2t}$
$= \dfrac{3}{1}$	$= \dfrac{3}{1}$

Example 3 and the definition of circumference suggest this.─┐

Theorem 11.9

> The ratio of the circumference to the length of a diameter is the same for all circles.

π (read pie) is a Greek letter.

π is the symbol used for the ratio of the circumference to the diameter.

$$\pi = \frac{c}{d}$$

π is an irrational number. One useful approximation for π is 3.14.

A more accurate approximation is 3.141592653589793.

> The circumference c of a circle with a diameter of length d is $c = \pi d$, where $\pi \doteq 3.14$.

EXAMPLE 4 If the length of a diameter of a circle is 3.5 cm, find the circumference. (Use 3.14 for π.)

$c = \pi d$ $\longrightarrow$ $c = (3.14)(3.5)$, or 10.990 cm.

EXAMPLE 5 If the circumference of a circle is 11π ft, find the length of a diameter.

$c = \pi d$ $\longrightarrow$

$$11\pi = \pi d$$
$$d = \frac{11\pi}{\pi}, \text{ or } 11 \text{ ft}$$

EXAMPLE 6 If a radius of a circle is 5 inches long, find the circumference in terms of π.

The length of a diameter is twice the length of a radius.
$d = 2r$ $\longrightarrow$

$$c = \pi d$$
$$c = \pi(2 \cdot 5), \text{ or } 10\pi \text{ inches}$$

EXAMPLE 7 The circumference of a circle is 20π. Find the length of a radius.

Example 6 suggests another formula.
$c = 2\pi r.$ $\longrightarrow$

$d = 2r$ $\longrightarrow$

$$20\pi = 2\pi r \qquad\qquad 20\pi = \pi d$$
$$r = \frac{20\pi}{2\pi} \qquad\qquad d = \frac{20\pi}{\pi}$$
$$r = 10 \qquad\qquad\quad d = 20$$
$$\qquad\qquad\qquad\qquad r = 10$$

Thus, the length of a radius is 10.

ORAL EXERCISES

Find the circumference in terms of π.

1. $d = 3$ in. **2.** $r = 5$ cm **3.** $r = 7$ yd **4.** $d = 8$ ft

Find the length of a diameter.

5. $r = 3$ ft **6.** $c = 5\pi$ yd **7.** $c = 12\pi$ cm **8.** $c = 3$ in.

Find the length of a radius.

9. $d = 5$ cm **10.** $c = 4\pi$ ft **11.** $c = 9\pi$ in. **12.** $c = 4$ yd

EXERCISES

PART A

Find the circumference in terms of π.

1. $r = 3.4$ in. **2.** $d = 7.2$ cm **3.** $r = .42$ yd **4.** $d = 420$ mi

Find each missing measurement. Use 3.14 for π.

	r	d	c
5.	2 in.	?	?
6.	?	8 cm	?
7.	.72 ft	?	?
8.	?	?	9.4 yd
9.	?	.64 yd	?
10.	32 mi	?	?
11.	?	?	27 cm
12.	?	?	4.7 ft
13.	?	?	13 ft
14.	?	6.2 cm	?

PART B

15. Estimate the length of the curve below.

For each given circumference approximate the lengths of a radius and the circumference to the nearest hundredth. (Use 3.14 for π.)

16. $\frac{3}{4}$ ft

17. $\frac{2}{3}$ cm

18. $\sqrt{3}$ in.

19. $\sqrt{7}$ yd

20. Two approximations, $3\frac{1}{7}$ and 3.14 are often used for π. Which is closer to π?

21. Archimedes found π to be between $3\frac{1}{7}$ and $3\frac{10}{71}$. Which is closer to π?

22. Find the length of the equator if the radius of the earth is 4000 miles.

23. If a radius of a circle is increased by d, express the increase in the circumference in terms of d.

PART C

24. Using the Pythagorean theorem, find the length of each side of a square inscribed in a circle with a 1 inch radius. Compare the perimeter of the square to the circumference of the circle.

25. Using the appropriate trigonometric ratio, find the length of each side of an octagon inscribed in a circle with a 1 inch radius. Compare the perimeter of the octagon with the circumference of the circle.

26. The circumference of a circle is equal to the perimeter of a square whose side is s. Show that the radius of this circle is $\frac{2s}{\pi}$.

27. The circumference of a circle is 20π. Find the perimeter and area of a regular inscribed hexagon.

An Area Problem

Two different methods are sometimes used to get a quick estimate of the area of a quadrilateral shaped land plot.

In most cases, however, the area obtained is only an approximation because they are not exactly rectangles nor rhombuses.

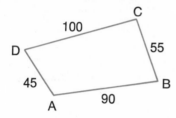

Sides (Rectangle) Method

$$\text{Area} = \left(\frac{55 + 45}{2}\right) \left(\frac{100 + 90}{2}\right)$$

$$= \frac{100}{2} \cdot \frac{190}{2}$$

$$= 50 \cdot 95$$

$$= 4750 \text{ sq units}$$

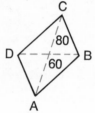

Diagonal (Kite) Method

$$\text{Area} = \frac{1}{2}(80)(60)$$

$$= \frac{1}{2}(4800)$$

$$= 2400 \text{ sq units}$$

To find the area of a rectangle shaped quadrilateral:

$$\text{Area} = \left(\frac{AB + CD}{2}\right)\left(\frac{AD + BC}{2}\right)$$

To find the area of a kite shaped quadrilateral:

$$\text{Area} = \frac{1}{2}(AC)(DB)$$

These formulas are based on the area of a rectangle and kite (rhombus) formulas.

For the two figures below measure carefully in centimeters.
Approximate the area of each using both formulas.
Which formula gives the best estimate. Why?

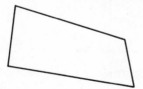

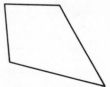

Area of a Circle

OBJECTIVE

■ To apply the formula for the area of a circle

▶ REVIEW CAPSULE

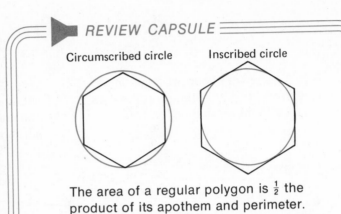

Circumscribed circle   Inscribed circle

The area of a regular polygon is $\frac{1}{2}$ the product of its apothem and perimeter.

EXAMPLE 1

Find the area of a regular hexagon if the perimeter is 48 cm and the apothem is $4\sqrt{3}$ cm.

Area $= \frac{1}{2}ap$ ⟶

$$\text{Area} = \frac{1}{2}(4\sqrt{3})(48)$$
$$\text{or } 96\sqrt{3} \text{ sq cm}$$

$4\sqrt{3}$

The area of a circle is very close to the area of a regular polygon with a very large number of sides.

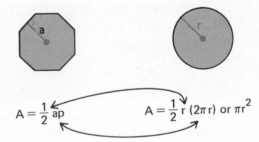

The apothem is approximately equal to the length of the radius.

The perimeter is approximately equal to the circumference.

$$A = \frac{1}{2}ap \qquad A = \frac{1}{2}r(2\pi r) \text{ or } \pi r^2$$

Theorem 11.10

The area of a circle with a radius of length r is πr^2.

(Area $= \pi r^2$)

The length of a diameter is twice the length of a radius.

Since $r = \frac{1}{2}d$ we can also write the area formula in terms of the diameter: $c = \pi\left(\frac{1}{2}d\right)^2$ or $c = \dfrac{\pi d^2}{4}$.

EXAMPLE 2 ⌠Find the area of a circle in terms of π if a radius is
4 inches long.

Area $= \pi r^2$ ⟶ Area $= \pi (4)^2$, or 16π square inches.

EXAMPLE 3 ⌠Find the area of a circle if a radius is 11 cm long.
(Use 3.14 for π.)

Area $= \pi r^2$ ⟶ Area $= (3.14)(11)^2$
$= (3.14)(121)$, or 399.94 sq cm

EXAMPLE 4 · Find the length of a radius of a circle if the area
is 48π.

Area $= \pi r^2$ ⟶ $48\pi = \pi r^2$
$48 = r^2$
$\sqrt{48} = \sqrt{16} \cdot \sqrt{3} = 4\sqrt{3}$ ⟶ $r = \sqrt{48}$, or $4\sqrt{3}$

EXAMPLE 5 · Find the area of a circle if the circumference is 5π. ^{38}

Find the length of a radius first.

$c = \pi d$, or $2\pi r$
$5\pi = 2\pi r$
$r = \frac{5}{2}$
Area $= \pi(\frac{5}{2})^2$, or $\frac{25}{4}\pi$

ORAL EXERCISES

Find the area in terms of π.

1. $r = 1$ in. **2.** $r = 5$ ft **3.** $d = 4$ yd **4.** $d = 16$ cm

Find the length of a radius of the circle whose area is given.

5. π sq ft **6.** 36π sq cm **7.** 49π sq in. **8.** 64π sq cm

Find the length of a diameter of the circle whose area is given.

9. 4π sq in. **10.** 25π sq cm **11.** 144π sq yd **12.** 36π sq ft

EXERCISES

PART A

Find the area of a circle with each given radius length. (Use 3.14 for π.)

1. $r = .7$ in. **2.** $r = 5.6$ yd **3.** $r = \frac{3}{4}$ cm **4.** $r = \sqrt{5}$ ft

Find the area of a circle with each given diameter length. (Use 3.14 for π.)

5. $d = 3$ cm **6.** $d = 4.7$ ft **7.** $d = \frac{1}{3}$ yd **8.** $d = \sqrt{3}$ in.

Find the area of a circle with each given circumference. (Use 3.14 for π.)

9. $c = 31.4$ in. **10.** $c = 6.28$ cm **11.** $c = 9$ yd **12.** $c = 100$ ft

Find the lengths of a radius and a diameter of a circle with each given area. (Use 3.14 for π.)

13. 314 sq cm **14.** 78.5 sq in. **15.** 1.1304 sq yd **16.** 4.5216 sq cm

PART B

17. Find the area of a square with an apothem of 1 in. and a perimeter of 8 in. Compare this to the area of a circle with a 1 in. radius.

18. Find the area of a regular octagon with an apothem of 1 in. and a perimeter of 6.08 in. Compare this with the area of a circle with a 1 in. radius.

Find the area of the shaded region. Each polygon is regular with sides 2 in. long. (Hint: Find the length of the radius of each circle. Then find the difference between the larger and smaller areas.)

19.

20.

21.
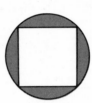

22.

Find the area of the shaded region.

23. $\overline{AB}$ is a diameter of $\odot O$, $\overline{AO}$ is a diameter of $\odot P$, $\overline{OB}$ is a diameter of $\odot Q$. $AB = 10$

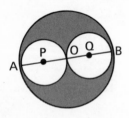

24. Each circle is tangent to the 2 adjacent circles and to the square. All $\odot$'s are $\cong$. $AB = 2$

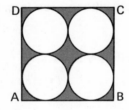

25. Each circle is tangent to the adjacent circles and to the square. All $\odot$'s are $\cong$. $AB = 2$

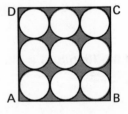

PART C

26. Prove or disprove: The ratio of the areas of two circles equals the ratio of the lengths of the radii.

27. Prove or disprove: The ratio of the areas of two circles equals the ratio of the squares of the circumferences.

28. Find the ratio of the area of a square inscribed in a circle to the area of a square circumscribed about the circle.

29. Find the ratio of the area of an equilateral triangle inscribed in a circle to the area of an equilateral triangle circumscribed about the circle.

Arc Lengths

OBJECTIVE
■ To apply a formula for the length of an arc

REVIEW CAPSULE

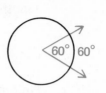

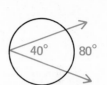

A central angle has the same measure as its intercepted arc.

An inscribed angle has one half the measure of its intercepted arc.

EXAMPLE 1

$m\widehat{AB}$ is the degree measure of $\widehat{AB}$.

$\widehat{AB}$ and $\widehat{CD}$ are not $\cong$.

These arcs have the same degree measure, but different lengths.

$m\angle COD = 40$.
Find $m\widehat{AB}$ and $m\widehat{CD}$.
Which arc is longer?

$m\widehat{AB} = m\widehat{CD} = 40$. *But,*
$\widehat{CD}$ is longer than $\widehat{AB}$.

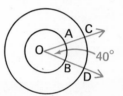

EXAMPLE 2

Find the length of an arc of a circle with a 6 in. radius if the degree measure of the arc is 60.

Find the circumference. $\longrightarrow$

$c = 2\pi(6)$ or 12π in.

The arc is $\frac{1}{6}$ of the $\odot$. $\longrightarrow$

Leave the answer in terms of π unless otherwise stated.

$\text{length} = \left(\frac{60}{360}\right)(12\pi)$
$= \frac{1}{6}(12\pi)$, or 2π in.

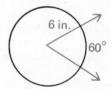

Theorem 11.11

If the degree measure of an arc is m and the length of a radius of the circle is r, the length ℓ of the arc is given by this formula. $\ell = \left(\dfrac{m}{360}\right)(2\pi r)$

EXAMPLE 3 Find the length of $\widehat{ST}$ if $m\widehat{ST} = 90$ and $r = 2$.

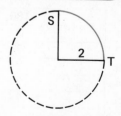

$\ell = \left(\frac{m}{360}\right)(2\pi r)$ $\longrightarrow$ $\text{length} = \left(\frac{90}{360}\right)(2\pi \cdot 2)$, or π.

EXAMPLE 4   Diameter $\overline{RP}$, $RP = 16$ cm,
$m \angle PRQ = 60$.
Find the length of $\overset{\frown}{PQ}$.

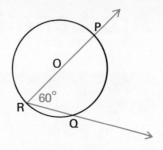

$\angle PRQ$ is an inscribed $\angle$. $\longrightarrow$ $m\overset{\frown}{PQ} = 120$

$\overline{RP}$ is a diameter. $\longrightarrow$ $r = 8$ cm

length $= \left(\frac{120}{360}\right)(2\pi \cdot 8)$

$\qquad = \frac{1}{3}(16\pi)$, or $\frac{16}{3}\pi$ cm.

EXAMPLE 5   Length of $\overset{\frown}{AB} = \frac{3}{4}\pi$,
$OA = 4\frac{1}{2}$ in.
Find $m\overset{\frown}{AB}$.

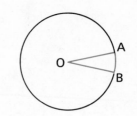

length $= \left(\frac{m}{360}\right)(2\pi r)$ $\longrightarrow$ $\dfrac{3}{4}\pi = \left(\dfrac{m}{360}\right)(2\pi)\left(4\frac{1}{2}\right)$

$\dfrac{3}{4}\pi = \left(\dfrac{m}{360}\right)(9\pi)$

Divide each side by π. $\longrightarrow$ $\dfrac{3}{4} = \dfrac{9m}{360}$

Prod. of extremes = prod. of means. $\longrightarrow$ $(4)(9m) = (3)(360)$

$36m = 1{,}080$

$m = 30$

Thus, $m\overset{\frown}{AB} = 30$.

EXERCISES

PART A

Complete the following chart. (Answers may be left in terms of π.)

	Degree Measure of Arc	Length of Radius	Length of Diameter	Length of Arc
1.	45	10 in.	?	?
2.	30	?	6 yd	?
3.	120	2.5 cm	?	?
4.	250	?	$\frac{4}{3}$ ft	?
5.	300	π cm	?	?
6.	15	?	?	10π ft
7.	60	?	?	4π yd
8.	75	?	?	4.5π cm
9.	120	?	?	$\frac{3}{4}\pi$ in.
10.	180	?	?	π in.
11.	?	8 yd	?	π yd
12.	?	?	10 cm	3π cm
13.	?	2.5 ft	?	5π ft
14.	?	?	$\frac{2}{3}$ cm	$\frac{\pi}{6}$ cm
15.	?	?	.8 yd	$.4\pi$ yd

16. In a circle with a 6 inch radius, find, correct to the nearest inch, the length of an arc with a measure of 120°.

17. In a circle with a 10 inch diameter, find, correct to the nearest inch, the length of an arc with a measure of 75°.

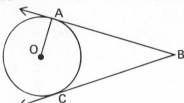

18. $\vec{BA}$ and $\vec{BC}$ are tangent to $\odot O$, $m\angle ABC = 48$, $OA = 8$. Find length of $\widehat{AC}$.

19. $\vec{BA}$ and $\vec{BC}$ are tangent to $\odot O$, $OA = 10$, length of $\widehat{AC} = 12$. Find $m\angle ABC$. Use 3.14 for π.

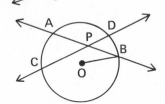

20. $m\widehat{BD} = 30$, $m\angle APC = 50$, radius $\overline{OB}$, $OB = 10$. Find length of $\widehat{AC}$.

21. $m\widehat{BD} = 40$, length of $\widehat{AC} = 12$, radius $\overline{OB}$, $OB = 10$. Find $m\angle APC$. Use 3.14 for π.

Algebra Review

OBJECTIVE

■ To simplify radical expressions like $\dfrac{3 + \sqrt{5}}{\sqrt{5}}$ and $\dfrac{1 + \sqrt{2}}{3 - \sqrt{7}}$

To simplify expressions like $\dfrac{3 + \sqrt{5}}{\sqrt{5}}$ and $\dfrac{1 + \sqrt{2}}{3 - \sqrt{7}}$:
1. Rationalize the denominator.
2. Write in simplest form.

EXAMPLE 1   Simplify $\dfrac{2 + \sqrt{7}}{\sqrt{3}}$.

Make the denominator a perfect square. $\longrightarrow$

$$\frac{2 + \sqrt{7}}{\sqrt{3}} \cdot \frac{\sqrt{3}}{\sqrt{3}} = \frac{2\sqrt{3} + \sqrt{21}}{3}$$

EXAMPLE 2   Simplify $\dfrac{2}{1 + \sqrt{3}}$.

$$\frac{2}{1 + \sqrt{3}} \cdot \frac{1 - \sqrt{3}}{1 - \sqrt{3}} = \frac{2 - 2\sqrt{3}}{1 - 3}$$

$$= \frac{2 - 2\sqrt{3}}{-2}, \text{ or } -1 + \sqrt{3}$$

Simplify.

1. $\dfrac{\sqrt{7} - 1}{\sqrt{7}}$

2. $\dfrac{4\sqrt{3} + 2}{\sqrt{3}}$

3. $\dfrac{4}{2 + \sqrt{5}}$

4. $\dfrac{2 + \sqrt{3}}{1 - \sqrt{6}}$

Flow Chart: Estimating π

π to a hundred and twenty decimal places.

3. | 14159 | 26535 | 89793 | 23846 | 26433 | 83279 | 50288 | 41971 |
|---|---|---|---|---|---|---|---|
| 69399 | 37510 | 58209 | 74944 | 59230 | 78164 | 06286 | 20899 |
| 86280 | 34825 | 34211 | 70679 | 82148 | 08651 | 32823 | 06647 |

Example
Let $n = 0, 1, 2$.

For $n = 0$, $(-1)^0 \left[\dfrac{1}{2(0)+1}\right] = (1)\left(\dfrac{1}{1}\right)$, or 1.

For $n = 1$, $(-1)^1 \left[\dfrac{1}{2(1)+1}\right] = (-1)\left(\dfrac{1}{3}\right)$, or $-\dfrac{1}{3}$.

For $n = 2$, $(-1)^2 \left[\dfrac{1}{2(2)+1}\right] = (1)\left(\dfrac{1}{5}\right)$, or $\dfrac{1}{5}$.

Add $1 - \dfrac{1}{3} + \dfrac{1}{5}$ as decimals.

$1 - .33 + .20 = .87$

Mult. by 4. $4(.87) = 3.48$
Is this the estimate for π? No.

Now let $n = 0, 1, 2,$ and 3.

For $n = 3$, $(-1)^3 \left[\dfrac{1}{2(3)+1}\right] = (-1)\left(\dfrac{1}{7}\right)$, or $-\dfrac{1}{7}$.

Add up all the terms in decimal form.

$$\underset{\underset{n=0}{\uparrow}}{1} \quad \underset{\underset{n=1}{\uparrow}}{-.33} \quad \underset{\underset{n=2}{\uparrow}}{+.20} \quad \underset{\underset{n=3}{\uparrow}}{-.14} \quad = .73$$

Multiply by 4. $4(.73) = 2.92$
Is this the estimate for π? No.

Let $n = 0, 1, 2, 3, 4$.
Continue.

[Hint: Carry this process out to at least ten terms in order to get an estimate for π.]

Read: store as Q

$Q \xleftarrow{} $ Multiply by 4.

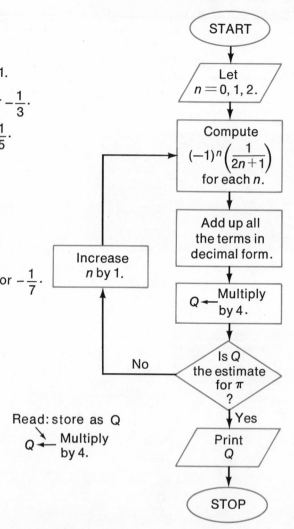

Areas of Sectors and Segments

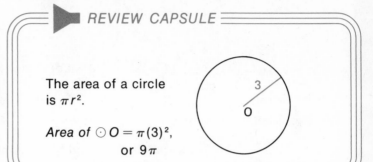

A sector is bounded by two radii and an arc.

A segment is bounded by a chord and an arc.

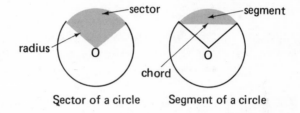

Sector of a circle   Segment of a circle

EXAMPLE 1

Find the area of a sector of a circle with a radius of 10 in. and an arc measure of 36°.

The area of the sector is $\frac{36}{360}$, or $\frac{1}{10}$ the area of the circle.

$$\text{Area of sector} = \left(\frac{36}{360}\right)(\text{area of circle})$$
$$= \left(\frac{1}{10}\right)(\pi 10^2), \text{ or } 10\pi \text{ sq in.}$$

Theorem 11.12

The area of a sector bounded by an arc of measure m and radii of length r is given by this formula.
$$\text{Area} = \left(\frac{m}{360}\right)(\pi r^2)$$

EXAMPLE 2

Find the area of a sector of a circle with a 5-cm radius and an arc length of 2π cm.

Use the formula for arc length to find $\frac{m}{360}$.

$$2\pi = \frac{m}{360}(2 \cdot 5\pi) \therefore \frac{m}{360} = \frac{1}{5}.$$

Substitute in the formula. ⟶

$$\text{Area} = \left(\frac{m}{360}\right)(\pi r^2) = \frac{1}{5} \cdot \pi(5^2) = 5\pi$$

Thus, the area of the sector is 5π sq cm.

EXAMPLE 3   Find the area of a segment of a circle with a 10-in. radius and an arc measure of 60°.

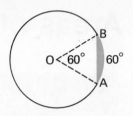

Area of segment = area of sector − area of △AOB.

△AOB is equilateral.

Leave the answer in this form. ⟶

Area of sector = $(\frac{60}{360})(\pi 10^2)$
= $(\frac{1}{6})(100\pi)$
= $\frac{50}{3}\pi$ sq in.

Area of △AOB
= $\frac{10^2}{4}\sqrt{3}$
= $25\sqrt{3}$ sq in.

Thus, area of segment = $\frac{50}{3}\pi - 25\sqrt{3}$ sq in.

EXAMPLE 4   Find the area of the region bounded by two concentric circles with 7-cm and 4-cm radii.

The region is called an *annulus,* or *ring.*

Area of ring = area of outer circle − area of inner circle.

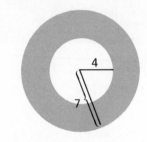

Area of outer circle = $\pi(7)^2$
= 49π
Area of inner circle = $\pi(4)^2$
= 16π

Thus, area of region = $49\pi - 16\pi$, or 33π sq cm.

ORAL EXERCISES

What fractional part of the area of a circle is the area of a sector with the given arc measure?

1. 10°   **2.** 36°   **3.** 90°   **4.** 120°

What is the area of a sector if the area of the circle is 120π and the arc of the sector has the given measure?

5. 10°   **6.** 36°   **7.** 90°   **8.** 120°
9. 20°   **10.** 72°   **11.** 180°   **12.** 45°

EXERCISES
PART A

1. Find the area of a sector of a circle with a 6-in. radius and an arc measure of 72°.

2. Find the area of a sector of a circle with a 5-cm radius and an arc measure of 60°.

Find the missing measures. $\overline{OX}$ **and** $\overline{OY}$ **are radii of** $\odot O$. **Answers may be left in terms of** π.

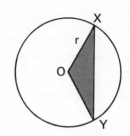

	$m\angle O$	Length of Radius r	$m\widehat{XY}$	Area of Sector Shown	Area of Segment Shown
3.	60	5 cm	?	?	?
4.	?	5 in.	90	?	?
5.	120	8 ft	?	?	?
6.	?	10 cm	?	25π sq cm	?
7.	?	?	120	12π sq in.	?

8. Find the area of a sector of a circle with a 10-in. radius and an arc length of 4π in.

9. Find the area of a sector of a circle with a 12-cm radius and an arc length of 3π cm.

10. Find the area of a segment of a circle with a 9-in. radius and an arc length of 3π in.

11. Find the area of a segment of a circle with an 8-cm radius and an arc length of 4π cm.

12. Find the area of a ring bounded by circles with 10-cm and 8-cm radii.

13. Find the area of a ring bounded by circles with 8-in. and 5-in. radii.

PART B

14. If the area of a ring is 48π *sq in. and the* outer circle has an 8-in. radius, find the length of a radius of the inner circle.

15. If the area of a ring is 48π sq in. and the inner circle has an 8-in. radius, find the length of a radius of the outer circle.

PART C

Find the change in the area of a sector of a circle.

16. The measure of the angle is doubled.

17. The length of the radius of the circle is doubled.

18. The measure of the angle is halved and the length of the radius is doubled.

19. Find a formula for the area of a ring bounded by two given concentric circles with radii of length R and r. $(R > r)$.

20. Show that in a circle of radius r the segment cut off by a $60°$ central angle has area $= \dfrac{r^2(2\pi - 3\sqrt{3})}{12}$.

21. Find the area of a segment of a circle with a 10-cm radius and an arc measure of $68°$. [Hint: Use the appropriate trigonometric ratio.]

22. Find the area of a segment of a circle with a 12-in. radius and an arc measure of $32°$. [Hint: Use the appropriate trigonometric ratio.]

Chapter Eleven Review

1. Trace the figures at the right. By direct comparison determine which is larger. [p. 359]

Find the area. [p. 359, 363, 367, 372]

2.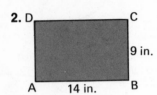
D, C, 9 in., A, 14 in., B

3.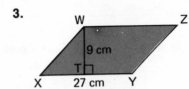
W, Z, 9 cm, T, X, 27 cm, Y

4.
O, N, L, 13 yd, M

5.
T, 9 ft, M, R, 7 ft, S

6.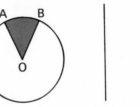
K, 14 cm, J, 9 cm, S, H, 18 cm, I

7.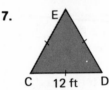
E, C, 12 ft, D

8. Regular pentagon ABCDE, AB = 4, apothem = 2.8. Find the area of ABCDE. [p. 379]

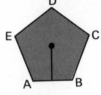
D, E, C, A, B

9. Regular hexagon FGHIJK, perimeter = 18. Find the area of FGHIJK. [p. 379]

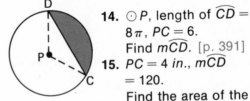
J, I, K, O, H, F, G

10. Find the circumference of a circle with a 6-in. radius. [p. 383]
[p. 391]

12. ⊙O, m∠AOB = 50, OA = 8. Find the length of $\overarc{AB}$.

13. OA = 8 cm, m$\overarc{AB}$ = 72. Find the area of the sector. [p. 395]

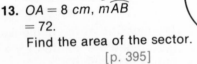
A, B, O

11. Find the area of a circle with a 12-cm radius. [p. 388]

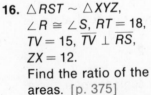
D, P, C

14. ⊙P, length of $\overarc{CD}$ = 8π, PC = 6. Find m$\overarc{CD}$. [p. 391]

15. PC = 4 in., m$\overarc{CD}$ = 120. Find the area of the segment. [p. 395]

16. △RST ~ △XYZ, ∠R ≅ ∠S, RT = 18, TV = 15, $\overline{TV} \perp \overline{RS}$, ZX = 12. Find the ratio of the areas. [p. 375]

T, R, V, S

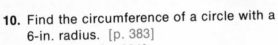
Y, Z, X

17. △RST ~ △XYZ, ∠R ≅ ∠S, RT = 21, RS = 18, YZ = 14. Find the ratio of the perimeters. [p. 375]

18. Find the area of a ring bounded by circles with 11-ft and 7-ft radii. [p. 395]

Chapter Eleven Test

1. Trace the figures at the right. By direct comparison, determine which is larger.

Find the area.

2.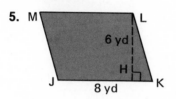
   M   L
   J 17 ft K

3.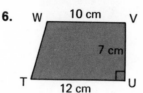
   E   D
   8 in.
   B 27 in. C

4.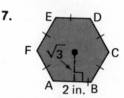
   Q
   18 cm
   O 12 cm P T

5.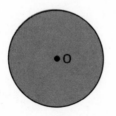
   M   L
   6 yd
   H
   J 8 yd K

6.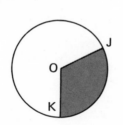
   W 10 cm V
   7 cm
   T 12 cm U

7.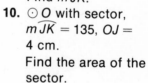
   E   D
   F $\sqrt{3}$ C
   A 2 in. B

8. Circle O. Circumference $= 6\pi$ in. Find the area.

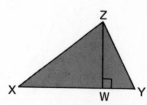

9. $\odot O$, length of $\overset{\frown}{JK} = 6\pi$, $OJ = 5$. Find $m\overset{\frown}{JK}$.

10. $\odot O$ with sector, $m\overset{\frown}{JK} = 135$, $OJ = 4$ cm. Find the area of the sector.

11. Equilateral $\triangle RST$, $RS = 10$ cm. Find the area.

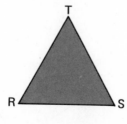

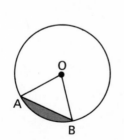

12. $\odot O$, $m\overset{\frown}{AB} = 100°$, $OA = 9$ in. Find the length of $\overset{\frown}{AB}$.

13. $m\overset{\frown}{AB} = 60°$, $OA = 10$ cm. Find the area of the segment.

14. $\triangle XYZ \sim \triangle ABC$, $\overline{CD} \perp \overline{AB}$, $AB = 8$, $CD = 6$, $WZ = 9$. Find the ratio of the areas of the two triangles.

15. Find the area of a ring bounded by circles with 9-cm and 5-cm radii.

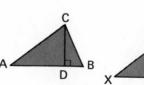

Curve Stitching

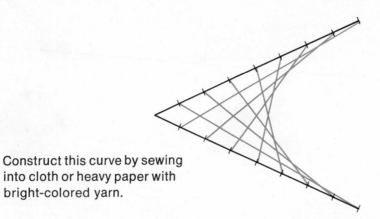

Construct this curve by sewing into cloth or heavy paper with bright-colored yarn.

Hint:

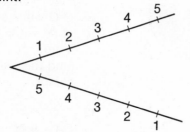

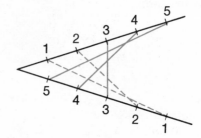

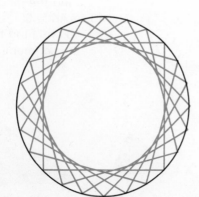

Now construct these.

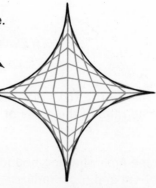

The Coordinate Plane

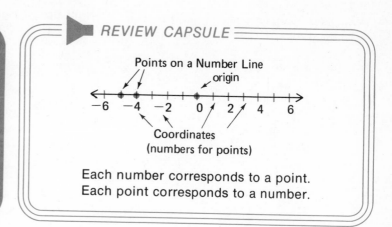

▶ *REVIEW CAPSULE*

Points on a Number Line

origin

Coordinates
(numbers for points)

Each number corresponds to a point.
Each point corresponds to a number.

Two perpendicular number lines determine a *coordinate plane.*

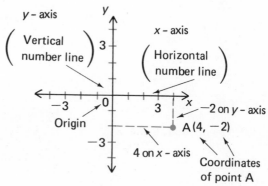

y – axis
(Vertical number line)

x – axis
(Horizontal number line)

Origin

−2 on y – axis

A (4, −2)

4 on x – axis

Coordinates of point A

Each point in the plane is described by two numbers.

We describe the position of point A by an *ordered pair,* (4, −2).

(4, −2)

x-coordinate (abscissa) y-coordinate (ordinate)

The x-coordinate is always written first.

EXAMPLE 1   Give the coordinates of each point graphed below.

(4, −3) and (−3, 4) describe two different points.

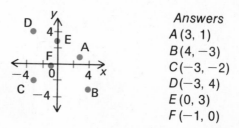

Answers
A (3, 1)
B (4, −3)
C (−3, −2)
D (−3, 4)
E (0, 3)
F (−1, 0)

EXAMPLE 2

A positive coordinate is right or up from the origin.

A negative coordinate is left or down from the origin.

Graph each point whose coordinates are given below.

To graph A(2, 4)
1. Start at origin.
2. Move right 2 units.
3. Move up 4 units.

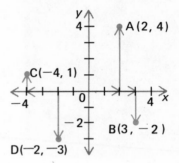

EXAMPLE 3

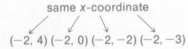

(−4, 3) (−1, 3) (0, 3) (2, 3)
The line is horizontal (parallel to the x-axis).

Graph each point. Then draw a line through the points.

A(−4, 3)
B(−1, 3)
C(0, 3)
D(2, 3)

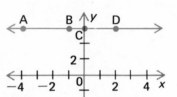

In Example 3, each y-coordinate is 3.

For a horizontal line, the y-coordinate of each point is the same.

EXAMPLE 4

same x-coordinate

(−2, 4) (−2, 0) (−2, −2) (−2, −3)
The line is vertical (parallel to the y-axis).

Graph each point. Then draw a line through the points.

E (−2, 4)
F (−2, 0)
G (−2, −2)
H (−2, −3)

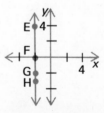

In Example 4, each x-coordinate is −2.

For a vertical line, the x-coordinate of each point is the same.

ORAL EXERCISES

Give the coordinates of each point graphed at the right.

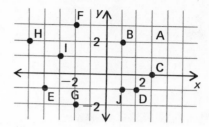

1. A	**2.** B
3. C	**4.** D
5. E	**6.** F
7. G	**8.** H
9. I	**10.** J

Tell in which directions to move from the origin in order to graph each point.

11. $A(3, 1)$ **12.** $B(-2, 5)$ **13.** $C(6, -4)$ **14.** $D(-3, -5)$ **15.** $E(0, 8)$ **16.** $F(0, -3)$
17. $G(5, 0)$ **18.** $H(-4, 0)$ **19.** $I(-3, 8)$ **20.** $J(0, 0)$ **21.** $K(-1, -4)$ **22.** $L(6, -2)$

EXERCISES
PART A

1. On the same coordinate system, graph and label each point in Exercises 11–16 above.

2. On the same coordinate system, graph and label each point in Exercises 17–22 above.

Is $\overleftrightarrow{PQ}$ a vertical line, a horizontal line, or neither?

3. $P(-2, 1)$, $Q(-2, 3)$ **4.** $P(4, 0)$, $Q(1, 0)$ **5.** $P(2, 6)$, $Q(6, 2)$ **6.** $P(-3, 4)$, $Q(-2, 4)$
7. $P(1, 5)$, $Q(1, -2)$ **8.** $P(5, 1)$, $Q(1, 2)$ **9.** $P(-3, 6)$, $Q(-3, -6)$ **10.** $P(4, -1)$, $Q(4, 1)$
11. $P(-3, 2)$, $Q(3, -2)$ **12.** $P(1, -1)$, $Q(1, -2)$ **13.** $P(4, -3)$, $Q(0, -3)$ **14.** $P(6, -1)$, $Q(1, 6)$

For what value of a will $\overleftrightarrow{AB}$ be vertical or horizontal, as indicated.

15. $A(8, 2)$, $B(-3, a)$; horizontal   **16.** $A(a, 6)$, $B(6, -6)$; vertical   **17.** $A(3, 1)$, $B(a, -1)$; vertical
18. $A(a, 2)$, $B(4, 5)$; vertical   **19.** $A(7, a)$, $B(-1, -3)$; horizontal   **20.** $A(6, 5)$, $B(-2, a)$; horizontal

PART B

The axes divide the coordinate plane into four quadrants. In which quadrant(s) will a point have the following?

Second Quadrant	First Quadrant
Third Quadrant	Fourth Quadrant

21. Negative x-coordinate
22. Positive x-coordinate and negative y
23. Positive y-coordinate and positive x
24. Negative x-coordinate and positive y
25. Negative x-coordinate and negative y

Give the coordinates of D so that $ABCD$ is a rectangle. Graph $ABCD$.

26. $A(2, 1)$, $B(6, 1)$, $C(6, 4)$, $D(?, ?)$ **27.** $A(-1, -6)$, $B(-5, -6)$, $C(-5, -2)$, $D(?, ?)$
28. $A(4, 0)$, $B(7, 0)$, $C(7, 3)$, $D(?, ?)$ **29.** $A(-3, -2)$, $B(-3, 4)$, $C(-4, -4)$ $D(?, ?)$

The Distance Formula

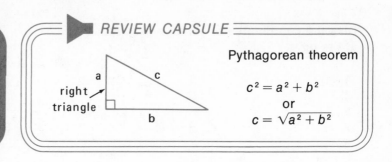

▶ *REVIEW CAPSULE*

Pythagorean theorem

$$c^2 = a^2 + b^2$$
or
$$c = \sqrt{a^2 + b^2}$$

EXAMPLE 1 Find the length of $\overline{AB}$.

$A(3, 2)$ $B(7, 2)$

same y-coordinate
$\overline{AB}$ is a horizontal segment.

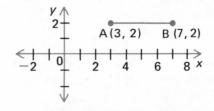

$$AB = BA$$
$$|7 - 3| = |3 - 7|$$
$$4$$

The length of $\overline{AB}$ is 4 units. $AB = 4$.

The length of a horizontal segment is the absolute value of the difference of the x-coordinates.

$A(x_1, y)$ and $B(x_2, y)$ determine a horizontal segment.

$$AB = |x_2 - x_1|$$

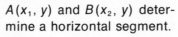

EXAMPLE 2

$C(4, 3)$ $D(4, -1)$

same x-coordinate
$\overline{CD}$ is a vertical segment.

Find the length of $\overline{CD}$.

The length of $\overline{CD}$ is 4 units. $CD = 4$.

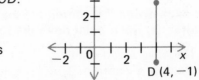

$$CD = DC$$
$$|-1 - 3| = |3 - (-1)|$$
$$4$$

$C(x, y_1)$ and $D(x, y_2)$ determine a vertical segment.

$$CD = |y_2 - y_1|$$

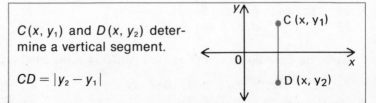

The length of a vertical segment is the absolute value of the difference of the y-coordinates.

EXAMPLE 3   Find the distance between points A and B.

Graph points A and B.
Form right $\triangle ABC$:
1. Draw horizontal segment $\overline{AC}$.
2. Draw vertical segment $\overline{BC}$.

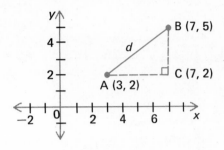

Use formulas for lengths of horizontal
and vertical segments.

$AC = |7 - 3|$ $BC = |2 - 5|$
$\quad\; = 4$ $\quad\; = 3$

Pythagorean theorem ───────────→

$$d = \sqrt{(AC)^2 + (BC)^2}$$
$$= \sqrt{4^2 + 3^2}$$
$$= \sqrt{16 + 9}$$
$$= \sqrt{25}$$
$$= 5$$

Thus, the distance is 5.

Theorem 12.1

The Distance Formula

The distance d between $P(x_1, y_1)$ and $Q(x_2, y_2)$ is
given by this formula.

$$d = \sqrt{(x_2 - x_1)^2 + (y_2 - y_1)^2}$$

EXAMPLE 4   Find the distance between $P(-1, -6)$ and $Q(3, -4)$.
Use the distance formula.

$$P(-1, -6) \qquad Q(3, -4)$$
$$\uparrow \;\; \uparrow \qquad\qquad \uparrow \;\; \uparrow$$
$$x_1 \;\; y_1 \qquad\qquad x_2 \;\; y_2$$

Distance formula ──────────────→
$3 - (-1) = 3 + 1 = 4$ ───────────→
$-4 - (-6) = -4 + 6 = 2$

$\sqrt{20} = \sqrt{4} \cdot \sqrt{5} = 2\sqrt{5}$ ───────→

$$d = \sqrt{(x_2 - x_1)^2 + (y_2 - y_1)^2}$$
$$= \sqrt{[3 - (-1)]^2 + [-4 - (-6)]^2}$$
$$= \sqrt{4^2 + 2^2}$$
$$= \sqrt{16 + 4}$$
$$= \sqrt{20}$$
$$= 2\sqrt{5}$$

Thus, the distance is $\sqrt{20}$, or $2\sqrt{5}$.

EXAMPLE 5 $\triangle ABC$ has vertices $A(-3, 5)$, $B(6, 3)$, and $C(-1, -3)$. Show that $\triangle ABC$ is isosceles.

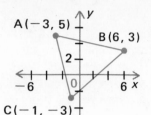

Use the Distance formula. ⟶

$$AB = \sqrt{[6 - (-3)]^2 + (3 - 5)^2}$$
$$= \sqrt{(9)^2 + (-2)^2}$$
$$= \sqrt{81 + 4}$$
$$= \sqrt{85}$$
$$AC = \sqrt{[-1 - (-3)]^2 + (-3 - 5)^2}$$
$$= \sqrt{(2)^2 + (-8)^2}$$
$$= \sqrt{4 + 64}$$
$$= \sqrt{68}$$
$$BC = \sqrt{(-1 - 6)^2 + (-3 - 3)^2}$$
$$= \sqrt{(-7)^2 + (-6)^2}$$
$$= \sqrt{49 + 36}$$
$$= \sqrt{85}$$

$AB = \sqrt{85}$ and $BC = \sqrt{85}$ ⟶ Since $AB = BC$, $\triangle ABC$ is isosceles.

ORAL EXERCISES

Find the length of $\overline{AB}$.

1. $A(3, 0)$, $B(1, 0)$ **2.** $A(2, -1)$, $B(2, 5)$ **3.** $A(6, 3)$, $B(-6, 3)$ **4.** $A(4, 1)$, $B(4, -1)$
5. $A(7, 2)$, $B(7, 5)$ **6.** $A(0, 3)$, $B(-3, 3)$ **7.** $A(6, -4)$, $B(-2, -4)$ **8.** $A(0, 8)$, $B(0, -3)$

EXERCISES

PART A

Find PQ.

1. $P(2, 3)$, $Q(5, 1)$ **2.** $P(-1, 3)$, $Q(7, -2)$ **3.** $P(6, -3)$, $Q(4, -5)$ **4.** $P(-1, 7)$, $Q(5, 0)$
5. $P(-2, -1)$, $Q(-5, 8)$ **6.** $P(4, 7)$, $Q(-3, -5)$ **7.** $P(-2, 8)$, $Q(6, -4)$ **8.** $P(0, 0)$, $Q(-8, -1)$
9. $P(7, -3)$, $Q(-6, 0)$ **10.** $P(1, 9)$, $Q(-1, 7)$ **11.** $P(2, 5)$, $Q(-4, 0)$ **12.** $P(3, -7)$, $Q(-4, 5)$

Find the length of each side of $\triangle ABC$. Then tell whether $\triangle ABC$ is isosceles or scalene.

13. $A(0, 0)$, $B(2, 5)$, $C(4, 0)$ **14.** $A(-3, 4)$, $B(2, -1)$, $C(4, 5)$ **15.** $A(3, 4)$, $B(5-3)$, $C(-2, 2)$
16. $A(1, 3)$, $B(-2, -1)$, $C(5, 0)$ **17.** $A(-6, 2)$, $B(5, -1)$, $C(4, 4)$ **18.** $A(-3, -3)$, $B(1, -6)$,
$$C(-2, -2)$$

PART B

19. Show that $\triangle RST$ is a right triangle for $R(-4, 3)$, $S(6, 1)$, and $T(2, -3)$. [Hint: Use the converse of the Pythagorean theorem.]

20. Show that the diagonals of $MNPQ$ are congruent for $M(3, 2)$, $N(3, -1)$, $P(7, -1)$, and $Q(7, 2)$.

The Midpoint Theorem

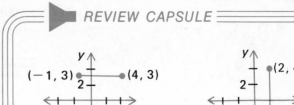
EXAMPLE 1   Graph the points $A(1, 3)$, $B(9, 3)$, and $C(9, 5)$. Find the coordinates of the midpoints of $\overline{AB}$ and $\overline{BC}$.

The midpoint of a segment lies halfway between the endpoints.

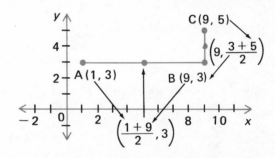

$\left(\dfrac{1+9}{2}, 3\right)$ is $(5, 3)$. ────────▶

$\left(9, \dfrac{5+3}{2}\right)$ is $(9, 4)$. ────────▶

Thus, the midpoint of $\overline{AB}$ has coordinates $(5, 3)$, and the midpoint of $\overline{BC}$ has coordinates $(9, 4)$.

EXAMPLE 2   Find the coordinates of M, the midpoint of the segment joining $A(1, 3)$ and $C(9, 5)$.

Form a rt. △ with $B(9, 3)$.

Use the midpoints of $\overline{AB}$ and $\overline{BC}$ as guides.

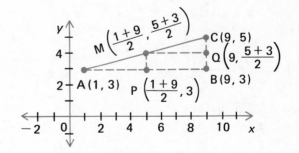

The x-coordinate of M is the average of the x-coordinates of A and C.

The y-coordinate of M is the average of the y-coordinates of A and C.

The coordinates of M are $\left(\dfrac{1+9}{2}, \dfrac{5+3}{2}\right)$, or $(5, 4)$.

The Midpoint Theorem

Let $P(x_1, y_1)$ and $Q(x_2, y_2)$ be any two points.
Then the midpoint of $\overline{PQ}$ has coordinates

$$\left(\frac{x_1 + x_2}{2}, \frac{y_1 + y_2}{2}\right).$$

EXAMPLE 3   Find the coordinates of the midpoint of $\overline{AB}$.

$$A(7, -3) \qquad\qquad B(-1, 5)$$
$$\uparrow\ \uparrow \qquad\qquad\qquad \uparrow\ \uparrow$$
$$x_1\ y_1 \qquad\qquad\qquad x_2\ y_2$$

Average x-coord. of A and B. $\dfrac{x_1 + x_2}{2} = \dfrac{7 + (-1)}{2}$ $\dfrac{y_1 + y_2}{2} = \dfrac{-3 + 5}{2}$

Average y-coord. of A and B.

$$= \frac{6}{2} \qquad\qquad\qquad\qquad = \frac{2}{2}$$
$$= 3 \qquad\qquad\qquad\qquad\quad = 1$$

x-coord. of midpoint   y-coord. of midpoint

Thus, the midpoint of $\overline{AB}$ has coordinates $(3, 1)$.

EXAMPLE 4 M is the midpoint of $\overline{AB}$. $A(-5, 4)$ and $M(-2, 1)$.
Find the coordinates of B.

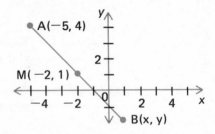

Let B have coordinates (x, y). $\longrightarrow$ $A(-5, 4) \qquad M(-2, 1) \qquad B(x, y)$

x-coord.   x-coord.   x-coord.   y-coord.   y-coord.   y-coord.
of A   of B   of M   of A   of B   of M

Average x-coord. of A and B.

Average y-coord. of A and B.

$$\frac{-5 + x}{2} = -2 \qquad\qquad \frac{4 + y}{2} = 1$$
$$-5 + x = -4 \qquad\qquad\quad 4 + y = 2$$
$$x = 1 \qquad\qquad\qquad\quad y = -2$$

Thus, B has coordinates $(1, -2)$.

EXAMPLE 5 $\triangle ABC$ has vertices $A(-4, -3)$, $B(4, -1)$, and $C(-2, 3)$. Find the coordinates of M, the midpoint of $\overline{AB}$. Find the length of the median from C to $\overline{AB}$.

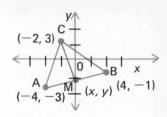

Let M have coordinates (x, y). Use the midpoint theorem.

Average the x-coord. of A and B. $\longrightarrow$ $x = \dfrac{-4 + 4}{2} = \dfrac{0}{2} = 0$

Average the y-coord. of A and B. $\longrightarrow$ $y = \dfrac{-3 + (-1)}{2} = \dfrac{-4}{2}$

$\dfrac{-4}{2} = -2$

Thus, M has coordinates $(0, -2)$.

Find CM for $C(-2, 3)$, $M(0, -2)$. Use the distance formula.

$CM = \sqrt{[0 - (-2)]^2 + (-2 - 3)^2}$
$= \sqrt{(2)^2 + (-5)^2}$
$= \sqrt{4 + 25}$
$= \sqrt{29}$

Thus, $CM = \sqrt{29}$.

EXERCISES

PART A

Find the coordinates of the midpoint of $\overline{AB}$.

1. $A(6, 0)$, $B(-4, 4)$ **2.** $A(5, 2)$, $B(-3, -6)$ **3.** $A(4, 7)$, $B(-2, 5)$ **4.** $A(3, 8)$, $B(-5, 2)$
5. $A(6, 1)$, $B(-3, 2)$ **6.** $A(5, -8)$, $B(4, 7)$ **7.** $A(-1, 5)$, $B(9, -2)$ **8.** $A(3, 7)$, $B(-3, -7)$
9. $A(0, 7)$, $B(-2, 4)$ **10.** $A(-3, 1)$, $B(8, -5)$ **11.** $A(4, -6)$, $B(3, -8)$ **12.** $A(-2, 6)$, $B(5, -5)$

M is the midpoint of $\overline{AB}$. Find the coordinates of B.

13. $M(-2, 3)$, $A(5, 8)$ **14.** $M(6, 1)$, $A(-8, 2)$ **15.** $M(-3, -1)$, $A(7, 5)$ **16.** $M(-4, 7)$, $A(8, -2)$
17. $M(0, 3)$, $A(-5, 1)$ **18.** $M(6, 4)$, $A(-2, -3)$ **19.** $M(5, 0)$, $A(-8, 2)$ **20.** $M(-6, 1)$, $A(0, -3)$

Find the coordinates of the midpoints of each side of $\triangle PQR$. Then find the length of the median to $\overline{PQ}$.

21. $P(-2, -4)$, $Q(6, -2)$, $R(2, 6)$ **22.** $P(-4, 1)$, $Q(2, -4)$, $R(-2, 5)$ **23.** $P(-1, -1)$, $Q(4, -2)$, $R(5, 4)$

PART B

24. In $\triangle ABC$, M is the midpoint of $\overline{AB}$. Show that $AM = MB = MC$ for $A(6, 0)$, $B(0, -8)$, and $C(0, 0)$.

25. In $\triangle PQR$, M is the midpoint of $\overline{PQ}$ and N is the midpoint of $\overline{QR}$. Show that $MN = \frac{1}{2}(PR)$ for $P(-3, -2)$, $Q(2, 2)$ and $R(3, -7)$.

26. Show that $\overline{AC}$ and $\overline{BD}$ have the same midpoint for $A(-3, -5)$, $B(2, -3)$, $C(3, 5)$, and $D(-2, 3)$.

27. M is the midpoint of $\overline{AD}$ and N is the midpoint of $\overline{BC}$. Show that $MN = AB = CD$ for $A(-1, -4)$, $B(2, 2)$, $C(-2, 6)$, and $D(-5, 0)$.

Reflections About the Y-Axis

EXPERIMENT

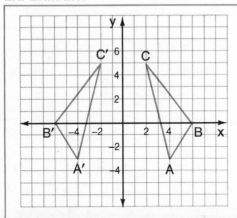

On graph paper, copy the axes, △ *ABC*, and △ *A'B'C'*.

1. Are the triangles congruent?

2. Give the coordinates of the vertices of △ *ABC* and △ *A'B'C'*.

3. Compare the x-coordinates of *A* and *A'*; *B* and *B'*; *C* and *C'*.

4. Similarly, compare the y-coordinates.

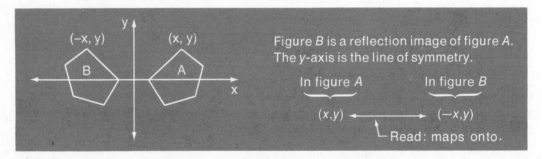

Figure *B* is a reflection image of figure *A*. The y-axis is the line of symmetry.

In figure *A*   In figure *B*

$(x,y) \longleftrightarrow (-x,y)$

Read: maps onto.

Copy each figure on graph paper. Draw the reflection of each figure with the y-axis the line of symmetry.

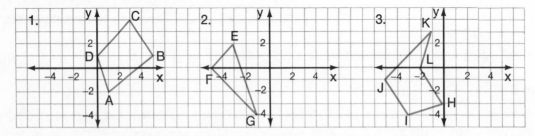

The coordinates of the vertices of a polygon are given.
Graph and label the polygon and the reflection about the y-axis.

4. *A*(2, 1), *B*(4, −3), *C*(3, 5)
6. *G*(−4, 1), *H*(−3, −5), *I*(−2, 4)

5. *J*(0, 0), *K*(1, 2), *L*(4, 3), *M*(2, −3)
7. *P*(0, 0), *Q*(0, −4), *R*(−3, −2), *S*(−1, 3)

Slope

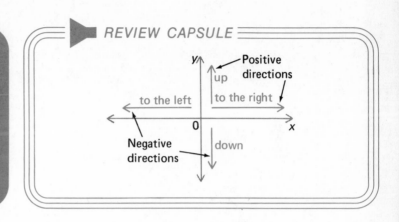

REVIEW CAPSULE

EXAMPLE 1   Find the directed distance from R to S.

$\overline{RS}$ is vertical.

$\vec{d}(RS)$ means the directed distance
from R to S. ———————————→ $\vec{d}(RS) = y$-coord. of $S - y$-coord. of R
Direction from R to S is down $(-)$. $= \quad -1 \quad - \quad 2$
Distance is $|-1-2| = 3$.   **Thus,** $\vec{d}(RS) = -3$.

Example 1 suggests this. ———————————→ If $\overline{RS}$ is vertical, with $R(x, y_1)$ and $S(x, y_2)$, then
$\vec{d}(RS) = y$-coord. of $S - y$-coord. of R.
$$\vec{d}(RS) = y_2 - y_1$$

EXAMPLE 2   Find $\vec{d}(MN)$.

$\overline{MN}$ is horizontal.

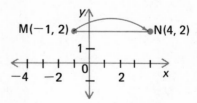

Direction from M to N is right $(+)$.
Distance is $|4 - (-1)| = 5$. $\vec{d}(MN) = x$-coord. of $N - x$-coord. of M
Read: The directed distance from $= \quad 4 \quad - (-1)$, or $+5$
M to N is 5. ———————————→ **Thus,** $\vec{d}(MN) = +5$, or 5.

Example 2 suggests this. ————————→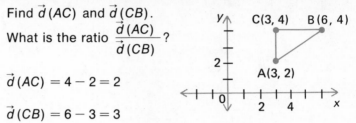

EXAMPLE 3

Find $\vec{d}(AC)$ and $\vec{d}(CB)$.

What is the ratio $\dfrac{\vec{d}(AC)}{\vec{d}(CB)}$?

$\overline{AC}$ is vertical. }
A to C is up: $+$ }

$\overline{CB}$ is horizontal. }
C to B is right: $+$ }

$\vec{d}(AC) = 4 - 2 = 2$

$\vec{d}(CB) = 6 - 3 = 3$

Thus, $\dfrac{\vec{d}(AC)}{\vec{d}(CB)} = \dfrac{2}{3}.$ ← vertical change
← horizontal change

We say that the *slope* of $\overline{AB}$ is $\frac{2}{3}$.

Write. ————————————————→ Slope $(\overline{AB}) = \dfrac{2}{3}$

EXAMPLE 4

Find the slope of $\overline{AB}$ for $A(2, -1)$ and $B(7, 3)$.

Graph A and B. Form right triangle ABC.

Find $\vec{d}(AC)$ and $\vec{d}(CB)$.
Slope $(\overline{AB}) = \dfrac{\text{vert.}}{\text{horiz.}} = \dfrac{\vec{d}(AC)}{\vec{d}(CB)}$

$\vec{d}(AC) = 3 - (-1) = 4$
$\vec{d}(CB) = 7 - 2 = 5$

Slope of $\overline{AB} = \dfrac{4}{5}$

$\vec{d}(AC) = 3 - (-1) = 4$ ————————————→
$\vec{d}(CB) = 7 - 2 = 5$ ————————————→

y-coord. B↘ ↙*y*-coord. A
Slope $(\overline{AB}) = \dfrac{3 - (-1)}{7 - 2} = \dfrac{4}{5}$
x-coord. B↗ ↖*x*-coord. A

Definition of slope ————————→

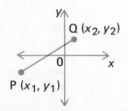

The *slope* of a segment is $\dfrac{\text{vertical change}}{\text{horizontal change}}.$

For $\overline{PQ}$ with $P(x_1, y_1)$ and $Q(x_2, y_2)$,

Slope $(\overline{PQ}) = \dfrac{y\text{-coord. of } Q - y\text{-coord. of } P}{x\text{-coord. of } Q - x\text{-coord. of } P}$

$= \dfrac{y_2 - y_1}{x_2 - x_1}$

EXAMPLE 5 Find slope $(\overline{CD})$ for $C(-3, 7)$ and $D(-2, -5)$.

$$\text{Slope } (\overline{CD}) = \frac{y_2 - y_1}{x_2 - x_1}$$

$$= \frac{-5 - 7}{-2 - (-3)}$$

$$= \frac{-12}{1}, \text{ or } -12$$

EXAMPLE 6 Find the slope of $\overline{AB}$, $\overline{BC}$, and $\overline{CD}$, for $A(-3, -1)$, $B(-1, 0)$, $C(3, 2)$, $D(5, 3)$.

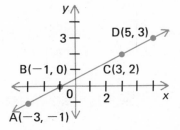

$$\text{Slope } (\overline{AB}) = \frac{0 - (-1)}{-1 - (-3)} = \frac{1}{2}$$

$$\text{Slope } (\overline{BC}) = \frac{2 - 0}{3 - (-1)} = \frac{2}{4} = \frac{1}{2}$$

$$\text{Slope } (\overline{CD}) = \frac{3 - 2}{5 - 3} = \frac{1}{2}$$

Definition of slope of a line ———→
In Example 6, slope $(\overleftrightarrow{AB}) = \frac{1}{2}$.

> The *slope of a line* is the slope of any segment on the line.

EXAMPLE 7 Find the slope of $\overleftrightarrow{AB}$ in each case. Then describe the position of the line.

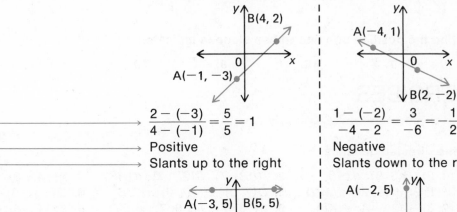

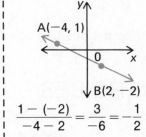

Slope ———→	$\dfrac{2 - (-3)}{4 - (-1)} = \dfrac{5}{5} = 1$ $\dfrac{1 - (-2)}{-4 - 2} = \dfrac{3}{-6} = -\dfrac{1}{2}$
Sign of slope ———→	Positive Negative
Position of line ———→	Slants up to the right Slants down to the right

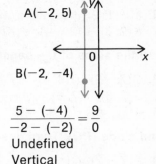

Slope ———→	$\dfrac{5 - 5}{5 - (-3)} = \dfrac{0}{8} = 0$ $\dfrac{5 - (-4)}{-2 - (-2)} = \dfrac{9}{0}$
	Zero Undefined
Position of line ———→	Horizontal Vertical

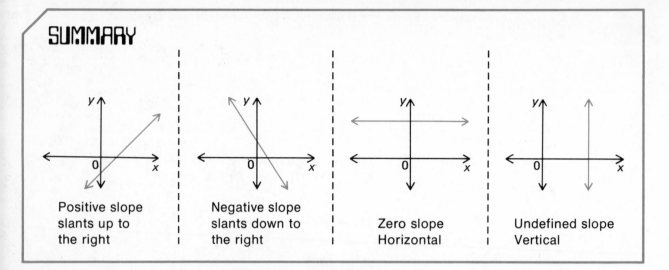

Positive slope slants up to the right | Negative slope slants down to the right | Zero slope Horizontal | Undefined slope Vertical

ORAL EXERCISES

Classify the slope of each line ℓ as positive, negative, zero, or undefined.

1.   **2.**   **3.**   **4.**   **5.**

Describe the position of a line whose slope is indicated.

6. 5   **7.** $\frac{0}{2}$ **8.** -1 **9.** $-\frac{7}{0}$ **10.** $\frac{5}{4}$ **11.** $-\frac{4}{7}$ **12.** $\frac{2}{0}$

EXERCISES

PART A

Find the directed distance.

1. $A(3, 2)$, $B(3, 8)$; $\vec{d}\,(AB)$ **2.** $R(5, -7)$, $S(2, -7)$; $\vec{d}\,(RS)$ **3.** $P(-4, -3)$, $Q(-4, -8)$; $\vec{d}\,(PQ)$
4. $M(-1, 2)$, $N(0, 2)$; $\vec{d}\,(MN)$ **5.** $C(7, 0)$, $D(-7, 0)$; $\vec{d}\,(CD)$ **6.** $G(-3, -9)$, $H(-3, 2)$; $\vec{d}\,(GH)$
7. $K(2, 3)$, $L(2, -4)$; $\vec{d}\,(KL)$ **8.** $S(-2, 7)$, $T(-6, 7)$; $\vec{d}\,(ST)$ **9.** $E(-1, -5)$, $F(6, -5)$; $\vec{d}\,(EF)$

Find the slope of the segment joining each pair of points.

10. $C(7, -2)$, $D(6, 4)$ **11.** $P(-1, 1)$, $Q(7, 4)$ **12.** $A(6, -7)$, $B(-3, -7)$
13. $S(0, 3)$, $T(7, 0)$ **14.** $R(-2, -3)$, $S(-2, 6)$ **15.** $E(6, 2)$, $F(-4, -1)$
16. $A(6, -4)$, $B(-6, -4)$ **17.** $G(1, -6)$, $H(5, 3)$ **18.** $K(-1, 3)$, $L(3, -1)$

Find slope ($\overleftrightarrow{PQ}$). Then describe the position of $\overleftrightarrow{PQ}$.

19. $P(7, -2)$, $Q(-3, 1)$ **20.** $P(1, 7)$, $Q(1, -7)$ **21.** $P(-2, 6)$, $Q(-6, 2)$

22. $P(6, 3)$, $Q(6, -2)$ **23.** $P(4, -1)$, $Q(3, -4)$ **24.** $P(-1, -4)$, $Q(-4, -1)$
25. $P(5, -1)$, $Q(-3, 8)$ **26.** $P(6, -3)$, $Q(-6, 3)$ **27.** $P(-2, 7)$, $Q(-2, 0)$

PART B

Find a so that $\overleftrightarrow{CD}$ will have the given slope.

28. $C(2, a)$, $D(3, -6)$; $\frac{2}{3}$ **29.** $C(5, -2)$, $D(-4, a)$; 0 **30.** $C(a, -1)$, $D(-3, 2)$; undefined
31. $C(4, -2)$, $D(6, a)$; 1 **32.** $C(3, a)$, $D(8, 1)$; -2 **33.** $C(3, -3)$, $D(-3, a)$; $-\frac{4}{3}$
34. $C(-3, -2)$, $D(1, a)$; 2 **35.** $C(-5, a)$, $D(1, -a)$; $-\frac{1}{3}$ **36.** $C(2, a)$, $D(-a, 3)$; $\frac{5}{4}$

PART C

Graph A, B, C, and D. Draw $\overline{AB}$ and $\overline{CD}$. Find slope ($\overline{AB}$) and slope ($\overline{CD}$). What relationship appears to exist between $\overline{AB}$ and $\overline{CD}$ in each case?

37. $A(-4, -6)$, $B(-1, -3)$, $C(2, 0)$, $D(6, 4)$ **38.** $A(-5, 7)$, $B(-1, 4)$, $C(3, 1)$, $D(7, -2)$
39. $A(-3, -3)$, $B(-1, 3)$, $C(1, -5)$, $D(3, 1)$ **40.** $A(-4, 1)$, $B(2, -3)$, $C(-3, 6)$, $D(3, 2)$

Algebra Review

OBJECTIVES
■ To square a binomial
■ To complete the square

To square a binomial:
Use $(a + b)^2 = a^2 + 2ab + b^2$.

To complete the square of an expression like $x^2 - 8x$:
1. Take one half of the middle coefficient.
2. Square it.

EXAMPLE 1   Simplify $(2x + 3)^2$

$$(a + b)^2 = a^2 + 2ab + b^2$$

$$\overbrace{(2x} + 3)^2 = \overbrace{(2x)^2} + 2\overbrace{(2x)}(3) + 3^2$$
$$= 4x^2 + 12x + 9$$

EXAMPLE 2   Complete the square: $x^2 - 6x + \underline{\quad ? \quad}$.

Use one half of the middle coefficient and square it.

$x^2 - 6x + 9 = (x - 3)^2$. $\longrightarrow$ $x^2 - 6x + \underline{(-\frac{6}{2})^2}$,   or $x^2 - 6x + \underline{\quad 9 \quad}$
$x^2 - 6x + 9$ is a perfect square.

Simplify.

1. $(x + 2)^2$ **2.** $(x - 4)^2$ **3.** $(2x - 5)^2$ **4.** $(4x + 1)^2$

Complete the square.

5. $x^2 - 4x + \underline{\quad ? \quad}$ **6.** $y^2 + 24y + \underline{\quad ? \quad}$ **7.** $x^2 + 9x + \underline{\quad ? \quad}$

Equation of a Line

OBJECTIVES
- To identify the slope and the *y*-intercept in the equation of a line
- To write the equation of a line
- To show that a point lies on a line with a given equation

 REVIEW CAPSULE

Find the slope of $\overleftrightarrow{CD}$ for $C(8, 2)$ and $D(3, 6)$.

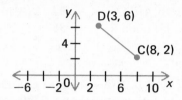

Slope $(\overleftrightarrow{CD}) = \dfrac{6 - 2}{3 - 8} = \dfrac{4}{-5} = -\dfrac{4}{5}$

EXAMPLE 1

The points on a line can be described by an equation. Find an equation of the line through $R(-1, -7)$ and $Q(4, 8)$.

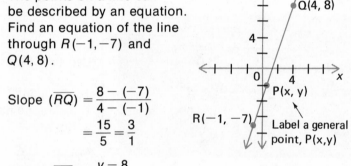

Label a general point, P(x,y)

The slope of $\overleftrightarrow{RQ}$ is the slope of any segment on $\overleftrightarrow{RQ}$.

Slope $(\overline{RQ}) = \dfrac{8 - (-7)}{4 - (-1)}$

$= \dfrac{15}{5} = \dfrac{3}{1}$

Find the slope of $\overleftrightarrow{RQ}$ in two different ways.

Slope $(\overline{PQ}) = \dfrac{y - 8}{x - 4}$

Both represent the slope of the same line. → *Slope* $(\overline{PQ}) =$ slope $(\overline{RQ})$

$\dfrac{y - 8}{x - 4} = \dfrac{3}{1}$

Solve for *y*.

$y - 8 = 3(x - 4)$
$y - 8 = 3x - 12$
$y = 3x - 4$

The equation describes any point (x, y) on $\overleftrightarrow{RQ}$. ——————→ **Thus,** an equation of $\overleftrightarrow{RQ}$ is $y = 3x - 4$.

EXAMPLE 2

Show that the point $T(1, -1)$ lies on $\overleftrightarrow{PQ}$ in Example 1.

Equation of $\overleftrightarrow{PQ}$ ——————→
Substitute 1 for *x*; −1 for *y*. ——————→

Checks ——————→

y	$3x - 4$
-1	$3(1) - 4$
	$3 - 4$
	-1

A point lies on a line if its coordinates satisfy the equation.

$(1, -1)$ satisfies $y = 3x - 4$. ——————→ **Thus,** $T(1, -1)$ lies on $\overleftrightarrow{PQ}$.

EXAMPLE 3 Find an equation of the line through $A(-4, 3)$ and $B(2, -1)$. Then write the equation in terms of y.

Graph $\overleftrightarrow{AB}$.

Label a general point $P(x, y)$.

$$\text{Slope } (\overleftrightarrow{AB}) = \frac{-1 - 3}{2 - (-4)} = \frac{-4}{6} = \frac{-2}{3}$$

$$\text{Slope } (\overline{AP}) = \frac{y - 3}{x - (-4)} = \frac{y - 3}{x + 4}$$

Slope $(\overleftrightarrow{AB})$ = Slope $(\overline{AP})$. $\longrightarrow$ $\dfrac{y - 3}{x + 4} = \dfrac{-2}{3}$

Prod. of extremes = prod. of means. $\longrightarrow$ $3(y - 3) = -2(x + 4)$

$$3y - 9 = -2x - 8$$
$$3y = -2x + 1$$

Divide each side by 3. $\longrightarrow$ $y = \dfrac{-2x + 1}{3}$

$\dfrac{-2x + 1}{3}$ is $\dfrac{-2x}{3} + \dfrac{1}{3}$. $\longrightarrow$ $y = -\dfrac{2}{3}x + \dfrac{1}{3}$

Equation is in terms of y. $\longrightarrow$ **Thus,** an equation of $\overleftrightarrow{AB}$ is $y = -\frac{2}{3}x + \frac{1}{3}$.

EXAMPLE 4 For $\overleftrightarrow{RQ}$ in Example 1, find the y-coordinate of the point where $\overleftrightarrow{RQ}$ crosses the y-axis.

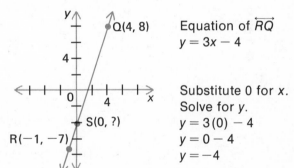

Equation of $\overleftrightarrow{RQ}$
$$y = 3x - 4$$

Substitute 0 for x.
Solve for y.
$$y = 3(0) - 4$$
$$y = 0 - 4$$
$$y = -4$$

$\overleftrightarrow{RQ}$ crosses the y-axis where $x = 0$.

$\overleftrightarrow{RQ}$ crosses the y-axis at $S(0, -4)$. $\longrightarrow$ **Thus,** -4 is the y-coordinate of S. -4 is called the y-intercept of $\overleftrightarrow{RQ}$.

Definition of y-intercept $\longrightarrow$

> The *y-intercept* of a line is the y-coordinate of the point where the line crosses the y-axis.

EXAMPLE 5 Find the y-intercept of $\overleftrightarrow{AB}$ in Example 3.

Equation of $\overleftrightarrow{AB}$ $\longrightarrow$ $y = -\frac{2}{3}x + \frac{1}{3}$

Substitute 0 for x and solve for y.
$$y = -\tfrac{2}{3}(0) + \tfrac{1}{3}$$
$$y = 0 + \tfrac{1}{3}$$
$$y = \tfrac{1}{3}$$

$\overleftrightarrow{AB}$ crosses the y-axis at $(0, \frac{1}{3})$. $\longrightarrow$ **Thus,** the y-intercept of $\overleftrightarrow{AB}$ is $\frac{1}{3}$.

Equation of $\overleftrightarrow{RQ}$: $y = 3x - 4$ Equation of $\overleftrightarrow{AB}$: $y = -\frac{2}{3}x + \frac{1}{3}$

Slope: 3 Slope: $-\frac{2}{3}$
y-intercept: -4 y-intercept: $\frac{1}{3}$

Theorem | **12.3** | If the equation of a line is $y = mx + b$, then m is the slope and b is the y-intercept.

$$y = mx + b$$

slope y-intercept

EXAMPLE 6 $-3x + 2y = -10$ is an equation for $\overleftrightarrow{CD}$. Find the slope and the y-intercept of $\overleftrightarrow{CD}$.

Solve for y. $\longrightarrow$
$$-3x + 2y = -10$$
$$2y = 3x - 10$$
$$y = \frac{3x - 10}{2}$$

$\frac{3x - 10}{2}$ $\frac{3x}{2} - \frac{10}{2}$. $\longrightarrow$
$$y = \frac{3}{2}x - 5, \text{ or } y = \frac{3}{2}x + (-5)$$

slope y-intercept

Use Theorem 12.3. $\longrightarrow$

Thus, the slope is $\frac{3}{2}$ and the y-intercept is -5.

The converse of Theorem 12.3 can also be proved.

Theorem | **12.4** | If a line has slope m and y-intercept b, then its equation is $y = mx + b$.

EXAMPLE 7   Write an equation of a line whose slope is $\frac{4}{3}$ and whose y-intercept is -2.

Slope-intercept form of equation $\longrightarrow$ $y = mx + b$

m is $\frac{4}{3}$; b is -2. $\longrightarrow$ $y = \frac{4}{3}x + (-2)$
$$y = \frac{4}{3}x - 2$$

Thus, an equation of the line is $y = \frac{4}{3}x - 2$.

ORAL EXERCISES

Give an expression for the slope of $\overleftrightarrow{AB}$.

1. $A(2,3)$, $B(x,y)$ **2.** $A(1,0)$, $B(x,y)$ **3.** $A(6,-2)$, $B(x,y)$ **4.** $A(-2,4)$, $B(x,y)$
5. $A(5,-7)$, $B(x,y)$ **6.** $A(3,-2)$, $B(x,y)$ **7.** $A(-1,-4)$, $B(x,y)$ **8.** $A(-5,-3)$, $B(x,y)$

Identify the slope and the y-intercept.

9. $y = 3x + 4$ **10.** $y = 7x - 2$ **11.** $y = -2x + 1$ **12.** $y = -4x - 8$
13. $y = \frac{1}{3}x + \frac{2}{3}$ **14.** $y = -\frac{4}{5}x - 3$ **15.** $y = x - \frac{3}{4}$ **16.** $y = -x - 2$
17. $y = 6x$ **18.** $y = x$ **19.** $y = -2$ **20.** $y = 0$

EXERCISES

PART A

Show that point P lies on the line with the given equation.

1. $y = 2x + 4$; $P(0,4)$ **2.** $y = -3x + 8$; $P(-1,11)$ **3.** $y = -x - 5$; $P(-2,-3)$
4. $y = \frac{1}{2}x - 5$; $P(8,-1)$ **5.** $y = -\frac{2}{3}x + 5$; $P(6,1)$ **6.** $y = -5x - \frac{1}{2}$; $P(2,-\frac{21}{2})$
7. $y = -\frac{1}{4}x - 3$; $P(4,-4)$ **8.** $y = 6x + \frac{1}{3}$; $P(-2,-\frac{35}{3})$ **9.** $y = -\frac{1}{2}x - \frac{3}{2}$; $P(4,-\frac{7}{2})$

Write an equation of the line with slope m and y-intercept b.

10. $m = 3$, $b = 5$ **11.** $m = 6$, $b = 2$ **12.** $m = -3$, $b = 4$ **13.** $m = 7$, $b = -2$
14. $m = -1$, $b = -2$ **15.** $m = 0$, $b = -\frac{1}{2}$ **16.** $m = 6$, $b = -\frac{1}{3}$ **17.** $m = 1$, $b = 0$
18. $m = -1$, $b = \frac{1}{4}$ **19.** $m = \frac{2}{3}$, $b = 0$ **20.** $m = -\frac{3}{4}$, $b = \frac{1}{4}$ **21.** $m = 0$, $b = 0$

Write each equation in the form $y = mx + b$. Identify the slope and the y-intercept.

22. $3y = 6x + 12$ **23.** $2y = -8x + 2$ **24.** $-4y = 2x - 3$ **25.** $6y = -3x - 9$
26. $5x + y = -2$ **27.** $-3x - y = 4$ **28.** $y - 5 = 0$ **29.** $5y = -10x$
30. $4x - 3y = 0$ **31.** $-2x = 6y + 3$ **32.** $8y - 2 = 0$ **33.** $7x - 4y = -12$

PART B

Graph $\overleftrightarrow{PQ}$. Then write an equation of $\overleftrightarrow{PQ}$ in the form $y = mx + b$. Identify the slope and the y-intercept.

34. $P(6,3)$, $Q(4,1)$ **35.** $P(-5,2)$, $Q(3,-2)$ **36.** $P(0,4)$, $Q(6,-2)$ **37.** $P(3,-1)$, $Q(5,-5)$
38. $P(4,7)$, $Q(0,-2)$ **39.** $P(6,-1)$, $Q(3,-2)$ **40.** $P(-4,8)$, $Q(7,-6)$ **41.** $P(0,3)$, $Q(-4,2)$
42. $P(-7,-2)$, $Q(-1,4)$ **43.** $P(5,0)$, $Q(6,-6)$ **44.** $P(-3,-1)$, $Q(-8,2)$ **45.** $P(0,-1)$, $Q(2,-4)$
46. $P(-5,0)$, $Q(0,6)$ **47.** $P(-3,1)$, $Q(-2,5)$ **48.** $P(6,-1)$, $Q(7,-3)$ **49.** $P(-5,2)$, $Q(1,0)$

PART C

50. Prove Theorem 12.3.   **51.** Prove Theorem 12.4.

Graphing Lines

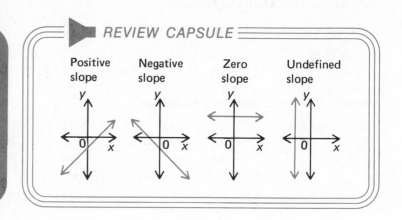

EXAMPLE 1

Graph the line whose equation is $y = \frac{4}{3}x + 1$.

slope $= \frac{4}{3}$ ← up 4
   ← right 3
Crosses y-axis at $(0, 1)$.

$$y = \frac{4}{3}x + 1$$
slope   y-intercept

Graph $(0, 1)$. Then use the slope to find another point on the line.

Graph $P(0, 1)$.

Begin at P. Move up 4 and right 3 to Q. Draw $\overleftrightarrow{PQ}$.

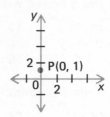

right 3

up 4 $Q(3, 5)$

$P(0, 1)$

Thus, $\overleftrightarrow{PQ}$ is the line whose equation is $y = \frac{4}{3}x + 1$.

EXAMPLE 2

Graph the line whose equation is $y = -3x - 2$.

slope $= \frac{-3}{1}$ ← down 3
   ← right 1
Crosses y-axis at $(0, -2)$.

$$y = -3x - 2$$
slope   y-intercept

Graph $P(0, -2)$.

Move down 3 and right 1 to Q. Draw $\overleftrightarrow{PQ}$.

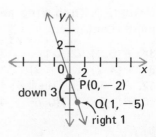

$P(0, -2)$

down 3

$Q(1, -5)$

right 1

Thus, $\overleftrightarrow{PQ}$ is the line whose equation is $y = -3x - 2$.

EXAMPLE 3   Graph the line whose equation is $y = 3$.

$$y = 3 \text{ is the same as}$$
$$y = 0 \cdot x + 3$$
$$\uparrow \qquad \uparrow$$
$$\text{slope} \qquad y\text{-intercept}$$

Begin at $P(0, 3)$.

Use any other point Q
with y-coordinate 3.

A line with 0 slope is horizontal. ⟶ Draw $\overleftrightarrow{PQ}$.

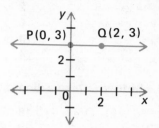

Thus, $\overleftrightarrow{PQ}$ is the line whose equation is $y = 3$.

EXAMPLE 4   Graph $\overleftrightarrow{RS}$ for $R(-2, 1)$ and $S(-2, -3)$. Give the slope and the y-intercept of $\overleftrightarrow{RS}$.

$\overleftrightarrow{RS}$ is a vertical line.
Its slope is undefined.
It has no y-intercept,
since it never crosses
the y-axis.

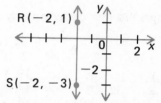

The equation of a vertical line cannot be of the form
$$y = mx + b.$$
$$\nearrow \qquad \uparrow$$
$$\text{undefined slope} \qquad \text{no } y\text{-intercept}$$

Every point on $\overleftrightarrow{RS}$ has x-coordinate -2. ⟶ The equation of $\overleftrightarrow{RS}$ in Example 4 is $x = -2$.
y can have any value.

EXAMPLE 5   Graph the line whose equation is $x = 5$.

$x = 5$ is the equation of a vertical line.

Plot two points with
x-coordinate 5.
$M(5, 3) \qquad N(5, -2)$

Every point has x-coordinate 5.

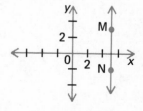

Draw $\overleftrightarrow{MN}$.

Thus, $\overleftrightarrow{MN}$ is the line whose equation is $x = 5$.

ORAL EXERCISES

Tell whether the line described by each equation slants up to the right, slants down to the right, is horizontal, or is vertical.

1. $y = 2x - 6$ **2.** $y = -7x + 3$ **3.** $y = 6x + 4$ **4.** $y = -3x - 5$
5. $y = x - 6$ **6.** $x = 2$ **7.** $y = 3x$ **8.** $y = -\frac{2}{3}x + 2$
9. $x = -5$ **10.** $y = -x + 5$ **11.** $y = 0$ **12.** $y = -3$
13. $y = \frac{3}{4}x - 1$ **14.** $y = -\frac{7}{2}x + \frac{3}{2}$ **15.** $y = x$ **16.** $y = -\frac{4}{5}x$

Tell whether $\overleftrightarrow{PQ}$ is vertical or horizontal. Then give its equation.

17. $P(6, -2)$, $Q(4, -2)$ **18.** $P(3, 8)$, $Q(3, -2)$ **19.** $P(5, 0)$, $Q(4, 0)$ **20.** $P(4, 5)$, $Q(-3, 5)$
21. $P(1, 1)$, $Q(1, 2)$ **22.** $P(0, 1)$, $Q(0, -6)$ **23.** $P(3, 6)$, $Q(-3, 6)$ **24.** $P(4, 7)$, $Q(4, -2)$
25. $P(5, -3)$, $Q(5, 3)$ **26.** $P(3, -1)$, $Q(-1, -1)$ **27.** $P(-6, 2)$, $Q(-6, -2)$ **28.** $P(-4, 4)$, $Q(-4, -4)$

EXERCISES

PART A

Graph the line described by each equation.

1. $y = 3x + 1$ **2.** $y = \frac{1}{2}x - 4$ **3.** $y = -\frac{4}{3}x - 2$ **4.** $y = -2x + 3$
5. $y = 4x - 2$ **6.** $x = -5$ **7.** $y = \frac{1}{3}x$ **8.** $y = -3$
9. $y = -x - 5$ **10.** $y = -\frac{2}{3}x + 4$ **11.** $y = 0$ **12.** $y = \frac{1}{2}x + \frac{1}{2}$
13. $2x + 3y = 6$ **14.** $6x - y = 0$ **15.** $-3x - 2y = 8$ **16.** $y + 3x = -\frac{1}{4}$
17. $x = 7$ **18.** $4x - 5y = 10$ **19.** $2x = -6y$ **20.** $2x = 4y + 16$

PART B

EXAMPLE   Graph the line which passes through $(2, -1)$ and has slope -3. Write an equation of the line.

Locate $(2, -1)$.

slope -3 means $\dfrac{-3}{1}$ $\begin{array}{l}\leftarrow \text{down } 3 \\ \leftarrow \text{right } 1\end{array}$

Locate second point and draw the line.

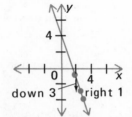

down 3   right 1

$m = -3 \rightarrow$

To find b,
let $x = 2$, $y = -1$

$y = mx + b$
$\downarrow$
$y = -3x + b$
$\downarrow$
$-1 = -3(2) + b$
$-1 = -6 + b$
$5 = b$

Thus, the equation is $y = -3x + 5$.

Graph the line which passes through P and has slope m. Write an equation of the line.

21. $P(1, 4)$; $m = \frac{1}{2}$ **22.** $P(-2, 5)$; $m = -\frac{3}{4}$ **23.** $P(6, 1)$; $m = 4$
24. $p(2, -3)$; $m = -2$ **25.** $P)3, 0)$; $m = 1$ **26.** $P(0, 0)$; $m = 3$
27. $P(0, -2)$; $m = -1$ **28.** $P(1, 1)$; $m = 0$ **29.** $P(-3, -1)$; $m =$ undefined
30. $P(2, -4)$; $m = -\frac{3}{2}$ **31.** $P(0, 0)$; m undefined   **32.** $P(0, 0)$; $m = 0$

Reflections About the X-Axis

EXPERIMENT

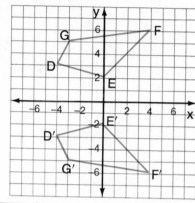

On graph paper, copy figures DEFG and D'E'F'G'.

1. Are the figures congruent?

2. Give the coordinates of the vertices of DEFG and D'E'F'G'.

3. Compare the x-coordinates of D and D'; E and E'; F and F'; G and G'.

4. Similarly, compare the y-coordinates.

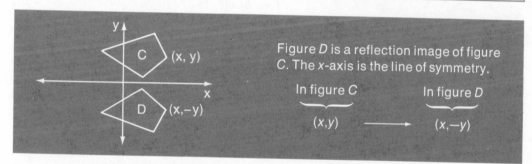

Figure D is a reflection image of figure C. The x-axis is the line of symmetry.

In figure C
(x, y)

In figure D
$(x, -y)$

$(x, y) \longrightarrow (x, -y)$

Copy each figure on graph paper. Draw the reflection of each figure with the x-axis the line of symmetry.

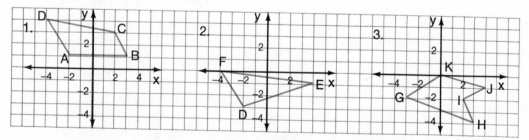

The coordinates of the vertices of a polygon are given.
Graph and label the polygon and the reflection about the x-axis.

4. $A(2, 1)$, $B(3, 3)$, $C(-4, 5)$

5. $J(0, 0)$, $K(4, 2)$, $L(1, 3)$, $M(-5, 2)$

6. $G(2, -3)$, $H(4, -1)$, $I(-3, 5)$

7. $P(0, 0)$, $Q(0, -4)$, $R(3, -3)$, $S(4, -1)$

Parallel and Perpendicular Lines

<table>
<tr><td>

OBJECTIVES

■ To determine if lines are parallel or perpendicular from their slopes

■ To find the slope of a line parallel or perpendicular to a given line

■ To write an equation of a line parallel or perpendicular to a given line

</td><td>

 REVIEW CAPSULE

Reciprocals

$\frac{2}{3}$ and $\frac{3}{2}$ $\frac{1}{4}$ and 4   1 and 1

$(\frac{2}{3})(\frac{3}{2}) = 1$ $(\frac{1}{4})(4) = 1$ $(1)(1) = 1$

Two numbers are *reciprocals* if their product is 1.

Negative Reciprocals

$-\frac{5}{4}$ and $\frac{4}{5}$ 3 and $-\frac{1}{3}$ 1 and -1

$(-\frac{5}{4})(\frac{4}{5}) = -1$ $(3)(-\frac{1}{3}) = -1$ $(1)(-1) = -1$

Two numbers are *negative reciprocals* if their product is -1.

</td></tr>
</table>

EXAMPLE 1

Examine the graphs of the lines described by $y = \frac{3}{2}x + 2$ and $y = \frac{3}{2}x - 4$. What conclusion can you draw?

$y = mx + b$
↑
slope

$$y = \frac{3}{2}x + 2 \qquad y = \frac{3}{2}x - 4$$
$$\underset{\text{same slope}}{\rule{3cm}{0.4pt}}$$

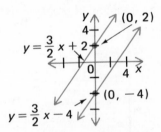

Example 1 suggests the theorem below.

It appears that the lines with equations $y = \frac{3}{2}x + 2$ and $y = \frac{3}{2}x - 4$ are parallel.

Theorem 12.5

If two lines have the same slope, then they are parallel.

EXAMPLE 2 Show that $\overleftrightarrow{PQ} \parallel \overleftrightarrow{RS}$ for $P(-3, 2)$, $Q(5, 0)$, $R(-4, -3)$, and $S(0, -4)$.

$$\text{Slope} = \frac{y_2 - y_1}{x_2 - x_1}$$

$$\text{Slope }(\overleftrightarrow{PQ}) = \frac{0 - 2}{5 - (-3)} = \frac{-2}{8} = -\frac{1}{4}$$

$$\text{Slope }(\overleftrightarrow{RS}) = \frac{-4 - (-3)}{0 - (-4)} = \frac{-1}{4} = -\frac{1}{4}$$

$$\text{Slope }(\overleftrightarrow{PQ}) = \text{slope }(\overleftrightarrow{RS})$$

Thus, $\overleftrightarrow{PQ} \parallel \overleftrightarrow{RS}$, by Theorem 12.5.

EXAMPLE 3 Examine the graphs of the lines described by $y = \frac{2}{3}x - 2$ and $y = -\frac{3}{2}x + 1$. What conclusion can you draw?

$$\left(\frac{2}{3}\right)\left(-\frac{3}{2}\right) = -1$$

(See Review Capsule.)

$$y = \frac{2}{3}x - 2 \qquad y = -\frac{3}{2}x + 1$$

slopes are negative reciprocals

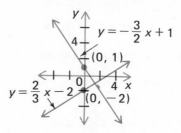

Example 3 suggests the theorem below.

It appears that the lines with equations $y = \frac{2}{3}x - 2$ and $y = -\frac{3}{2}x + 1$ are perpendicular.

Theorem 12.6

If the slopes of two lines are negative reciprocals, then the lines are perpendicular.

EXAMPLE 4 Give the slope of a line perpendicular to $\overleftrightarrow{CD}$.

$$C(-5, 3) \qquad D(1, -2)$$

Find the slope of $\overleftrightarrow{CD}$. ⟶ $\text{Slope }(\overleftrightarrow{CD}) = \frac{-2 - 3}{1 - (-5)} = \frac{-5}{6}$, or $-\frac{5}{6}$

Use Theorem 12.6.

The negative reciprocal of $-\frac{5}{6}$ is $\frac{6}{5}$.

Thus, the slope of a line perpendicular to $\overleftrightarrow{CD}$ is $\frac{6}{5}$.

ORAL EXERCISES

Give the negative reciprocal of each number.

1. 2   **2.** $\frac{1}{3}$ **3.** 1   **4.** $-\frac{3}{5}$ **5.** $\frac{5}{2}$ **6.** -6 **7.** -1 **8.** 0

Give the slope of a line parallel to the line with the given equation.

9. $y = 2x - 3$ **10.** $y = -4x + 7$ **11.** $y = x - 2$ **12.** $y = -\frac{3}{5}x + \frac{1}{5}$

Give the slope of a line perpendicular to the line with given equation.

13. $y = -3x + 8$ **14.** $y = \frac{1}{4}x - 7$ **15.** $y = -x + 9$ **16.** $y = \frac{2}{3}x$

EXERCISES

PART A

Give the slope of a line parallel to $\overleftrightarrow{AB}$.

1. $A(1, 6)$, $B(2, 5)$ **2.** $A(-3, 2)$, $B(6, -1)$ **3.** $A(0, -5)$, $B(7, 2)$ **4.** $A(-3, -1)$, $B(5, -8)$
5. $A(3, 5)$, $B(-2, 5)$ **6.** $A(4, -5)$, $B(6, 0)$ **7.** $A(2, -8)$, $B(2, 9)$ **8.** $A(-4, 3)$, $B(7, -1)$

Give the slope of a line perpendicular to $\overleftrightarrow{CD}$.

9. $C(-3, 1)$, $D(4, 2)$ **10.** $C(1, -5)$, $D(0, 8)$ **11.** $C(-6, -1)$, $D(2, -3)$ **12.** $C(4, 3)$, $D(0, -1)$
13. $C(6, -2)$, $D(-5, -3)$ **14.** $C(0, 4)$, $D(-6, 4)$ **15.** $C(8, 5)$, $D(-1, -4)$ **16.** $C(3, -7)$, $D(3, -2)$

Use slopes to show that $\overline{AB} \parallel \overline{CD}$ and $\overline{AD} \parallel \overline{BC}$.

17. $A(-1, 0)$, $B(4, 5)$, $C(3, 9)$, $D(-2, 4)$ **18.** $A(5, -8)$, $B(7, -6)$, $C(6, 1)$, $D(4, -1)$
19. $A(1, -6)$, $B(6, -1)$, $C(4, 1)$, $D(-1, -4)$ **20.** $A(-2, 5)$, $B(4, 9)$, $C(0, -1)$, $D(-6, -5)$

Use slopes to show that $\overline{PR} \perp \overline{SQ}$.

21. $P(2, -1)$, $Q(5, 3)$, $R(1, 6)$, $S(-2, 2)$ **22.** $P(-2, -2)$, $Q(6, -1)$, $R(0, 4)$, $S(-6, 3)$

PART B

EXAMPLE   Write an equation of a line passing through $(1, 6)$ and perpendicular to the line with equation $y = \frac{1}{2}x - 5$.

For $y = \frac{1}{2}x - 5$, $m = \frac{1}{2}$
For a $\perp$ line, $m = -2$ $\longrightarrow$

$y = mx + b$ Now find b.
    $\downarrow$ $(1, 6)$ satisfies $y = -2x + b$
$y = -2x + b$

$6 = -2(1) + b$
$6 = -2 + b$
$8 = b$

Thus, the equation is $y = -2x + 8$.

Write an equation of a line passing through the given point and perpendicular to the line whose equation is given.

23. $(5, -2)$; $y = -6x + 1$ **24.** $(-3, 1)$; $y = \frac{2}{3}x - 4$
25. $(0, 6)$; $2x + 4y = 10$ **26.** $(-4, -5)$; $3x + 2y = -7$

Using Coordinates in Geometry

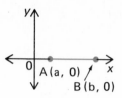

$\overline{AB}$ is horizontal. Both y-coordinates are 0.
$AB = |b - a|$.

EXAMPLE 1 Show that the quadrilateral with vertices $A(0, 4)$, $B(6, 8)$, $C(2, -2)$, $D(-4, -6)$ is a parallelogram.

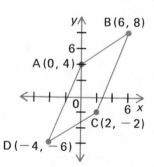

Use slopes to show that $\overline{AB} \parallel \overline{CD}$ and $\overline{AD} \parallel \overline{BC}$.

Slope $(\overline{AB}) = \dfrac{8 - 4}{6 - 0} = \dfrac{4}{6}$, or $\dfrac{2}{3}$

Slope $(\overline{CD}) = \dfrac{-6 - (-2)}{-4 - 2} = \dfrac{-4}{-6}$, or $\dfrac{2}{3}$

They have the same slope $(\frac{2}{3})$. ⟶
$\therefore \overline{AB} \parallel \overline{CD}$.

Slope $(\overline{AD}) = \dfrac{-6 - 4}{-4 - 0} = \dfrac{-10}{-4}$, or $\dfrac{5}{2}$

Slope $(\overline{BC}) = \dfrac{8 - (-2)}{6 - 2} = \dfrac{10}{4}$, or $\dfrac{5}{2}$

They have the same slope $(\frac{5}{2})$. ⟶
$\therefore \overline{AD} \parallel \overline{BC}$

Opposite sides are $\parallel$. ⟶ **Thus,** quadrilateral $ABCD$ is a parallelogram.

EXAMPLE 2 Show that $ABCD$ is a rectangle for $A(-1,-2)$, $B(3,2)$, $C(1,4)$, and $D(-3,0)$.

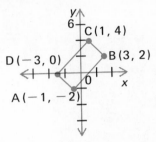

Use slopes to show that $\overline{AD} \parallel \overline{BC}$ and $\overline{AB} \parallel \overline{DC}$. Then show that $\angle A$ is a right $\angle$.

Slope $(\overline{AD}) = \dfrac{0-(-2)}{-3-(-1)} = \dfrac{2}{-2}$, or -1

Slope $(\overline{BC}) = \dfrac{4-2}{1-3} = \dfrac{2}{-2}$, or -1

$\therefore \overline{AD} \parallel \overline{BC}$

Slope $(\overline{AB}) = \dfrac{2-(-2)}{3-(-1)} = \dfrac{4}{4}$, or 1

Slope $(\overline{DC}) = \dfrac{4-0}{1-(-3)} = \dfrac{4}{4}$, or 1

$\therefore \overline{AB} \parallel \overline{DC}$

Opposite sides are $\parallel$. $\longrightarrow$ *ABCD* is a parallelogram.

slope $(\overline{AD}) \times$ slope $(\overline{AB})$
$= (-1) \times (1)$, or -1. $\longrightarrow$ The slopes of $\overline{AD}$ and $\overline{AB}$ are negative reciprocals.
$\therefore \overline{AD} \perp \overline{AB}$, and $\angle A$ is a right angle.

A $\square$ with a right $\angle$ is a rectangle. $\longrightarrow$ **Thus, *ABCD* is a rectangle.**

EXAMPLE 3

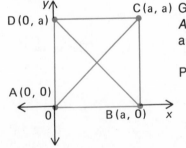

Given: square *ABCD* with $A(0,0)$, $B(a,0)$, $C(a,a)$, and $D(0,a)$

Prove: $\overline{AC} \perp \overline{BD}$

The square is placed in a convenient position in the coordinate plane.

Show that slope $(\overline{AC})$ and slope $(\overline{BD})$ are negative reciprocals.

Slope $(\overline{AC}) = \dfrac{a-0}{a-0} = \dfrac{a}{a} = 1$

Slope $(\overline{BD}) = \dfrac{0-a}{a-0} = \dfrac{-a}{a} = -1$

$(1)(-1) = -1$ $\longrightarrow$ **Thus, $\overline{AC} \perp \overline{BD}$.**

In Example 3, we used coordinate geometry to prove that the diagonals of a square are perpendicular.

EXAMPLE 4 Use coordinate geometry to prove that the diagonals of a rectangle are congruent.

The rectangle is placed in a convenient position: two of its sides lie on the axes.

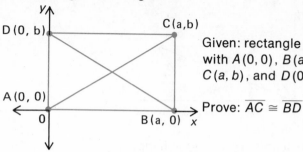

Given: rectangle $ABCD$ with $A(0,0)$, $B(a,0)$, $C(a,b)$, and $D(0,b)$

Prove: $\overline{AC} \cong \overline{BD}$

Distance formula ⟶ $AC = \sqrt{(x_2 - x_1)^2 + (y_2 - y_1)^2}$
Substitute $A(0,0)$ and $C(a,b)$. ⟶ $= \sqrt{(a - 0)^2 + (b - 0)^2}$
$= \sqrt{a^2 + b^2}$

$BD = \sqrt{(a - 0)^2 + (0 - b)^2}$
Substitute $B(a,0)$ and $D(0,b)$. ⟶ $= \sqrt{a^2 + (-b)^2}$
$= \sqrt{a^2 + b^2}$
$AC = BD$
Thus, $\overline{AC} \cong \overline{BD}$.

EXERCISES

PART A

Show that *ABCD* is a parallelogram.

1. $A(-2, -5)$, $B(0, -3)$, $C(-1, 4)$, $D(-3, 2)$

2. $A(2, -7)$, $B(7, -2)$, $C(6, 2)$, $D(1, -3)$

Show that *EFGH* is a rectangle.

3. $E(1, 4)$, $F(7, 0)$, $G(9, 3)$, $H(3, 7)$

4. $E(-4, -5)$, $F(1, 0)$, $G(-1, 2)$, $H(-6, -3)$

Show that the diagonals of *PQRS* are congruent.

5. $P(2, 3)$, $Q(8, -1)$, $R(10, 2)$, $S(4, 6)$

6. $P(-2, -8)$, $Q(3, -3)$, $R(1, -1)$, $S(-4, -6)$

Show that the diagonals of *WXYZ* bisect each other.

7. $W(1, -7)$, $X(3, -5)$, $Y(2, 2)$, $Z(0, 0)$

8. $W(1, -3)$, $X(6, 2)$, $Y(5, 6)$, $Z(0, 1)$

Show that *MNPQ* is a rhombus.

9. $M(5, -2)$, $N(8, 2)$, $P(4, 5)$, $Q(1, 1)$

10. $M(0, -3)$, $N(6, -2)$, $P(5, 4)$, $Q(-1, 3)$

Use coordinate geometry to prove each statement.

11. The diagonals of a parallelogram bisect each other.

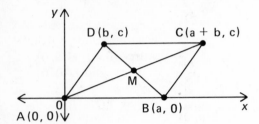

12. The midpoint of the hypotenuse of a right triangle is equidistant from the vertices.

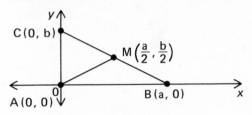

13. The segment joining the midpoint of two sides of a triangle is parallel to the third side.

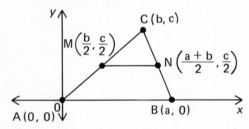

14. The diagonals of an isosceles trapezoid are congruent.

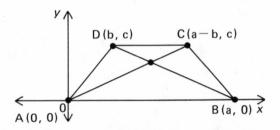

Algebra Review

$|a|$ is read the absolute value of a.
$|a| = 6$ means $a = 6$, or $a = -6$.

EXAMPLE   Solve $|2x - 1| = 5$.

Think of $2x - 1$ as some number a. ⟶

$$|2x - 1| = 5 \text{ means}$$
$$2x - 1 = 5 \text{ or } 2x - 1 = -5$$
$$2x = 6 \qquad\qquad 2x = -4$$
$$x = 3 \text{ or } \qquad x = -2$$

Thus, the solutions are 3 and -2.

Solve.

1. $|x - 2| = 7$ **2.** $|x + 6| = 10$ **3.** $|7 - x| = 4$ **4.** $|2 + x| = 9$
5. $|2x - 6| = 4$ **6.** $|5 - 3y| = 7$ **7.** $|2z - 14| = 1$ **8.** $|2 - 5y| = 8$
9. $|3k + 2| = 10$ **10.** $|4 + 2y| = 0$ **11.** $|5a + 3| = 6$ **12.** $|6z - 8| = 4$

Equation of a Circle

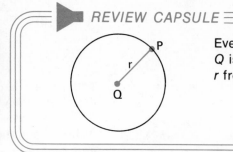

▶ REVIEW CAPSULE

Every point P on circle
Q is the same distance
r from Q.

EXAMPLE 1   Circle Q has its center at the origin and a radius of
length 6. Write an equation which describes all points
$P(x, y)$ on circle Q.

Choose $P(x, y)$ as a general point on
circle Q. ⟶ The distance from P to Q
is always 6.

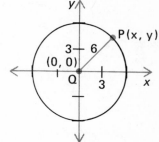

Use the Distance formula. ⟶
Substitute $P(x, y)$, $Q(0, 0)$.

$$\sqrt{(x_1 - x_2)^2 + (y_1 - y_2)^2} = d$$
$$\sqrt{(x - 0)^2 + (y - 0)^2} = 6$$
$$\sqrt{x^2 + y^2} = 6$$

Square each side. ⟶
$$x^2 + y^2 = 36$$

Thus, an equation of circle Q is $x^2 + y^2 = 36$.

EXAMPLE 2   Write an equation for the circle with center at $(3, 1)$
and radius of length 2.

Substitute $P(x, y)$ and $Q(3, 1)$ in the
distance formula. ⟶
Square each side. ⟶
$$\sqrt{(x - 3)^2 + (y - 1)^2} = 2$$
$$(x - 3)^2 + (y - 1)^2 = 4$$

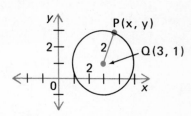

Thus, an equation is
$(x - 3)^2 + (y - 1)^2 = 4$.

Theorem   12.7

The equation of a circle
with center (h, k) and
radius r is

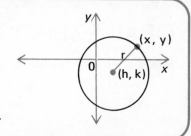

$$\sqrt{(x - h)^2 + (y - k)^2} = r,$$
or $(x - h)^2 + (y - k)^2 = r^2$.

EXAMPLE 3

EXAMPLE 3   Show that $R(4,-3)$ and $S(-2, \sqrt{21})$ lie on the circle with equation $x^2 + y^2 = 25$.

$R(4,-3)$
Let $x = 4$, $y = -3$ ⟶

$x^2 + y^2$	25
$4^2 + (-3)^2$	25
$16 + 9$	
25	

$S(-2, \sqrt{21})$
Let $x = -2$,
$y = \sqrt{21}$

$x^2 + y^2$	25
$(-2)^2 + (\sqrt{21})^2$	25
$4 + 21$	
25	

The coordinates of each point satisfy the equation.

Thus, $R(4,-3)$ and $S(-2, \sqrt{21})$ lie on the circle with equation $x^2 + y^2 = 25$.

EXAMPLE 4   Write an equation of a circle with center at $(2,-1)$ and with radius of length 4. Simplfy the equation.

$$(x - h)^2 + (y - k)^2 = r^2$$

center $(h, k) = (2,-1)$; $r = 4$ ⟶

$$(x - 2)^2 + [y - (-1)]^2 = 4^2$$
$$(x - 2)^2 + (y + 1)^2 = 16$$

Square each binomial. ⟶ $x^2 - 4x + 4 + y^2 + 2y + 1 = 16$
Add -4 and -1 to each side. ⟶ $\qquad x^2 - 4x + y^2 + 2y = 11$

$Q(2, -1)$

Only the variable terms remain on the left side.

Thus, the equation is $x^2 - 4x + y^2 + 2y = 11$.

EXAMPLE 5   Find the center and the radius length of the circle whose equation is $x^2 + y^2 - 6x + 24y = -53$.

$$x^2 + y^2 - 6x + 24y = -53$$

Group x-terms and y-terms. ⟶ $(x^2 - 6x + \quad) + (y^2 + 24y + \quad) = -53$

Add 9 and 144 to each side to form two perfect squares.

$$(x^2 - 6x + 9) + (y^2 + 24y + 144) = -53 + 9 + 144$$
$$(x - 3)^2 + (y + 12)^2 = 100,$$
$$\text{or } (x - 3)^2 + [y - (-12)]^2 = 10^2$$
$$\qquad\quad \uparrow \qquad\qquad\quad \uparrow \qquad\quad \uparrow$$
$$\qquad\quad h \qquad\qquad\quad k \qquad\quad r$$

Thus, the center is $(3,-12)$ and the radius length is 10.

ORAL EXERCISES

Identify the center and the radius of each circle whose equation is given.

1. $(x - 2)^2 + (y - 4)^2 = 6^2$
3. $(x - 1)^2 + (y + 2)^2 = 49$
5. $(x + 10)^2 + (y + 5)^2 = 16$
7. $x^2 + (y + 8)^2 = 7$

2. $(x - 8)^2 + (y - 3)^2 = 5^2$
4. $(x + 4)^2 + (y - 6)^2 = 4$
6. $(x - 6)^2 + y^2 = 1$
8. $x^2 + y^2 = 5,$

EXERCISES

Write an equation of a circle with center A and radius of length r. Leave the equation in the second form of Theorem 12.7.

1. $A(0,0)$; $r=2$ **2.** $A(2,1)$; $r=3$ **3.** $A(-1,4)$; $r=1$ **4.** $A(-2,-6)$; $r=5$
5. $A(4,-2)$; $r=4$ **6.** $A(-3,-8)$; $r=\sqrt{12}$ **7.** $A(5,5)$; $r=8$ **8.** $A(6,-2)$; $r=\sqrt{10}$

Write an equation of a circle with center A and radius of length r. Simplify the equation as in Example 4.

9. $A(1,2)$; $r=6$ **10.** $A(0,3)$; $r=2$ **11.** $A(6,-4)$; $r=9$ **12.** $A(-3,5)$; $r=5$
13. $A(-8,-1)$; $r=\sqrt{15}$ **14.** $A(7,0)$; $r=8$ **15.** $A(-2,-9)$; $r=\sqrt{7}$ **16.** $A(6,-7)$; $r=20$

Show that point P lies on the circle with the given equation.

17. $P(4,0)$; $x^2+y^2=16$ **18.** $P(0,-2)$; $x^2+y^2=4$ **19.** $P(5,-3)$; $x^2+y^2=34$
20. $P(-3,-1)$; $x^2+y^2=10$ **21.** $P(5,-3)$; $(x-1)^2+y^2=25$
22. $P(-1,-1)$; $(x-2)^2+(y+1)^2=9$ **23.** $P(\sqrt{2},7)$; $x^2+(y-2)^2=27$
24. $P(-\sqrt{3},-2)$; $x^2+y^2+6y=-5$ **25.** $P(-3,4)$; $x^2+y^2+2x-8y=-13$

Find the center and the radius of the circle with the given equation. Graph the circle.

26. $x^2+y^2=9$ **27.** $x^2+y^2=49$ **28.** $x^2+y^2=10$
29. $(x-1)^2+y^2=4$ **30.** $(x-3)^2+(y+4)^2=16$ **31.** $(x+2)^2+(y-6)^2=64$
32. $x^2+y^2=12$ **33.** $x^2+y^2+8x=9$ **34.** $x^2+y^2+2x-10y=1$
35. $x^2+y^2-12y=4$ **36.** $x^2+y^2-16x-6y=-72$ **37.** $x^2+y^2+18x-20y=-177$

Write an equation of the circle which has center Q and passes through the origin. Graph the circle.

38. $Q(3,4)$ **39.** $Q(-1,2)$ **40.** $Q(-2,-\sqrt{5})$

Write an equation of the circle for which R and S are the endpoints of a diameter. Graph the circle.

41. $R(-5,-2)$, $S(3,4)$ **42.** $R(-2,-5)$, $S(6,-1)$ **43.** $R(1,2)$, $S(-3,-4)$

Show that the circles with the given equations are congruent.

44. $x^2+y^2+4x=32$; $x^2+y^2-2x+6y=26$ **45.** $x^2+y^2-8y=1$; $x^2+y^2+10x=-8$

Show that the circles with the given equations are concentric.

46. $(x-3)^2+(y+2)^2=10$; $x^2+y^2-6x+4y=52$ **47.** $x^2+(y-8)^2=7$; $x^2+y^2-16y=46$

Find the coordinates of all common points of the circles with the given equations.

48. $(x-4)^2+(y+5)^2=16$; $(x-4)^2+(y-2)^2=9$ **49.** $x^2+y^2=10$; $(x+3)^2+(y+3)^2=4$

Coordinates in Space

OBJECTIVES
■ To graph points in a three-dimensional coordinate system
■ To find the distance between a pair of points in a three-dimensional coordinate system

▶ REVIEW CAPSULE

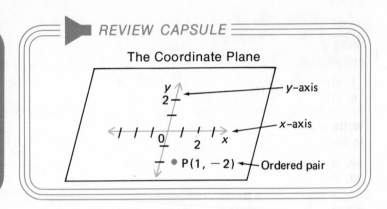

The Coordinate Plane

Suppose we tip the coordinate plane forward. Then we add a third axis, called the *z-axis*, perpendicular to the plane. We now have a three-dimensional coordinate system. On it, we can graph points in space by means of *ordered triples* of numbers.

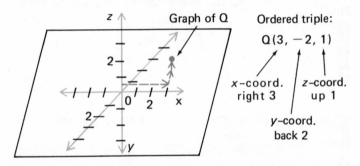

Graph of Q

Ordered triple:
Q(3, −2, 1)

x-coord. right 3   z-coord. up 1
y-coord. back 2

EXAMPLE 1   Graph R(−4, 1, −2) on a three-dimensional coordinate system.

We do not need to show the *xy*-plane.

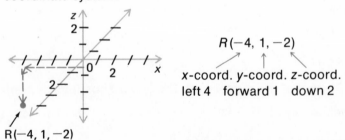

R(−4, 1, −2)

R(−4, 1, −2)
x-coord. y-coord. z-coord.
left 4   forward 1   down 2

The Display and Example 1 suggest this. ─────→

Coordinate ─────→
Sign ─────→
Direction to move from origin ─────→

GRAPHING ORDERED TRIPLES

x-coordinate		y-coordinate		z-coordinate	
Positive	Negative	Positive	Negative	Positive	Negative
Right	Left	Forward	Back	Up	Down

Distance formula for a plane:
$$d = \sqrt{(x_2 - x_1)^2 + (y_2 - y_1)^2}$$

We can find the distance between two points in a three-dimensional coordinate system.

Theorem 12.8

(See Exercise 20.)

If d is the distance between points $A(x_1, y_1, z_1)$ and $B(x_2, y_2, z_2)$, then
$$d = \sqrt{(x_2 - x_1)^2 + (y_2 - y_1)^2 + (z_2 - z_1)^2}.$$

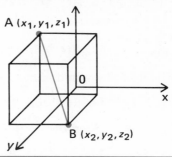

EXAMPLE 2   Find the distance between $P(2, 3, 4)$ and $Q(1, 5, -3)$.

$P(2, 3, 4) \qquad Q(1, 5, -3)$
$\uparrow \uparrow \uparrow \qquad \uparrow \uparrow \uparrow$
$x_1 \, y_1 \, z_1 \qquad x_2 \, y_2 \, z_2$

$\sqrt{54} = \sqrt{9} \cdot \sqrt{6} = 3\sqrt{6}$ ⟶

$$d = \sqrt{(x_x - x_1)^2 + (y_2 - y_1)^2 + (z_2 - z_1)^2}$$
$$PQ = \sqrt{(1 - 2)^2 + (5 - 3)^2 + (-3 - 4)^2}$$
$$= \sqrt{(-1)^2 + (2)^2 + (-7)^2}$$
$$= \sqrt{1 + 4 + 49}$$
$$= \sqrt{54}, \text{ or } 3\sqrt{6}$$

Thus, PQ is $\sqrt{54}$, or $3\sqrt{6}$.

EXERCISES

PART A

Graph each point on a three-dimensional coordinate system.

1. $A(2, 4, 1)$ **2.** $B(3, -4, 2)$ **3.** $C(-2, 1, 5)$ **4.** $D(4, -1, -5)$ **5.** $E(-3, -2, 1)$
6. $F(5, -2, 0)$ **7.** $G(0, 4, -1)$ **8.** $H(-3, 0, -5)$ **9.** $J(-1, 0, 0)$ **10.** $K(0, -4, 0)$

Find the distance between each pair of points.

11. $A(2, 4, 1)$, $B(5, -3, 7)$ **12.** $C(6, 2, 8)$, $D(-3, 4, -2)$ **13.** $E(-7, -3, 0)$, $F(4, -1, 6)$
14. $G(7, 3, -8)$, $H(2, 0, -1)$ **15.** $J(-5, 1, 0)$, $K(7, -6, 3)$ **16.** $L(0, 8, 0)$, $M(-5, -2, 1)$
17. $P(3, -7, 4)$, $Q(-1, 2, 0)$ **18.** $R(0, -6, 5)$, $S(3, -8, 4)$ **19.** $T(0, -2, -1)$, $U(-3, -7, 0)$

PART B

20. Prove Theorem 12.8.

Chapter Twelve Review

On the same coordinate system, graph and label each point. [p. 401]

1. $A(5, 2)$ **2.** $B(-4, 1)$ **3.** $C(-3, -2)$ **4.** $D(0, -5)$

Is $\overleftrightarrow{AB}$ a vertical line, a horizontal line, or neither? [p. 401]

5. $A(-3, 1), B(-3, 2)$ **6.** $A(1, 5), B(2, 5)$ **7.** $A(1, -6), B(-6, 1)$ **8.** $A(5, 0), B(-3, 0)$

Find CD. [p. 404]

9. $C(2, 5), D(3, 1)$ **10.** $C(4, -6), D(5, 0)$ **11.** $C(7, -2), D(-8, 3)$ **12.** $C(0, -4), D(3, 2)$

Find the coordinates of the midpoint of $\overline{AB}$. [p. 407]

13. $A(6, 5), B(-2, 3)$ **14.** $A(-1, 2), B(-3, 4)$ **15.** $A(5, 6), B(-2, 8)$ **16.** $A(-7, 0), B(2, -5)$

M is the midpoint of $\overline{AB}$. Find the coordinates of B. [p. 407]

17. $M(2, 3), A(-4, 6)$ **18.** $M(-5, 1), A(3, 0)$ **19.** $M(-2, -4), A(-5, 7)$ **20.** $M(6, -1), A(0, 3)$

Find $\vec{d}(PQ)$. [p. 411]

21. $P(5, 1), Q(5, -3)$ **22.** $P(2, 6), Q(-3, 6)$ **23.** $P(-1, 3), Q(0, 3)$ **24.** $P(4, -2), Q(4, 4)$

Find slope $(\overleftrightarrow{RS})$. Then describe its position. [p. 411]

25. $R(2, 8), S(2, -6)$ **26.** $R(4, 3), S(-1, -3)$ **27.** $R(-1, 6), S(2, -3)$ **28.** $R(-1, 0), S(3, 0)$

Identify the slope m and the y-intercept b. [p. 416]

29. $y = 6x + 2$ **30.** $y = -x - 4$ **31.** $-4y = 2x - 5$ **32.** $6x + 3y = -9$

**Graph $\overleftrightarrow{PQ}$. Then write an equation for $\overleftrightarrow{PQ}$ in the form $y = mx + b$.
Identify the slope and the y-intercept.** [p. 416]

33. $P(2, 3), Q(5, 6)$ **34.** $P(-4, 1), Q(3, 0)$ **35.** $P(-2, -5), Q(4, -3)$ **36.** $P(0, 6), Q(-4, 1)$

Graph the line described by each equation. [p. 420]

37. $y = 2x + 3$ **38.** $y = -x - 5$ **39.** $y = \frac{1}{3}x - 8$ **40.** $2x + 3y = -6$

Give the slope of a line parallel to $\overleftrightarrow{AB}$. [p. 424]

41. $A(2, 6), B(1, 5)$ **42.** $A(-3, 4), B(2, -1)$ **43.** $A(5, 7), B(-3, 7)$ **44.** $A(3, -8), B(-2, -8)$

Give the slope of a line perpendicular to $\overleftrightarrow{CD}$. [p. 424]

45. $C(2, 5), D(-3, 1)$ **46.** $C(4, -6), D(-2, 3)$ **47.** $C(-5, 0), D(2, 0)$ **48.** $C(3, -6), D(3, -2)$

49. Show that $ABCD$ is a rectangle, for $A(-2, -6), B(3, -1), C(1, 1), D(-4, -4)$ [p. 427]

Write an equation of a circle with center A and radius of length r. [p. 431]

50. $A(0, 0); r = 3$ **51.** $A(5, 1); r = 2$ **52.** $A(-3, 1); r = 1$ **53.** $A(-2, -4); r = \sqrt{5}$

Find the center and the radius of the circle with the given equation. Graph the circle. [p. 431]

54. $x^2 + y^2 = 16$ **55.** $x^2 + (y - 3)^2 = 36$ **56.** $x^2 + y^2 + 4x - 6y = 30$

Chapter Twelve Test

On the same coordinate system graph and label each point.

1. $A(-2, 3)$ **2.** $B(4, 1)$ **3.** $C(2, 0)$ **4.** $D(-1, -5)$

Is $\overleftrightarrow{RS}$ a vertical line, a horizontal line, or neither?

5. $R(-2, 3), S(3, -2)$ **6.** $R(-4, 1), S(-4, 3)$ **7.** $R(7, 0), S(-2, 0)$

Find AB.

8. $A(-3, 4), B(2, -7)$ **9.** $A(6, 0), B(-4, 1)$

Find the coordinates of the midpoint of $\overline{PQ}$.

10 $P(3, -6), Q(-1, 4)$ **11.** $P(5, 2), Q(-4, 3)$

M is the midpoint of $\overline{CD}$. Find the coordinates of D.

12. $M(4, 2), C(-1, 5)$ **13.** $M(-3, 1), C(0, -2)$

Find $\vec{d}(AB)$.

14. $A(2, -6), B(2, -8)$ **15.** $A(-3, -1), B(3, -1)$

Find slope ($\overleftrightarrow{CD}$). Then describe its position.

16. $C(-2, -4), D(5, 3)$ **17.** $C(0, 6), D(0, -3)$ **18.** $C(2, 5), D(-3, 5)$ **19.** $C(-1, 4), D(3, -2)$

Identify the slope m and the y-intercept b.

20. $y = x - 3$ **21.** $2x + 4y = 7$

Graph $\overleftrightarrow{PQ}$. Then write an equation for $\overleftrightarrow{PQ}$ in the form $y = mx + b$. Identify the slope and the y-intercept.

22. $P(4, 3), Q(0, -1)$ **23.** $P(-6, 4), Q(-2, -3)$

Graph the line described by each equation.

24. $y = -3x + 2$ **25.** $5x - 2y = 8$

Give the slope of a line parallel to $\overleftrightarrow{PQ}$.

26. $P(2, 1), Q(-3, 4)$ **27.** $P(-3, 6), Q(3, 6)$

Give the slope of a line perpendicular to $\overleftrightarrow{RS}$.

28. $R(3, 7), S(-4, 2)$ **29.** $R(5, 2), S(-3, 2)$

30. Show that $MNPQ$ is a parallelogram, for $M(5, -8), N(10, -3), P(9, 1), Q(4, -4)$.

Write an equation of a circle with center A and radius of length r.

31. $A(0, 0); r = 2$ **32.** $A(-1, 3); r = \sqrt{2}$

Find the center and the radius of the circle with the given equation. Graph the circle.
33. $x^2 + y^2 = 49$ **34.** $x^2 + y^2 - 10x + 2y = 39$

Slides and Coordinates

EXPERIMENT

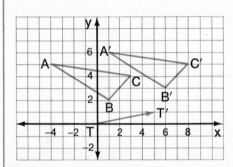

On graph paper, copy the axes, $\triangle ABC$, $\triangle A'B'C'$, and the slide arrow, TT'.

1. Are the triangles congruent?

2. Give the coordinates of the vertices of $\triangle ABC$ and $\triangle A'B'C'$. Give the coordinates of the tail and the tip of the slide arrow, TT'.

3. Compare the x-coordinates of A and A'; B and B'; C and C'; T and T'.

4. Similarly, compare the y-coordinates.

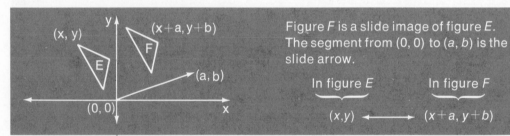

Figure F is a slide image of figure E. The segment from $(0, 0)$ to (a, b) is the slide arrow.

In figure E In figure F

$(x, y) \longleftrightarrow (x+a, y+b)$

Copy each figure and the slide arrow on graph paper. Draw the slide image of each.

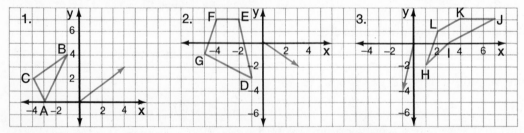

The coordinates of the vertices of a polygon and the tip of a slide arrow are given. Graph and label the polygon, the slide arrow, and the slide image.

4. $A(5, 4)$, $B(3, 1)$, $C(2, 0)$
   tip of slide arrow: $(3, -1)$

5. $D(6, 1)$, $E(4, 3)$, $F(2, -3)$, $G(1, -1)$
   tip of slide arrow: $(-4, 2)$

Locus of Points

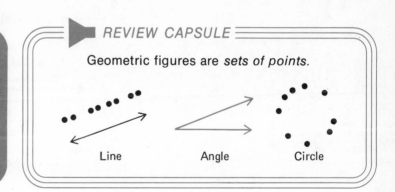

REVIEW CAPSULE

Geometric figures are *sets of points.*

Line   Angle   Circle

All points are coplanar. ————→ In this chapter, we assume that all points lie in the same plane unless otherwise stated.

EXAMPLE 1   Locate all points which are $\frac{1}{2}$ inch from a given point P.

Locate several points $\frac{1}{2}$ inch from P.

Draw a smooth dashed curve through the points.

$\frac{1}{2}$ in.

$\frac{1}{2}$ in.

Start with a given point P. ————→

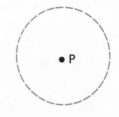

• P

Fully describe the figure. ————→ The figure formed is a circle with center P and a $\frac{1}{2}$-inch radius.

The *locus of points* $\frac{1}{2}$ inch from a given point P is a circle with center P and a $\frac{1}{2}$-inch radius.

Definition of *locus of points* ————→

A *locus of points* is a geometric figure containing all points, and only those points, which satisfy given conditions. [plural: loci (lō′ sī)]

Example 1 suggests this. ┐
                          └→

Postulate 25

The locus of points at a given distance from a given point is a circle with the given point as a center and the given distance as a radius.

EXAMPLE 2 Sketch and describe the locus of points 1 cm from a given line ℓ.

Locate a few points 1 cm | Draw dashed lines
from line ℓ. | through the points.

Start with a given line ℓ. ⟶

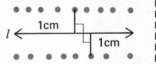

Fully describe the figure. ⟶ The locus is a pair of lines each parallel to ℓ and 1 cm from it.

Postulate 26

The locus of points at a given distance from a given line is a pair of lines each parallel to the given line and at the given distance from it.

EXAMPLE 3 Sketch and describe the locus of points equidistant from two given parallel lines, m and n.

Locate several points the | Draw a dashed line
same distance from m as | through the points.
from n. |

Start with two given parallel lines, m and n. ⟶

Fully describe the figure. ⟶ The locus is a line parallel to m and n and midway between them.

Postulate 27

The locus of points equidistant from two given parallel lines is a line parallel to each of the given lines and midway between them.

SUMMARY

To determine a locus of points:
1. **Start with the given figure(s).**
2. **Locate several points which satisfy the given conditions.**
3. **Draw a smooth dashed curve through all points which satisfy the given conditions.**
4. **Fully describe the locus.**

ORAL EXERCISES

Fully describe each locus sketched below. Then tell which postulate applies.

1.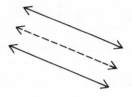

2.

3.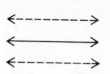

4.

EXERCISES

PART A

Sketch and describe each locus.

1. The locus of points 3 inches from a given point

2. The locus of points 3 inches from a given line

3. The locus of points equidistant from two given parallel lines which are 5 cm apart

4. The locus of points equidistant from points *A* and *B* which are 2 inches apart

5. The locus of points equidistant from the sides of a given angle

6. The locus of points $1\frac{1}{2}$ cm from a given point *Q*

7. The locus of points equidistant from two given points *P* and *Q*

8. The locus of points 4 cm from a given line

PART B

EXAMPLE   Sketch and describe the locus of points less than 1 inch from a given point.

Locate several points less than 1 inch from *P*. | Shade all such points.

Start with a given point *P*. ⟶

Fully describe the figure. ⟶ The locus is the interior of a circle with center *P* and a 1-inch radius.

Sketch and describe each locus.

9. The locus of points less than 2 cm from a given point

10. The locus of points less than $\frac{1}{2}$ inch from a given point

Locus Proofs

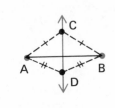

REVIEW CAPSULE

$\overrightarrow{CD}$ is the ⊥ bisector of $\overline{AB}$.

Two points each equidistant
from the endpoints of a segment determine the perpendicular bisector of the
segment.

EXAMPLE 1   Sketch and describe the locus of points equidistant
from two given points A and B.

Locate several points the same distance from A as from B.	Draw a smooth dashed line through the points.

Start with two points A and B. ⟶

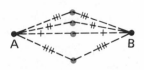

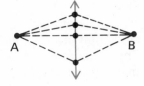

Fully describe the figure. ⟶   The locus is the perpendicular bisector of $\overline{AB}$.

Theorem 13.1

(See Exercise 13)

The locus of points equidistant from two given points
is the perpendicular bisector of the segment joining
the two points.

PART I	PART II
If a point lies on the perpendicular bisector of a segment, then it is equidistant from the endpoints of the segment.	If a point is equidistant from the endpoints of a segment, then it lies on the perpendicular bisector of the segment.

GIVEN
P is on the ⊥
bisector of $\overline{AB}$.
PROVE
$PA = PB$

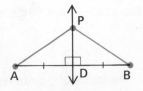

GIVEN: $PA = PB$
PROVE: P lies on the
⊥ bisector
of $\overline{AB}$.

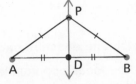

A locus consists of *all points* and *only those points* which satisfy the conditions. }

Every locus proof consists of two parts.

PART I Every point on the locus satisfies the conditions.

PART II Every point which satisfies the conditions lies on the locus.

Theorem 13.2

The locus of points in the interior of an angle equidistant from the sides is the angle bisector.

PART I

Every point on the locus must satisfy the conditions.

If a point is on the bisector of an angle, then it is equidistant from the sides of the angle.

ANALYSIS

Show $\triangle PFB \cong \triangle PGB$ by AAS for $\cong$ $\triangle$'s.

GIVEN
$\overrightarrow{BE}$ bisects $\angle ABC$, P is on $\overrightarrow{BE}$
$\overline{PF} \perp \overrightarrow{BC}$, $\overline{PG} \perp \overrightarrow{BA}$.
PROVE
$PF = PG$

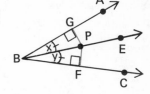

PROOF

STATEMENTS	REASONS
1. $\angle PFB \cong \angle PGB$	1. $\overline{PF} \perp \overrightarrow{BC}$ and $\overline{PG} \perp \overrightarrow{BA}$
2. $\angle x \cong \angle y$	2. Def. of $\angle$ bisector
3. $\overline{BP} \cong \overline{BP}$	3. Reflexive property
4. $\triangle PFB \cong \triangle PGB$	4. AAS for $\cong$ $\triangle$'s
5. $PF = PG$	5. Corr. sides of $\cong$ $\triangle$'s are $\cong$.

PART II

Every point which satisfies the conditions must lie on the locus.

If a point is equidistant from the sides of an angle, then it lies on the bisector of the angle.

ANALYSIS

Show $\triangle PFB \cong \triangle PGB$ by HL for $\cong$ rt. $\triangle$'s.

GIVEN
$\overline{PF} \perp \overrightarrow{BC}$, $\overline{PG} \perp \overrightarrow{BA}$, $PF = PG$
PROVE
$\overrightarrow{BP}$ is the $\angle$ bisector of $\angle ABC$. (P lies on $\overrightarrow{BP}$.)

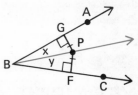

PROOF

STATEMENTS	REASONS
1. $\triangle PFB$ and $\triangle PGB$ are rt. $\triangle$'s.	1. $\overline{PF} \perp \overrightarrow{BC}$ and $\overline{PG} \perp \overrightarrow{BA}$
2. $\overline{PF} \cong \overline{PG}$	2. Def. of $\cong$ segments
3. $\overline{BP} \cong \overline{BP}$	3. Reflexive property
4. $\triangle PFB \cong \triangle PGB$	4. HL for $\cong$ rt. $\triangle$'s
5. $\angle x \cong \angle y$	5. Corr. $\angle$'s of $\cong$ $\triangle$'s are $\cong$.
6. $\overrightarrow{BP}$ is the bisector of $\angle ABC$.	6. Def. of $\angle$ bisector

EXAMPLE 2   Sketch and describe the locus of the midpoints of all radii of a given circle. Then give the postulate or theorem which applies.

Locate the midpoints of the radii.	Draw a smooth dashed curve through the midpoints.

Start with a given circle and several radii. ⟶

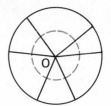

Fully describe the figure. ⟶

All points on the locus are equidistant from point O.

The locus is a circle concentric to the given circle and with a radius one-half the length of the radius of the given circle. This is an application of Postulate 25.

EXAMPLE 3   Sketch and describe the locus of the centers of all circles which pass through two given points. Then give the postulate or theorem which applies.

Draw several circles through A and B. Mark their centers.	Draw a smooth dashed line through the centers.

Start with two given points A and B. ⟶

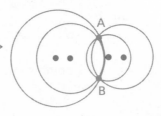
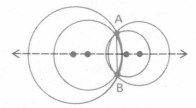

Fully describe the figure. ⟶

Each point on the locus is equidistant from A and B. ⟶

The locus is the perpendicular bisector of $\overline{AB}$.

The locus is an application of Theorem 13.1.

EXERCISES

PART A

Sketch and describe each locus. Then give the postulate or theorem which applies.

1. The locus of the midpoints of all chords of the same length in a given circle

2. The locus of the centers of all circles of the same size which are tangent to a given line

3. The locus of the centers of all circles which are tangent to each of two parallel lines

4. For all triangles with a given base and a given altitude, the locus of the vertices opposite the base

5. The locus of points equidistant from two intersecting lines

6. The locus of the midpoints of all chords parallel to a given chord of a circle

7. The locus of the centers of all circles which are tangent to both sides of a given angle

8. The locus of points within a circle which are equidistant from the endpoints of a given chord

PART B

Sketch and describe each locus of points. Then write the locus as a theorem. Then write Part I and Part II of the theorem.

9. The locus of the centers of all circles tangent to a given line at a given point

10. The locus of the midpoints of all chords drawn from a given point of a circle

PART C

Prove each locus statement as a theorem.

11. The locus of the centers of all circles tangent to a given line at a given point is a line perpendicular to the given line at the given point.

12. The locus of the vertex of the right angle of a right triangle with a given hypotenuse is a circle with the hypotenuse as a diameter.

13. Prove Theorem 13.1.

Algebra Review

To find the solution set of a quadratic equation like $x^2 + 7x + 12 = 0$:
1. Factor
2. Use: if $a \cdot b = 0$, $a = 0$ or $b = 0$.

EXAMPLE   Find the solution set of $6x^2 + x - 2 = 0$.

Factor.   ⟶

Set each factor equal to 0.   ⟶

Solve.   ⟶

$$(3x + 2)(2x - 1) = 0$$
$$3x + 2 = 0 \quad \text{or} \quad 2x - 1 = 0$$
$$3x = -2 \qquad\qquad 2x = 1$$
$$x = -\tfrac{2}{3} \qquad\qquad x = \tfrac{1}{2}$$

Thus, the solution set is $\{-\tfrac{2}{3}, \tfrac{1}{2}\}$.

Find the solution set.

1. $x^2 + 10x + 25 = 0$
2. $x^2 - 49 = 0$
3. $x^2 - 9x + 14 = 0$
4. $2x^2 - 11x + 5 = 0$
5. $3x^2 + 8x - 3 = 0$
6. $2x^2 + 3x - 9 = 0$

More Conditions for Loci

OBJECTIVE

■ To sketch and describe loci determined by specific conditions

▶ REVIEW CAPSULE

Locus of points 4″ from a given point | Locus of points 4″ from a given line

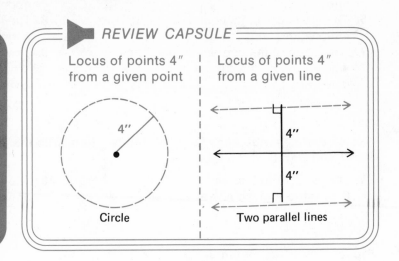

Circle | Two parallel lines

The distance from a point to a circle is the *shortest* distance measured along the line joining the point to the center of the circle.

PA is the *distance* from point *P* to circle *O*.
It is measured along $\overleftrightarrow{PO}$.

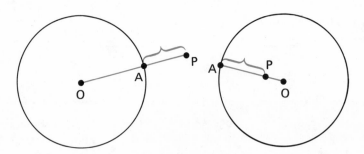

EXAMPLE 1

Sketch and describe the locus of points 8 inches from a circle with a 6-inch radius.

Step 1 Start with a circle with a 6-inch radius.

Step 2 Locate several points 8 inches from the circle. The points will lie outside the circle.

Step 3 Draw a smooth dashed curve through the points.

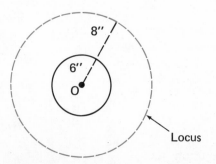

Step 4 Describe the locus. ⟶ The locus is *a circle* concentric to the given circle and with a 14-inch radius.

EXAMPLE 2 Sketch and describe the locus of points 6 inches from a circle with a 6-inch radius.

Follow steps 1–4.

The center is also 6 inches from the given circle.

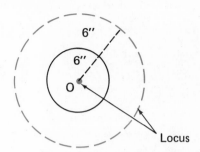

The locus is *a circle* concentric to the given circle and with a 12-inch radius and *the center* of the given circle.

EXAMPLE 3 Sketch and describe the locus of points 4 inches from a circle with a 6-inch radius.

Follow steps 1–4.

The points of the locus form an outer and an inner circle.

The locus is *two circles* concentric to the given circle, one with a 10-inch radius and one with a 2-inch radius.

EXAMPLE 4 Sketch and describe the locus of points 4 inches from line *m* and 6 inches from point *P* on line *m*.

Use Post. 26 for the locus 4″ from line *m*.
Use Post. 25 for the locus 6″ from point *P*.

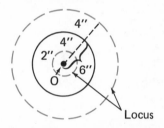

Look for the intersection of the parallel lines and the circle. ⟶ *A*, *B*, *C*, and *D* are the only points 4″ from *m and* 6″ from *P*.

Thus, The locus is the set of points {*A, B, C, D*}.

EXAMPLE 5   Points *A* and *B* are 3 inches apart. Sketch and describe the locus of points 2 inches from *A* and 2 inches from *B*.

Use Post. 25 to sketch each locus.

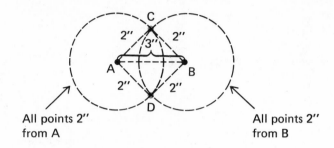

All points 2" from A

All points 2" from B

Look for the intersection of the two circles. ⟶ *C* and *D* are the only points 2" from *A* and 2" from *B*.

Thus, the locus is the set of points {*C*, *D*}.

EXAMPLE 6   Point *P* is 4 cm above line ℓ. Sketch and describe the locus of points 1 cm from *P* and 2 cm from ℓ.

Sketch the two loci. Use Post. 25 and Post. 26.

There are no points which are 1 cm from *P* and 2 cm from ℓ.

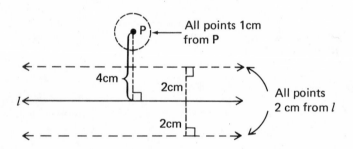

All points 1cm from P

4cm

2cm

l

2cm

All points 2 cm from *l*

There are no points in the intersection. ⟶ **Thus,** the locus is the empty set.

EXERCISES

PART A

Sketch and describe each locus of points.

1. The locus of points 5 inches from circle *O*
2. The locus of points 2 inches from circle *O*
3. The locus of points 1 inch from circle *O*

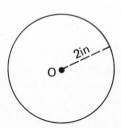

O • ⟋ 2in

4. The locus of points 3 cm from *A* and 4 cm from *B*
5. The locus of points 1 cm from *A* and 5 cm from *B*
6. The locus of points $1\frac{1}{2}$ cm from *A* and 4 cm from *B*

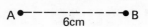

7. The locus of points equidistant from *m* and *n* and 2 inches from

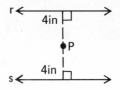

8. The locus of points equidistant from *r* and *s* and 3 inches from *P*

9. The locus of points equidistant from *r* and *s* and 4 inches from *P*

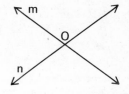

10. The locus of points 2 cm from ℓ and 4 cm from *P*
11. The locus of points 2 cm from ℓ and 3 cm from *P*
12. The locus of points 2 cm from ℓ and 7 cm from *P*
13. The locus of points 2 cm from ℓ and 9 cm from *P*
14. The locus of points 2 cm from ℓ and 2 cm from *P*

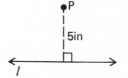

PART B

Sketch and describe each locus of points.

15. The locus of points 4 inches from a circle with a 3-inch radius

16. The locus of points 5 cm from a circle with a 5-cm radius

17. The locus of points 2 feet from a circle with a 7-foot radius

18. The locus of points equidistant from two concentric circles

19. The locus of points 3 inches from point *A* and 2 inches from point *B*, where *A* and *B* are 4 inches apart

20. Repeat Exercise 19 but with *A* and *B* 5 inches apart.

PART C

Sketch and describe each locus of points.

21. The locus of points equidistant from intersecting lines *r* and *s*, and 3 inches from line ℓ which is 2 inches above *r*

22. The locus of points equidistant from lines *m* and *n* and 8 inches from point *P*, where *P* is 3 inches above *m*, *m* ∥ *n*, and *m* is 6 inches above *n*

23. Repeat Exercise 22, but with *P* 5 inches above *m*.

24. Repeat Exercise 22, but with *P* 6 inches above *m*.

Compound Locus

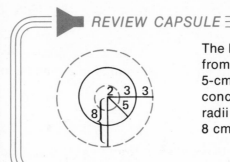

▶ REVIEW CAPSULE

The locus of points 3 cm from a circle with a 5-cm radius is two concentric circles with radii of length 2 cm and 8 cm, respectively.

EXAMPLE 1 Sketch and describe the locus of points at a distance *d* from a circle with radius of length *r*.

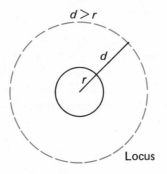

$d > r$

The locus is a circle concentric to the given circle with radius of length $r + d$.

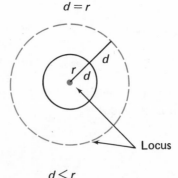

$d = r$

The locus is a circle concentric to the given circle with radius $2r$ *and* the center of the given circle.

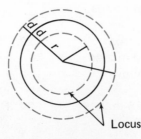

$d < r$

The locus is two circles concentric to the given circle and with radii $r + d$ and $r - d$ respectively.

EXAMPLE 2   Sketch and describe the locus of points p cm from line m and q cm from point A on line m.

There are three possibilities.

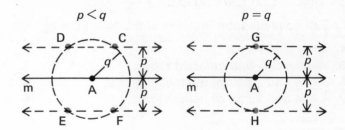

The locus is $\{C, D, E, F\}$.   The locus is $\{G, H\}$.

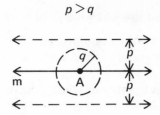

The locus is the empty set.

EXAMPLE 3   Points A and B are d inches apart. Sketch and describe the locus of points x inches from A and y inches from B.

There are three possibilities.

$x + y > d$ $x + y = d$

The locus is $\{E, F\}$.   The locus is $\{G\}$.

$x + y < d$

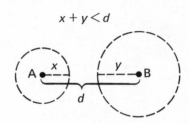

The locus is the empty set.

ORAL EXERCISES

Give all possible intersections of the following figures.

1. A ray and a circle
2. Two lines
3. Two circles with different radii
4. Two circles with the same radii
5. A line and a pair of intersecting lines
6. A circle and a pair of parallel lines
7. A line and a pair of parallel lines
8. A line and a pair of concentric circles

EXERCISES

PART A

Sketch and describe each locus of points. Show all possible cases.

1. The locus of points equidistant from the sides of $\angle A$ and d inches from point A

2. The locus of points r feet from point A and r feet from point B, where A and B are d feet apart

3. The locus of points equidistant from intersecting lines p and q and x units from A, the point of intersection of p and q

4. The locus of points equidistant from two parallel lines m and n and d feet from point A on line m, where m and n are f feet apart.

5. The locus of points equidistant from points A and B and h inches from point A, where A and B are d inches apart

6. The locus of points equidistant from intersecting lines r and s and y units from line r

PART B

EXAMPLE   Sketch and describe the locus of points equidistant from two given points and at a given distance from a third given point.

Let A, B, and P be the given points.

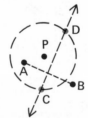

The locus is $\{C, D\}$.

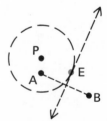

The locus is $\{E\}$.

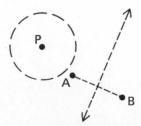

The locus is the empty set.

452   COMPOUND LOCUS

Sketch and describe each locus of points. Show all possible cases.

7. The locus of points equidistant from two given points and equidistant from two given parallel lines

8. The locus of points at a given distance from a given point and equidistant from the sides of a given angle

9. The locus of points equidistant from two given parallel lines and at a given distance from another given line

10. The locus of points equidistant from a pair of intersecting lines and at a given distance from a given point

11. The locus of points at a given distance d_1 from a given point and at a given distance d_2 from a second given point, where $d_1 \neq d_2$

12. The locus of points equidistant from two given concentric circles and at a given distance from two given parallel lines

13. The locus of points equidistant from a pair of intersecting lines and at a given distance from a given line

14. The locus of points equidistant from the sides of a given angle and equidistant from two given parallel lines

PART C

Sketch and describe each locus of points. Show all possible cases.

15. The locus of points equidistant from three given points [Hint: Take the points two at a time.]

16. The locus of points equidistant from the sides of a given triangle [Hint: Take the sides two at a time.]

17. The locus of points at the distance of a radius from a given circle and equidistant from two given points

18. The locus of points at a given distance from a given circle and equidistant from two given lines that intersect at the center of the given circle

---

Algebra Review

OBJECTIVE
■ To find the solution set of a quadratic equation by using the quadratic formula

The solutions of $ax^2 + bx + c = 0$ are given by the quadratic formula.

$$x = \frac{-b \pm \sqrt{b^2 - 4ac}}{2a}$$

EXAMPLE   Find the solution set of $2x^2 + 5x - 2 = 0$.

$$a = 2, \quad b = 5, \quad c = -2$$

Use quadratic formula. $\longrightarrow$ $x = \dfrac{-5 \pm \sqrt{5^2 - 4(2)(-2)}}{2(2)}$, or $\dfrac{-5 \pm \sqrt{41}}{4}$

Find the solution set.

1. $x^2 + 2x - 3 = 0$
2. $x^2 + x - 6 = 0$
3. $x^2 - 12x = 13$
4. $2x^2 - 11x + 12 = 0$
5. $3x^2 + 5x - 2 = 0$
6. $5x^2 - 3x = 2$

Conic Sections

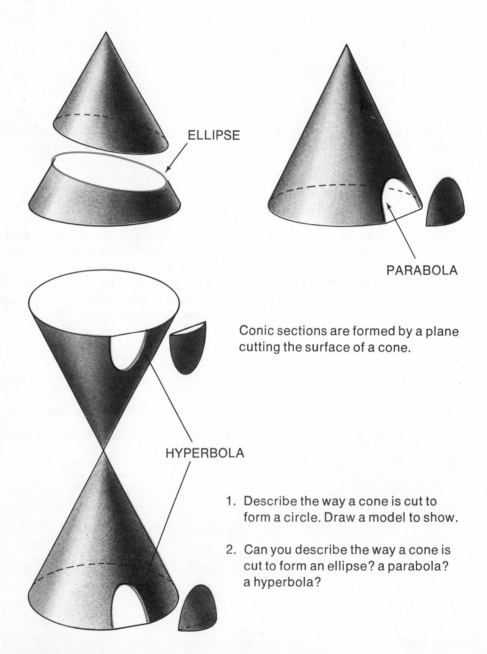

ELLIPSE

PARABOLA

Conic sections are formed by a plane cutting the surface of a cone.

HYPERBOLA

1. Describe the way a cone is cut to form a circle. Draw a model to show.

2. Can you describe the way a cone is cut to form an ellipse? a parabola? a hyperbola?

Each conic section is also defined as a locus.

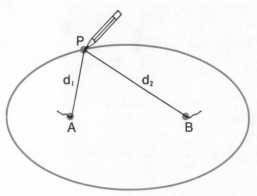

An *ellipse* is the locus of points in a plane the sum of whose distances from two fixed points is always a constant.
$$(d_1 + d_2 = \text{constant})$$

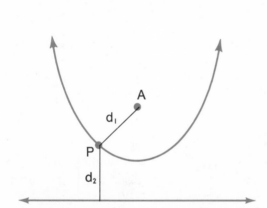

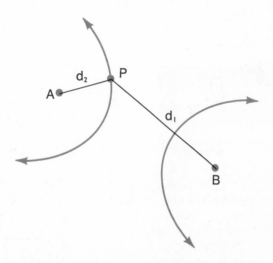

A *parabola* is the locus of points in the plane equidistant from a fixed point and a fixed line.
$$(d_1 = d_2)$$

A *hyperbola* is the locus of points in a plane the difference of whose distances from two fixed points is a constant.
$$(d_1 - d_2 = \text{constant})$$

Can you figure out a way to draw any of these conic sections by using the definition and a piece of string? Why is it easier to draw a circle using a piece of string?

Bisectors in a Triangle

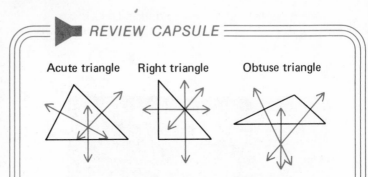

REVIEW CAPSULE

Acute triangle   Right triangle   Obtuse triangle

Perpendicular bisectors of the sides are shown.

Concurrent lines ⟶

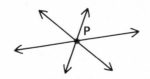

Lines are *concurrent* if they pass through the same point.

The Review Capsule suggests this.

Theorem 13.3

The perpendicular bisectors of the sides of a triangle are concurrent at a point which is equidistant from the vertices.

ANALYSIS

Let P be the point of intersection of two of the ⊥ bisectors. Show that the third ⊥ bisector passes through P.

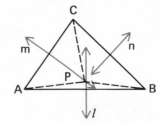

GIVEN
$\triangle ABC$ with ℓ, m, and n the ⊥ bisectors of the sides
PROVE
ℓ, m, and n are concurrent at a point equidistant from A, B, and C.

PROOF

STATEMENTS	REASONS
1. ℓ and m will intersect at a point P	1. $\ell \parallel m$, or $\ell \nparallel m$. ℓ cannot be $\parallel m$ by Th. 3.1 and Corollary to Th. 3.3.
2. $PB = PA$, and $PA = PC$	2. A point on the bisector of a segment is equidistant from the endpoints.
3. $PB = PC$	3. Transitive property
4. P lies on n.	4. A point equidistant from the endpoints of a segment lies on the bisector.
5. ℓ, m, and n are concurrent at a point equidistant from A, B, and C.	5. Steps 1–4.

EXAMPLE 1   Circumscribe a circle about △*ABC*.

Strategy: Find a point equidistant from the three vertices by finding the intersection of the perpendicular bisectors.

Construct the perpendicular bisectors of $\overline{AB}$ and of $\overline{AC}$. Label the intersection *P*. | With *PA* as a radius length, draw circle *P*.

Draw △*ABC*. ──────────────────→

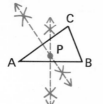

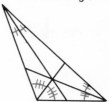

EXAMPLE 2   For each triangle, the angle bisectors are shown. What appears to be true about the angle bisectors?

Acute triangle   Right triangle   Obtuse triangle

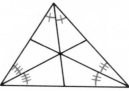

The angle bisectors appear to be concurrent.

Example 2 suggests this. ──────┐
                                      ↓

Theorem 13.4

The bisectors of the angles of a triangle are concurrent at a point which is equidistant from the sides.

ANALYSIS

Consider the point of intersection of two of the angle bisectors. Show that the third bisector passes through the intersection. Use Th. 13.2.

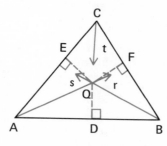

GIVEN
△*ABC* with rays *r*, *s*, and *t* bisecting the angles
PROVE
r, *s*, and *t* are concurrent at a point equidistant from $\overline{AB}$, $\overline{AC}$, and $\overline{BC}$.

PROOF
(See Exercise 15)

EXAMPLE 3   Inscribe a circle in △ABC.

Strategy: Bisect two angles. The intersection of the bisectors is the center of the inscribed circle.

Construct a perpendicular ⎪ With $\overline{QR}$ as a radius length,
$\overline{QR}$ from Q to $\overline{AB}$. ⎪ draw circle Q.

Bisect ∠A and ∠B.
Label the intersection Q.

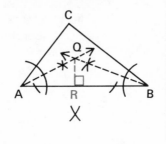

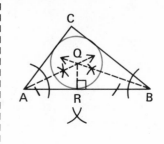

Every triangle has a circumcircle and an incircle.

Circumcircle of △ABC   Incircle of △DEF

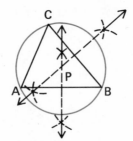

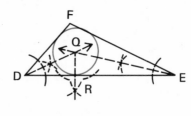

Circle P is *circumscribed* about △ABC. P is the *circumcenter* of △ABC

Circle Q is *inscribed* in △DEF. Q is the *incenter* of △DEF.

EXERCISES

PART A

1. Copy △ABC. Construct the perpendicular bisector of each side. Label the point of intersection P.

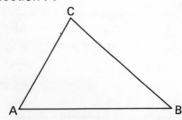

2. Copy △DEF. Construct the bisector of each angle. Label the point of intersection Q.

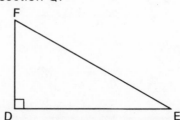

3. Copy △RST. Inscribe a circle in △RST. Label the incenter I.

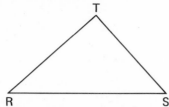

4. Copy △JKL. Circumscribe a circle about △JKL. Label the circumcenter C.

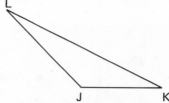

5. Draw three noncollinear points. Construct a circle which passes through all three points.

6. Draw a triangle PQR. Construct a circle tangent to all three sides.

7. Construct an isosceles triangle. Construct the incenter and the circumcenter. Where do the two centers appear to lie?

8. Construct an equilateral triangle. Construct the incenter and the circumcenter. What appears to be true of the two centers?

9. Trace a circle by drawing around a fifty-cent piece or similar object. Locate the center of the circle by construction. [HINT: Select three points on the circle.]

10. Consider an acute, a right, and an obtuse triangle. For each triangle, tell whether the circumcenter lies in the interior, on, or in the exterior of the triangle.

11. Repeat Exercise 10, but for the incenter instead of the circumcenter.

12. Given three noncollinear points, where is the point in their plane equidistant from all three?

13. Sketch and describe the locus of points equidistant from three noncollinear points.

14. Sketch and describe the locus of points equidistant from the three sides of a triangle.

PART B

15. Supply a reason for each step 2–5 in the proof of Theorem 13.4 below.

Statements	Reasons
1. r and s will intersect at a point Q.	1. r ∥ s, or r ∦ s, r cannot be ∥ s by Th. 3.2.
2. Draw $\overline{QD} \perp \overline{AB}$, $\overline{QE} \perp \overline{AC}$, $\overline{QE} \perp \overline{BC}$.	2.
3. QE = QD, QD = QF	3.
4. QE = QF	4.
5. Q lies on t.	5.
6. r, s, and t are concurrent at a point equidistant from $\overline{AB}$, $\overline{AC}$, and $\overline{BC}$.	6. Steps 1–5

PQRS is any convex quadrilateral.

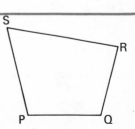

16. Explain how to locate a point equidistant from $\overleftrightarrow{PQ}$ and $\overleftrightarrow{PS}$ and also equidistant from S and R.

17. Explain how to locate a point equidistant from $\overleftrightarrow{PQ}$, $\overleftrightarrow{PS}$, and $\overleftrightarrow{SR}$.

18. Do the points of Exercises 16 and 17 necessarily coincide?

Altitudes and Medians

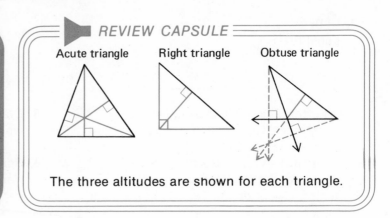

▶ REVIEW CAPSULE

Acute triangle   Right triangle   Obtuse triangle

The three altitudes are shown for each triangle.

Theorem 13.5

The altitudes of a triangle are concurrent.

ANALYSIS

Form another △ and show that the given altitudes are the ⊥ bisectors of its sides and are therefore concurrent by Th. 13.3.

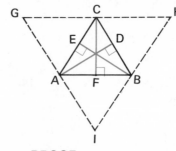

GIVEN
△ABC with altitudes $\overline{AD}$, $\overline{BE}$, and $\overline{CF}$
PROVE
$\overline{AD}$, $\overline{BE}$, and $\overline{CF}$ are concurrent.

PROOF

STATEMENTS	REASONS
1. Through C draw $\overleftrightarrow{GH} \parallel \overline{AB}$; through B draw $\overleftrightarrow{HI} \parallel \overline{AC}$; through A draws $\overleftrightarrow{GI} \parallel \overline{BC}$.	1. Parallel postulate
2. ABCG and ABHC are ▱'s.	2. Def. of ▱
3. $\overline{GC} \cong \overline{AB}$ and $\overline{AB} \cong \overline{CH}$	3. Opp. sides of a ▱ are ≅.
4. $\overline{GC} \cong \overline{CH}$	4. Transitive property
5. $\overline{CF} \perp \overline{AB}$	5. Def. of altitude
6. $\overline{CF} \perp \overline{GH}$	6. If a line is ⊥ to one of two ∥ lines, it is ⊥ to the other.
7. $\overline{CF}$ is the ⊥ bisector of $\overline{GH}$.	7. Def. of ⊥ bisector
8. Similarly. $\overline{AD}$ is the ⊥ bisector of $\overline{GI}$; $\overline{BE}$ is the ⊥ bisector of $\overline{HI}$.	8. Steps 2–7
9. $\overline{AD}$, $\overline{BE}$, and $\overline{CF}$ are concurrent	9. The ⊥ bisectors of the sides of a △ are concurrent.

"Ortho" comes from the Greek word "orthos." It means straight or right.

P is the *orthocenter* of △ABC above. It is the point at which the altitudes are concurrent.

EXAMPLE 1 For each triangle, the medians are shown. What appears to be true about the medians?

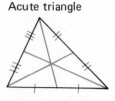

Acute triangle Right triangle Obtuse triangle

The medians appear to be concurrent.

EXAMPLE 2 $\overline{AD}$ and $\overline{BE}$ are medians of $\triangle ABC$. H is the midpoint of $\overline{AO}$ and K is the midpoint of $\overline{BO}$. $AD = 12$. Find AO.

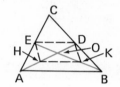

$HKDE$ is a $\square$. $\longleftarrow$ $\begin{cases} \overline{HK} \parallel \overline{AB}; \overline{HK} = \frac{1}{2}(AB) \\ \overline{ED} \parallel \overline{AB}; ED = \frac{1}{2}(AB) \\ \text{So } \overline{HK} \parallel \overline{ED}; \overline{HK} \cong \overline{ED} \end{cases}$ by Th. 7.9

Diag. of a $\square$ bisect each other. $\longrightarrow$ So, $HO = OD$

H is the midpoint of $\overline{AO}$. $\longrightarrow$ But, $AH = HO$

$AD = 12$ $\longrightarrow$ So, $AO = \frac{2}{3}(AD) = \frac{2}{3}(12) = 8$

Thus, $AO = 8$.

Theorem 13.6

The medians of a triangle are concurrent at a point which is two thirds of the distance from each vertex to the midpoint of the opposite side.

ANALYSIS
Construct a $\square$ within $\triangle ABC$. Use Th. 7.4. (The diagonals of a $\square$ bisect each other.)

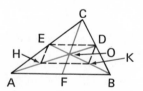

PROOF
(See Exercise 19)

GIVEN
$\triangle ABC$ with medians $\overline{AD}$, $\overline{BE}$, and $\overline{CF}$
PROVE
$\overline{AD}$, $\overline{BE}$, and $\overline{CF}$ are concurrent at a point O.
$AO = \frac{2}{3}(AD)$; $BO = \frac{2}{3}(BE)$; $CO = \frac{2}{3}(CF)$.

A triangular board will balance at its centroid.

O is the *centroid* of $\triangle ABC$ above. It is the point at which the medians are concurrent. The centroid is the center of gravity of a triangle.

EXAMPLE 3   In $\triangle PQR$, medians $\overline{QE}$ and $\overline{PD}$ intersect at S. If $PD = 3x$ and $PS = 8x - 12$, find PD, PS, and SD.

Use Theorem 13.6. ⟶

$$PS = \tfrac{2}{3}(PD)$$
$$8x - 12 = \tfrac{2}{3}(3x)$$
$$8x - 12 = \frac{6x}{3}$$

$\dfrac{6x}{3} = 2x$ ⟶

$$8x - 12 = 2x$$
$$6x = 12, \text{ or } x = 2$$

$PD = 3x$ ⟶ **Thus,** $PD = 3(2) = 6$

$PS = 8x - 12$ ⟶ $PS = 8(2) - 12 = 4,$

$SD = PD - PS$ ⟶ $SD = 6 - 4 = 2.$

EXERCISES

PART A

1. Draw an acute triangle. Construct the median to each side. Label the centroid P.
2. Draw an obtuse triangle. Construct the altitude to each side. Label the orthocenter Q.
3. Construct an isosceles triangle. Construct the centroid and the orthocenter. Where do the two centers appear to lie?
4. Construct an equilateral triangle. Construct the centroid. What is true of the centroid, the orthocenter, the incenter, and the circumcenter?
5. Consider an acute, a right, and an obtuse triangle. Tell whether the orthocenter lies in the interior, on, or in the exterior of each triangle.
6. Repeat Exercise 5, but for the centroid instead of the orthocenter.

Consider $\triangle ABC$ **with medians** $\overline{AD}$**,** $\overline{BE}$**, and** $\overline{CF}$ **concurrent at centroid** P**.**

7. If $AD = 15$, find AP.
8. If $CF = 20$, find PF.
9. If $PD = 4$, find PA.
10. If $PE = 12$, find BE.
11. If $CP = 11$, find CF.
12. If $AP = 9$, find PD.

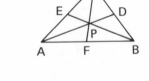

13. If $BP = 2x$ and $BE = 5x - 4$, find BP and BE.
14. If $PF = 3x$ and $PC = 7x - 5$, find PF and PC.
15. If $PD = 2x + 6$ and $AD = 10x$, find PD and AD.

Consider $\triangle RST$ **with median** $\overline{TM}$**, centroid** Q**, and altitude** $\overline{TA}$**.**

16. If $TA = 12$ and $AM = 5$, find QM.
17. If $TQ = 10$ and $TA = 12$, find AM.
18. If $QM = 2$ and $AM = 3$, find TA.

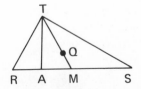

19. Give a reason for each step 2–10 in the proof of Theorem 13.6 below.

	Statements		Reasons
1.	$\overline{AD}$ and $\overline{BE}$ meet in a point O.	1.	$\overline{AD} \nparallel \overline{BE}$ by Th. 3.2.
2.	Let H be the midpoint of $\overline{AO}$; let K be the midpoint of $\overline{BO}$.	2.	
3.	Draw $\overline{HK}, \overline{KD}, \overline{DE}$, and $\overline{EH}$.	3.	
4.	In $\triangle ABC$, $\overline{ED} \parallel \overline{AB}$ and $ED = \frac{1}{2}(AB)$.	4.	
5.	In $\triangle AOB$, $\overline{HK} \parallel \overline{AB}$ and $HK = \frac{1}{2}(AB)$.	5.	
6.	$\overline{ED} \parallel \overline{HK}$ and $ED = HK$	6.	
7.	$HKDE$ is a $\square$.	7.	
8.	$HO = OD$ and $EO = OK$	8.	
9.	$AH = HO$ and $OK = KB$	9.	
10.	$AH = HO = OD$ and $EO = OK = KB$	10.	
11.	$AO = \frac{2}{3}(AD)$; $BO = \frac{2}{3}(BE)$	11.	Step 10
12.	$\overline{AD}$ and $\overline{CF}$ meet in a point P. Let J be the midpoint of $\overline{CP}$. Draw $\square JHFD$. Then $AP = \frac{2}{3}(AD)$; $CP = \frac{2}{3}(CF)$.	12.	Steps 1–11
13.	$O = P$, and $\overline{AD}, \overline{BE}$, and $\overline{CF}$ are concurrent.	13.	P is the only point on $\overline{AD}$ such that $AP = \frac{2}{3}(AD)$.
14.	$CO = \frac{2}{3}(CF)$	14.	Substitution

20. An isosceles triangle has sides measuring 10 in., 13 in., and 13 in. How far above the base is the centroid?

21. Each side of an equilateral triangle measures 8 ft. Find the lengths of the radius of the incircle and the circumcircle.

22. Given: $\triangle ABC$ with median CD
Prove: Area $\triangle ADC$ = area $\triangle BDC$

23. Given: $\triangle ABC$ with median $\overline{CD}$, centroid P, and altitudes $\overline{CE}$ and $\overline{PF}$
Prove: $\dfrac{PF}{CE} = \dfrac{1}{3}$, or $PF = \dfrac{1}{3}(CE)$

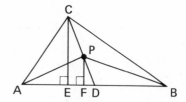

24. Prove that the medians of a triangle divide the triangle into six triangles which are equal in area.

25. Explain why it is logical that the centroid of a triangle is its center of gravity.

Justifying Constructions

<table>
<tr><td>

OBJECTIVE

■ To prove that constructions are valid

</td><td>

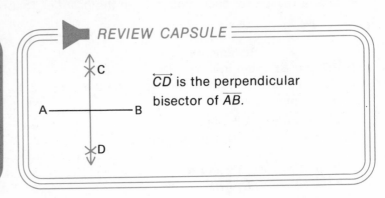
</td></tr>
</table>

EXAMPLE 1   The construction of the bisector of $\angle ABC$ is shown below. Prove that $\overrightarrow{BD}$ bisects $\angle ABC$.

ANALYSIS
Show $\triangle BED \cong \triangle BFD$

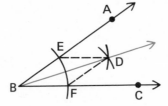

Given: $\angle ABC$ with $\overrightarrow{BD}$ constructed as shown.

Prove: $\overrightarrow{BD}$ bisects $\angle ABC$.

PROOF

$\overarc{EF}$ is an arc of a circle with center B. ⟶
Both arcs at D have the same radius.

STATEMENTS	REASONS
1. Draw $\overline{DE}$ and $\overline{DF}$.	1. Two points determine a line.
2. $\overline{BE} \cong \overline{BF}$	2. Radii of the same ⊙ are ≅.
3. $\overline{ED} \cong \overline{FD}$	3. Radii of ≅ ⊙'s are ≅.
4. $\overline{BD} \cong \overline{BD}$	4. Reflexive property
5. $\triangle BED \cong \triangle BFD$	5. SSS for ≅ △'s
6. $\angle EBD \cong \triangle FBD$	6. Corr. ∠'s of ≅ △'s are ≅.
7. $\overrightarrow{BD}$ bisects $\angle ABC$.	7. Def. of ∠ bisector

The proof in Example 1 *justifies* the angle bisector construction.

EXAMPLE 2   Give an analysis to justify the construction of the perpendicular to line ℓ through point M.

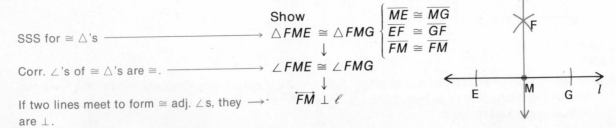

SSS for ≅ △'s ⟶ Show $\triangle FME \cong \triangle FMG$ $\begin{cases} \overline{ME} \cong \overline{MG} \\ \overline{EF} \cong \overline{GF} \\ \overline{FM} \cong \overline{FM} \end{cases}$

↓

Corr. ∠'s of ≅ △'s are ≅. ⟶ $\angle FME \cong \angle FMG$

↓

If two lines meet to form ≅ adj. ∠s, they ⟶ $\overrightarrow{FM} \perp \ell$
are ⊥.

EXAMPLE 3 Write a proof to justify the construction of a circle circumscribed about a triangle.

See the construction for circumscribing a circle about a triangle.

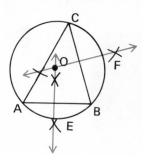

Given:
$\overrightarrow{OE}$ is the ⊥ bisector of $\overline{AB}$.
$\overrightarrow{OF}$ is the ⊥ bisector of $\overline{BC}$.

Prove:
A, B, and C lie on ⊙ O.
(⊙ O is circumscribed about △ ABC.)

Proof

Statements

1. The ⊥ bisectors intersect at O, and OA = OB = OC.

A, B, and C are all equidistant from O. ⟶ 2. A, B, and C lie on ⊙ O.

Reasons

1. The ⊥ bisectors of the sides of a △ are concurrent at a point equidistant from the vertices. (Th. 13.3)

2. Def. of ⊙

EXERCISES

PART A

Perform each construction. Then write a proof to justify the construction.

1. Construction of an angle congruent to a given angle
2. Construction of a perpendicular from a point to a line
3. Construction of a line parallel to a given line through a point not on the line
4. Construction of the perpendicular bisector of a segment
5. Construction of a 60° angle
6. Construction of a 15° angle
7. Construction of a 45° angle
8. Construction of a 105° angle [HINT: 60 + 45 = 105]

PART B

Perform each construction. Then write a proof to justify the construction.

9. Construction of a tangent to a circle through an external point
10. Construction of a circle with a given radius tangent to a given line at a given point on the line
11. Construction of a circle tangent to a given line at a given point on the line and passing through a given point not on the line

Loci in Space

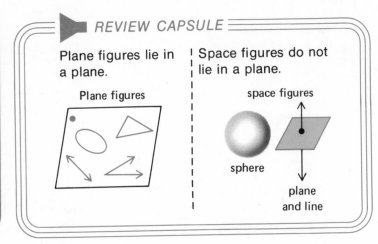

▶ REVIEW CAPSULE

Plane figures lie in a plane. | Space figures do not lie in a plane.

Plane figures | space figures

sphere | plane and line

EXAMPLE 1   Sketch and describe the locus of points in space equidistant from two parallel planes.

Locate points the same distance from each plane. | Sketch the figure formed by all such points.

Start with two parallel planes. ⟶

The locus is a plane parallel to each of the given planes and midway between them.

EXAMPLE 2   Sketch and describe the locus of points in space at a given distance *d* from a given point *P*.

Locate several points at a distance *d* from point *P*. | Sketch the figure formed by all such points

Start with a given point *P* and a given distance *d*. ⟶

(The points can be off the plane and into space.)

The locus is a sphere with center *P* and radius *d*.

EXAMPLE 3   Sketch and describe the locus of points in space equidistant from two given points.

Locate points the same distance from *A* as from *B*.

Sketch the figure formed by all such points.

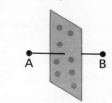

Start with given points *A* and *B*. ——→

The locus is a plane which bisects and is perpendicular to $\overline{AB}$.

EXERCISES

PART A

Sketch and describe each locus of points in space.

1. The locus of points in space 2 inches from a given point *Q*
2. The locus of points in space equidistant from two given points *C* and *D*
3. The locus of points equidistant from two given parallel planes *r* and *s* which are 4 cm apart
4. The locus of points in space 3 inches from a given line *ℓ*
5. The locus of points in space 5 cm from a given plane
6. The locus of points equidistant from the faces of a dihedral angle
7. The locus of points in space equidistant from two given parallel lines
8. The locus of points in space equidistant from the vertices of a given triangle
9. The locus of points in space equidistant from the sides of a given triangle
10. The locus of points in space equidistant from all the points of a given circle

PART B

Sketch and describe each locus of points in space.

11. The locus of points in space less than 3 in. from a given point *P*
12. The locus of points in space less than 2 cm from a given line *ℓ*
13. The locus of the centers of all circles tangent to a given line *ℓ* at a given point *Q* on *ℓ*
14. The locus of the centers of all circles with a given radius *r* and which pass through a given point *S*

PART C

Sketch and describe each locus of points in space.

15. The locus of points in space 5 cm from a given segment $\overline{AB}$
16. The locus of points in space 3 in. from point *A* and 4 in. from point *B*, where *A* and *B* are 5 in. apart

Chapter Thirteen Review

Sketch and describe each locus of points.

1. The locus of points 1 inch from a given point A [p. 439]

2. The locus of points equidistant from the sides of a 30° angle [p. 439]

3. The locus of points less than 2 cm from a given line [p. 439]

4. The locus of points equidistant from two intersecting lines [p. 439]

5. The locus of the centers of all circles tangent to a given line at a given point [p. 442]

6. The locus of points 7 cm from P and 2 cm from Q [p. 446]

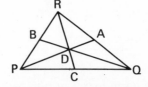

7. The locus of points 4 inches from ℓ and 2 inches from A [p. 446]

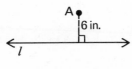

8. The locus of points 3 inches from a circle with a 4-inch radius [p. 446]

Sketch and describe each locus of points. Show all possible cases. [p. 450]

9. The locus of points x cm from point P and x cm from point Q, where P and Q are d cm apart

10. The locus of points equidistant from points C and D and r feet from point C, where C and D are f feet apart

11. The locus of points equidistant from intersecting lines ℓ and m and y inches from P, the point of intersection of ℓ and m

12. The locus of points equidistant from two given concentric circles and at a given distance from a given line

Construct. [p. 456]

13. Copy $\triangle ABC$. Construct the bisector of each angle.

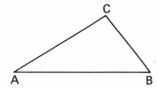

14. Copy $\triangle PQR$. Circumscribe a circle about the triangle.

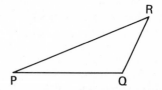

15. Draw an acute triangle. Construct the median to each side. [p. 460]

16. Construct a right triangle. Locate the orthocenter of the triangle. [p. 460]

In $\triangle PQR$ $\overline{PA}$, $\overline{QB}$, and $\overline{RC}$ are medians. [p. 460]

17. If $PA = 18$, find DP.
18. If $DB = 8$, find BQ.
19. If $DC = 2x$ and $DR = 3x + 5$, find RC.

Perform each construction. Then write a proof to justify the construction. [p. 464]

20. Construction of the perpendicular bisector of a segment

21. Construction of a 45° angle

Chapter Thirteen Test

Sketch and describe each locus of points.

1. The locus of points equidistant from two given points

2. The locus of points 2 inches from a given line

3. The locus of points less than 3 feet from a given point

4. The locus of the centers of all circles tangent to both sides of a given angle.

5. The locus of points equidistant from ℓ and m and 2 cm from A

6. The locus of points 4 inches from circle Q

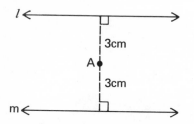

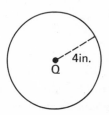

Sketch and describe each locus of points. Show all possible cases.

7. The locus of points equidistant from intersecting lines t and u and x units from P, the point of intersection of t and u

8. The locus of points equidistant from two parallel lines and at a given distance from a given point

Construct.

9. Copy $\triangle XYZ$. Construct the perpendicular bisector of each side.

10. Copy $\triangle MNO$. Inscribe a circle in the triangle

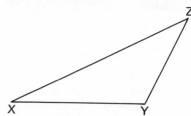

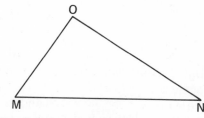

11. Construct a right triangle. Construct the altitude to each side.

12. Draw an acute triangle. Construct the centroid of the triangle.

In $\triangle XYZ$, $\overline{XA}$, $\overline{YB}$, and $\overline{ZC}$ are medians.

13. If $ZC = 24$, find ZQ.
14. If $BQ = x$ and $QY = 4x - 27$, find BY.

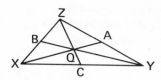

Perform the construction. Then write a proof to justify it.

15. Construction of a line parallel to a given line through a point not on the line

Men of Mathematics

David Hilbert was a German mathematician who exerted a great influence on modern mathematics. Hilbert was born on Jan. 23, 1862 in Königsberg, East Prussia (now Kalingrad USSR). He studied at the University of Königsberg and later taught there until he finally settled at the University of Göttingen. Under his leadership, Göttingen became one of the leading European centers of mathematics.

David Hilbert (1862-1943)

David Hilbert was unhappy with the postulates of Euclid's geometry. There were many inconsistencies and omissions. Hilbert developed a new set of postulates using five primitive terms (point, line, on, between, congruent) and fifteen postulates. Many high school geometry texts today use Hilbert's postulational structure rather than Euclid's.

Hilbert was also an expert in mathematical physics and made contributions to the fields of relativity and the kinetic theory of gasses.

Properties of Inequalities

EXAMPLE 1 Given: $AE > CF$; $EB = FD$
Compare AB and CD.

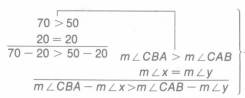

$$AE + EB > CF + FD$$

Thus, $AB > CD$.

EXAMPLE 2 Given: $m\angle CBA > m\angle CAB$
$m\angle x = m\angle y$
Compare $m\angle z$ and $m\angle w$.

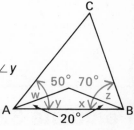

$$
\begin{array}{l}
70 > 50 \\
20 = 20 \\
\hline
70 - 20 > 50 - 20 \\
\end{array}
\qquad
\left.
\begin{array}{l}
m\angle CBA > m\angle CAB \\
m\angle x = m\angle y \\
\hline
m\angle CBA - m\angle x > m\angle CAB - m\angle y
\end{array}
\right\}
\;\rightarrow\;
m\angle CBA - m\angle x > m\angle CAB - m\angle y
$$

Thus, $m\angle z > m\angle w$.

EXAMPLE 3 Given: $\odot O$ with $AB < CD$,
E bisects AB,
F bisects CD.
Compare CF and AE.

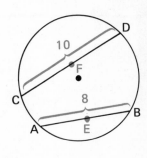

$$
\begin{array}{l}
10 > 8 \\
\frac{1}{2}(10) > \frac{1}{2}(8)
\end{array}
\qquad
\left.
\begin{array}{l}
CD > AB \\
\frac{1}{2}(CD) > \frac{1}{2}(AB)
\end{array}
\right\}
\;\longrightarrow\;
\begin{array}{c}
CD > AB \\
\frac{1}{2}(CD) > \frac{1}{2}(AB)
\end{array}
$$

$$
\left.
\begin{array}{l}
F \text{ bisects } \overline{CD}. \\
CF = \frac{1}{2}(CD)
\end{array}
\quad
\begin{array}{l}
E \text{ bisects } \overline{AB}. \\
AE = \frac{1}{2}(AB)
\end{array}
\right\}
\;\longrightarrow\;
\textbf{Thus, } CF > AE.
$$

Postulate 28	If $a > b$ and $c = d$, then $a + c > b + d$.
Postulate 29	If $a > b$ and $c = d$, then $a - c > b - d$.
Postulate 30	If $a > b$ and $c > 0$, then $ac > bc$.
Postulate 31	If $a > b$ and $c > 0$, then $\dfrac{a}{c} > \dfrac{b}{c}$.

EXAMPLE 4

Given: $m \angle x < m \angle z$
Prove: $m \angle ABE < m \angle CBD$

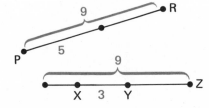

ANALYSIS

$m \angle z > m \angle x$
Add $m \angle y$ to each side and use
Postulate 28.

$\left. \begin{array}{l} m \angle CBD = m \angle z + m \angle y \\ m \angle ABE = m \angle x + m \angle y \end{array} \right\}$

Proof

Statements	Reasons
1. $m \angle x < m \angle z$	1. Given
2. $m \angle z > m \angle x$	2. $a < b$ means $b > a$.
3. $m \angle y = m \angle y$	3. Reflexive prop.
4. $m \angle z + m \angle y > m \angle x + m \angle y$	4. Post. 28
5. $m \angle CBD > m \angle ABE$	5. Substitution
6. $m \angle ABE < m \angle CBD$	6. $a > b$ means $b < a$.

EXAMPLE 5

Given: $PR = XZ$
$PQ > XY$
Compare QR and YZ.

$PR - PQ < XZ - XY$

Thus, $QR < YZ$.

$\left. \begin{array}{ll} 9 = 9 & PR = XZ \\ 5 > 3 & PQ > XY \\ \hline 9 - 5 < 9 - 3 & \overline{PR - PQ < XZ - XY} \end{array} \right\}$

The order reverses.

| Postulate 32 | If $a = b$ and $c > d$, then $a - c < b - d$. |
| | If $a = b$ and $c < d$, then $a - c > b - d$. |

EXAMPLE 6

Given: $m \angle A > m \angle B$
$m \angle B > m \angle C$
Compare $m \angle A$ and $m \angle C$.

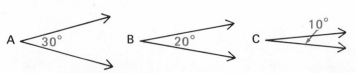

$m \angle A > m \angle C$

If $30 > 20$ and $20 > 10$, then $30 > 10$.

Postulate 33

Transitive Postulate for Inequalities
If $a < b$ and $b < c$, then $a < c$.
If $a > b$ and $b > c$, then $a > c$.

EXAMPLE 7 If $\overline{AB}$ and $\overline{CD}$ are two segments, give the possible relationships between AB and CD.

The length of $\overline{AB}$ may be less than, equal to, or greater than the length of $\overline{CD}$. $\Big\} \rightarrow$ $\quad AB < CD$ or $AB = CD$ or $AB > CD$

Postulate 34

Trichotomy Postulate
For any two numbers a and b,
$a < b$ or $a = b$ or $a > b$.

EXERCISES

PART A

Write an inequality to show each comparison. Give the postulate that applies.

1. Given: $AB > CD$
Compare AC and BD.

2. Given: $RS < PQ$
M is the midpoint of $\overline{RS}$.
N is the midpoint of $\overline{PQ}$.
Compare RM and PN.

3. Given: $m \angle AEC > m \angle BED$
Compare $m \angle x$ and $m \angle z$.

4. Given: $\angle x$ and $\angle y$
Give the possible relationships between $m \angle x$ and $m \angle y$.

5. Given: $AB < BC$ and
$BC < CD$
Compare AB and CD.

6. Given: $EF = GH$ and
$EX < GY$
Compare XF and YH.

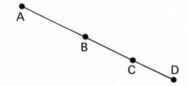
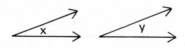
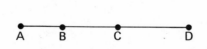

7. Given: $m \angle ABC = m \angle BCD$
$m \angle x > m \angle y$
Compare $m \angle z$ and $m \angle w$.

8. Given: $m \angle x = m \angle y$ and
$m \angle w < m \angle z$
Compare $m \angle ABC$ and
$m \angle ADC$.

9. Given: $AE < FC$ and
$EB = EF$
Compare AB and BC.

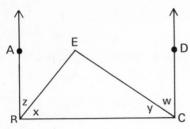

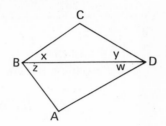

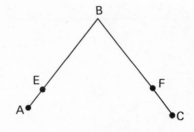

PART B

10. Given: $\overline{AB} \cong \overline{BC}$ and
$m \angle DAC < m \angle DCA$
Prove: $m \angle BCD >$
$m \angle BAD$

11. Given: $\overline{AC} \cong \overline{CB}$ and
$m \angle x > m \angle y$
Prove: $m \angle z > m \angle w$

12. Given: $\odot O$ with $AB > CD$,
$\overline{OE} \perp \overline{AB}, \overline{OF} \perp \overline{CD}$
Prove: $CF < AE$

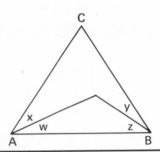

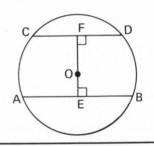

Algebra Review

Adding the same number to each side of a true
inequality does not reverse the order.
Dividing each side of a true inequality by the same
positive number does not reverse the order.

EXAMPLE   Find the solution set of $4x - 5 < 19$.

$$4x - 5 < 19$$

Add 5 to each side. ————————→ $4x < 24$

Divide each side by 4. ————————→ $x < 6$

Thus, the solution set is $\{x \mid x < 6\}$.

Find the solution set.

1. $5x + 2 > -8$ **2.** $9z - 8 < -17$ **3.** $3x - 7 > -8$ **4.** $7x - 18 < -7$

5. $3x - 11 < 7$ **6.** $4x + 8 > -16$ **7.** $8z + 8 > 8$ **8.** $4x - 4 < 12$

9. $2y + 13 > 7$ **10.** $7x - 24 < -3$ **11.** $3z - 18 > -6$ **12.** $5y - 17 < 3$

The Triangle Inequality

OBJECTIVES
■ To determine if a triangle can be constructed with sides having given measures
■ To apply the Triangle Inequality Theorem

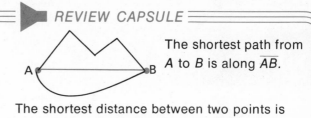

REVIEW CAPSULE

The shortest path from A to B is along $\overline{AB}$.

The shortest distance between two points is the length of the segment joining them.

EXAMPLE 1 Can a triangle be constructed with segments 8 inches, 5 inches, and 2 inches long?

Use the longest segment as a base.

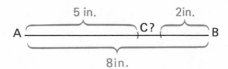

$5 + 2 < 8$ ─────────→ No. The 5-inch and the 2-inch segments will never meet to form the third vertex C.

EXAMPLE 2 Can a triangle be constructed with segments 14 cm, 9 cm, and 5 cm long?

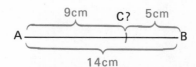

$9 + 5 = 14$ ─────────→ No. The 9-cm and the 5-cm segments meet on $\overline{AB}$, so the third vertex, C, will lie on $\overline{AB}$.

EXAMPLE 3 Can a triangle be constructed with segments 2 feet, 3 feet, and 4 feet long?

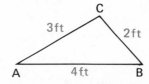

$2 + 3 > 4$ ─────────→ Yes. The 2-foot and the 3-foot segments meet at a point not on $\overline{AB}$ to form the third vertex C.

Theorem 14.1

If three segments have lengths such that the sum of any two is greater than the third, then a triangle can be constructed from the segments.

Theorem 14.2

The Triangle Inequality Theorem
In a triangle, the sum of the measures of any two sides is greater than the measure of the third side.

ANALYSIS

Consider the shortest distance between each pair of vertices.

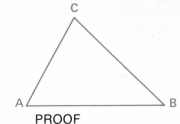

GIVEN
$\triangle ABC$
PROVE
$AC + CB > AB$
$AB + BC > AC$
$AC + AB > BC$

PROOF

STATEMENTS	REASONS
1. AB is the shortest distance from A to B, so $AC + CB > AB$.	1. The shortest distance between two points is the length of the segment joining them.
2. AC is the shortest distance from A to C, so $AB + BC > AC$.	2. Same as 1
3. BC is the shortest distance from B to C, so $AC + AB > BC$.	3. Same as 1

EXAMPLE 4

Can a triangle be constructed with segments 6 inches, 11 inches, and 8 inches long?

Testing only the sum of the two shortest lengths is enough. ⟶

$$6 + 8 > 11$$

Use Theorem 14.1. ⟶ **Thus,** a triangle can be constructed.

EXAMPLE 5

ANALYSIS

By Theorem 14.2
$PN + NO > PO.$

Given: $\odot O$, segments $\overline{PO}$ and $\overline{PN}$, and radius $\overline{NO}$
Prove: $PN > PM$

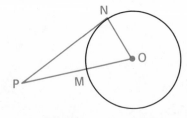

Proof

Statements	Reasons
1. $PN + NO > PO$	1. Triangle Inequality (Th. 14.2)
2. $PN + NO > PM + MO$	2. Segment addition postulate, substitution
3. $NO = MO$	3. Radii of the same $\odot$ are $\cong$.
4. $PN > PM$	4. If $a > b$ and $c = d$, $a - c > b - d$.

M is between P and O.
Replace PO with $PM + MO$. ⟶ (for statement 2)

Subtract NO and MO from 2. ⟶ (for statement 4)

476   THE TRIANGLE INEQUALITY

EXAMPLE 6

Given: $MN < QR$
$NP < RS$
Compare MP and QS.

$$2 < 3$$
$$\underline{5 < 8}$$
$$2 + 5 < 3 + 8$$

$$MN < QR$$
$$\underline{NP < RS}$$
$$MN + NP < QR + RS$$

$$MN + NP < QR + RS$$

Thus, $MP < QS.$

Postulate 35

If $a < b$ and $c < d$, then $a + c < b + d$.
If $a > b$ and $c > d$, then $a + c > b + d$.

ORAL EXERCISES

Tell whether a triangle can be constructed with segments having these measures.

1. 7, 12, 20   **2.** 6, 8, 10   **3.** 8, 11, 19
4. 4 ft., 6 ft., 1 ft.   **5.** 12 cm, 9 cm, 4 cm   **6.** 16 in., 11 in., 6 in.
7. $1\frac{1}{2}$, $2\frac{1}{2}$, $3\frac{1}{2}$ **8.** 8.2 m, 6.1 m, 2.1 m   **9.** 6 in., 9 in., 1 ft.

EXERCISES

PART A

Explain why each of the following is true.

1. People often cut across vacant lots rather than go around a corner.

2. The measure of a diagonal of a rectangle is less than the sum of the measures of two adjacent sides.

3. If two sides of a triangle have measures 5 and 7, then the measure of the third side is between 0 and 12.

4. The difference between the measures of two sides of a triangle is less than the measure of the third side.

5. Given: $ED = EC$
Prove: $AB + AD > BC$

6. Given: $\triangle ABC$ with
D between A and B
Prove: $2(CD) < AB + BC + CA$

7. Given: Quadrilateral $ABCD$
Prove: $AB + BC + CD + DA > AC + BD$

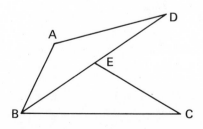

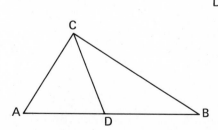

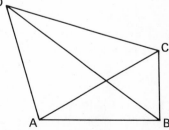

PART B

8. Given: Quadrilateral *ABCD*
Prove: $AB + AD > DC - CB$

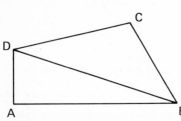

9. Given: $\triangle ABC$ with
P in the interior
Prove: $AP + BP + CP > \frac{1}{2}(AB + BC + CA)$

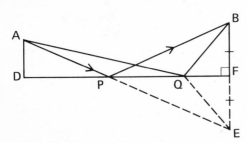

10. Given: $\triangle ABC$ with
D in the interior
Prove: $AC + CB > AD + DB$

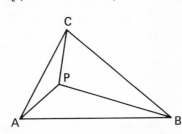

PART C

11. Light reflected from a mirror surface *DF* from point *A* to point *B* will take the path *APB*. Show that path *APB* is shorter than any other path, say path *AQB*.

12. Prove that the length of a median of a triangle is less than $\frac{1}{2}$ the sum of the lengths of the two adjacent sides.
[Hint: Extend median $\overline{CD}$ to *E* so that $CD = DE$. Draw $\overline{AE}$ and $\overline{BE}$. Compare *CE* with $CB + BE$. Prove $AC = BE$.]

Algebra Review

<table>
<tr><td>

OBJECTIVE
■ To solve an inequality like $x + 8 < 3x - 4$

</td><td>

Multiplying or dividing each side of a true inequality by the same negative number reverses the order.

</td></tr>
</table>

EXAMPLE   Solve $2x + 5 > 8x + 23$.

$$2x + 5 > 8x + 23$$

Add -5 to each side. $\longrightarrow$ $\quad 2x > 8x + 18$
Add $-8x$ to each side. $\longrightarrow$ $\quad -6x > 18$
Divide each side by -6. $\longrightarrow$ $\quad x < -3$

Solve.

1. $2z + 8 < 8z - 88$
2. $x + 15 > 2x + 10$
3. $9x - 4 > 17x + 28$
4. $2 + x < 5x - 38$
5. $55 + 5x > 12x - 8$
6. $-3x - 8 < 6 + 4x$

Inequalities in Scalene Triangles

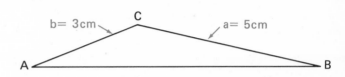

▶ REVIEW CAPSULE

$m \angle x = m \angle A + m \angle C$
So, $m \angle x > m \angle A$
and $m \angle x > m \angle C$

An exterior angle of a triangle has greater measure than either opposite interior angle.

EXAMPLE 1   In the triangle below, $a > b$. Compare $m \angle A$ and $m \angle B$. Measure, if necessary.

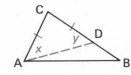

b= 3cm   C   a= 5cm

A   B

Thus, $m \angle A > m \angle B$.

Theorem 14.3

If two sides of a triangle are unequal in measure, then the angle opposite the longer side has the greater measure.

ANALYSIS
Construct isos. $\triangle ACD$.
Then, $m \angle x = m \angle y$,
$m \angle BAC > m \angle x$, and
$m \angle y > m \angle B$.

GIVEN
$\triangle ABC$ with $BC > AC$
PROVE
$m \angle BAC > m \angle B$

PROOF

STATEMENTS	REASONS
1. On $\overline{CB}$, let $CD = AC$.	1. Postulate 5
2. Draw $\overline{AD}$.	2. Two points are contained in exactly one line.
3. $m \angle x = m \angle y$	3. Base $\angle$'s of an isos. $\triangle$ are $\cong$.
4. $m \angle BAC > m \angle x$	4. Angle addition postulate
5. $m \angle BAC > m \angle y$	5. Substitution
6. $m \angle y > m \angle B$	6. An exterior $\angle$ of a $\triangle$ has greater measure than either opp. int. $\angle$.
7. $m \angle BAC > m \angle B$	7. Trans. post. for inequalities

EXAMPLE 2 For △ABC, list the angle measures in order from largest to smallest.

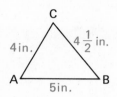

By Th. 14.3, ∠s opp. longer sides have greater measure. ⟶

$AB > BC > AC$
Thus, $m\angle C > m\angle A > m\angle B$.

EXAMPLE 3 In the triangle below, $m\angle B > m\angle A$. Compare AC and BC. Measure, if necessary.

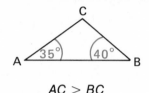

This example leads to the theorem below (Converse of Th. 14.3).

$AC > BC$

Theorem **14.4**

If two angles of a triangle are unequal in measure, then the side opposite the angle with greater measure is the longer side.

ANALYSIS
Use an indirect proof. By Post. 34, $BC < AC$, or $BC = AC$, or $BC > AC$. Show the first two possibilities lead to contradictions.

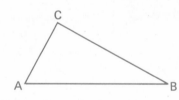

GIVEN
△ABC with
$m\angle A > m\angle B$
PROVE
$BC > AC$

EXAMPLE 4

ANALYSIS
Show $m\angle z > m\angle x$.
Then use Th. 14.4.

∠z is an ext. ∠ of △DBC. Thus, $m\angle z > m\angle y$.

Given: △ABC with $\overline{CD}$ bisecting ∠ACB.
Prove: $AC > AD$

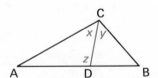

Proof

Statements	Reasons
1. $\overline{CD}$ bisects ∠ACB	1. Given
2. $m\angle x = m\angle y$	2. Def. of ∠ bisector
3. $m\angle z > m\angle y$	3. Ext. ∠ of a △ > either opp. int. ∠.
4. $m\angle z > m\angle x$	4. Substitution
5. $AC > AD$	5. Sides opp. greater ∠'s are longer. (Th. 14.4)

ORAL EXERCISES

List the angles, according to their measures, from largest to smallest.

1.

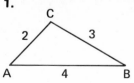

2.

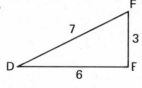

List the sides, according to their measures, from largest to smallest.

3.

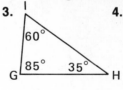

4.

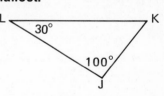

EXERCISES

PART A

1. Given: Equilateral $\triangle ABC$
Prove: $DB > DC$

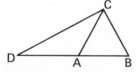

2. Given: $\angle ABC$ is obtuse.
Prove: $AC > AB$ and $AC > BC$

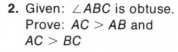

3. Given: $\triangle ABC$ with $BC > AC$ and $m\angle C > m\angle A$
Prove: $m\angle C > m\angle B$

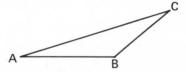

4. Given: $EB > AE$ and $CD > BC$
Prove: $m\angle A > m\angle D$

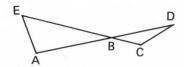

5. Given: $AC > CB$,
$\overrightarrow{AD}$ bisects $\angle CAB$,
$\overrightarrow{BD}$ bisects $\angle ABC$.
Prove: $AD > DB$

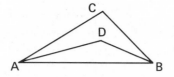

6. Given: $\triangle BAC$ with
$m\angle A < m\angle B$ and
$CD < CB$
Prove: $m\angle A < m\angle CDA$

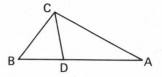

PART B

7. Given: $m\angle A > m\angle C$
Prove: $DC > DB$

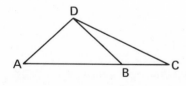

8. Given: $DB > AC$ and
$\overrightarrow{AD}$ bisects $\angle CAB$.
Prove: $DB > DC$

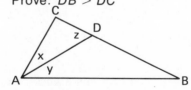

9. Given: $AC = CB$ and
$DB > DA$
Prove: $m\angle w < m\angle z$

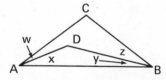

The Hinge Theorem

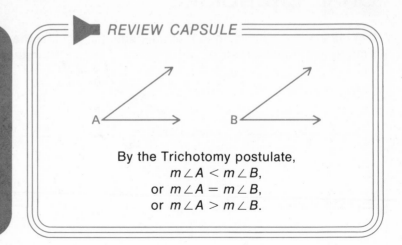

EXAMPLE 1   Two sticks are hinged together and connected with an elastic band. What happens to the elastic band as the sticks are opened wider and wider?

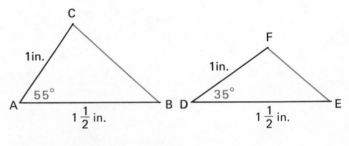

The elastic band will stretch to a greater length.

EXAMPLE 2   In the triangles below, $AC = DF$, $AB = DE$, and $m \angle A > m \angle D$. Compare CB and FE.

Compare the elastic models in Example 1.

$$CB > FE$$

Examples 1 and 2 suggest the next theorem.

The Hinge Theorem

If two sides of one triangle are congruent, respectively, to two sides of another triangle, and the included angle of the first triangle has a greater measure than the included angle of the second triangle, then the third side of the first triangle has a greater measure than the third side of the second triangle.

ANALYSIS

Construct $\triangle ACG \cong \triangle DFE$.
Let $\overrightarrow{CH}$ bisect $\angle GCB$.
$AH + HG > AG$
Prove $\triangle GCH \cong \triangle BCH$
and substitute
to show $AB > AG$.

GIVEN

$\triangle$'s ABC and DEF, $\overline{AC} \cong \overline{DF}$,
$\overline{CB} \cong \overline{FE}$, $m \angle ACB > m \angle F$.

PROVE

$AB > DE$

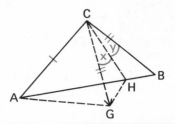
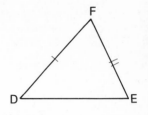

EXAMPLE 3 C is the midpoint of $\overline{AD}$ and $\overline{AB} \cong \overline{DE}$. Compare CE and BC.

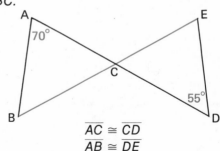

C is the midpoint. ──────────→ $\overline{AC} \cong \overline{CD}$

                                      $\overline{AB} \cong \overline{DE}$

$70 > 55$ ──────────────→ $m \angle A > m \angle D$

Use Theorem 14.5. ──────────→   So, $BC > CE$.

$a > b$ means $b < a$. ──────────→ **Thus,** $CE < BC$.

EXAMPLE 4

ANALYSIS

Use $\triangle ADC$ and $\triangle DBC$.
Apply Theorem 14.5.

Given: $\square ABCD$ with
            $m \angle ADC > m \angle DCB$
Prove: $AC > BD$

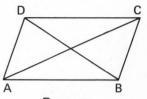

Proof

Statements	Reasons
1. $ABCD$ is a $\square$.	1. Given
2. $\overline{AD} \cong \overline{BC}$	2. Opp. sides of a $\square$ are $\cong$.
3. $\overline{DC} \cong \overline{DC}$	3. Reflexive property
4. $m \angle ADC > m \angle DCB$	4. Given
5. $AC > BD$	5. Theorem 14.5

Theorem 14.6

If two sides of one triangle are congruent, respectively, to two sides of another triangle, and the third side of the first has a greater measure than the third side of the second, then the angle opposite the third side of the first triangle has a greater measure than the angle opposite the third side of the second triangle.

ANALYSIS

Use an indirect proof. Either $m\angle C < m\angle F$, or $m\angle C = m\angle F$, or $m\angle C > m\angle F$. Show that the first two cases lead to contradictions.

GIVEN

$\triangle$'s ABC and DEF, $\overline{AC} \cong \overline{DF}$, $\overline{CB} \cong \overline{FE}$, $AB > DE$

PROVE

$m\angle C > m\angle F$

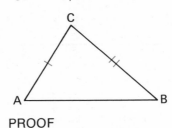
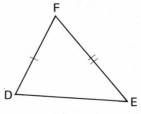

PROOF

STATEMENTS	REASONS
1. $m\angle C < m\angle F$ or $m\angle C = m\angle F$ or $m\angle C > m\angle F$	1. Trichotomy postulate
2. If $m\angle C < m\angle F$, then $AB < DE$.	2. Theorem 14.5
3. Thus, $m\angle C$ is *not* $< m\angle F$.	3. Given: $AB > DE$
4. If $m\angle C = m\angle F$, then $\triangle ABC \cong \triangle DEF$.	4. SAS for $\cong$ $\triangle$'s
5. Then $AB = DE$	5. Corr. parts of $\cong$ $\triangle$'s are $\cong$.
6. Thus, $m\angle C \neq m\angle F$	6. Given: $AB > DE$
7. $\therefore m\angle C > m\angle F$	7. Steps 1, 3, and 6

EXAMPLE 5

ANALYSIS

In $\triangle AMD$ and $\triangle BME$, show that $m\angle A > m\angle B$, Then use Th. 14.4.

Use $\triangle ACB$. ———————————→

Given: $\triangle ABC$ with M the midpoint of $\overline{AB}$, $\overline{AD} \cong \overline{BE}$, and $DM > EM$
Prove: $BC > AC$

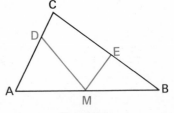

Proof

Statements	Reasons
1. M is the midpoint of $\overline{AB}$.	1. Given
2. $\overline{AM} \cong \overline{MB}$	2. Def. of midpoint
3. $\overline{AD} \cong \overline{BE}$	3. Given
4. $DM > EM$	4. Given
5. $m\angle A > m\angle B$	5. Theorem 14.6
6. $BC > AC$	6. In a $\triangle$, the longer side is opp. the angle with greater measure.

ORAL EXERCISES

Compare the measures.

1. *BC* and *CD*   **2.** *m ∠ x* and *m ∠ y*   **3.** *AD* and *DC*   **4.** *m ∠ w* and *m ∠ z*

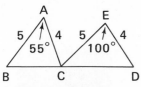
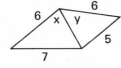
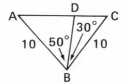

EXERCISES

PART A

1. Given: *AD = CD* and
AB > CB
Prove: *m ∠ ADB >*
m ∠ CDB

2. Given: *AC = BC* and
m ∠ ACD > m ∠ DCB
Prove: *AD > DB*

3. Given: ▱*ABCD* with
m ∠ BAD > m ∠ ADC
Prove: *BD > AC*

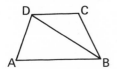

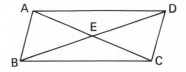

4. Given: *CD* is a median
to *AB* and *CB < CA*.
Prove: *m ∠ y < m ∠ x*

5. Given: ⊙*O* with
AB > CD
Prove: *m ∠ x > m ∠ y*

6. Given: *AB = DC*, $\overline{AB} \parallel \overline{DC}$,
m ∠ AED < m ∠ DEC
Prove: *AD < DC*

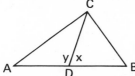

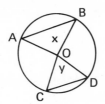

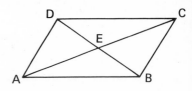

PART B

7. Given: *M* is the midpoint
of $\overline{AB}$, *AD = EB*,
MD < ME.
Prove: *AC > CB*

8. Given: *AD = EB* and
DB > AE
Prove: *CB > CA*

PART C

9. Given: *m ∠ x = m ∠ y*
and *BC > AB*
Prove: *m ∠ BDC >*
m ∠ BDA

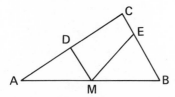

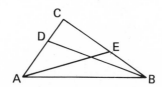

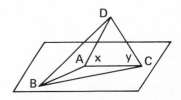

Mathematics in Biology

A biologist at a chlorodometer is determining the amount of chloride ions in a blood sample.

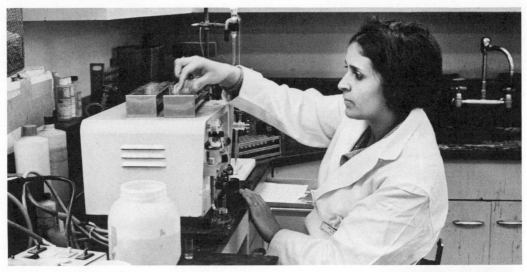

Pictured is a model of a DNA Molecule.
According to one three-dimensional model, the molecule consists of a double chain of particles which are parallel to one another and arranged in a spiral. Such models help advance the science of genetics which uses the branch of mathematics called *probability*.

Inequalities in Circles

OBJECTIVE

■ To apply inequality relationships to circles

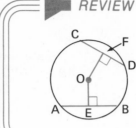

If $\overline{AB} \cong \overline{CD}$, then $OE = OF$.

In a circle, congruent chords are equidistant from the center.

EXAMPLE 1

In circle O, $CD > AB$.
Compare OF and OE.
Measure, if necessary.

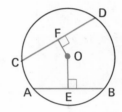

$OF < OE$

Example 1 suggests this. ⌐→

Theorem 14.7

If two chords of a circle are unequal in measure, then the longer chord is nearer the center.

ANALYSIS

Suppose the two chords have a common endpoint. (If not, construct chords $\cong$ to the given ones which do have a common endpoint.) Use $\triangle OEF$ and $\triangle BEF$.

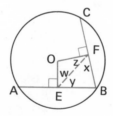

GIVEN
$\odot O$ with $AB > BC$
$\overline{OF} \perp \overline{BC}$ and $\overline{OE} \perp \overline{AB}$
PROVE
$OE < OF$

PROOF

STATEMENTS	REASONS
1. Draw $\overline{EF}$.	1. Two points are contained in exactly one line.
2. $\overline{OE} \perp \overline{AB}$, $\overline{OF} \perp \overline{BC}$	2. Given
3. $EB = \frac{1}{2}(AB)$; $BF = \frac{1}{2}(BC)$	3. A radius $\perp$ to a chord bisects the chord.
4. $AB > BC$	4. Given
5. $EB > BF$	5. If $a > b$, then $\frac{1}{2}a > \frac{1}{2}b$.
6. $m\angle x > m\angle y$	6. Theorem 14.3
7. $\angle OEB$ and $\angle OFB$ are rt. $\angle$'s	7. Def. of $\perp$ segments
8. $m\angle OEB = m\angle OFB$	8. All rt. $\angle$'s are $\cong$.
9. $m\angle z < m\angle w$	9. If $a = b$ and $c > d$, then $a - c < b - d$.
10. $OE < OF$	10. In a $\triangle$, sides opp. larger $\angle$'s are longer. (Use $\triangle OEF$.)

EXAMPLE 2

Given: $\odot O$ with $AB > CD$,
$\overline{OE} \perp \overline{AB}$, $\overline{OF} \perp \overline{CD}$, and $\overline{EB} \cong \overline{BF}$
Prove: $m \angle x > m \angle y$

ANALYSIS
Use $\triangle OEB$ and $\triangle OFB$.
Apply Theorem 14.6.

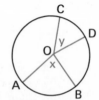

Proof

Statements	Reasons
1. $AB > CD$, $\overline{OE} \perp \overline{AB}$, and $\overline{OF} \perp \overline{CD}$	1. Given
2. $OE < OF$	2. Theorem 14.7
3. $OF > OE$	3. $a < b$ means $b > a$.
4. $\overline{EB} \cong \overline{BF}$	4. Given
5. $\overline{OB} \cong \overline{OB}$	5. Reflexive property
6. $m \angle x > m \angle y$	6. Theorem 14.6

Use $\triangle OEB$ and $\triangle OFB$. ⟶ 6.

Theorem 14.8

If two chords of a circle are unequally distant from the center, then the chord nearer the center is the longer chord.

EXAMPLE 3

Given: $\odot O$ with $\overline{OE} \perp \overline{AB}$,
$\overline{OF} \perp \overline{CD}$, and $OF < OE$
Prove: $m \angle COD > m \angle AOB$

ANALYSIS
Use $\triangle COD$ and $\triangle AOB$.
Apply Theorem 14.6.

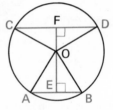

Proof

Statements	Reasons
1. $\overline{OE} \perp \overline{AB}$, $\overline{OF} \perp \overline{CD}$, $OF < OE$	1. Given
2. $CD > AB$	2. Theorem 14.8
3. $\overline{OA} \cong \overline{OC}$; $\overline{OB} \cong \overline{OD}$	3. Radii of the same $\odot$ are $\cong$.
4. $m \angle COD > m \angle AOB$	4. Theorem 14.6

EXAMPLE 4

ANALYSIS
$m \angle x = m\overarc{AB}$
$m \angle y = m\overarc{CD}$
Use substitution.

Given: $\odot O$ with $m \angle x > m \angle y$
Prove: $m\overarc{AB} > m\overarc{CD}$

Proof

Statements	Reasons
1. $m \angle x > m \angle y$	1. Given
2. $m \angle x = m\overarc{AB}$ $m \angle y = m\overarc{CD}$	2. A minor arc is measured by its central angle.
3. $m\overarc{AB} > m\overarc{CD}$	3. Substitution

ORAL EXERCISES

Compare the measures.

1.

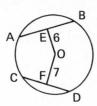

AB and CD,
FD and EB

2.

AO and CO,
m$\widehat{AB}$ and m$\widehat{BC}$

3.

OP and OR,
PN and NR

4.

RS and TU,
WT and VS

EXERCISES

PART A

1. Given: ⊙O with $\overline{OE} \perp \overline{AB}$, $\overline{OF} \perp \overline{CD}$, $m\angle COD <$ $m\angle AOB$
Prove: $OF > OE$

2. Given: ⊙O with $\overline{OE} \perp \overline{AB}$, $\overline{OF} \perp \overline{CD}$, $m\angle x > m\angle y$, $\overline{AE} \cong \overline{AF}$
Prove: $AB > CD$

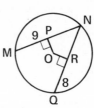

3. Given: ⊙O with m$\widehat{AB}$ < m$\widehat{CD}$
Prove: $m\angle x < m\angle y$

4. Given: ⊙O with $\overline{OE} \perp \overline{AB}$, $\overline{OF} \perp \overline{BC}$, $AE > BF$
Prove: $OE < OF$

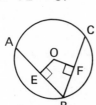

5. Given: ⊙O with $m\angle B > m\angle A$
Prove: m$\widehat{AC}$ > m$\widehat{BC}$

6. Given: ⊙O with $\overline{OE} \perp \overline{AB}$ and $\overline{OF} \perp \overline{CD}$
Prove: $AB < CD$

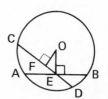

PART B

7. Prove that if two noncongruent chords (not diameters) intersect on a circle, the longer chord makes the angle of smaller measure with the diameter through the point of intersection.

8. Prove that if a square and an equilateral triangle are inscribed in the same circle, the apothem of the square is longer than the apothem of the triangle.

Chapter Fourteen Review

Write an inequality to show each comparison. Give the postulate which applies. [p. 471]

1. Given: $AC > BD$
Compare AB and CD.

2. Given: $m \angle x < m \angle y$
and $m \angle y < m \angle z$
Compare $m \angle x$ and $m \angle z$.

3. Given: $EF > GH$
M is the midpoint of $\overline{EF}$.
N is the midpoint of $\overline{GH}$.
Compare EM and NH.

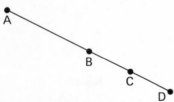

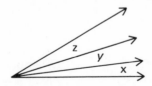

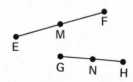

Determine whether a triangle can be constructed with segments having these measures.

4. 6, 8, 10   **5.** 5 ft, 2 ft, 7 ft   **6.** 3 in., 1 in., 5 in.   [p. 475]

List the angles, according to their measures, from largest to smallest. [p. 479]

7.

8.

9.

10.
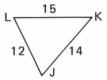

List the sides, according to their measures, from largest to smallest. [p. 479]

11.

12.
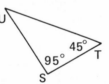

13.

14.
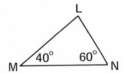

Compare the measures. [p. 482, 487]

15. AB and BC **16.** $m \angle x$ and $m \angle y$ **17.** AB and CD **18.** $m\overset{\frown}{RS}$ and $m\overset{\frown}{ST}$

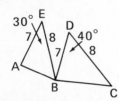

19. Given: Quadrilateral $ABCD$
Prove: $AC + BD <$
$AB + BC + CD + DA$
[p. 475]

20. Given: $\triangle ABC$ with $m \angle B$
$< m \angle A$ and $CD < CA$
Prove: $m \angle B < m \angle CDB$
[p. 482]

21. Given: $\odot O$ with $\overline{OE} \perp \overline{AB}$,
$\overline{OF} \perp \overline{CD}$, $AE < CF$
Prove: $OE > OF$ [p. 487]

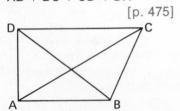

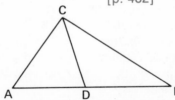

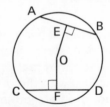

Chapter Fourteen Test

Write an inequality to show each comparison. Give the postulate which applies.

1. Given: $m \angle x > m \angle y$
Compare $m \angle ABD$ and $m \angle CBE$.

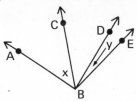

2. Given: $AB = CD$, $AE < CF$
Compare EB and FD.

Tell whether a triangle can be constructed with segments having these measures.

3. 2 ft, 4 ft, 6 ft

4. 5, 2, 4

List the angles, according to their measures, from largest to smallest.

5.

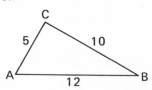

6.

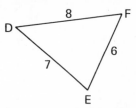

List the sides, according to their measures, from largest to smallest.

7.

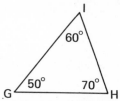

8.

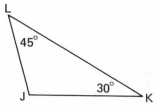

Compare the measures.

9. $m \angle x$ and $m \angle y$

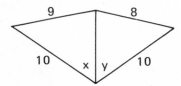

10. OF and OE if $AB = 8$ and $BD = 10$

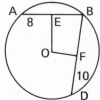

11. Given: $AC < CB$, $\overrightarrow{AE}$ bisects $\angle CAB$,
$\overrightarrow{BE}$ bisects $\angle ABC$.
Prove: $AE < EB$

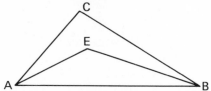

12. Given: $\square ABCD$ with $m \angle BAD < m \angle ADC$
Prove: $BD < AC$

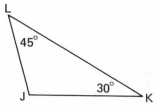

Regular Polyhedrons

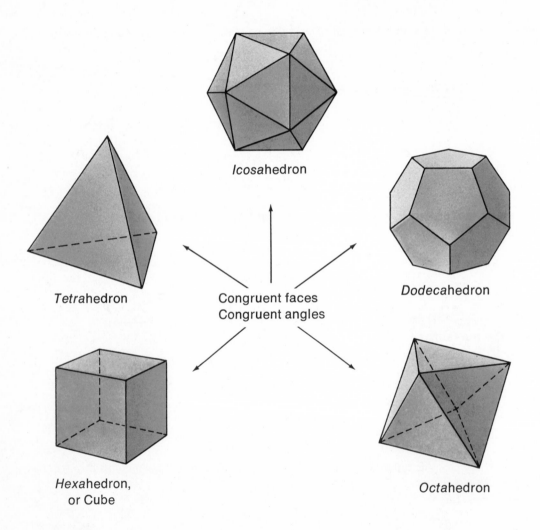

Icosahedron

Tetrahedron

Dodecahedron

Congruent faces
Congruent angles

Hexahedron,
or Cube

Octahedron

For each polyhedron, count the number of faces (F), edges (E), and vertices (V). Find a formula relating F, E, and V.

Space Figures — Prisms

▶ *REVIEW CAPSULE*

Space Figures

Space figures contain points of more than one plane.

Prisms

A prism is a type of space figure.

EXAMPLE 1 A prism has two *bases*. The bases of a triangular prism are congruent *triangular regions*. Give the type of base of each of these prisms.

bases

See sketches above.

                       Answers

Quadrangular prism	Quadrilateral regions
Pentagonal prism	Pentagonal regions
Hexagonal prism	Hexagonal regions

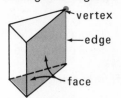
vertex
edge
face

EXAMPLE 2 A triangular prism has 9 *edges*, 5 *faces*, and 6 *vertices*. Give the number of edges, faces, and vertices for each of these prisms.

The bases of a prism are two of its faces.

Answers

	Edges	Faces	Vertices
Quadrangular prism	12	6	8
Pentagonal prism	15	7	10
Hexagonal prism	18	8	12

EXAMPLE 3 A triangular prism has three lateral edges and three lateral faces. Give the number of lateral edges and lateral faces for each of these prisms.

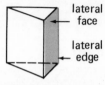
lateral face

lateral edge

Answers

	Lateral edges	Lateral faces
Quadrangular prism	4	4
Pentagonal prism	5	5
Hexagonal prism	6	6

The lateral faces of a right prism are rectangular regions.

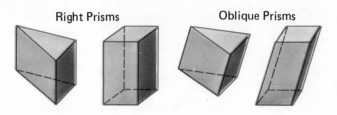

Right Prisms   Oblique Prisms

The lateral edges are ⊥ to the bases. ⟶ In a right prism, each lateral edge is an altitude of the prism.

EXAMPLE 4 Sketch a right pentagonal prism.

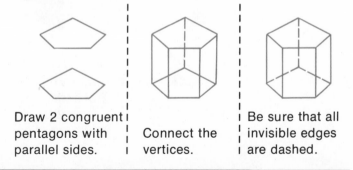

Draw 2 congruent pentagons with parallel sides.

Connect the vertices.

Be sure that all invisible edges are dashed.

ORAL EXERCISES

1. Explain the difference between a plane figure and a space figure.

2. Name five plane figures. Name five space figures.

Identify each figure as completely as you can.

3.

4.

5.

6.

7.

8.

EXERCISES

Copy and complete the chart.

	Type of Prism	Sketch	No. of Lateral Edges	No. of Edges	No. of Vertices	No. of Bases	No. of Lateral Faces	No. of Faces	Type of Base
1.	Quadrangular				8				
2.	Pentagonal		5					7	
3.	Hexagonal					2			
4.	Octagonal			24					octagonal region
5.	Decagonal						10		

Sketch each of the following.

6. A right triangular prism whose bases are right triangles
7. A right triangular prism whose bases are equilateral triangles
8. A right quadrangular prism whose bases are rectangles (a rectangular solid)
9. A rectangular solid with all edges congruent (a cube)
10. A right hexagonal prism
11. An oblique pentagonal prism

PART B

True or false? Refer to the chart above.

12. A prism has as many base edges as lateral edges.
13. A prism has twice as many vertices as lateral faces.
14. A prism has two more lateral edges than faces.
15. A prism has the same number of lateral faces and lateral edges.
16. In a prism, the ratio of the number of vertices to the number of edges is $2:3$.
17. A hexagonal prism has twice as many edges as a triangular prism.

PART C

18. Let V be the number of vertices, F be the number of faces, and E be the number of edges of a prism. What relationship exists between V, F, and E?
19. Suppose a prism has n lateral faces. Represent V, F, and E in terms of n and prove what you discovered in Exercise 18.

Surface Areas of Prisms

OBJECTIVE

■ To find the lateral area and the total area of a prism

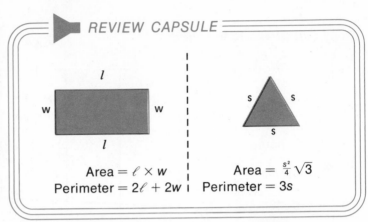

$$\text{Area} = \ell \times w$$
$$\text{Perimeter} = 2\ell + 2w$$

$$\text{Area} = \tfrac{s^2}{4}\sqrt{3}$$
$$\text{Perimeter} = 3s$$

EXAMPLE 1

Lateral area = sum of areas of lateral faces.

Find the lateral area of the right triangular prism shown.

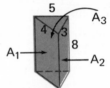

First Method	Second Method
Each lateral face is a rectangle. Find the three areas, A_1, A_2, and A_3.	"Unfold" the lateral faces. A large rectangle is formed.

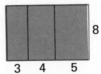

Formula for area of a rectangle ⟶ $A = \ell \times w$

$A_1 = 4 \times 8 \;\;= 32$

$A_2 = 3 \times 8 \;\;= 24$

$A_3 = 5 \times 8 \;\;= \underline{40}$

Add the three areas to get the lateral area. ⟶ $A_1 + A_2 + A_3 = 96$

The lateral area (L) is the area of the large rectangle.

$$L = \ell \times w$$
$$= \binom{\text{perimeter}}{\text{of base}} \times \binom{\text{length of}}{\substack{\text{altitude} \\ \text{of prism}}}$$
$$= (3 + 4 + 5) \times \quad (8)$$
$$= \qquad 12 \quad \times \quad 8$$

The second method suggests this.

Thus, the lateral area is 96 square units.

Theorem 15.1

For any right prism, lateral area
= perimeter of base × measure of altitude of prism.
$L = ph$

EXAMPLE 2   Find the lateral area of the
right prism shown.

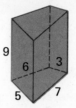

$$L = ph$$
$$= (21)(9)$$
$$= 189$$

$$\left.\begin{array}{l} p = 5 + 7 + 3 + 6 = 21 \\ h = 9 \end{array}\right\} \longrightarrow$$

Thus, the lateral area is 189 sq. units.

EXAMPLE 3   Find the total area of the
rectangular solid shown.

Total area = lateral area + areas of both bases

$$\left.\begin{array}{l} p = 2\ell + 2w \\ \quad = 2(9) + 2(4) \\ \quad = \ \ 18 \ + \ 8 \\ \quad = 26 \\ h = 5 \end{array}\right\} \longrightarrow$$

Lateral area	Area of each base
$L = ph$	$B = \ell w$
$= (26)(5)$	$= (9)(4)$
$= \ \ 130$	$= \ \ 36$

A prism has 2 ≅ bases. $\longrightarrow$

Total area = $130 + 2(36)$, or 202

Thus, the total area is 202 square units.

Theorem 15.2

For any prism,,
total area = lateral area + 2 times base area.
$$T = L + 2B$$

EXAMPLE 4   Find the total area of a right triangular prism whose
altitude measures 5 cm and whose bases are
equilateral triangles with sides measuring 8 cm.

$$T = L + 2B$$

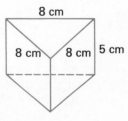

$$\left.\begin{array}{l} p = 3s \\ \quad = 3(8) \\ \quad = 24 \\ h = 5 \end{array}\right\} \longrightarrow$$

$$L = \ ph \qquad B = \frac{s^2}{4}\sqrt{3}$$
$$= (24)(5) \qquad \ = \frac{8^2}{4}\sqrt{3}$$
$$= 120 \qquad\qquad = 16\sqrt{3}$$

$T = L + 2B \longrightarrow T = 120 + 2(16\sqrt{3})$, or $120 + 32\sqrt{3}$

Thus, the total area is $120 + 32\sqrt{3}$ sq cm.

EXERCISES

PART A

Find the lateral area of each right prism.

1.

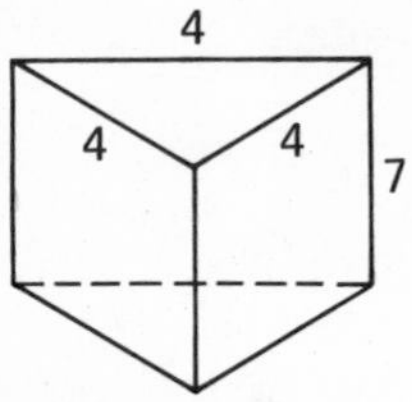

2.

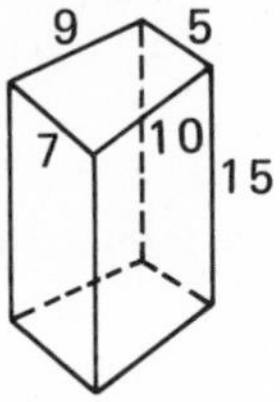

3.

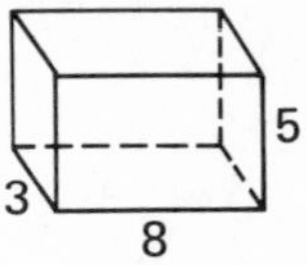

4.

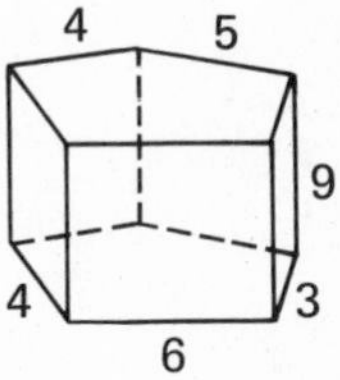

5. A lateral edge of a right prism measures 10 feet and the perimeter of the base is 32 feet. Find the lateral area.

6. Find the total area of a right prism whose base is a square 6 inches on a side and whose altitude measures 9 inches.

7. Find the total area of a right prism whose bases are equilateral triangles with sides measuring 4 cm and whose altitude measures 15 cm.

8. The bases of a prism are regular pentagons with sides measuring 7 feet. The altitude measures 12 feet. Find the lateral area of the prism.

9. Find the total area of a rectangular solid whose dimensions are 6 inches, 8 inches, and 11 inches.

10. How many square yards must be covered to paint the walls and ceiling of a warehouse 120 feet by 96 feet with a 9-foot ceiling?

PART B

11. The altitude of a right prism measures 12 inches, and the base is a right triangle with legs measuring 6 inches and 8 inches. Find the total area.

12. The base of a prism is a rhombus with diagonals measuring 10 feet and 24 feet. The altitude measures 15 feet. Find the lateral area.

13. Find the total area of a prism whose bases are regular hexagons with 8-inch sides and whose altitude measures 16 inches.

14. The total area of a right prism is 210 square cm. The base is a square 5 cm on a side. Find the length of the altitude of the prism.

PART C

15. In a truncated prism, the bases are not parallel. Find the total area of the truncated right prism shown.

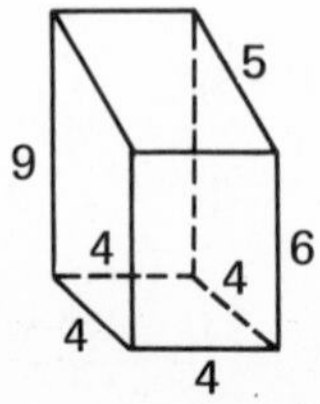

16. A truncated right prism has a square base with 5-foot sides. Two of the lateral edges measure 8 feet and the other two measure 20 feet. Find the lateral area and the total area.

Volumes of Prisms

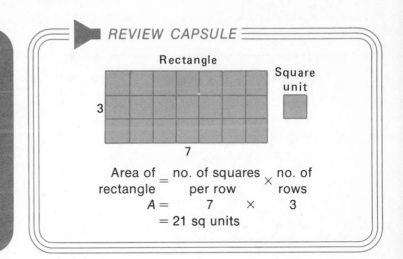

Rectangle

Square unit

3

7

$$\text{Area of rectangle} = \text{no. of squares per row} \times \text{no. of rows}$$
$$A = 7 \times 3$$
$$= 21 \text{ sq units}$$

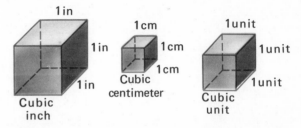

1 in
1 in
1 in
Cubic inch

1 cm
1 cm
1 cm
Cubic centimeter

1 unit
1 unit
1 unit
Cubic unit

A cube is a rectangular solid with
congruent edges.

EXAMPLE 1   Find the number of cubic units in the rectangular
solid below.

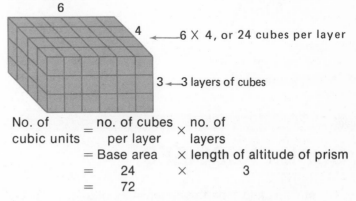

6

4 ⟵ 6 × 4, or 24 cubes per layer

3 ⟵ 3 layers of cubes

$$\text{No. of cubic units} = \text{no. of cubes per layer} \times \text{no. of layers}$$
$$= \text{Base area} \times \text{length of altitude of prism}$$
$$= 24 \times 3$$
$$= 72$$

Thus, the rectangular solid contains 72 cubic units.

Definition of volume ⟶
The volume of the solid in Example 1 is
72 cubic units.

> The *volume* of a solid is the number of cubic
> units in the solid.

<table>
<tr><td>

Theorem | **15.3**

</td><td>

For any prism,
volume = base area × measure of altitude.
$$V = Bh$$

</td></tr>
</table>

EXAMPLE 2   Find the volume of the prism below.

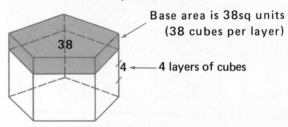

Base area is 38 sq units
(38 cubes per layer)

4 ←——— 4 layers of cubes

$$\text{volume} = \frac{\text{no. of cubes}}{\text{per layer}} \times \left.\frac{\text{no. of}}{\text{layers}}\right\} \longrightarrow$$

Volume = base area × length of altitude
$$V = \quad 38 \quad \times \quad 4$$
$$= 152$$

Thus, the volume is 152 cubic units.

EXAMPLE 3   The bases of a prism are equilateral triangular regions with
each side measuring 4 feet. The
altitude measures 7 feet. Find
the volume of the prism.

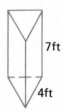

7ft

4ft

$$V = Bh$$

Find the area of the base. ————————→

$$B = \frac{s^2}{4}\sqrt{3} \qquad h = 7$$

$$= \frac{4^2}{4}\sqrt{3}$$

$$= 4\sqrt{3}$$

$28\sqrt{3} \doteq 28(1.73)$, or 48.5 ————————→

$$V = (4\sqrt{3}) \quad \times \quad (7), \text{ or } 28\sqrt{3}$$

Thus, the volume is $28\sqrt{3}$ cubic feet.

ORAL EXERCISES

1. Let ℓ, w, and h be the dimensions of a rectangular solid. Give a formula for the volume.

2. Let s be the length of an edge of a cube. Give a formula for the volume.

Find the volume of each prism. The area of the base (B) and the altitude length (h) are given.

3. $B = 7$ sq cm, $h = 2$ cm

4. $B = 12$ sq ft, $h = 3$ ft

5. $B = 10$ sq in., $h = 14$ in.

6. $B = 8$ sq ft, $h = 8$ ft

7. $B = 9\sqrt{2}$ sq yd, $h = 5$ yd

8. $B = 5\sqrt{3}$ sq m, $h = 4$ m

EXERCISES

Find the volume of each right prism.

1.   **2.**   **3.** 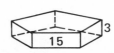 **4.**   **5.**

6. Find the volume of a cube whose edges measure 6 feet.

7. Find the volume of a rectangular solid whose dimensions are 4, 7, and 11.

8. A lateral edge of a right prism measures 5 inches. The area of the base is 32 square inches. Find the volume.

9. Find the volume of a prism whose base is a square 8 cm on a side and whose altitude measures 12 cm.

10. The bases of a prism are equilateral triangles with sides measuring 8 inches. The altitude measures 5 inches. Find the volume.

11. The bases of a prism are isosceles right triangles with legs measuring 10 yards. The altitude measures 16 yards. Find the volume.

12. A room is 18 feet wide, 30 feet long, and 9 feet high. Find its volume in cubic yards.

13. Find the weight of a wooden beam 6 inches by 9 inches by 8 feet if the wood weighs 46 pounds per cubic foot.

PART B

14. The total area of a cube is 384 square feet. Find the volume.

15. The base of a rectangular solid measures 7 by 12. Find the altitude if the volume is 504 cubic units.

16. The altitude of a prism measures 8 cm and the base is a right triangle with one leg measuring 5 cm and the hypotenuse measuring 13 cm. Find the volume.

17. How many bricks 8 inches by 4 inches by 2 inches are needed to build a wall 20 feet long, 6 feet high, and 1 foot thick, if 10 per cent of the wall is mortar?

18. A cistern in the form of a rectangular solid measures 5 feet by 6 feet by 9 feet. How many gallons of water will it hold? [1 cu ft = 7.5 gal]

19. Find the volume of a prism whose bases are regular hexagons with 10-inch sides and whose altitude measures 12 inches.

PART C

20. The volume of a rectangular solid is 432 cubic units. Each side of its square base is $\frac{1}{2}$ the measure of the altitude. Find the area of the base.

21. Each lateral edge of a prism measures 14 cm and makes an angle of 45° with the plane of the base. The area of the base is 62 sq cm. Find the volume.

Inscribed Regular Polyhedrons

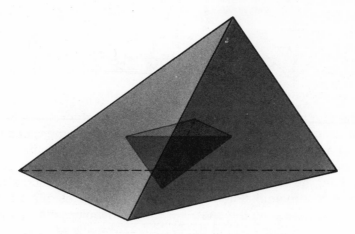

A regular tetrahedron can be *inscribed* in a larger regular tetrahedron. Each vertex of the smaller one will intersect the center of a face of the larger.

Draw a regular octahedron inscribed in a regular hexahedron.

Draw a regular hexahedron inscribed in a regular octahedron.

Draw a regular dodecahedron inscribed in a regular icosahedron.

Complete the chart. Look for a pattern that tells which polygons can be inscribed in each other.

Polygon	Number of Faces	Number of Vertices
Tetrahedron	4	
Hexahedron		8
Octahedron		
Dodecahedron		20
Icosahedron	20	

Cylinders

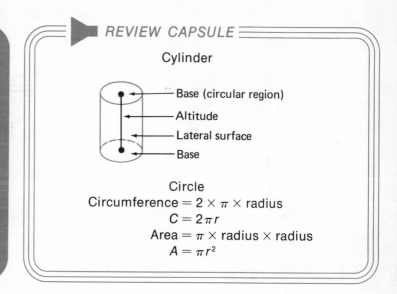

▶ *REVIEW CAPSULE*

Cylinder

Base (circular region)
Altitude
Lateral surface
Base

Circle
Circumference = 2 × π × radius
$C = 2\pi r$
Area = π × radius × radius
$A = \pi r^2$

EXAMPLE 1 The radius of the base of a cylinder is 6 inches long and the altitude is 8 inches long. Find the lateral area.

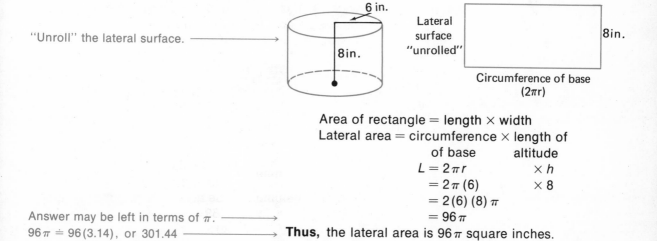

"Unroll" the lateral surface. ⟶

Lateral surface "unrolled"   8 in.

Circumference of base
$(2\pi r)$

Area of rectangle = length × width
Lateral area = circumference × length of
$\qquad\qquad$ of base $\qquad$ altitude
$\qquad\qquad L = 2\pi r \qquad\quad \times h$
$\qquad\qquad\quad = 2\pi(6) \qquad \times 8$
$\qquad\qquad\quad = 2(6)(8)\pi$

Answer may be left in terms of π. ⟶ $\qquad = 96\pi$
$96\pi \doteq 96(3.14)$, or 301.44 ⟶ **Thus,** the lateral area is 96π square inches.

Theorem 15.4

For a cyclinder, lateral area
$\quad$ = circumference of base × measure of altitude.
$L = 2\pi rh$

EXAMPLE 2   Find the total area of the cylinder in Example 1.

Total area = lateral area + areas of both bases
$$T = \quad L \quad + \quad 2B$$

From Example 1 ⟶

$$L = 96\pi \quad \binom{\text{Bases are}}{\text{circles.}} \quad \begin{aligned} B &= \pi r^2 \\ &= 6^2\pi \\ &= 36\pi \end{aligned}$$

$$\begin{aligned} T &= L + 2 \ B \\ &= 96\pi + 2(36\pi) \\ &= 96\pi + 72\pi \end{aligned}$$

Use the distributive property. ⟶
$$\begin{aligned} &= (96 + 72)\pi \\ &= 168\pi \end{aligned}$$

$168\pi \doteq 168(3.14)$, or 527.52 ⟶ **Thus,** the total area is 168π square inches.

Theorem 15.5

For a cylinder,
total area = lateral area + 2 times base area.
$$T = \quad L \quad + 2B$$
$$T = \quad 2\pi rh \quad + 2\pi r^2$$
$$T = 2\pi r(h + r)$$

EXAMPLE 3   A water tank is in the shape of a large cylinder. Its base has an area of 86π square meters, and its altitude measures 5 meters. Find the volume.

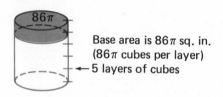

Base area is 86π sq. in.
(86π cubes per layer)
← 5 layers of cubes

A cylinder is like a prism with circular bases. ⟶

$$\text{Volume} = \frac{\text{no. of cubes}}{\text{per layer}} \times \frac{\text{no. of}}{\text{layers}}$$
$$\text{Volume} = \text{base area} \times \text{length of altitude}$$
$$V = \quad 86\pi \quad \times \quad 5$$
$$= 430\pi$$

$430\pi \doteq 430(3.14)$, or $1,350.20$ ⟶ **Thus,** the volume is 430π cubic meters.

Theorem 15.6

For a cylinder
volume = base area × measure of altitude.
$$V = \pi r^2 h$$

---

504   CYLINDERS

EXAMPLE 4   The radius of a base of a cylinder is 3 feet long and the altitude is 7 feet long. Find the lateral area, total area, and volume.

Use the formulas. $\longrightarrow$

$r = 3, h = 7$ $\longrightarrow$

$$L = 2\pi rh \qquad T = 2\pi r(h + r) \qquad V = \pi r^2 h$$
$$= 2(3)(7)\pi \qquad = 2(3)\pi(7 + 3) \qquad = (3^2)(7)\pi$$
$$= 42\pi \qquad\qquad = 6\pi \quad (10) \qquad = (9)(7)\pi$$
$$\qquad\qquad\qquad = 60\pi \qquad\qquad = 63\pi$$

Thus, the lateral area is 42π sq ft,
       the total area is 60π sq ft,
and   the volume is 63π cu ft.

SUMMARY

Formulas for a Cylinder
Lateral area: $L = 2\pi rh$
Total area: $T = 2\pi r(h + r)$
Volume: $V = \pi r^2 h$

EXERCISES

PART A

Find the lateral area, total area, and volume of each cylinder. Leave answers in terms of π.

1.

2.

3.

4.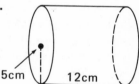

Leave answers in terms of π.

5. A cylindrical oil tank is 28 feet long and the radius of its base is 4 feet long. Find the volume.

6. Find the total area of a cylinder whose altitude measures 8 inches and whose base has a radius 3 inches long.

7. The diameter of the base of a cylinder is 12 cm long and its altitude measures 18 cm. Find the lateral area.

8. A cylindrical pail is 10 inches deep and the radius of its base is 5 inches long. Find the volume.

9. How many square inches of tin are required to make the pail in Exercise 8?

10. A concrete roller is 6 feet long. Its diameter is 2 feet long. How much area will it cover in 400 revolutions?

Leave answers in terms of π.

11. A diameter of a cylindrical gas tank is 1 yard long. The tank is 2 feet long. About how many gallons of gas will it hold? [1 cu ft = 7.5 gal.]

12. When a piece of iron is submerged in a cylindrical tank, the water is raised 6 inches. The diameter of the tank is 18 inches long. What is the volume of the piece of iron?

EXAMPLE A cylinder of revolution is formed when a rectangle is revolved about one of its sides as an axis. Find the volume of the cylinder of revolution formed when a rectangle 4 inches by 10 inches is revolved about a 10-inch side.

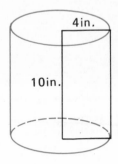
4 in.

10 in.

$V = \pi r^2 h$

$r = 4$ and $h = 10 \longrightarrow$ $= \pi (4^2)(10)$
$= (16)(10)\pi$
$= 160\pi$

Thus, the volume is 160π cubic inches.

13. Suppose the rectangle in the Example above is revolved about a 4-inch side. Compare the volume of the resulting cylinder of revolution to the volume of the one in the Example. Sketch the figure.

14. Consider the cylinder of revolution in the Example and the one in Exercise 13. Compare their lateral areas.

15. The measures of the sides of a rectangle are in the ratio 3:1. It is possible to form two cylinders of revolution with the rectangle. What is the ratio of the lateral areas of the two cylinders? [HINT: Let x and $3x$ represent the sides.]

16. Consider the two cylinders of revolution in Exercise 15. What is the ratio of the volumes of the two cylinders?

Cylinder inscribed in cube

Cylinder circumscribed about cube

PART C

17. A cylinder may be inscribed in a cube, as shown. What is the ratio of the volume of the cylinder to the volume of the cube?

18. A cylinder may be circumscribed about a cube as shown. What is the ratio of the volume of the cube to the volume of the cylinder?

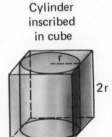
r

2r

r

?

Pyramids

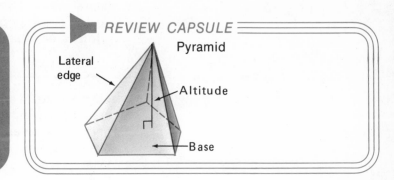

▶ REVIEW CAPSULE

Pyramid

Lateral edge

Altitude

Base

In a regular pyramid,
1. the base is a regular
polygonal region.
2. the lateral faces are
congruent isosceles
triangular regions.
3. the altitude meets
the base at its center.
4. the slant height is the
altitude of each lateral
face.

Triangular

Slant height

Equilateral triangle

Quadrangular

Slant height

Square

Pentagonal

Slant height

Regular pentagon

EXAMPLE 1 Each edge of the base of a
regular quadrangular pyramid is
16 feet and a slant height is
12 feet. Find the lateral area.

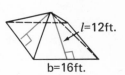

l=12ft.

b=16ft.

First Method	Second Method

Find the area of a lateral face. The slant
height is the altitude of each ⟶
lateral face.

$A = \frac{1}{2}b\ell$

$A = \frac{1}{2}(16)(12)$

$= (8)(12)$

$= 96$

The lateral area is 4 times the area of a
lateral face. ⟶
(All 4 lateral faces are ≅.)

$L = 4A$

$= 4(96)$

$= 384$

$L = (\frac{1}{2}b\ell) \times 4 \leftarrow 4 \times$ Area of
$= (\frac{1}{2}\ell) \times (4b)$ lateral face

$= (\frac{1}{2}\ell) \times p \leftarrow 4b$ is the perimeter
   of the base.
$= \frac{1}{2}\ell p$

$= \frac{1}{2}(12)(64) \leftarrow \begin{cases} \ell = 12 \\ p = 4(16), \text{ or } 64 \end{cases}$

$= (6)(64)$

$= 384$

Thus, the lateral area is 384 square feet.

<table>
<tr><td>

Theorem   **15.7**
</td><td>

For a regular pyramid,
lateral area $= \frac{1}{2} \times$ slant height $\times$ perimeter of base.
$$L = \frac{1}{2}\ell p$$
total area $=$ lateral area $+$ base area
$$T = L + B$$
</td></tr>
</table>

EXAMPLE 2   Find the lateral area and the total area of a pyramid whose slant height measures 10 and whose base is a regular pentagon with sides measuring 7 and apothem measuring 4.

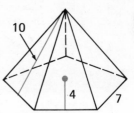

A regular pentagon has 5 sides. Perimeter is 5 times 7.

$T = L + B$

$$L = \frac{1}{2}\ell p$$
$$= \frac{1}{2}(10)(5 \times 7)$$
$$= 5(35)$$
$$= 175$$

$$T = L + B$$
$$L = 175 \quad B = \frac{1}{2}ap \longleftarrow$$
$$= \frac{1}{2}(4)(35)$$
$$= 70$$

$\begin{cases} \text{Use area} \\ \text{formula for} \\ \text{regular polygon.} \end{cases}$

$$T = 175 + 70$$
$$= 245$$

Thus, the lateral area is 175 square units, and the total area is 245 square units.

EXAMPLE 3   Each edge of the base of a regular quadrangular pyramid measures 10 meters and each lateral edge measures 13 meters. Find the total area.

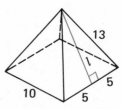

$$T = L + B$$

$L = \frac{1}{2}\ell p$ ⟶ To find L, we need ℓ (the slant height).

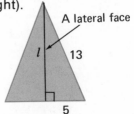

A lateral face

Use the Pythagorean theorem. ⟶

$$\ell^2 + 5^2 = 13^2$$
$$\ell^2 + 25 = 169$$
$$\ell^2 = 144$$
$$\ell = 12$$

The base is a square.
$p = 4 \times 10$

$$L = \frac{1}{2}\ell p \qquad\qquad B = 10^2 \quad \begin{cases} \text{Area of} \\ \text{square base} \end{cases}$$
$$= \frac{1}{2}(12)(4 \times 10) \qquad = 100$$
$$= (6)(40)$$
$$= 240$$

$T = L + B$ ⟶

$$T = 240 + 100, \text{ or } 340$$

Thus, the total area is 340 square meters.

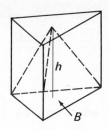

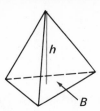

Volume of prism = Bh
Volume of pyramid = $\frac{1}{3}Bh$

Any pyramid can be converted into a prism with the same base and altitude. The volume of the pyramid is $\frac{1}{3}$ the volume of the prism.

Theorem 15.8

For any pyramid,
volume = $\frac{1}{3}$ × base area × measure of altitude
$V = \frac{1}{3}Bh$

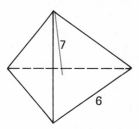

EXAMPLE 4 Each edge of the base of a regular triangular pyramid is 6 cm long and the altitude is 7 cm long. Find the volume.

$$V = \frac{1}{3}Bh$$

Use area formula for an equilateral triangle; $s = 6$. ————————→

$$B = \frac{s^2}{4}\sqrt{3} \qquad h = 7$$

$$= \frac{6^2}{4}\sqrt{3}$$

$$= \frac{36}{4}\sqrt{3}$$

$$= 9\sqrt{3}$$

$V = \frac{1}{3}Bh$ ————————————→

$$V = \frac{1}{3}(9\sqrt{3})(7)$$
$$= (3\sqrt{3})(7)$$
$$= 21\sqrt{3}$$

$21\sqrt{3} \doteq 21(1.73)$, or 36.33 ————————→

Thus, the volume is $21\sqrt{3}$ cubic cm.

SUMMARY

Formulas for a Pyramid

Lateral Area: $L = \frac{1}{2}\ell p$ $\begin{cases} \text{Regular} \\ \text{pyramid only} \end{cases}$

Total Area: $T = L + B$

Volume: $V = \frac{1}{3}Bh$

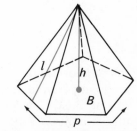

EXERCISES

Find the lateral area, the total area, and the volume of each regular pyramid.

1.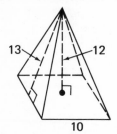

2.

3.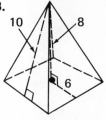

4.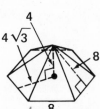

5. Find the lateral area of a regular pyramid whose slant height is 8 cm and whose base has a perimeter of 19 cm.

6. Find the volume of a pyramid whose base is a square with 5-inch sides and whose altitude measures 18 inches.

7. The sides of the base of a regular triangular pyramid measure 6 feet. Each lateral edge measures 5 feet. Find the total area of the pyramid.

8. The altitude of a pyramid measures 15 meters. The base is a right triangle with legs measuring 7 meters and 10 meters. Find the volume.

9. Each side of the base of a regular quadrangular pyramid measures 12 inches and each lateral edge measures 10 inches. Find the lateral area and the total area of the pyramid.

10. The base of a pyramid is a rhombus with diagonals measuring 7 and 8. The altitude of the pyramid measures 21. Find the volume.

PART B

11. The perimeter of the base of a regular pyramid is 70 feet and the lateral area is 315 square feet. Find the slant height.

12. The lateral area of a regular pyramid is 476 square units and the slant height is 14 units. Find the perimeter of the base.

13. The slant height of a regular quadrangular pyramid is 26 feet and one side of the base measures 20 feet. Find the lateral area, total area, and volume.

14. Find the lateral area and the total area of a regular hexagonal pyramid whose lateral edges measure 25 inches and whose base has sides measuring 14 inches.

PART C

15. Each side of the base of a regular triangular pyramid measures 12 units. The slant height makes an angle of 45° with the altitude. Find the total area and the volume of the pyramid.

16. Derive a formula for the total area of a regular pyramid in terms of its slant height, apothem, and perimeter of the base.

Cones

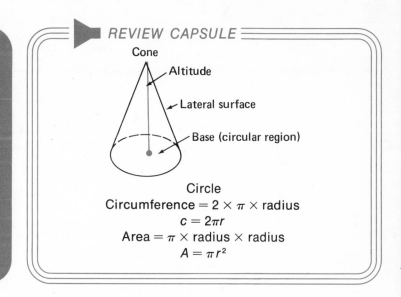

▶ *REVIEW CAPSULE*

Cone

— Altitude

— Lateral surface

— Base (circular region)

Circle
Circumference = 2 × π × radius
$c = 2\pi r$
Area = π × radius × radius
$A = \pi r^2$

Regular Pyramids

Cone

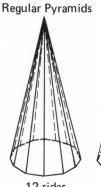

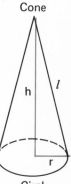

A cone is like a regular pyramid with a circular base.

Bases ⟶

6 sides   12 sides   24 sides   Circle

Circumference is like perimeter, $c = 2\pi r$.

The base of a cone is a circle, $B = \pi r^2$.

Formulas	Regular Pyramid	Cone
Lateral area	$L = \frac{1}{2}\ell p$	$L = \frac{1}{2}\ell c$ $= \frac{1}{2}\ell(2\pi r)$ $= \pi r\ell$
Total area	$T = L + B$	$T = L + B$ $= \pi r\ell + \pi r^2$ $= \pi r(\ell + r)$
Volume	$V = \frac{1}{3}Bh$	$V = \frac{1}{3}Bh$ $= \frac{1}{3}(\pi r^2)h$ $= \frac{1}{3}\pi r^2 h$

<table>
<tr><td>

Theorem 15.9

</td></tr>
</table>

For a cone,
lateral area (L) is $\pi r \ell$
total area (T) is $\pi r(\ell + r)$,
volume (V) is $\frac{1}{3}\pi r^2 h$.

EXAMPLE 1

Find the lateral area, the total area, and the volume of the cone shown at the right.

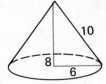

$$r = 6 \qquad \ell = 10 \qquad h = 8$$

$L = \pi r \ell$	$T = \pi r(\ell + r)$	$V = \frac{1}{3}\pi r^2 h$
$= \pi(6)(10)$	$= \pi(6)(10 + 6)$	$= \frac{1}{3}\pi(6^2)(8)$
$= 60\pi$	$= \pi(6)(16)$	$= \frac{1}{3}\pi(36)(8)$
	$= 96\pi$	$= 96\pi$

Thus, the lateral area is 60π square units,
the total area is 96π square units,
and the volume is 96π cubic units.

EXAMPLE 2

The radius of the base of a cone is 7 cm and the slant height is 14 cm. Find the lateral area, total area, and volume.

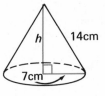

$$r = 7 \qquad \ell = 14 \qquad h = ?$$

Find h: $h^2 + 7^2 = (14)^2$
$h^2 + 49 = 196$
$h^2 = 147$
$h = \sqrt{147}$, or $7\sqrt{3}$

$\sqrt{147} = \sqrt{49} \cdot \sqrt{3} = 7\sqrt{3} \longrightarrow$

$r = 7, \ell = 14, h = 7\sqrt{3} \longrightarrow$

$L = \pi r \ell$	$T = \pi r(\ell + r)$	$V = \frac{1}{3}\pi r^2 h$
$= \pi(7)(14)$	$= \pi(7)(14 + 7)$	$= \frac{1}{3}\pi(7^2)(7\sqrt{3})$
$= 98\pi$	$= \pi(7)(21)$	$= \frac{1}{3}\pi(49)(7\sqrt{3})$
	$= 147\pi$	$= \frac{343}{3}\pi\sqrt{3}$

Thus, the lateral area is 98π sq cm,
the total area is 147π sq cm,
and the volume is $\frac{343}{3}\pi\sqrt{3}$ cu cm.

ORAL EXERCISES

1. Explain why the formulas for a regular pyramid are similar to the formulas for a cone.
2. In a cone, what corresponds to the perimeter of the base of a regular pyramid?
3. Give the formula for the circumference of the base of a cone.
4. Give the formula for the area of the base of a cone.

EXERCISES

PART A

Find the lateral area, total area, and volume of each cone. Leave answers in terms of π.

1.

2.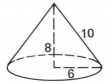

3.

4.

Leave answers in terms of π, wherever possible.

5. The slant height of a cone is 16 inches and the radius of the base measures 5 inches. Find the lateral area and the total area.
6. The radius of the base of a cone measures 3 units and the altitude measures 7 units. Find the volume.
7. The altitude of a cone measures 10 cm and the radius of the base measures 4 cm. Find the slant height.
8. The slant height of a cone is 18 feet and the altitude measures 9 feet. Find the length of the base.
9. The slant height of a cone is 15 meters and the radius of the base measures 9 meters. Find the volume.
10. The altitude of a cone measures 24 units and the slant height is 26 units. Find the lateral area and the total area.
11. A cone and a cylinder have congruent bases, and their altitudes have the same measure. Compare their volumes.
12. A cone and a cylinder have congruent bases. The altitude of the cone is three times as long as the altitude of the cylinder. Compare their volumes.

Leave answers in terms of π.

13. The area of the base of a cone is 81π square units and the slant height is 41 units. Find the measure of the altitude.

14. The volume of a cone is 320π square cm and the altitude measures 15 cm. Find the length of the radius of the base.

EXAMPLE A cone of revolution is formed when a right triangle is revolved about one of its legs as an axis. Find the volume of the cone of revolution formed when a right triangle with legs measuring 5 and 12 is revolved about the 12-unit leg.

$r = 5, h = 12$ ——————————→

$$V = \tfrac{1}{3}\pi r^2 h$$
$$= \tfrac{1}{3}\pi (5^2)(12)$$
$$= \tfrac{1}{3}(12)(25)\pi$$
$$= (4)(25)\pi$$
$$= 100\pi$$

Thus, the volume is 100π cubic units.

15. Suppose the triangle in the Example above is revolved about the 5-unit leg. Compare the volume of the resulting cone of revolution with the volume of the one in the Example.

16. Consider the cone of revolution in the Example and the one in Exercise 15. Compare their lateral areas.

17. The measures of the legs of a right triangle are in a ratio of 4:1. It is possible to form two cones of revolution with the right triangle. What is the ratio of the lateral areas of the two cones? [Hint: Let x and $4x$ represent the legs]

18. Consider the two cones of revolution in Exercise 17. What is the ratio of the volumes of the two cones?

PART C

19. Suppose a square with 6-inch sides is revolved about a diagonal as an axis. Find the volume.

20. Suppose a 3-4-5 right triangle is revolved about its hypotenuse as an axis. Find the volume.

Spheres

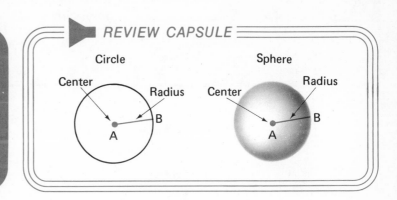

Circle

Sphere

Great circle of a sphere

Plane intersecting sphere and passing through its center

Definition of *great circle* ⟶ A *great circle of a sphere* is a circle which is formed when a plane intersects a sphere and passes through its center.

EXAMPLE 1 Find the area of a great circle of a sphere whose radius is 8.

$$A = \pi r^2$$
$$A = \pi (8)^2$$
$$A = 64\pi$$

Thus, the area is 64π square units.

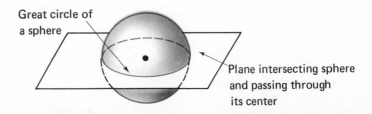

One quadrant $\left(\frac{1}{4}\right)$ of a sphere

Two intersecting great circles formed by perpendicular planes

This can be proved in advanced geometry. ⟶ The surface area of a quadrant is equal to the area of a great circle.

Thus, Area of quadrant $= \pi r^2$

Theorem 15.10

The *area of a sphere* is 4 times the area of a great circle.

$$\text{Area} = 4 \times \pi r^2$$
$$A = 4\pi r^2$$

EXAMPLE 2 Find the area of a sphere with a 6-inch radius

$$A = 4\pi r^2$$

 $r = 6$

$$= 4\pi (6^2)$$
$$= 4\pi (36)$$
$$= 144\pi$$

Thus, the area is 144π sq in.

We can cut up a solid sphere into pyramid-like figures to help us find its volume.

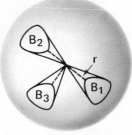

Use enough pyramids to cover the entire sphere. (Only 3 are shown.)

Let B_1, B_2, B_3, $\cdots$, B_n be the areas of the bases of the pyramids.

Vol. of pyramid $= \frac{1}{3}Bh$ (For each pyramid, h is the radius of the sphere.)

The sum of the base areas is the area of the sphere. (The pyramids cover the sphere.)

Volume of a pyramid $= \frac{1}{3}Bh$
Volume of shaded pyramid $= \frac{1}{3}B_1 r$

Volume of sphere $=$ Sum of volumes of pyramids
$$V = \frac{1}{3}B_1 r + \frac{1}{3}B_2 r + \frac{1}{3}B_3 r + \cdots + \frac{1}{3}B_n r$$
$$= \frac{1}{3}r(B_1 + B_2 + B_3 + \cdots + B_n)$$
$$= \frac{1}{3}r \text{ (area of sphere)}$$
$$= \frac{1}{3}r(4\pi r^2)$$
$$= \frac{4}{3}\pi r^3$$

Theorem 15.11

The volume of a sphere is $\frac{4}{3}\pi r^3$.

$$V = \frac{4}{3}\pi r^3$$

EXAMPLE 3 Find the volume of a sphere with a 6-inch radius.

$r = 6$ ⟶

$6^3 = 6 \times 6 \times 6$, or 216 ⟶

$\dfrac{4}{3} \times \dfrac{216}{1} = \dfrac{4}{\overset{1}{\cancel{3}}} \times \dfrac{\overset{72}{\cancel{216}}}{1} = 288$

$$V = \tfrac{4}{3}\pi r^3$$
$$= \tfrac{4}{3}\pi (6)^3$$
$$= \tfrac{4}{3}(216)\pi$$
$$= 288\pi$$

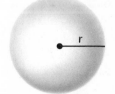

Thus, the volume is 288π cubic inches.

SUMMARY

Formulas for a Sphere

Area: $A = 4\pi r^2$
Volume: $V = \tfrac{4}{3}\pi r^3$

EXERCISES

PART A

Find the area and volume of each sphere. Leave answers in terms of π.

1.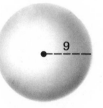
9

2.
4

3.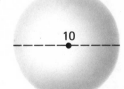
10

4.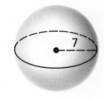
7

5. A baseball has a radius 7 cm long. Find its surface area.

6. Find the volume of a sphere with a 3 inch radius.

7. The area of a great circle of a sphere is 62π square cm. Find the area of the sphere.

8. How many cubic inches of air can be pumped into a basketball if its maximum diameter is 12 in.?

9. The diameter of a sphere is 8 feet long. Find the area and the volume.

10. Two spheres have radii of lengths 1 inch and 3 inches. What is the ratio of their surface areas?

PART B

11. Find the length of a radius of a sphere whose area is 196π square cm.

12. A great circle of a sphere has an area of 64π square units. Find the volume.

13. If the number of square inches in the area of a sphere is equal to the number of cubic inches in its volume, find the length of a radius of the sphere.

14. Find the volume of a hollow metal ball if its outside diameter measures 12 and its inside diameter measures 10.

PART C

15. If a sphere with radius of length r is inscribed in a cube, what is the ratio of the volume of the sphere to the volume of the cube? [Hint: The height of the cube equals the length of a diameter of the sphere.]

16. If a sphere with radius of length r is inscribed in a cylinder, what is the ratio of the volume of the sphere to the volume of the cylinder? [Hint: The height of the cylinder equals the length of a diameter of the sphere.]

Algebra Review

OBJECTIVE
■ To solve systems of equations

To solve a system of equations:
1. Get one equation with only one variable.
2. Solve it.   3. Substitute.

EXAMPLE Solve this system.

$$5x - 3y = 2$$
$$4x + 2y = 6$$

Multiply each side by 2. $\longrightarrow$ $2(5x - 3y) = 2(2)$
Multiply each side by 3. $\longrightarrow$ $3(4x + 2y) = 3(6)$

Now the coefficients of y are opposites. $\longrightarrow$

$$10x - 6y = 4$$
$$\underline{12x + 6y = 18}$$

Add the equations. $\longrightarrow$

$$22x = 22$$
$$x = 1$$

Substitute 1 for x in either of the original equations. $\longrightarrow$

$$5x - 3y = 2$$
$$5(1) - 3y = 2$$

Solve for y. $\longrightarrow$

$$5 - 3y = 2$$
$$-3y = -3$$
$$y = 1$$

Thus, $(1, 1)$ is the solution.

Solve.

1. $x - y = 7$
$x + y = 9$

2. $-2x + y = 6$
$2x + 3y = 10$

3. $3x - y = 5$
$2x + y = 5$

4. $3x - 4y = 4$
$2x + 4y = 16$

5. $-x + y = -4$
$3x - 2y = 12$

6. $2x + y = 9$
$3x + 2y = 16$

7. $5x + 2y = 14$
$2x - y = 3$

8. $-12x - y = 14$
$5x + 3y = -11$

Constructing A Mobile

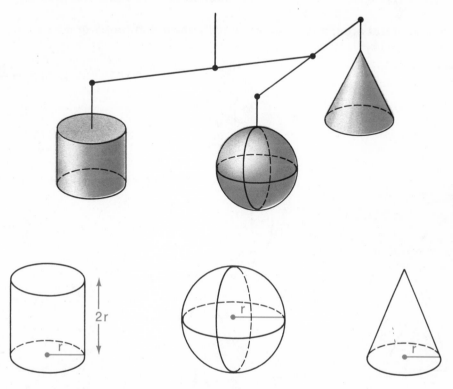

The cylinder balances the sphere and the cone.

Volume of cylinder		Volume of sphere		Volume of cone
$V = \pi r^2 h \leftarrow h = 2r$	$=$	$V = \dfrac{4}{3}\pi r^3$	$+$	$V = \dfrac{1}{3}\pi r^2 h \leftarrow h = 2r$
$\downarrow$				$\downarrow$
$V = \pi r^2 (2r)$				$V = \dfrac{1}{3}\pi r^2 (2r)$
$V = 2\pi r^3$				$V = \dfrac{2}{3}\pi r^3$

$$2\pi r^3 \;=\; \frac{4}{3}\pi r^3 \;+\; \frac{2}{3}\pi r^3$$

Construct a mobile with hollow figures similar to the ones shown.
Why is the balance system different?

Chapter Fifteen Review

Sketch each of the following. Then state how many edges, vertices, and faces each has. [p. 493]

1. A right pentagonal prism

2. A rectangular solid with all edges congruent

Find the lateral area, total area, and volume. Leave answers in terms of π.
[p. 496, 499, 503, 507, 511]

3.
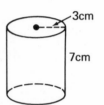
16, 9, 5

4.
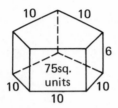
10, 10, 10, 10, 10, 6, 75sq. units

5.
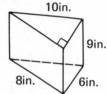
10in., 9in., 8in., 6in.

6.
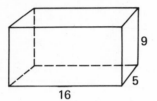
3cm, 7cm

7.
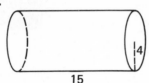
4, 15

8. Regular pyramid
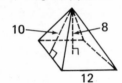
10, 8, h, 12

9.
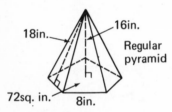
18in., 16in. Regular pyramid, 72sq. in., 8in., h

10.
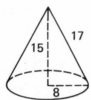
15, 17, 8

11.
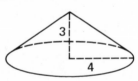
3, 4

Find the area and the volume. Leave answers in terms of π. [p. 515]

12.

6″

13.

4cm

Leave answers in terms of π.

14. The slant height of a cone is 18 inches and the radius of the base is 4 inches long. Find the lateral area. [p. 511]

15. The base of a triangular prism is an equilateral triangle with sides 6 cm long. The altitude is 7 cm long. Find the volume. [p. 499]

16. The volume of a rectangular solid is 300 cubic feet. The base is a rectangle 4 feet by 15 feet. Find the length of the altitude. [p. 499]

17. A rectangle 7 inches by 9 inches is revolved about a 9-inch side as an axis. Find the total area of the cylinder of revolution formed. [p. 503]

Chapter Fifteen Test

Sketch each of the following. Then state how many edges, vertices, and faces each has.

1. A rectangular solid

2. A right hexagonal prism

Find the lateral area, total area, and volume. Leave answers in terms of π.

3.

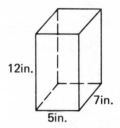

12in.
7in.
5in.

4.

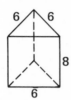

6   6
8
6

5.

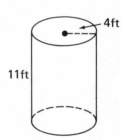

4ft
11ft

6.   Regular   pyramid

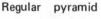

15
12
18

7.

25
24
7

8.

10cm
6cm

Find the area and volume. Leave answers in terms of π.

9.

3ft

Leave answers in terms of π.

10. The bases of a prism are regular hexagons with sides 7 feet long. The altitude is 10 feet long. Find the total area.

11. The total area of a cube is 150 square yards. Find the volume.

12. The diameter of the base of a cylinder is 30 cm long and its altitude is 20 cm long. Find the lateral area.

13. A right triangle with legs measuring 9 inches and 14 inches is revolved about its 9-inch leg as an axis. Find the volume of the cone of revolution.

POSTULATES
THEOREMS
and COROLLARIES

POSTULATES
THEOREMS
and COROLLARIES

Postulate 1 For any two points, there is only one line containing them. [35]

Theorem 2.1 Two lines intersect in at most one one point. [35]

Postulate 2 Three noncollinear points are contained in exactly one plane. [35]

Theorem 2.2 A line and a point not on the line are contained in exactly one plane. [36]

Theorem 2.3 Two intersecting lines are contained in exactly one plane. [36]

Postulate 3 If two points of a line are in a given plane, then the line itself is contained in the plane. [36]

Theorem 2.4 If a line intersects a plane, but is not contained in the plane, then the intersection is exactly one point. [36]

Postulate 4 If two planes intersect, then their intersection is exactly one line. [36]

Postulate 5 Given a line and a point on it, there is a segment congruent to any given segment with the given point as endpoint. [37]

Postulate 6 Given a line and a point on it, there is an angle congruent to any given angle with the given point as vertex. [37]

Postulate 7 Every segment has exactly one midpoint. [37]

Postulate 8 Every angle, except a straight angle, has exactly one bisector. [37]

Postulate 9 If $\overrightarrow{BD}$ is in the interior of $\angle ABC$, then $m\angle ABC = m\angle ABD + m\angle DBC$. [46]

Postulate 10   If point P is between points A and B, then $AB = AP + PB$. [47]

Postulate 11   Given a point and a line in a plane, there is exactly one line through the point perpendicular to the given line. [52]

Postulate 12   The sum of the measures of the angles with the same vertex on one side of a line is 180°. [53]

Theorem   2.5   If two lines form congruent adjacent angles, then they are perpendicular. [53]

Theorem   2.6   Supplements of congruent angles are congruent. [55]

Corollary   Supplements of the same angle are congruent. [56]

Theorem   2.7   Complements of congruent angles are congruent. [56]

Corollary   Complements of the same angle are congruent. [56]

Theorem   2.8   Vertical angles are congruent. [57]

Postulate 13   If two parallel lines are intersected by a transversal, then alternate interior angles are congruent. [76]

Theorem   3.1   If two parallel lines are intersected by a transversal, then corresponding angles are congruent. [76]

Theorem   3.2   If two parallel lines are intersected by a transversal, the interior angles on the same side of the transversal are supplementary. [77]

Postulate 14   If two lines are intersected by a transversal so that two alternate interior angles are congruent, then the lines are parallel. [80]

Theorem   3.3   If two lines are intersected by a transversal so that corresponding angles are congruent, then the lines are parallel. [81]

Corollary   Two coplanar lines perpendicular to the same line are parallel. [81]

Theorem   3.4   If two lines are intersected by a transversal so that two interior angles on the same side of the transversal are supplementary, then the lines are parallel. [82]

Postulate 15   Through point P not on line ℓ, there is exactly one line parallel to ℓ. [86]

Theorem   3.5   The sum of the measures of the three angles of a triangle is 180°. [89]

Theorem   3.6   In a plane, two lines parallel to the same line are parallel to each other. [90]

Theorem	3.7	If two parallel planes are intersected by a third plane, then the lines of intersection are parallel. [96]
Theorem	4.1	If two angles of a triangle are congruent to two angles of a second triangle, then the third angles of the triangle are also congruent. [104]
Theorem	4.2	The measure of an exterior angle of a triangle is the sum of the measures of its two opposite interior angles. [105]
Corollary		The measure of an exterior angle of a triangle is greater than the measure of either of its opposite interior angles. [105]
Theorem	4.3	There is at most one line perpendicular to a given line from a given point. [106]
Postulate 16		Two triangles are congruent if the three sides of one are congruent respectively to the three sides of the other. (side-side-side congruence) [115]
Postulate 17		Two triangles are congruent if two sides and an included angle of one are congruent respectively to two sides and an included angle of the other. [123]
Theorem	4.4	Two triangles are congruent if two angles and an included side of one are congruent respectively to two angles and an included side of the other. [124]
Theorem	4.5	Two triangles are congruent if two angles and a side opposite one of them are congruent respectively to two angles and the corresponding side of the other. [127]
Theorem	5.1	If two sides of a triangle are congruent, then the angles opposite these sides are congruent. [138]
Corollary		An equilateral triangle is also equiangular. [139]
Theorem	5.2	If two angles of a triangle are congruent, then the sides opposite these angles are congruent. [139]
Corollary		An equiangular triangle is also equilateral. [140]
Theorem	5.3	Two right triangles are congruent if the hypotenuse and a leg of one are congruent respectively to the hypotenuse and a leg of the other. [148]
Theorem	5.4	A point on the perpendicular bisector of a segment is equidistant from the endpoints of the segment. [157]

Theorem	5.5	Two points each equidistant from the endpoints of a segment determine the perpendicular bisector of the segment. [158]
Theorem	6.1	The sum of the measures of the angles of a convex quadrilateral is 360°. [178]
Theorem	6.2	The sum of the measures of the interior angles of a convex polygon with n sides is $(n-2)180$. [180]
Theorem	6.3	The sum of the measures of the exterior angles, one at each vertex, of any convex polygon is 360. [183]
Theorem	6.4	The measure of an angle of a regular polygon with n sides is $\dfrac{(n-2)180}{n}$. [186]
Corollary		The measure of an exterior angle of a regular polygon with n sides is $\dfrac{360}{n}$. [187]
Theorem	7.1	Two quadrilaterals are congruent if any three sides and the included angles of one are congruent respectively to three sides and the included angles of the other. [199]
Theorem	7.2	Opposite sides of a parallelogram are congruent. [202]
Theorem	7.3	Opposite angles of a parallelogram are congruent. [203]
Theorem	7.4	The diagonals of a parallelogram bisect each other. [204]
Theorem	7.5	If opposite sides of a quadrilateral are congruent, then the quadrilateral is a parallelogram. [206]
Theorem	7.6	If opposite angles of a quadrilateral are congruent, then the quadrilateral is a parallelogram. [207]
Theorem	7.7	If two sides of a quadrilateral are both parallel and congruent, then the quadrilateral is a parallelogram. [207]
Theorem	7.8	If the diagonals of a quadrilateral bisect each other, then the quadrilateral is a parallelogram. [208]
Theorem	7.9	The segment joining the midpoints of two sides of a triangle is parallel to the third side and is half as long. [209]
Theorem	7.10	If three parallel lines cut off congruent segments on one transversal, then they cut off congruent segments on any transversal. [212]

Corollary		If any number of parallel lines cut off congruent segments on one transversal, then they cut off congruent segments on any transversal. [213]
Postulate 18		The shortest curve joining two points is a segment. [214]
Theorem	7.11	Parallel lines are equidistant at all points. [214]
Theorem	7.12	The median of a trapezoid is parallel to its bases, and its length is half the sum of the lengths of the bases. [221]
Postulate 19		The line of symmetry of a symmetric figure is the perpendicular bisector of a segment joining two corresponding points. [224]
Theorem	7.13	Corresponding sides of symmetric polygons are congruent. [225]
Theorem	7.14	Corresponding angles of symmetric polygons are congruent. [225]
Theorem	7.15	The diagonals of an isosceles trapezoid are congruent. [228]
Theorem	7.16	If a trapezoid has a pair of congruent legs which are not parallel, then it is isosceles. [229]
Theorem	7.17	If a trapezoid has at least one pair of congruent base angles, then it is isosceles. [229]
Theorem	7.18	If two triangles are reflections, then they are congruent. [240]
Postulate 20		In $\triangle ABC$, if $\overline{A'B'} \parallel \overline{AB}$, then $\dfrac{AB}{A'B'} = \dfrac{BC}{B'C} = \dfrac{CA}{CA'}$. [257]
Theorem	8.1	A line parallel to one side of a triangle divides the other two sides proportionally. [258]
Theorem	8.2	A line which divides two sides of a triangle proportionally is parallel to the third side. [258]
Theorem	8.3	If two angles of a triangle are congruent to two angles of a second triangle, then the two triangles are similar. [260]
Theorem	8.4	If $\angle X \cong \angle U$ and $\dfrac{XZ}{UT} = \dfrac{XY}{UV}$, then $\triangle XYZ \sim \triangle UVT$. [263]
Theorem	8.5	If $\dfrac{XY}{TU} = \dfrac{YZ}{UV} = \dfrac{ZX}{VT}$, then $\triangle XYZ \sim \triangle TUV$. [264]
Theorem	8.6	Corresponding medians of similar triangles are proportional to corresponding sides. [272]

Theorem	8.7	Corresponding altitudes of similar triangles are proportional to corresponding sides. [273]
Theorem	8.8	The bisector of an angle of a triangle divides the opposite side into segments proportional to the other sides of the triangle. [273]
Theorem	8.9	If a tetrahedron is cut by a plane parallel to its base, then the triangle formed by the intersection is similar to the base. [280]
Theorem	9.1	In a right triangle, the altitude to the hypotenuse forms two triangles, each similar to the original triangle, and each similar to the other. [285]
Corollary	1	In a right triangle, the length of the altitude to the hypotenuse is the geometric mean of the lengths of the segments of the hypotenuse. [286]
Corollary	2	In a right triangle, the length of either leg is the geometric mean of the lengths of the hypotenuse and the segment of the hypotenuse bounded by the altitude and that leg. [286]
Theorem	9.2	If a triangle is a right triangle, then the square of the length of the hypotenuse is equal to the sum of the squares of the lengths of the two legs. [288]
Theorem	9.3	If the sum of the squares of the lengths of two sides of a triangle is equal to the square of the length of the third side, then the triangle is a right triangle. [292]

Theorem 9.4 In an isosceles right triangle, the length ℓ of a leg is $\frac{\text{hyp.}}{2}\sqrt{2}$. [297]

$$\ell = \frac{\text{hyp.}}{2}\sqrt{2}$$

Theorem 9.5 In a 30 –60° rt. triangle, the length ℓ of the leg opposite the 30° angle is $\frac{\text{hyp.}}{2}$. $\ell = \frac{\text{hyp.}}{2}$

The length ℓ' of the leg opposite the 60° angle is $\frac{\text{hyp.}}{2}\sqrt{3}$. [298]

$$\ell' = \frac{\text{hyp.}}{2}\sqrt{3}$$

Theorem	10.1	Any two radii of a circle are congruent. [316]
Theorem	10.2	In a circle, a radius perpendicular to a chord bisects the chord. [316]
Theorem	10.3	If chords of a circle (or congruent circles) are congruent, then they are equidistant from the center(s). [319]
Theorem	10.4	If chords of a circle (or congruent circles) are equidistant from the center(s), then the chords are congruent. [320]

Theorem 10.5   If a line is perpendicular to a radius at its endpoint on the circle, then it is tangent to the circle. [322]

Theorem 10.6   If a line is tangent to a circle, then it is perpendicular to a radius which ends at the point of tangency. [322]

Theorem 10.7   Tangent segments to a circle from the same point are congruent. [323]

Postulate 21   If point P is on $\overset{\frown}{AB}$, then $m\overset{\frown}{AP} + m\overset{\frown}{PB} = m\overset{\frown}{AB}$. [328]

Theorem 10.8   Congruent arcs determine congruent chords. [332]

Theorem 10.9   Congruent chords of the same circle (or congruent circles) determine congruent minor arcs. [332]

Theorem 10.10   The measure of an inscribed angle is one half the measure of its intercepted arc. [337]

Theorem 10.11   The measure of an angle formed by two secants intersecting in the interior of a circle is one half the sum of the measures of the arcs intercepted by the angle and its vertical angle. [342]

Theorem 10.12   The measure of an angle formed by two secants intersecting in the exterior of a circle is one half the difference of the measures of the intercepted arcs. [343]

Theorem 10.13   The measure of an angle formed by a secant and a tangent intersecting at the point of tangency is one half the measure of the intercepted arc. [345]

Theorem 10.14   The measure of an angle formed by a secant and a tangent intersecting outside the circle is one half the difference of the measures of the intercepted arcs. [346]

Theorem 10.15   The measure of an angle formed by two intersecting tangents is one half the difference of the measures of the intercepted arcs. [346]

Theorem 10.16   If two chords of a circle intersect, then the product of the lengths of the segments of one equals the product of the lengths of the segments of the other. [349]

Theorem 10.17   If two secants intersect outside a circle, then the product of the lengths of one secant segment and its external secant segment equals the product of the lengths of the other secant segment and its external secant segment. [350]

Theorem 10.18	If a tangent and a secant intersect outside a circle, then the square of the length of the tangent segment equals the product of the lengths of the secant segment and its external secant segment. [351]
Postulate 22	The area of a rectangle is the product of the lengths of two consecutive sides. [360]
Corollary	The area of a square is the square of the length of a side. [360]
Postulate 23	If a region is the union of two or more nonoverlapping regions, then its area is the sum of the areas of these nonoverlapping regions. [360]
Postulate 24	Congruent figures have the same area. [363]
Theorem 11.1	The area of a right triangle is one half the product of the lengths of the two legs. [363]
Theorem 11.2	The area of any triangle is one half the product of the lengths of a base and the corresponding altitude. [364]
Corollary	Triangles with congruent bases and congruent corresponding altitudes have the same area. [364]
Theorem 11.3	The area of a parallelogram is the product of the length of a base and the length of its corresponding altitude. [367]
Corollary	Parallelograms with congruent bases and congruent corresponding altitudes have the same area. [368]
Theorem 11.4	The area of a trapezoid is one half the product of the length of an altitude and the sum of the lengths of the two bases. [372]
Theorem 11.5	The ratio of the areas of two similar triangles is the square of the ratio of the lengths of two corresponding sides. [375]
Theorem 11.6	The ratio of the perimeters of two similar polygons is the same as the ratio of the lengths of two corresponding sides. [376]
Theorem 11.7	The area of an equilateral triangle having sides of length s is $\frac{s^2}{4}\sqrt{3}$. [379]
Theorem 11.8	The area of a regular polygon is one half the product of the apothem and the perimeter. [380]
Theorem 11.9	The ratio of the circumference to the length of a diameter is the same for all circles. [384]
Theorem 11.10	The area of a circle with a radius of length r is πr^2. [388]

Theorem 11.11   If the degree measure of an arc is m and the length of a radius of the circle is r, then the length ℓ of the arc is given by this formula. [391]
$$\ell = \left(\frac{m}{360}\right)(2\pi r)$$

Theorem 11.12   The area of a sector bounded by an arc of measure m and radii of length r is given by this formula. [395]
$$\text{Area} = \left(\frac{m}{360}\right)(\pi r^2)$$

Theorem 12.1   The distance formula.
The distance d between $P(x_1, y_1)$ and $Q(x_2, y_2)$ is given by this formula. [405]
$$d = \sqrt{(x_2 - x_1)^2 + (y_2 - y_1)^2}$$

Theorem 12.2   The Midpoint Theorem
Let $P(x_1, y_1)$ and $Q(x_2, y_2)$ be any two points. Then the midpoint of $\overline{PQ}$ has coordinates $\left(\dfrac{x_1 + x_2}{2}, \dfrac{y_1 + y_2}{2}\right)$. [408]

Theorem 12.3   If the equation of a line is $y = mx + b$, then m is the slope and b is the y-intercept. [418]
$$y = mx + b$$
slope⟋   ⟍ y-intercept

Theorem 12.4   If a line has slope m and y-intercept b, then its equation is $y = mx + b$. [418]

Theorem 12.5   If two lines have the same slope, then they are parallel. [424]

Theorem 12.6   If the slopes of two lines are negative reciprocals, then the lines are perpendicular. [425]

Theorem 12.7   The equation of a circle with center (h, k) and radius of length r is $\sqrt{(x - h)^2 + (y - k)^2} = r$, or $(x - h)^2 + (y - k)^2 = r^2$. [431]

Theorem 12.8   If d is the distance between points $A(x_1, y_1, z_1)$ and $B(x_2, y_2, z_2)$, then $d = \sqrt{(x_2 - x_1)^2 + (y_2 - y_1)^2 + (z_2 - z_1)^2}$. [435]

Postulate 25   The locus of points at a given distance from a given point is a circle with the given point as a center and the given distance as a radius. [439]

Postulate 26   The locus of points at a given distance from a given line is a pair of lines each parallel to the given line and at the given distance from it. [440]

Postulate 27   The locus of points equidistant from two given parallel lines is a line parallel to each of the given lines and midway between them. [440]

TABLES

Table of Roots and Powers

No.	Sq.	Sq. Root	Cube	Cu. Root	No.	Sq.	Sq. Root	Cube	Cu. Root
1	1	1.000	1	1.000	51	2,601	7.141	132,651	3.708
2	4	1.414	8	1.260	52	2,704	7.211	140,608	3.733
3	9	1.732	27	1.442	53	2,809	7.280	148,877	3.756
4	16	2.000	64	1.587	54	2,916	7.348	157,564	3.780
5	25	2.236	125	1.710	55	3,025	7.416	166,375	3.803
6	36	2.449	216	1.817	56	3,136	7.483	175,616	3.826
7	49	2.646	343	1.913	57	3,249	7.550	185,193	3.849
8	64	2.828	512	2.000	58	3,364	7.616	195,112	3.871
9	81	3.000	729	2.080	59	3,481	7.681	205,379	3.893
10	100	3.162	1,000	2.154	60	3,600	7.746	216,000	3.915
11	121	3.317	1,331	2.224	61	3,721	7.810	226,981	3.936
12	144	3.464	1,728	2.289	62	3,844	7.874	238,328	3.958
13	169	3.606	2,197	2.351	63	3,969	7.937	250,047	3.979
14	196	3.742	2,744	2.410	64	4,096	8.000	262,144	4.000
15	225	3.875	3,375	2.466	65	4,225	8.062	274,625	4.021
16	256	4.000	4,096	2.520	66	4,356	8.124	287,496	4.041
17	289	4.123	4,913	2.571	67	4,489	8.185	300,763	4.062
18	324	4.243	5,832	2.621	68	4,624	8.246	314,432	4.082
19	361	4.359	6,859	2.668	69	4,761	8.307	328,509	4.102
20	400	4.472	8,000	2.714	70	4,900	8.357	343,000	4.121
21	441	4.583	9,261	2.759	71	5,041	8.426	357,911	4.141
22	484	4.690	10,648	2.802	72	5,184	8.485	373,248	4.160
23	529	4.796	12,167	2.844	73	5,329	8.544	389,017	4.179
24	576	4.899	13,824	2.884	74	5,476	8.602	405,224	4.198
25	625	5.000	15,625	2.924	75	5,625	8.660	421,875	4.217
26	676	5.099	17,576	2.962	76	5,776	8.718	438,976	4.236
27	729	5.196	19,683	3.000	77	5,929	8.775	456,533	4.254
28	784	5.292	21,952	3.037	78	6,084	8.832	474,552	4.273
29	841	5.385	24,389	3.072	79	6,241	8.888	493,039	4.291
30	900	5.477	27,000	3.107	80	6,400	8.944	512,000	4.309
31	961	5.568	29,791	3.141	81	6,561	9.000	531,441	4.327
32	1,024	5.657	32,768	3.175	82	6,724	9.055	551,368	4.344
33	1,089	5.745	35,937	3.208	83	6,889	9.110	571,787	4.362
34	1,156	5.831	39,304	3.240	84	7,056	9.165	592,704	4.380
35	1,225	5.916	42,875	3.271	85	7,225	9.220	614,125	4.397
36	1,296	6.000	46,656	3.302	86	7,396	9.274	636,056	4.414
37	1,369	6.083	50,653	3.332	87	7,569	9.327	658,503	4.431
38	1,444	6.164	54,872	3.362	88	7,744	9.381	681,472	4.448
39	1,521	6.245	59,319	3.391	89	7,921	9.434	704,969	4.465
40	1,600	6.325	64,000	3.420	90	8,100	9.487	729,000	4.481
41	1,681	6.403	68,921	3.448	91	8,281	9.539	753,571	4.498
42	1,764	6.481	74,088	3.476	92	8,464	9.592	778,688	4.514
43	1,849	6.557	79,507	3.503	93	8,649	9.644	804,357	4.531
44	1,936	6.633	85,184	3.530	94	8,836	9.695	830,584	4.547
45	2,025	6.708	91,125	3.557	95	9,025	9.747	857,375	4.563
46	2,116	6.782	97,336	3.583	96	9,216	9.798	884,736	4.579
47	2,209	6.856	103,823	3.609	97	9,409	9.849	912,673	4.595
48	2,304	6.928	110,592	3.634	98	9,604	9.899	941,192	4.610
49	2,401	7.000	117,649	3.659	99	9,801	9.950	970,299	4.626
50	2,500	7.071	125,000	3.684	100	10,000	10.000	1,000,000	4.642

Trigonometric Ratios

Angle Measure	Sin	Cos	Tan	Angle Measure	Sin	Cos	Tan
0°	0.000	1.000	0.000	46°	.7193	.6947	1.036
1°	.0175	.9998	.0175	47°	.7314	.6820	1.072
2°	.0349	.9994	.0349	48°	.7431	.6691	1.111
3°	.0523	.9986	.0524	49°	.7547	.6561	1.150
4°	.0698	.9976	.0699	50°	.7660	.6428	1.192
5°	.0872	.9962	.0875	51°	.7771	.6293	1.235
6°	.1045	.9945	.1051	52°	.7880	.6157	1.280
7°	.1219	.9925	.1228	53°	.7986	.6018	1.327
8°	.1392	.9903	.1405	54°	.8090	.5878	1.376
9°	.1564	.9877	.1584	55°	.8192	.5736	1.428
10°	.1736	.9848	.1763	56°	.8290	.5592	1.483
11°	.1908	.9816	.1944	57°	.8387	.5446	1.540
12°	.2079	.9781	.2126	58°	.8480	.5299	1.600
13°	.2250	.9744	.2309	59°	.8572	.5150	1.664
14°	.2419	.9703	.2493	60°	.8660	.5000	1.732
15°	.2588	.9659	.2679	61°	.8746	.4848	1.804
16°	.2756	.9613	.2867	62°	.8829	.4695	1.881
17°	.2924	.9563	.3057	63°	.8910	.4540	1.963
18°	.3090	.9511	.3249	64°	.8988	.4384	2.050
19°	.3256	.9455	.3443	65°	.9063	.4226	2.145
20°	.3420	.9397	.3640	66°	.9135	.4067	2.246
21°	.3584	.9336	.3839	67°	.9205	.3907	2.356
22°	.3746	.9272	.4040	68°	.9272	.3746	2.475
23°	.3907	.9205	.4245	69°	.9336	.3584	2.605
24°	.4067	.9135	.4452	70°	.9397	.3420	2.747
25°	.4226	.9063	.4663	71°	.9455	.3256	2.904
26°	.4384	.8988	.4877	72°	.9511	.3090	3.077
27°	.4540	.8910	.5095	73°	.9563	.2924	3.270
28°	.4695	.8829	.5317	74°	.9613	.2756	3.487
29°	.4848	.8746	.5543	75°	.9659	.2588	3.732
30°	.5000	.8660	.5774	76°	.9703	.2419	4.010
31°	.5150	.8572	.6009	77°	.9744	.2250	4.331
32°	.5299	.8480	.6249	78°	.9781	.2079	4.704
33°	.5446	.8387	.6494	79°	.9816	.1908	5.145
34°	.5592	.8290	.6745	80°	.9848	.1736	5.671
35°	.5736	.8192	.7002	81°	.9877	.1564	6.314
36°	.5878	.8090	.7265	82°	.9903	.1392	7.115
37°	.6018	.7986	.7536	83°	.9925	.1219	8.144
38°	.6157	.7880	.7813	84°	.9945	.1045	9.514
39°	.6293	.7771	.8098	85°	.9962	.0872	11.43
40°	.6428	.7660	.8391	86°	.9976	.0698	14.30
41°	.6561	.7547	.8693	87°	.9986	.0523	19.08
42°	.6691	.7431	.9004	88°	.9994	.0349	28.64
43°	.6820	.7314	.9325	89°	.9998	.0175	57.29
44°	.6947	.7193	.9657	90°	1.000	0.000	
45°	.7071	.7071	1.000				

INDEX

INDEX

SELECTED ANSWERS

PAGE 5

1. Answers may vary. **3.** coll. **5.** copl. but not coll. **7.** coll. **9.** segment **11.** Answers may vary. **13.** Answers may vary. **15.** T **17.** F **19.** F

PAGE 8

1. -2.5 **6.** .4 in.; 1 cm **13.** 3 **19.** DE

PAGE 12

1. $\ncong$ **5.** $\cong$ **9.** $\ncong$ **12.** $\cong$ **15.** See constr., p. 10 and Example 5, p. 11. **17.** See constr., p. 10 and Example 5, p. 11. **19.** 5 **22.** 4 **25.** See constr. and Example 4, p. 10. **27.** See constr. and Example 4, p. 10. **29.** N **32.** Q or C

ALGEBRA REVIEW

1. 3 **4.** 1 **7.** $\dfrac{4}{3}$ **10.** -1

PAGE 16

1. vertex R; sides $\overrightarrow{RX}$ and $\overrightarrow{RT}$ **3.** $43°$ **7.** See Example 4, p. 15. **10.** See Example 4, p. 15. **13.** $\cong$ **16.** See constr., p. 16. **19.** $40°$ **20.** $107°$ **21.** $110°$ **22.** $77°$ **23.** $115°$ **24.** $75°$ **25.** See constr., p. 16.

PAGE 22

1. G **3.** G; B **5.** E; I **7.** F **9.** G;B **11.** See constr., p. 21. **13.** 28 **15.** See constr., p. 21. **17.** 13

PAGE 24

1. $\overleftrightarrow{RT}$ **5.** $\overline{XW}$ **7.** T **9.** $\angle STV$ **11.** $\overrightarrow{VW}$ **13.** 3 **15.** 9 **17.** yes **19.** 30 **20.** 110 **21.** no **22.** no **25.** See constr., p. 11.

PAGE 25

1. $\overline{ST}$ **4.** $\overline{AD}$ **6.** $\{B\}$ **8.** -2 **10.** 6 **12.** yes **14.** 45 **15.** 63 **16.** yes **17.** yes **20.** 2 in.; 5 cm **21.** 110

PAGE 30

1. Answers may vary. **3.** $\angle SJY$ **5.** adj. **6.** no com. side **13.** Answers may vary. **15.** Answers may vary. **17.** F **19.** F **21.** T **23.** T **25.** T

PAGE 33

1. $140°$ **4.** $22°$ **7.** $65°$ **9.** $81\frac{1}{2}°$ **11.** $60°$ **13.** $90°$ **15.** $45°$ **17.** $44\frac{1}{3}°$ **19.** $62°$ **21.** $47°$

PAGE 38

1. 6 **3.** yes, if they are collinear **5.** yes **7.** no **9.** yes **11.** F **13.** F **15.** T **17.** F **19.** Assume that the 2 intersecting lines l and m are contained in 2 planes. Then pt. A on line l, pt. B on line m, and pt. C, their pt. of intersection, are 3 noncollinear pts. contained in 2 planes. This contradicts Post. 2.

ALGEBRA REVIEW

1. 7 **4.** 7

PAGE 44

1. $\angle DUT \cong \angle TUB$; def. of $\angle$ bis. **4.** $AB = CD$; subtr. prop. **7.** See Example 3, p. 42. **9.** See Example 4, p. 42. **12.** $m\angle YVW + m\angle RST = m\angle LMN + m\angle RST$ (trans. prop.); $m\angle YVW = m\angle LMN$ (subtr. prop.); $\angle YVW \cong \angle LMN$ (def. of $\cong$ $\angle$'s)

PAGE 48

1. 120 **4.** 75 **6.** 11 cm **8.** See Example 5, p. 47. **10.** See Example 8, p. 48. **12.** $m\angle 1 = m\angle 3$ (given and def. of $\cong$ $\angle$'s); $m\angle 1 + m\angle 2 = m\angle 3 + m\angle 2$ (add. prop.); $m\angle LVC = m\angle 1 + m\angle 2$ and $m\angle RVQ = m\angle 2 + m\angle 3$ (Post. 9); $m\angle LVC = m\angle RVQ$ (subst. prop.) **14.** $BR = CS$ and $RV = SV$ (given and def. of $\cong$ segments); $BR + RV = CS + RV$ (add. prop.); $BR + RV = CS + SV$ (subst. prop.); $BR + RV = BV$ and $CS + SV = CV$ (Post. 10); $BV = CV$ (subst. prop.); $\overline{BV} \cong \overline{CV}$ (def. of $\cong$ segments) **16.** $XZ = AC$ (given and def. of $\cong$ segments); $XY = \frac{1}{2} \times z$ (given); $xy = \frac{1}{2} AC$ (subst. prop.); $AB = \frac{1}{2} AC$ (given); $XY = AB$ (Subst. prop.); $\overline{XY} \cong \overline{AB}$ (def. of $\cong$ segments)

18. $JL = LK$ and $TS = SR$ (given and def. of seg. bis.); $JK = TR$ (given and def. of $\cong$ segments); $JK = JL + LK$ and $TR = TS + SR$ (Post. 10); $JL + LK = TS + SR$ (subst. prop.); $JL + JL = SR + SR$ (subst. prop.); $2JL = 2SR$ (add. prop.); $JL = SR$ (div. prop.); $\overline{JL} \cong \overline{SR}$ (def. of $\cong$ segments)

ALGEBRA REVIEW

1. $3x + 3y$ **4.** $-15x + 10y$ **7.** $2x^2 - 5x - 3$ **10.** $9x^2 + 24x + 16$ **13.** $a^2 - b^2$

PAGE 54

1. ∤ **5.** $\overrightarrow{OA} \perp \overrightarrow{OD}$; $\overrightarrow{OD} \perp \overrightarrow{OG}$; $\overrightarrow{OB} \perp \overrightarrow{OE}$ **7.** See constr., p. 51. **9.** $135 = 90 + \frac{1}{2}(90)$ **11.** $\angle TRY$ and $\angle TRX$ are rt. $\angle$'s (given and def. of $\perp$ lines); $\angle TRX \cong \angle TRY$ (all rt. $\angle$'s are $\cong$.)

PAGE 58

1. 120 **3.** 30 **5.** $\angle AOC \cong \angle BOD$ **8.** $m\angle TOP + m\angle POX = 180$ and $m\angle TOQ + m\angle QOX = 180$ (Post. 12); $\angle POX$ is suppl. of $\angle TOP$ and $\angle QOX$ is suppl. of $\angle TOQ$ (def. of suppl. $\angle$'s); $\angle TOP \cong \angle TOQ$ (given); $\therefore \angle POX \cong \angle QOX$ (Th. 2.6) **11.** Answers may vary. **13.** $\angle CBE \cong \angle CDE$ (given); $\angle ABF \cong \angle CBE$ (vert. $\angle$'s); $\angle ABF \cong \angle CDE$ (subst. prop.) **15.** $m\angle 1 + m\angle 2 = 180$ and $\angle 1 \cong \angle 2$ (given); $m\angle 1 = \angle 2$ (def. of $\cong \angle$'s); $m\angle 1 + m\angle 1 = 180$ (subst. prop.); $2m\angle 1 = 180$ (subst. prop.); $m\angle 1 = 90$ (div. prop.); $\therefore \angle 1$ and $\angle 2$ are rt. $\angle$'s. **17.** Need; $\angle AOB$ is comp. of $\angle BOC$; then use corollary to Th. 2.7.

PAGE 62

1. 78 **3.** 104 **5.** $90°$ **9.** $90°$ **13.** Answers may vary. **14.** T **15.** F **16.** F **17.** Answers may vary.

ALGEBRA REVIEW

1. 5 **4.** $x^5 + x^4 + x^3 - x^2 + x - 2$

PAGE 64

1. acute **4.** neither **7.** F **9.** T **11.** $m\angle RWS = m\angle SWT$ and $m\angle SWT = m\angle TWU$ (given and def. of $\cong$ $\angle$'s); $m\angle RWS = m\angle TWU$ (trans. prop.); $\angle RWS \cong \angle TWU$ (def. of $\cong \angle$'s) **13.** $LC = PQ$ (given); $LC + CP = PQ + CP$ (add. prop.) **15.** $110°$ **17.** 40 **19.** See Exercise 19, p. 38. **21.** See constr., p. 51.

PAGE 65

1. obtuse **4.** compl. **7.** T **9.** F **11.** F **13.** $CS = NT$ (given and def. of $\cong$ segments); $CS + SN = SN + NT$ (add. prop.); $CS + SN = CN$ and $SN + NT = ST$ (Post. 10); $CN = ST$ (subst. prop.); $\overline{CN} \cong \overline{ST}$ (def. of $\cong$ segments) **15.** $120°$ **17.** 38 **19.** **19.** Answers may vary. **21.** Bisect a $90°$ $\angle$.

PAGE 69

1. $\overleftrightarrow{XY} \parallel \overleftrightarrow{ZW}$ **4.** $\overleftrightarrow{AB} \parallel \overline{CD}$; $\overleftrightarrow{AB} \parallel \overrightarrow{EF}$; $\overline{CD} \parallel \overrightarrow{EF}$ **7.** F **9.** F **11.** F **13.** T **15.** ST **17.** AT **19.** ST **21.** ST **23.** AT

PAGE 72

1. $\overleftrightarrow{MS}$ **4.** none of these **5.** none of these **6.** alt. ext. **7.** alt. int. **8.** corr. **19.** F

PAGE 78

1. $m\angle s = 121$; $m\angle t = 59$; $m\angle u = 59$; $m\angle v = 121$; $m\angle w = 121$; $m\angle y = 59$; $m\angle z = 121$ **4.** Answers may vary. **5.** 70 **7.** $\angle TWU \cong \angle WYX$; $\angle UWY \cong \angle XYZ$; $\angle TWV \cong \angle WYS$; $\angle YWV \cong \angle ZYS$; $\angle UWY \cong \angle WYS$; $\angle VWY \cong \angle WYX$; $\angle TWV \cong \angle XYZ$; $\angle TWU \cong \angle SYZ$ **10.** $\angle ABC \cong \angle GFK$ (alt. ext. $\angle$'s); $\angle GFK \cong \angle HIK$ (corr. $\angle$'s); $\therefore \angle ABC \cong \angle HIK$ (trans. of $\cong$) **12.** $m\angle BEH = m\angle BED + m\angle DEH$ (Post. 9); $\angle CBE \cong \angle BED$ and $\angle EHJ \cong \angle DEH$ (alt. int. $\angle$'s); $m\angle CBE = m\angle BED$ and $m\angle EHJ = m\angle DEH$ (def. of $\cong \angle$'s); $\therefore m\angle BEH = m\angle CBE + m\angle EHJ$ (subst. prop.) **14.** $m\angle n = 117$; $m\angle l = 63$; $m\angle k = 117$; $m\angle y = 63$; $m\angle z = 117$; $m\angle x = 63$; $m\angle w = 117$; $m\angle u = 63$; $m\angle v = 117$; $m\angle t = 63$; $m\angle s = 117$; $m\angle q = 63$; $m\angle r = 117$; $m\angle p = 63$; $m\angle o = 117$ **17.** $m\angle w + m\angle x = 180$ and $m\angle y + m\angle z = 180$ (Th. 3.2); $\therefore m\angle w + m\angle x + m\angle y + m\angle z = 360$ (add. prop.). **20.** See diagram accompanying Example 5, p. 76. Given $l \parallel m$. Prove $\angle 1$ and $\angle 2$ are suppl. $\angle 1 \cong \angle 3$ (corr. $\angle$'s); $\angle 2$ and $\angle 3$ are suppl. (Post. 12); $\therefore \angle 1$ and $\angle 2$ are suppl. (subst. prop.). **21.** Alt. int. $\angle$'s are $\cong$ (Post. 13); vert. $\angle$'s are $\cong$ (Th. 2.8); $\therefore$ alt. ext. $\angle$'s are $\cong$ (subst. prop.);

PAGE 83

1. If the sum of the measures of two $\angle$'s is 180, then the $\angle$'s are suppl. T. **3.** If two coplanar lines are $\parallel$, then they are $\perp$ to the same line. F **5.** $\overleftrightarrow{BD} \parallel \overleftrightarrow{EH}$; $\cong$ vert. $\angle$'s: $\angle ACB$ and $\angle DCG$; $\angle ACD$ and $\angle BCG$; $\angle AFE$ and $\angle HFG$, $\angle EFG$ and $\angle AFH$; $\cong$ alt. int. $\angle$'s: $\angle DCG$ and $\angle AFH$, $\angle BCG$ and $\angle AFE$; $\cong$ alt. ext. $\angle$'s: $\angle ACD$ and $\angle HFG$, $\angle ACB$ and $\angle EFG$; $\cong$ corr. $\angle$'s: $\angle ACD$ and $\angle HFG$ **8.** $\angle CNV \cong \angle AOV$ (corr. $\angle$'s); $\angle ALR \cong \angle CNV$ (given); $\angle AOV \cong \angle ALR$ (trans. prop.); $RS \parallel VW$ (Th. 3.3) **11.** $l \not\parallel m$ **13.** $l \not\parallel m$ **15.** $\angle ADB \cong \angle DBC$ (given and alt. int. $\angle$'s); $m\angle ADB = m\angle DBC$ (def. of $\cong \angle$'s); $m\angle ABC = m\angle ADC$ (given and def. of $\cong \angle$'s); $m\angle ABC = m\angle ABD + m\angle DBC$ and $m\angle ADC = m\angle ADB + m\angle BDC$ (Post. 9); $m\angle ABD + m\angle DBC = m\angle ADB + m\angle BDC$ (subst. prop.); $m\angle ABD = m\angle BDC$ (subst. prop. and subtr. prop.); $\angle ABD \cong \angle BDC$ (def. of $\cong \angle$'s); $\overline{AB} \parallel \overline{DC}$ (Post. 14)

ALGEBRA REVIEW (PAGE 83)

1. $3x(x^2 - 5)$ **4.** $4b(b^2 - 6b + 12)$
7. $9m(2m^3 - 3m^2 - 5m + 4)$

PAGE 87

1. $\neq$ **2.** $=$ **3.** $\neq$ **10.** cannot tell **12.** cannot tell

PAGE 91

1. $m\angle A = m\angle B = 45$; $m\angle C = 90$ **3.** $m\angle A = 50$; $m\angle B = 60$; $m\angle C = 70$ **5.** 70 **6.** 133 **7.** too little info. **8.** too little info. **17.** $m\angle C = 90$ (given); $m\angle A + m\angle B = m\angle C = 180$ (Th. 3.5); $m\angle A + m\angle B = 90$ (subtr. prop.) **20.** Answers may vary. **22.** If $\angle A$ and $\angle B$ are both obtuse, then $m\angle A + m\angle B > 180$. But $m\angle A + m\angle B + m\angle C = 180$. **24.** If a transversal intersects the $\parallel$ lines at A and B, then $m\angle A + m\angle B = 180$ (int. $\angle$'s are suppl.) But $m\angle A + m\angle B + m\angle C = 180$.

PAGE 94

1. See constr., p. 93. **4.** See Exercise 3 and Example p. 94.

PAGE 97

1. T **3.** F **5.** F (Line could be contained in plane.) **7.** F (Line could be contained in either plane.) **9.** F **11.** F (Line could be contained in plane.) **13.** p and q have no pts. in common (def.); l on p (given); $l \parallel q$ (l and q have no pts. in common.) **15.** Line l intersects plane p in pt. X; line m on p. Assume $l \parallel m$; l and m are coplanar. But only pt. X on l is contained in plane p $\therefore$ $l \nparallel m$.

PAGE 98

1. $m\angle x = 50$; $m\angle v = 130$ **3.** 140 **5.** $\overleftrightarrow{AB} \parallel \overleftrightarrow{CD}$ **8.** F **10.** T **12.** $\nparallel$ **13.** $\parallel$ **15.** $m\angle URS = m\angle 1 + m\angle 3$ and $m\angle PQS = m\angle 2 + m\angle 4$ ($\angle$ add. post.); $m\angle 1 + m\angle 3 = m\angle 2 + m\angle 4$ (add. prop. of equations); $\angle URS \cong \angle PQS$ (subst. prop.); $\overrightarrow{RU} \parallel \overrightarrow{QP}$ (Th. 3.3)

PAGE 99

1. 46; 64 **3.** 60 **5.** T **7.** T **9.** T **11.** F **12.** If lines are coplanar, then they are $\parallel$. **14.** See Th. 3.5. **16.** Similar to Exercise 15, p. 84.

PAGE 103

1. Answers may vary. **3.** Answers may vary. **5.** T **7.** T **9.** T **11.** F **13.** T **15.** F **17.** J; $\overline{SJ}$, $\overline{JL}$; $\overline{SL}$; $\angle S, \angle L$ **19.** all isosceles rt. $\triangle$'s **21.** U; A; B; D **23.** Use def. of obtuse $\angle$, equiangular $\triangle$ and Th. 3.5.

PAGE 107

1. 30 **4.** 144 **7.** Use Ths. 2.8 and 2.4. **10.** $m\angle C + m\angle CDE + m\angle CED = 180 = m\angle C + m\angle A + m\angle B$ (Th. 3.5); $2m\angle CDE = 2m\angle A$ (subst., trans., substr. prop.); $m\angle CDE = m\angle A$ (div. prop.); use Th. 3.3. **12.** See Example 1, p. 104.

PAGE 113

1. b **2.** c **3.** $\triangle DEF$ **6.** $\triangle SMT$ **9.** Answers may vary. **12.** 17

PAGE 116

1. not necessarily $\cong$ **4.** $\cong$ **7.** yes; SSS **10.** 5 **13.** Use SSS. **16.** $\overline{SM}, \overline{VP}; \overline{MN}, \overline{PR}; \overline{NS}, \overline{RV}$ **18.** See const., p. 115. **20.** Use def. of equilateral $\triangle$ and SSS. **23.** See constr., p. 115. **25.** Consider two of the $\triangle$'s at a time and see Exercise 14.

PAGE 125

1. $\overline{LJ} \cong \overline{CP}$; $\overline{JK} \cong \overline{PQ}$; $\overline{LK} \cong \overline{CQ}$ **3.** $\cong$; SAS **6.** See Example 1, p. 122 and Example 5, p. 124. **8.** Use SAS. **11.** Use SAS. **14.** See Example 1, p. 122. **16.** Use ASA.

ALGEBRA REVIEW

1. $(x-5)(x-2)$ **4.** $(x+6)(x-6)$
7. $(2x-1)(x-3)$

PAGE 130

1. yes; SAS **2.** yes; AAS **3.** not necessarily **4.** not necessarily **5.** yes; AAS **6.** yes; SSS **7.** yes; ASA **8.** yes; SAS **9.** not necessarily **10.** yes; ASA **11.** Use ASA. **14.** Use ASA. **17.** $\angle VAQ \cong \angle AQP$ (alt. int. $\angle$'s); $\angle AQP \cong \angle TSP$ (corr. $\angle$'s); use AAS. **20.** Use Th. 4.1; ASA.

PAGE 132

1. equilateral; equiangular **5.** 93 **9.** congruent; ASA **12.** See Oral Exercise 7, p. 103. **14.** 82 **16.** yes; SSS **19.** Use SAS.

1. scalene; obtuse **5.** 50 **8.** yes; ASA **11.** See Exercise 4, p. 132. **13.** 95 **15.** Use SAS.

1. $m\angle R = 68$ **4.** See p. 135. **7.** Use SAS and corr. parts. **10.** 72 **12.** $\triangle APG \cong \triangle GCA$ (SAS); $\angle 1 \cong \angle 3$ (corr. parts); use Post. 14. **14.** $\triangle ADC \cong \triangle BDC$ (SAS); use corr. parts and def. of isos. $\triangle$.

1. $m\angle X = 70$; $m\angle Y = 70$; $m\angle Z = 40$ **3.** $m\angle t = 66$; $m\angle r = 114$ **6.** Use alt. int. $\angle$'s; corr. $\angle$'s; Th. 5.1. **9.** See Th. 5.2. diagram; use AAS; corr. parts. **11.** Use Th. 5.1; corr. $\angle$'s; Th. 5.2. **13.** Use Th. 5.1; ASA; corr. parts.

1. Answers may vary. **4.** Use Th. 5.1; SAS. **7.** Use ASA; corr. parts. **10.** Use Th. 2.6; Post. 10; ASA. **13.** $R\triangle GEC$ **14.** $R\triangle ABG$ **15.** $R\triangle DGC$ **16.** $R\triangle ABG$ **17.** $R\triangle AFG$

ALGEBRA REVIEW

1. $\dfrac{x-4}{x+3}$ **4.** $\dfrac{3(b-2)}{b+2}$

1. $\triangle DOA \cong \triangle BOC$ **4.** Use hyp–leg. **6.** Use SAS; corr. parts; def. of isos. $\triangle$. **8.** Use hyp–acute angle; corr. parts. **10.** Use corr. parts; hyp–acute angle; corr. parts.

1. $\overline{AB} = \overline{CD}$; $\overline{AE} \cong \overline{CE}$; $\overline{BE} \cong \overline{DE}$; $\angle EAB \cong \angle ECD$; $\angle ABE \cong \angle CDE$; $\angle BEA \cong \angle DEC$; $\triangle AED \cong \triangle CEB$ **4.** See Exercises 10–11, p. 150. **7.** $\triangle RQV \cong \triangle KAJ$ (SSS); See Exercise 10, p. 150. **10.** 54 **13.** $\triangle CBF \cong \triangle DAE$ (hyp–leg); $\triangle CBA \cong \triangle DAB$ (corr. parts and SAS); use corr. parts. **22.** $m\angle x = 42$ **25.** $\triangle WYM \cong \triangle TZM$ (Th. 5.1 and ASA); $\overline{WM} \cong \overline{TM}$ (corr. parts); $\angle WMZ \cong \angle TMY$ (Th. 2.6); use SAS and corr. parts. **28.** $\triangle ZXT \cong \triangle YXT$ (SSS); $\angle ZWX \cong \angle YXW$ (corr. parts); $\triangle ZXW \cong \triangle YXW$ (SAS); use corr. parts.

1. $\overline{TQ}$ is the $\perp$ bis. of $\overline{SM}$. **4.** Answers may vary. **6.** Answers may vary. **8.** Use SAS; corr. parts. **10.** Use ASA; corr. parts; def. of isos. $\triangle$. **12.** See Examples 4 and 5, p. 157. **14.** Use hyp–acute angle; corr. parts. **16.** Given isos. $\triangle ABC$ with base angles A and B and bisectors $\overline{AD}$ and $\overline{BE}$ intersecting at O; $\overline{AO} \cong \overline{BO}$ (Th. 5.2); $\triangle BDO \cong \triangle AEO$ (ASA); $\overline{OD} \cong \overline{OE}$ (corr. parts); $\overline{AD} \cong \overline{BE}$ (Post. 10) **18.** $\overline{EC} \cong \overline{EA}$ and $\overline{CD} \cong \overline{AD}$ (Th. 5.4); $\triangle EBC \cong \triangle EBA$ (hyp–leg); $\overline{BC} \cong \overline{BA}$ (corr. parts); use Th. 5.5. **20.** $\overline{DC} \cong \overline{BC}$ (Th. 5.2); $\angle ADX \cong \angle ABX$ (Post. 9 and subtr. prop.); $\overline{AD} \cong \overline{AB}$ (Th. 5.2); use Th. 5.5.

1. 50 **4.** $\overline{ZI}$, $\overline{LV}$; $\overline{WR}$, $\overline{JK}$; $\overline{TU}$, $\overline{QC}$ **6.** Use Th. 3.5; subtr. prop. **8.** Use ASA; corr. parts. **11.** Use hyp–acute angle; corr. parts. **13.** Use SAS; corr. parts. **15.** Use SSS; corr. parts; Th. 2.5; def. of altitude. **17.** Use SSS; corr. parts. **19.** T; use SAS; corr. parts. **21.** T; in $\triangle ABC$ with median $\overline{AD}$, draw $\perp$'s $\overline{DE}$ and $\overline{DF}$ to $\overline{AB}$ and $\overline{AC}$ resp.; $\triangle ADE \cong \triangle ADF$ (hyp–acute angle); $\triangle EDB \cong \triangle FDC$ (hyp–leg); use corr. parts and Th. 5.2. **23.** $\overline{CE} \cong \overline{AE}$ (Th. 5.4); $\triangle CBE \cong \triangle ABE$ (hyp–leg); $\overline{AB} \cong \overline{CB}$ (corr. parts); $\triangle CDB \cong \triangle ADB$ (SSS); $\angle CDB \cong \angle ADB$ (corr. parts); use Th. 2.5; def. of $\perp$ bisector. **26.** Use SAS. **27.** Use SAS. **28.** Use corr. parts from Exercises 26, 27; SSS.

1. Answers may vary. **3.** Answers may vary. **5.** Answers may vary. **7.** Answers may vary; no **8.** T **10.** F **12.** F **14.** Intersection is a point.

ALGEBRA REVIEW

1. $\dfrac{y+4}{3y-5}$ **4.** $\dfrac{x-3}{x+2}$

1. $\overline{XR}$, $\overline{QL}$; $\overline{RT}$, $\overline{LS}$; $\overline{TX}$, $\overline{SQ}$ **3.** $\overline{KC}$; $\overline{KA}$, $\overline{CA}$; $\overline{JN}$; $\overline{JY}$, $\overline{NY}$ **4.** leg–leg **7.** median; altitude; neither **8.** Use SAS; corr. parts. **10.** $\triangle CJQ \cong \triangle PQJ$ (hyp–leg); use corr. parts. **12.** 40 **14.** Answers may vary. **16.** Answers may vary.

PAGE 169

1. $\overline{PQ}, \overline{XY}$; $\overline{QR}, \overline{YZ}$; $\overline{RP}, \overline{ZX}$ 2. $\angle P, \angle X$; $\angle Q, \angle Y$; $\angle R, \angle Z$ 3. $\overline{DF}$; $\overline{DE}, \overline{FE}$ 4. $\overline{DE}$ or $\overline{FE}$; $\overline{EG}$
5. hypacute angle. 7. Answers may vary. 9. 43
11. Use LA; corr. parts; def. of isos. $\triangle$. 14. Answers may vary.

PAGE 173

1. not a union of segments 5. 1 endpoint shared by 4 segments 9. triangle 13. 7

PAGE 176

1. concave 5. convex 9. Answers may vary.
13. Answers may vary. 16. Answers may vary.
19. F 21. F 23. F

PAGE 180

1. $m\angle A = 80$; $m\angle B = 90$; $m\angle C = 90$; $m\angle D = 100$
4. 123 7. 540 10. 8,640 13. Answers may vary.
16. 5 20. 120 22. 156 24. Generalize from Examples 4 and 5, p. 179. 26. They are equal; use Post. 12 and Post. 9 to show the sum of the $\angle$'s having central pt. as vertex is 360; then use subtr. prop. 27. measures may vary; no; no

PAGE 183

1. 360 4. 360; yes 7. $7(180) - 5(180) = 360$
10. 60 12. $\dfrac{360}{n}$ 14. $m\angle p = 24$; $m\angle q = 48$;
$m\angle r = 72$; $m\angle s = 96$; $m\angle t = 120$

ALGEBRA REVIEW

1. $\dfrac{26 - 5y}{y^2 - 16}$

PAGE 187

1. Answers may vary. 5. 60 9. $128\frac{4}{7}$ 13. 120
17. 30 21. 3 25. 6 29. 4 35. not possible
41. F 43. F

ALGEBRA REVIEW

1. -15 4. 4 7. $\dfrac{5}{2}$

PAGE 191

1. See p. 189. 4. See p. 189. 10. $45 + 30$
16. Answers may vary. 18. Use a $135°$ angle.
20. Construct $45°$ angles at each end of the segment.

PAGE 192

1. polygon 6. convex 11. 540 13. 360
15. 120 17. T 19. F 21. $m\angle A = 80$; $m\angle B = 70$; $m\angle C = 100$; $m\angle D = 110$ 23. 9 25. See p. 189.

PAGE 193

1. not a union of segments 5. convex 9. 3,600
11. 108 13. F 15. $m\angle X = 80$; $m\angle Y = 90$; $m\angle Z = 100$; $m\angle W = 90$ 17. 10 19. See p. 190.

PAGE 197

1. $\overline{AC}, \overline{BD}$; yes 5. Answers may vary. 7. Answers may vary. 9. no 11. not necessarily
13. Opposite segments are parallel

PAGE 200

1. quad. $ABCD \cong$ quad. $EFGH$ 4. $\overline{BC}, \overline{MN}$; $\overline{CD}, \overline{NO}$; $\overline{DE}, \overline{OP}$; $\overline{EB}, \overline{PM}$; $\angle B, \angle M$; $\angle C, \angle N$; $\angle D, \angle O$; $\angle E, \angle P$ 6. $\overline{WX} \cong \overline{DE}, \angle X \cong \angle E$, and $\overline{XY} \cong \overline{EF}$ (given); $\triangle WXY \cong \triangle DEF$ (SAS) 8. 10 cm; 133
10. Use Th. 7.1. 12. Use Th. 7.1. 14. Use corr. parts; subtr. prop. of equations; Ths. 2.6, 2.8, 7.1.
16. Answers may vary. 18. Proof is similar to that for Th. 7.1

ALGEBRA REVIEW

1. 2

PAGE 205

1. $\overline{JM} \parallel \overline{KL}$; $\overline{JK} \parallel \overline{ML}$ 3. $\angle J \cong \angle L$; $\angle M \cong \angle K$
5. $m\angle S = m\angle U = 50$; $m\angle T = 130$ 7. $m\angle S = 60$; $m\angle B = 120$ 9. $m\angle P = 135$; $m\angle W = 45$ 11. $\cong$; Ths. 2.8, 7.4; SAS 14. See Exercise 13. 16. Use Ths. 3.2, 2.6. 17. yes; $\triangle XOD \cong \triangle YOB$ (ASA)
18. yes; $\triangle TOZ \cong \triangle UOX$ (ASA)

PAGE 208

1. yes 4. yes; def. 6. not necessarily 8. not necessarily 10. yes; Th. 7.6 12. yes; Th. 7.8
14. Use hypotheses; Th. 6.1; subst. prop.; div. prop. of equations; Th. 3.4 to show each pair of opposite sides are parallel. 16. yes; use Th. 3.4.
18. Use Ths. 7.2, 7.3; Post. 13; subst. prop. to prove 2 triangles formed by $\angle$ bisectors are congruent. Then use corr. parts; segment add. post; Th. 7.5.

PAGE 211

7. 1 **9.** $NW = \frac{1}{2} RY = RI$ and $IW = \frac{1}{2} RQ = RN$
(Th. 7.9 and def. of midpt.); use Th. 7.5. **11.** *Use*
Th. 7.8. **13.** Use Ths. 3.1, 7.3; subst. prop.; Th. 7.6.
15. Join midpoints of adjacent sides also; then use
Example 4, p. 210 and Th. 7.4.

PAGE 215

1. 5 **2.** 7 **3.** 4 **4.** $4\frac{1}{2}$ **5.** 12 **6.** $53\frac{1}{3}$ **7.** 24

8. $4\frac{1}{2}$ **9.** $12\frac{1}{2}$ **10.** $13\frac{3}{5}$ **11.** 10 **13.** 26 **15.** See
constr., p. 213. **18.** Use Ths. 3.3, 7.10. **20.** See constr.,
p. 213. **23.** F; draw isos. $\triangle ABC$ with median $\overline{CD}$;
draw $\overline{EF}$ the $\perp$ bis. of $\overline{CD}$.

PAGE 218

1. yes **4.** yes **7.** Use hyp–leg as in Example 4,
p. 218. **10.** not necessarily; see Example 3, p. 217.
12. not necessarily; see Example 3, p. 217.
14. yes; see Example 4, p. 210. **16.** yes; use Th. 7.8.

ALGEBRA REVIEW
1. 15

PAGE 223

1. 7 **3.** 15 **5.** 15 **7.** 10 **9.** 21 **11.** WZ = 14;
XY = 26. **13.** $MN = \frac{1}{2}(AB + DC)$ **15.** Refer to fig.
for Exercise 13; use def. of median, Ths. 7.12, 7.10 to
show $\overline{MN}$ bisects $\overline{BD}$; draw $\overline{AC}$ and use similar proof.
18. Draw rectangle $URPT$ with $UR = 1$ in., $RP = 2$ in.;
draw $\overline{PS}$ collinear with $\overline{RP}$ so that $PS = 1$ in.; draw
$\overline{ST}$. **20.** no

PAGE 226

1. one line thorugh each vertex $\perp$ opposite
side **5.** $\angle R, \angle V$; $\overline{RS}, \overline{VU}$; $\angle S, \angle U$; $\overline{ST}, \overline{UT}$
9. yes; no; yes; no **11.** yes; they are equal.
13. Use same strategy as for Th. 7.13 and $\angle$ add.
post. **14.** no

PAGE 230

1. $m\angle B = 72$; $m\angle C = 108$ **4.** $m\angle PON = 70$;
$m\angle PNO = 45$ **7.** Use Ths. 5.1, 7.17. **9.** yes;
properties of isos. trapezoid; SAS **11.** T; use Th.
3.2; properties of isos. trapezoid; subst. prop.
13. T; use Ths. 3.2, 2.6, 7.17

PAGE 233

1. parallelogram, rhombus, rectangle, square **3.** isos.
trapezoid, rectangle, square **5.** parallelogram,
rhombus, rectangle, square **7.** rhombus, square
9. isos. trapezoid, rectangle, square **11.** T **13.** T **15.** T
15. T **17.** $m\angle B = 100$; $m\angle C = 80$ **19.** See Example 2,
p. 232. **21.** See Example 3, p. 232. **22.** $\overline{TZ} \cong \overline{VZ}$
and $\overline{XT} \cong \overline{YV}$ by Example 2, p. 232, Th. 7.9, subst.
prop.; use segment add. post.

PAGE 236

1. isos. trapezoid, rectangle, square **3.** rhombus,
square **5.** rectangle **7.** none of these **9.** rectangle
11. rectangle **13.** use Th. 7.7; Example 2, p. 234.
15. Use Example 2, p. 234; Example 2, p. 232; def.
of square. **17.** $RSTU$ is a parallelogram by Example 4,
p. 210; draw $\overline{RT}$ and $\overline{US}$; $DRTC$ is a parallelogram (Th.
7.7); $\overline{RT} \cong \overline{DC}$ (Th. 7.2); similarly, $UDAS$ is a parallelogram and $\overline{DA} \cong \overline{US}$. Use Example 2, p. 232 to
show $\overline{RT} \cong \overline{US}$; then use Example 2, p. 234.
19. T; use Th. 7.5; def. of rhombus. **21.** F; see
Th. 7.4.

PAGE 238

1. Construct $90°$ angle; see Example 1, p. 237.
3. See Examples 1 and 2, p. 237. **5.** See Example
2, p. 237. **7.** Copy segment s with end points A and B.
Construct $\perp$ at A; using d as radius and B as center draw
arc intersecting $\perp$ at C; using C as center and s as radius
and using B as center and $\overline{AC}$ as radius draw arcs intersecting at D; $ABDC$ is required rectangle. **9.** Use construction for Exercise 8 through constructing $\perp$'s; then,
using A as center and d as radius, draw an arc intersecting $\overrightarrow{DF}$ at H; using B as center and d as radius,
draw an arc intersecting $\overrightarrow{CE}$ at G; $ABHG$ is required trapezoid. **11.** Construct $60°$ angle with
vertex A and sides $\overrightarrow{AB}$ and $\overrightarrow{AC}$; mark off $\overline{AD}$ on
$\overrightarrow{AB}$ and $\overline{AE}$ on $\overrightarrow{AC}$ with lengths b' and l respectively;
draw $\overrightarrow{EF} \parallel \overrightarrow{AB}$ with F on same side of $\overrightarrow{AC}$ as B;
mark off $\overline{EG}$ on $\overrightarrow{EF}$ with length b; $AEGD$ is
required trapezoid. **13.** See Exercise 10.

PAGE 241

1. reflections **4.** not reflections **7.** $\overrightarrow{AJ}$,
$\overrightarrow{BQ}$; $\overline{AC}, \overline{BL}$; $\overline{JC}, \overline{QL}$; $\angle A, \angle B$; $\angle J, \angle Q$; $\angle C, \angle L$
10. yes; Th. 7.18. **13.** T **15.** F **17.** Use Th.
7.18; $\angle$ add. post; SASAS. **18.** Construct $\perp$ bis. for
the segment joining any 2 corr. points.

PAGE 242

1. $\angle A, \angle C$; $\angle B, \angle D$ **3.** $\overline{DA}, \overline{AB}$; $\overline{AB}, \overline{BC}$; $\overline{BC}, \overline{CD}$; $\overline{CD}, \overline{DA}$ **5.** quadrilateral, trapezoid, parallelogram, rhombus, rectangle, square **10.** T **12.** T **14.** F **16.** F **18.** F **20.** T **22.** Use ASASA. **25.** Answers may vary. **27.** See constr., p. 213.

PAGE 243

1. $\angle A, \angle B$; $\angle B, \angle C$; $\angle C, \angle D$; $\angle D, \angle A$ **2.** $\overline{EF}$ **3.** $\overline{RQ}$ **4.** quadrilateral, trapezoid **7.** F **9.** T **11.** T **13.** F **15.** See Th. 7.15. **17.** See constr., p. 213.

PAGE 248

1. ST **3.** ST **5.** AT **7.** 15 in. **9.** yes **11.** T; use def. of parallelogram; Th. 7.2; SSS.

PAGE 251

1. T **5.** T **9.** 10 **13.** 2 **17.** Answers may vary. **21.** $\frac{4}{6}$ **23.** $\frac{9}{7}$ **27.** 36; 54 **29.** 55; 66 **31.** T; use product of means = product of extremes and comm. prop. for mult. **33.** T; $\frac{b}{b} = \frac{d}{d} = 1$; use add. prop. **35.** T; follows from Exercises 33 and 31. **37.** T; $\frac{n}{n} = \frac{m}{m} = 1$; $x \cdot 1 = x$

PAGE 255

1. $\angle A, \angle D$; $\angle B, \angle E$; $\angle C, \angle F$ **3.** yes **5.** $3\frac{1}{2}$; $DF = 3$ **8.** $TS = 12$; $LK = 18$ **11.** yes; ratios of corr. sides are all $\frac{1}{1}$. **13.** yes

ALGEBRA REVIEW

1. $2\sqrt{2}$ **5.** $6\sqrt{5}$ **9.** $\sqrt[r]{s}$

PAGE 259

1. $8\frac{3}{4}$ **3.** 26 **5.** TQ **7.** $\frac{NX}{NC}$ or $\frac{XT}{CQ}$ **9.** 12 **11.** $\frac{9\sqrt{3}}{7\sqrt{5} - 3\sqrt{3}}$ **13.** Use Ths. 8.2, 3.1; subst. prop. **15.** $\frac{MB}{WM} = \frac{XT}{WX}$ and $\frac{WX}{XT} = \frac{SN}{NT}$ (Th. 8.1); use Exercise 31, p. 252 and subst. prop.

PAGE 262

1. Use Th. 8.3. **4.** 10 **6.** yes **8.** Use Ths. 2.8, 8.3. **11.** $m\angle TQC = m\angle TMC = 90$; $\angle T$ and $\angle QCM$ are supplements (Th. 6.1); $\angle JCP$ and $\angle JCQ$ are supplements; use corollary to Th. 2.6 to show $\angle T \cong \angle JCP$; similarly, $\angle X \cong \angle PJC$; use Th. 8.3.

PAGE 265

1. $\sim$; AA **4.** yes **7.** no **10.** yes **12.** no **14.** no **16.** yes **18.** yes **20.** yes **22.** If measure of vertex angle $= x$, then measure of base angle $= \frac{1}{2}(180 - x)$; use Th. 8.3. **24.** $\triangle D'E'C \cong \triangle DEF$ (SAS); $\frac{D'C}{AC} = \frac{E'C}{BC}$ (subst. prop.); $AC = AD' + D'C$ and $BC = BE' + E'C$ (segment add. post.); $\frac{D'C}{AD' + D'C} = \frac{E'C}{BE' + E'C}$ (subst. prop.); $\frac{AD'}{D'C} + \frac{D'C}{D'C} = \frac{BE'}{E'C} + \frac{E'C}{E'C}$ (algebraic properties); $\frac{AD'}{D'C} = \frac{BE'}{E'C}$ (subtr. prop. of equations); $\overline{D'E'} \parallel \overline{AB}$ (Th. 8.2); $\angle D \cong \angle D' \cong \angle A$ and $\angle E \cong \angle E' \cong \angle B$ (corr. parts and Th. 3.1); use Th. 8.3. **25.** See sketch for Exercise 24; $\frac{DE}{AB} = \frac{FE}{CB} = \frac{FD}{CA}$ (given); construct $\overline{CD'} \cong \overline{FD}$ and $\overline{CE'} \cong \overline{FE}$; $\frac{CD'}{CA} = \frac{CE'}{CB}$ (subst. prop.); $\triangle ABC \sim \triangle D'E'C$ (Th. 8.4); $\frac{D'E'}{AB} = \frac{CD'}{CA}$ (def. of $\sim \triangle$'s); $\frac{D'E'}{AB} = \frac{FD}{CA}$ (subst. prop.); $\frac{FD}{CA} = \frac{DE}{AB}$ (given); $\frac{D'E'}{AB} = \frac{DE}{AB}$ (subst. prop.); $D'E' = DE$ (mult. prop. of equations); $\triangle D'E'C \cong \triangle DEF$ (SSS); $\angle C \cong \angle F$ (corr. parts); use Th. 8.4.

PAGE 269

1. $\angle J, \angle P$; $\angle Q, \angle R$; $\angle C, \angle D$; $\angle V, \angle T$; $\angle N, \angle L$ **3.** $m\angle Q = 39$; $m\angle G = 162$ **6.** 12 **8.** $NO = 2$; $OL = 1$ **11.** 3 sides and 2 angles or 2 sides and 3 angles **13.** Use def. of $\sim$ polygons.

PAGE 271

1. $\angle ZTS \cong \angle X$ (def. of $\sim \triangle$'s); use Th. 3.3, 3.1, 8.3. **3.** Use def. of $\perp$ lines; Ths. 2.8, 8.3. **5.** Use defs. of altitude, $\perp$ lines; Th. 8.3. **7.** Use Post. 13; Ths. 7.3, 8.3. **10.** Use def. of $\sim \triangle$'s; def. of $\angle$ bis; Th. 8.3. **12.** Use Th. 5.1; def. of $\perp$ lines; Th. 8.3. **15.** Given equilateral triangles ABC and $A'B'C'$: Prove $\triangle ABC \sim \triangle A'B'C'$.

1. $AC = 4\frac{1}{2}$; $CL = 7\frac{1}{2}$ 3. 49 5. $LC = 21$;
$CQ = 35$ 7. $\frac{XT}{LP} = \frac{TC}{PQ} = \frac{CX}{QL}$ 8. Use Th. 8.3;
def. of $\sim \triangle$'s. 11. Use Post. 13; Th. 8.3; def of $\sim \triangle$'s.
14. See constr., p. 274. 16. See Exercise 12.

PAGE 277
1. 96 3. Use Th. 8.3; def. of $\sim \triangle$'s; product of
means = product of extremes. 6. Use Post. 13;
Th. 8.3; def. of $\sim \triangle$'s; product of means = product
of extremes. 9. 128 12. $\angle 1 + \angle 2 = \angle 3 + \angle 4 = 90°$ (def. of $\perp$ lines); $\angle 2 = \angle 3$ (Th. 2.7); use Th. 8.8;
product of means = product of extremes. 15. $\triangle XFZ$
$\sim \triangle RFP$ (Post. 13, Th. 8.3); $\frac{ZF}{PF} = \frac{XF}{RF}$ (def. of $\sim \triangle$'s);
$\frac{RF}{FX} = \frac{RZ}{ZX}$ (Th. 8.8); use Exercise 31, p. 252 and substitution; product of means = product of extremes.

PAGE 281
1. $10\frac{2}{7}$ 3. $DE = 6$; $EF = 9$ 5. 12 7. Using
def. of $\sim \triangle$'s, show $\frac{BX}{BA} = \frac{BZ}{BF} = \frac{BY}{BC}$; use Th. 8.4.
9. $\frac{AS}{AY} = \frac{AT}{AZ}$ (given); $\angle TAS \cong \angle YAZ$ (Th. 2.8);
$\triangle ATS \sim \triangle AZY$ (Th. 8.4) 11. $\frac{NT}{TW} = \frac{RQ}{QW}$ and $\frac{AC}{CW} = \frac{NT}{TW}$ (Th. 8.1); use subst. prop.

PAGE 282
1. $\not\sim$ 4. 10 8. $\sim$; SAS 11. AT 13. 9
16. $NP = 20$; $NC = 30$ 18. Use Th. 8.3.

PAGE 283
1. $\sim$ 4. 15 6. $\sim$; AA 9. 15 11. Use
Post. 13; Th. 8.3. 14. ST

PAGE 287
1. $\triangle RJD \sim \triangle DJC \sim \triangle RDC$ 3. 2 5. 9
7. 4 9. 3 11. 8 13. 9 15. $8\sqrt{2}$ 17. 10
19. See Example 1, p. 285. 21. $\triangle SVL \sim \triangle LVC$
and $\triangle LVC \sim \triangle LTV$ (Th. 9.1); use def. of $\sim \triangle$'s; Th.
8.3. 23. $ZH = 8$; $XZ = 8\sqrt{5}$ 25. $HY = 4$; $ZY = 2\sqrt{13}$ 27. Use Th. 9.1; def. of $\sim \triangle$'s; product of
means = product of extremes.

PAGE 290
1. can 5. cannot 9. can 13. cannot 17. 13
21. 5 25. $\sqrt{5}$ 29. 10 in. 31. 39 cm 33. $s\sqrt{2}$
35. $9\frac{3}{13}$ 37. $14\frac{1}{12}$ 39. Use Th. 9.2; add. prop.
of equations. 42. 13 45. $2\frac{2}{5}$

PAGE 293
1. yes 5. yes; $\angle B$ 8. no 11. yes 14. Multiply
each side of equation by v^2g^2; use Th. 9.3. 16. yes
19. no 22. $(AD)^2 + (CD)^2 = (AC)^2$ and $(CD)^2 + (DB)^2 = (CB)^2$ (Th. 9.2); $(AC)^2 + (CB)^2 = (AD)^2 + 2(CD)^2 + (DB)^2$ (add. prop. of equations); $AD \cdot DB = (CD)^2$ since $\frac{AD}{CD} = \frac{CD}{DB}$ (given and product of means
= product of extremes); use subst. and distr. proper-
ties to show $(AC)^2 + (CB)^2 = (AD + DB)^2 = (AB)^2$;
use Th. 9.3. 24. Use indirect proof; Th. 9.2.

ALGEBRA REVIEW
1. $15\sqrt{2}$ 4. $\sqrt{2}$ 7. $8\sqrt{5}$ 10. 5 13. 8

PAGE 299
1. $BC = 18$; $CA = 18\sqrt{3}$ 3. $AB = 18$; $CA = 9\sqrt{3}$
5. $AB = 12$; $BC = 6$ 7. $XZ = YZ = 6\sqrt{2}$ 9. $XY = 6$; $YZ = 3\sqrt{2}$ 11. $XY = 4\sqrt{2}$; $XZ = 4$ 13. $10\sqrt{3}$
15. $LM = 6\sqrt{2}$; $JK = 12\sqrt{2}$ 17. See Example 1,
p. 297. 19. Using properties of rhombi obtained in
Chapter 7, $\angle URV = 30°$ and $\angle RUV = 60°$; in $\triangle RUV$,
$RU = $ hyp., $UV = l$, $RV = l'$; then $RS + ST + TU + UR = 4$(hyp.), $RT = 2l'$, and $SU = 2l$. Use Th. 9.5
and subst. prop. to disprove.

PAGE 302
1. .416, .384, .923, 2.400, .923, .384 4. 1.118,
.745, .666, .894, .666, .745 7. 1.732 8. .866
9. .500 13. .434, .400, .916, 2.291, .916, .400
16. $\sin B = \frac{b}{c} = \cos A$ 18. $\tan B = \frac{b}{a} = \frac{1}{\tan A}$
20. See Exercise 18.

PAGE 304
1. 15° 4. 7° 7. 65° 10. 54° 13. T 16. T
19. T 22. F 24. T 26. F 28. Hypotenuse is
longest side. 30. $\frac{\sin A}{\cos A} = \left(\frac{a}{c}\right) \div \left(\frac{b}{c}\right) = \frac{a}{b} = \tan A$

PAGE 307

1. 5.3 **5.** 19.3 **9.** 1.9 **11.** 37° **13.** 41°
15. 13.8 **17.** 22.5 **19.** 6.2 **21.** 37° **23.** 39°
25. $AB \doteq 7.9$; $BC = 1.3$; $m\angle A = 28$ **28.** $AB \doteq 5.4$;
$m\angle A \doteq 68$; $m\angle B \doteq 22$

PAGE 310

1. 46.6 ft **5.** 10.4 m **7.** 8° **9.** 93.2 ft
11. 55.6 ft **13.** 17.5 **15.** 50°; 50°; 80°

PAGE 312

1. $\triangle RJB \sim \triangle TRB \sim \triangle TJR$ **3.** $\sqrt{89}$ **5.** yes **8.** $YZ = 2$; $XZ = 2\sqrt{3}$ **10.** $RS = TS = 3\sqrt{2}$ **12.** .750
14. .5299 **17.** 28° **20.** 5.5 **22.** 18.1 ft

PAGE 313

1. $\triangle XBP \sim \triangle XPH \sim \triangle PBH$ **3.** $\sqrt{65}$ **5.** yes
8. $JT = 6$; $LJ = 6\sqrt{3}$ **10.** .923 **11.** 2.400
12. .4695 **14.** 18.0 **16.** 46.2 ft

PAGE 317

1. $\triangle AOB \cong \triangle COB$ **3.** 6 **4.** $\sqrt{39}$ **7.** Use Ths.
10.1, 5.1. **9.** Use def. of radius, circle. **11.** Use
Ths. 10.1, 7.8, 7.2. **13.** Use def. of $\perp$ lines, Th. 3.2
to show $OY \perp TU$; then use Th. 10.2. **16.** half as far

PAGE 320

1. $\cong$ **3.** $\not\cong$ **5.** $\not\cong$ **7.** $\not\cong$ **9.** 16 **11.** $\overline{RM} \cong$
$\overline{MS} \cong \overline{NT} \cong \overline{NU}$; $\overline{AM} \cong \overline{BN}$ **14.** 6 **16.** $\triangle XRT$
$\cong \triangle YOT \cong \triangle WOU \cong \triangle ZOU$ (Th. 10.1, hyp–leg); use
corr. parts; segment add. post.; SSS. **18.** See Example
1, p. 319. **20.** Use Th. 10.2; SAS; corr. parts; def.
of congruent circles.

PAGE 325

1. 8 **4.** 40 **7.** $\overline{PQ} \cong \overline{PW} \cong \overline{PH}$ **10.** Draw $\overline{OX}$,
$\overline{OC}$; see proof of Th. 10.7; use corr. parts.
13. $m\angle OXT = \frac{1}{2} m\angle JXT$ and $m\angle OTX = \frac{1}{2} m\angle VTX$
(Exercise 10); $m\angle OXT + m\angle OTX = 90$ (Th. 3.5);
use add., mult. properties of equations; Th.3.4. **16.** 24

ALGEBRA REVIEW

1. 25 **4.** 16 **7.** 4

PAGE 330

1. 80 **5.** $\overarc{AB}$; $\overarc{BC}$; $\overarc{AC}$; $\overarc{CD}$; $\overarc{DA}$ **6.** $\overarc{ADB}$;
$\overarc{BDC}$; $\overarc{ADC}$; $\overarc{CBD}$; $\overarc{DCA}$ **7.** $\overarc{DAB}$; $\overarc{DCB}$ **10.** $m\overarc{LQ}$
$= m\overarc{VC} = 56$; $m\angle V = m\overarc{CQ} = 124$ **12.** 101 **13.** 79
14. 180 **15.** 101 **20.** $m\overarc{KJ} = 62$, $m\overarc{JI} = 27$, and
$m\overarc{IH} = 79$ contradict $\overline{HK}$ is a diameter; $m\overarc{JI} = 27$,
$m\overarc{IH} = 79$, and $m\overarc{HG} = 74$ contradict $\overline{GJ}$ is a diameter.

PAGE 333

1. no **2.** yes **3.** no **5.** $\overline{CD} \cong \overline{PQ}$; $\overline{PD} \cong \overline{CQ}$;
$\overarc{PQD} \cong \overarc{CDQ}$ **8.** $\overarc{AB} \cong \overarc{CD}$; $\overarc{AB} \cong \overarc{FG}$; $\overarc{BC} \cong \overarc{HI}$;
$\overarc{DF} \cong$ none **9.** Use Th. 10.8. **11.** 108 **13.** Use Ths.
5.2, 10.9; def. of minor arc measure. **15.** Use def. of
minor arc measure to show $\angle KOL \cong \angle MOL$; use Th.
2.6; SAS; corr. parts. **17.** See Example 2, p. 331.
19. Draw $\overline{ON}$; use def. of minor arc measure; hypacute angle; corr. parts.

PAGE 338

1. 43 **5.** 90 **9.** $m\angle K = 54$; $m\angle KTW = 72$
12. Similar to proof for Case I; use $\angle$ add. post.
14. Angle intercepts minor arc; thus, angle
measure is less than $\frac{1}{2}(180) = 90$.

PAGE 340

1. 31 **2.** 43 **3.** 137 **4.** 12 **9.** $m\angle J = 67$;
$m\angle B = 94$ **12.-13.** 122 **14.** 61 **15.** 116
19. Use Th. 2.8; def. of minor arc measure; Th.
10.10. **22.** $m\angle BLX = 90$ (Th. 10.10); use Th.
9.1. **24.** Given $\triangle ABC$ and $\triangle A'B'C'$ with $\angle A \cong$
$\angle A'$, $\angle B \cong \angle B'$; $\overarc{BC} \cong \overarc{B'C'}$ (Th. 10.10); use Th. 10.8;
AAS. **26.** Given inscribed quad. $ABCD$ with
$\angle A \cong \angle B$; $\angle B$ and $\angle C$ are supplementary and $\angle C \cong$
$\angle D$ (Example 5, p. 340 and subst. prop.); use Th.
3.4., 7.17.

PAGE 344

1. 21 **3.** 84 **5.** $m\angle KRT = 6$; $m\angle C = 109$
8. 109 **11.** Use. Th. 10.11; mult. prop. of equations.
14. See Example 3, p. 343.

PAGE 347

1. 76 **2.** 109 **5.** 71 **6.** 238 **9.** 32
10. 141 **11.** 90 **12.** 99 **13.** 72 **14.** 50
15. $m\angle CAD = 60$; $m\angle DBA = 30$ **18.** See Example 2, p. 346. **20.** $m\widehat{US} = m\widehat{VS}$ (Th. 10.9);
$m\angle U = \frac{1}{2}m\widehat{VS}$ (Th. 10.10); $m\angle USR = \frac{1}{2}\,m\widehat{US}$
(Th. 10.13); use subst. prop.; Post. 14. **22.** Use Ths. 10.13, 2.8.

PAGE 351

1. 3 **2.** 18 **3.** 12 **7.** 6 **9.** 12 **11.** $RW = 13\frac{1}{3}$;
$SX = 11$ **14.** Use Ths. 10.10, 8.3; product of
means = product of extremes. **16.** $LP = 28$; $SP = 21$ **18.** Show $\triangle XZT \sim \triangle LXT$ as in proof of
Th. 10.18; use product of means = product of extremes.
21. $MC \cdot MG = (MT)^2 = MB \cdot MF$ (Th. 10.18)

PAGE 355

1. Answers may vary. **3.** See constr., p. 353.
5. Construct $\perp$ at the point, designated A; mark off
1 in. segment $\overline{AO}$ on $\perp$; desired circle has center O.
8. Answers may vary. **10.** Use Th. 5.4; def. of
circle. **11.** Center of circle will be intersection of
diagonals; length of radius = $\frac{1}{2}$ length of side.

13. Find s so that $s^2 + \frac{s^2}{4} = r^2$; then mark point P

at a distance of $\frac{s}{2}$ from O along the diameter; at P

draw a perpendicular; the line intersects the semicircle at Q, a vertex of the square; $PQ = s$; at
Q, draw a perpendicular of length s; the point R
where this perpendicular intersects the circle is the
third vertex; finally construct the perpendicular
from R to the diameter of the semicircle. **15.** See
Exercise 14; $x = \sqrt{ab}$ **18.** Use Exercise 14.

PAGE 356

1. $\overline{OE}$; $\overline{OF}$; $\overline{OG}$ **3.** $\overrightarrow{BD}$ **5.** $\overline{EG}$ **7.** no
8.-9. yes **10.** no **11.** no **15.** 82 **16.** 64
19. $32\frac{1}{2}$ **20.** 115 **23.** 119; 50 **27.** See
constr., p. 353. **28.** $\angle A \cong \angle B \cong \angle C \cong \angle D$ (Th. 5.1);
$\triangle AOB \cong \triangle CPD$ (AAS); use corr. parts; Th. 10.9.

PAGE 357

1. $\overline{CD}$ **2.** $\odot O$ **3.** $\overleftrightarrow{HJ}$ **4.** $\widehat{CBD}$ **5.** Answers
may vary. **6.** yes **7.** no **8.** yes **12.** 160 **13.** 57
16. 20 **19.** $\overline{CJ} \cong \overline{PT}$ (Th. 10.8); $m\widehat{CP} = 180 - m\widehat{CJ} = 180 - m\widehat{PT} = m\widehat{JT}$; use Th. 10.10;
Post. 14; Th. 7.7 to show a parallelogram;
$\angle C$ is a rt. $\angle$ (Th. 10.10); use def. of rectangle.

PAGE 361

1. figure on left **3.** 18.75 sq yd **6.** 7.875
sq m **9.** 36 sq yd **12.** $x^2 - y^2$ **15.** 46 cm
18. $x + 1$ **21.** 12 **23.** $6\sqrt{10}$ **25.** 84 sq in.
28. 128 sq in. **30.** Use div. prop. of equations.

ALGEBRA REVIEW

1. $\frac{b}{5}$ **4.** $6a$ **7.** $3 - x$

PAGE 365

1. 6 sq in. **5.** 9.69 sq in. **9.** 16 cm **10.** $2\sqrt{5}$ in.
11. 18 ft **12.** 1.6 yd **13.** $2\frac{1}{4}$ in. **14.** $x^2 - 9$
15. $2(x + 4)$ **16.** $4(x + 2)$ **17.** $16\sqrt{3}$ sq ft
19. 6 **21.** $4\frac{2}{3}$ **23.** 30 sq cm **26.** Choose similar
triangles with noncongruent bases. **28.** similar to
Exercise 31, p. 362 **30.** Each of smaller triangles
has same height as original triangle; base of each is of
length one half that of original; thus, areas are
equal (mult. prop. of equations).

PAGE 369

1. 63 sq in. **5.** 8 cm **6.** .08 in. **7.** $\frac{8}{9}$ ft
8. $\sqrt{7}$ yd **9.** $3x^2 + 5x - 2$ **10.** $3x + 4$
11. $4x - 1$ **12.** 9 **14.** $14\frac{2}{5}$ **16.** no **20.** 20

PAGE 374

1. 28 sq in. **5.** $103\frac{1}{2}$ sq ft **6.** 6 cm **7.** 3 in.
8. $4x^2 - 2x - 2$ **9.** $x - 4$ **10.** $2x - 1$ **11.** 15 cm;
19 cm **13.** $100\sqrt{3}$ **15.** See Example 1, p. 372.
16. 36.1 **18.** $s = \frac{(a + b)h}{2}$ and $s' = \frac{(a' + b')h'}{2}$
(Th. 11.4); $\frac{(a + b)h}{2} = \frac{(a' + b')h'}{2}$ and
$\frac{(a + b)}{(a' + b')} = \frac{h'}{h}$ (subst. prop. and mult., div. properties)

PAGE 378

1. 21 **4.** $4(2x + 1)$ **7.** $\frac{36}{16}$; $\frac{6}{4}$ **10.** 24 sq in.
12. See Exercise 27, p. 366. **14.** Use strategy of proof of Exercise 27, p. 366.

PAGE 381

1. $\frac{25\sqrt{3}}{4}$ sq cm **5.** 79.21 sq ft **9.** $9\sqrt{3}$ **10.** $\sqrt{3}$
11. $192\sqrt{3}$ **12.** 100 **13.** 3 **14.** 7 **15.** $\frac{7}{2}$
16. $216\sqrt{3}$ **17.** $2\sqrt{3}$ **18.** 484 **19.** 1.2 **20.** 3 cm
24. 5; $75\sqrt{3}$ **25.** $12\sqrt{3}$; $324\sqrt{3}$ **26.** $2\sqrt{2}$; 32
27. $4\sqrt{2}$; 64 **28.** $4\sqrt{3}$; $96\sqrt{3}$ **29.** 8; $96\sqrt{3}$
30. 4; 2; $4\sqrt{3}$ **31.** $\frac{5\sqrt{2}}{2}$; $\frac{5}{2}$; 5 **32.** $\frac{4\sqrt{3}}{3}$; 2;
$\frac{4\sqrt{3}}{3}$ **33.** See Example 4, p. 380. **34.** Consider
equilateral $\triangle$'s with sides of length $2\sqrt{3}$ and $4\sqrt{3}$
respectively. **36.** apothem: 3.24; area: 38.04
37. radius: 4.94; area: 58.12 **38.** radius 1.30;
apothem: 1.05 **39.** apothem: 5.64; area: 104.18
40. radius: 10.64; area: 327.60 **41.** radius: 2.04;
apothem: 1.91 **42.** apothem: 7.61; area: 188.09
43. radius: 6.31; area: 116.99 **44.** radius: 1.84;
apothem: 1.75

PAGE 385

1. 6.8π in. **5.** $d = 4$ in.; $C \doteq 12.56$ in. **6.** $r = 4$ cm; $C \doteq 25.12$ cm **7.** $d = 1.44$ ft; $C \doteq 4.5216$ ft
8. $r \doteq 1.496$ yd; $d \doteq 2.993$ yd **9.** $r = .32$ yd; $C \doteq 2.0096$ yd **10.** $d = 64$ mi; $C \doteq 200.96$ mi **11.** $r \doteq 4.299$ cm; $d \doteq 8.598$ cm **12.** $r \doteq .748$ ft; $d \doteq 1.496$ ft
13. $r \doteq 2.070$ ft; $d \doteq 4.140$ ft **14.** $r = 3.10$ cm; $C \doteq 19.468$ cm **15.** Answers may vary. **16.** $r \doteq .12$ ft; $C = .75$ ft **20.** $3\frac{1}{7}$ **22.** $8,000\pi$ **24.** $S = \sqrt{2}$; $P = 4\sqrt{2}$; $C = 2\pi$; $C > P$ **26.** If $2\pi r = 4s$,
then $r = \frac{4s}{2\pi} = \frac{2s}{\pi}$.

PAGE 389

1. 1.5386 sq in. **5.** 7.065 sq cm **9.** 78.50 sq in.
13. $r \doteq 10$ cm; $d \doteq 20$ cm **17.** area of square = 4 sq in.; area of circle $\doteq$ 3.14 sq in. **19.** $\sqrt{3}$
$-\frac{1}{3}\pi$ sq in. **23.** $12\frac{1}{2}\pi$ **26.** Consider circles with
radii 1 and 2 respectively. **28.** $\frac{1}{2}$

PAGE 392

1. 20 in.; $\frac{5\pi}{2}$ in. **2.** 3 yd; $\frac{\pi}{2}$ yd **3.** 5 cm; $\frac{5\pi}{3}$ cm
4. $\frac{2}{3}$ ft; $\frac{25\pi}{27}$ ft. **5.** 2π cm; $\frac{5\pi^2}{3}$ cm **6.** 120 ft;
240 ft **7.** 12 yd; 24 yd **8.** 10.8 cm; 21.6 cm
9. $1\frac{1}{8}$ in.; $2\frac{1}{4}$ in. **10.** 1 in. 2 in. **11.** $22\frac{1}{2}$;
16 yd **12.** 108; 5 cm **13.** 360; 5 ft **14.** 90;
$\frac{1}{3}$ cm **15.** 180; .4 yd **16.** 13 in. **18.** $\frac{88\pi}{15}$
20. $\frac{35\pi}{9}$

ALGEBRA REVIEW

1. $1 - \frac{\sqrt{7}}{7}$

PAGE 396

1. 7.2π sq in. **3.** 60, $\frac{25\pi}{6}$ sq cm; $\frac{50\pi - 75\sqrt{3}}{12}$
sq cm **4.** 90, $\frac{25\pi}{4}$ sq in.; $\frac{25\pi}{4} - 12.5983$ sq in.
5. 120; $\frac{64\pi}{3}$ sq ft; $\frac{64\pi}{3} - 16\sqrt{3}$ sq ft **6.** 90;
90; $25\pi - 50$ sq cm **7.** 120; 6 in.; $12\pi - 9\sqrt{3}$ sq in.
8. 20π sq in. **10.** $\frac{27\pi}{2} - \frac{81\sqrt{3}}{4}$ sq in. **12.** 36π
sq cm **14.** 4 in. **16.** doubled **19.** $\pi(R^2 - r^2)$
21. $\frac{170\pi}{9} - 46.3577$ sq cm

PAGE 398

1. left **2.** 126 sq in. **5.** $31\frac{1}{2}$ sq ft **8.** 28
10. 12π in. **12.** $\frac{20\pi}{9}$ **13.** $\frac{64\pi}{5}$ sq cm **16.** 9:4
18. 72π sq ft

PAGE 399

1. left **2.** 289 sq ft **5.** 48 sq yd **8.** 9π sq in.
11. $25\sqrt{3}$ sq cm **14.** 54:24 **15.** 56π sq cm

PAGE 403

1. See Example 2, p. 402 **3.** vertical **7.** vertical
11. neither **15.** 2 **18.** 4 **21.** 2; 3 **22.** 4
23. 1 **24.** 2 **25.** 3 **26** (2, 4) **28.** (4, 3)

PAGE 406

1. $\sqrt{13}$ **5.** $3\sqrt{10}$ **9.** $\sqrt{178}$ **13.** $AB = BC = \sqrt{29}$, $AC = 4$; isos. **16.** $AB = AC = 5$, $BC = 2\sqrt{5}$: isos. **19.** $RS = \sqrt{104}$, $ST = \sqrt{32}$, $RT = \sqrt{72}$; $(RS)^2 = (ST)^2 + (RT)^2$

PAGE 409

1. $(1, 2)$ **5.** $(1\frac{1}{2}, 1\frac{1}{2})$ **9.** $(-1, 5\frac{1}{2})$ **13.** $(-9, -2)$ **17.** $(5, 5)$ **21.** $\overline{PQ}$: $(2, -3)$, $\overline{QR}$: $(4, 2)$, $\overline{PR}$: $(0, 1)$; 9 **24.** $AM = MB = MC = 5$ **26.** midpoint $= (0, 0)$

PAGE 414

1. 6 **4.** 1 **7.** -7 **10.** -6 **13.** $-\frac{3}{7}$ **16.** 0 **19.** $-\frac{3}{10}$; slants down to the right. **22.** undefined; vertical **25.** $-\frac{7}{8}$; slants down to the right. **28.** $-\frac{20}{3}$ **31.** 0 **34.** 6 **37.** slope $(\overline{AB}) = $ slope $(\overline{CD}) = 1$; ‖

ALGEBRA REVIEW

1. $x^2 + 4x + 4$ **5.** 4

PAGE 419

1. $4 = 2(0) + 4$ **4.** $-1 = \frac{1}{2}(8) - 5$ **7.** $-4 = -\frac{1}{4}(4) - 3$ **10.** $y = 3x + 5$ **14.** $y = -x - 2$ **18.** $y = -x + \frac{1}{4}$ **22.** $y = 2x + 4$; 2, 4 **26.** $y = -5x - 2$; $-5, -2$ **30.** $y = \frac{4}{3}x$; $\frac{4}{3}, 0$ **34.** $y = x - 3$; $1, -3$ **38.** $y = \frac{9}{4}x - 2$; $\frac{9}{4}, -2$ **42.** $y = x + 5$; $1, 5$ **46.** $y = \frac{6}{5}x + 6$; $\frac{6}{5}, 6$ **50.** Let l be a line with equation $y = mx + b$; let $P(x_1, y_1)$ and $Q(x_2, y_2)$ be points on l; thus, $y_1 = mx_1 + b$ and $y_2 = mx_2 + b$; use def. of slope and substitute to show slope $= m$; def. of y-intercept, point where line crosses y-axis is $A(0, y\text{-intercept})$; substitute in $y = mx + b$ to show y-intercept $= b$.

PAGE 422

17. Answers may vary. **21.** $y = \frac{1}{2}x + \frac{7}{2}$ **24.** $y = -2x + 1$ **27.** $y = -x - 2$ **30.** $y = -\frac{3}{2}x - 1$

PAGE 426

1. -1 **5.** 0 **9.** -7 **13.** -11 **17.** slope $(\overline{AB}) = $ slope $(\overline{CD}) = 1$; slope $\overline{AD} = $ slope $(\overline{BC}) = -4$ **19.** slope $(\overline{AB}) = $ slope $(\overline{CD}) = 1$; slope $(\overline{AD}) = $ slope $(\overline{BC}) = -1$ **21.** slope $(\overline{PR})$, -7, is negative reciprocal of slope $(\overline{SQ})$, $\frac{1}{7}$ **23.** $y = \frac{1}{6}x - \frac{17}{6}$ **25.** $y = 2x + 6$

PAGE 429

1. slope $(\overline{AB}) = $ slope $(\overline{CD}) = 1$; slope $(\overline{AD}) = $ slope $(\overline{BC}) = -7$ **3.** slope $(\overline{EF}) = $ slope $(\overline{GH}) = -\frac{2}{3}$; slope $(\overline{EH}) = $ slope $(\overline{FG}) = \frac{3}{2}$; $(-\frac{2}{3})(\frac{3}{2}) = -1$ **5.** $PR = QS = \sqrt{65}$ **7.** Write equations for $\overleftrightarrow{WY}$, $\overleftrightarrow{XZ}$; solve simultaneously for intersection point $P(\frac{3}{2}, -\frac{5}{2})$; $WP = PY = \frac{\sqrt{82}}{2}$; $ZP = PX = \frac{\sqrt{34}}{2}$ **9.** $MN = NP = PQ = QM = 5$; $\overline{MN} \parallel \overline{PQ}$ and $\overline{NP} \parallel \overline{QM}$ **11.** midpoint of $\overline{AC} = $ midpoint of $\overline{DB} = (\frac{a+b}{2}, \frac{c}{2})$ **13.** slope $(\overline{MN}) = $ slope $(\overline{AB}) = 0$

ALGEBRA REVIEW

1. $\{9, -5\}$ **5.** $\{5, 1\}$ **9.** $\{\frac{8}{3}, -4\}$

PAGE 433

1. $(x - 0)^2 + (y - 0)^2 = 2^2$ **5.** $(x - 4)^2 + [y - (-2)]^2 = 4^2$ **9.** $x^2 - 2x + y^2 - 4y = 31$ **13.** $x^2 + 16x + y^2 + 2y = -50$ **17.** $4^2 + 0^2 = 16$ **20.** $(-3)^2 + (-1)^2 = 10$ **23.** $(\sqrt{2})^2 + 5^2 = 27$ **26.** $(0, 0)$; 3 **29.** $(1, 0)$; 2 **32.** $(0, 0)$; $2\sqrt{3}$ **35.** $(0, 6)$; $2\sqrt{10}$ **38.** $(x - 3)^2 + (y - 4)^2 = 25$ **41.** $(x + 1)^2 + (y - 1)^2 = 25$ **44.** Show radius for each is 6. **46.** Show center for each has coordinates $(3, -2)$. **48.** $(4, -1)$

PAGE 435

1. Answers may vary. **6.** Answers may vary. **11.** $\sqrt{94}$ **14.** $\sqrt{83}$ **17.** $\sqrt{113}$ **20.** Given any two points $A(x_1, y_1, z_1)$ and $B(x_2, y_2, z_2)$; $C(x_1, y_1, z_2)$ is a point such that $(AC)^2 + (CB)^2 = (AB)^2$ (Pythagorean Th.); $AC = \sqrt{(z_2 - z_1)^2}$; $CB = \sqrt{(x_2 - x_1)^2 + (y_2 - y_1)^2}$; solve for AB

PAGE 436

1. Answers may vary. **5.** vertical **9.** $\sqrt{17}$
13. $(2,4)$ **17.** $(8,0)$ **21.** -4 **25.** undefined;
vertical **29.** $m=6$; $b=2$ **33.** $y=x+1$;
$m=1$, $b=1$ **37.** Answers may vary. **41.** 1
45. $\dfrac{-5}{4}$ **49.** slope $(\overline{AB})=$ slope $(\overline{CD})=1$;
slope $(\overline{AD})=$ slope $(\overline{BC})=-1$; $(1)(-1)=-1$
50. $x^2+y^2=9$ **54.** $(0,0)$; 4

PAGE 437

1. Answers may vary. **5.** neither **8.** $\sqrt{146}$
10. $(1,-1)$ **12.** $(9,-1)$ **14.** -2 **16.** 1; slants
up to the right **20.** $m=1$; $b=-3$ **22.** $y=x-1$;
$m=1$, $b=-1$ **24.** Answers may vary.
26. $\dfrac{-3}{5}$ **28.** $\dfrac{-7}{5}$ **30.** slope $(\overline{MN})=$ slope $(\overline{PQ})$
$=1$; slope $(\overline{MQ})=$ slope $(\overline{NP})=-4$ **31.** x^2+
$y^2=4$ **33.** $(0,0)$; 7

PAGE 441

1. See Post. 25. **3.** See Post. 27. **5.** bis. of
the angle **7.** $\perp$ bis of $\overline{PQ}$ **9.** interior of circle
with 2–cm radius

PAGE 444-445

1. circle concentric to given circle and with radius
equal to the distance from the center of the given
circle to one of the given chords; Post. 25 **3.** line
parallel to each of the given lines and midway between them; Post. 27 **5.** bisectors of the angles
formed; Th. 13.2 **7.** bis. of the angle; Th. 13.2
9. line $\perp$ given line at given pt.; the locus of the
centers of all circles tangent to a given line at a
given point is a line $\perp$ the given line at the given
point; Part I: A point on the perpendicular to a
given line at a given point is the center of a circle
tangent to the given line at the given point. Part II:
The center of a circle tangent to a given line at a
given point is a point on the perpendicular to the
given line at the given point. **11.** Part I: Use
Th. 10.5. Part II: Use Th. 10.6. **13.** Part I: Use
SAS; corr. parts. Part II: Use SSS; corr. parts;
Th. 2.5.

ALGEBRA REVIEW

1. $\{-5\}$ **4.** $\{\frac{1}{2}, 5\}$

PAGE 448

1. circle concentric to circle O and with 7–in. radius
2. circle concentric to circle O and with 4–in. radius,
and pt. at center **3.** 2 circles concentric to circle O,
one with 1–in. radius, other with 3–in. raduis **4.** $\{2$
pts. as in Example 5, p. 448$\}$ **5.** $\{$pt. on $\overline{AB}$ 1 cm
from A and 5 cm from $B\}$ **6.** empty set **7.** $\{4$ pts.,
one on each $\angle$ bis. 2 in. from $O\}$ **8.** $\{2$ pts., each
3 in. from P and on the line parallel to and midway between r and $s\}$ **9.** same as exercise 8 except 4 in.
from P **10.** $\{2$ pt. intersection of a line 2 cm above
l and a circle with center at P and 4–cm radius$\}$
11. $\{$pt. of tangency of line 2 cm above l and circle
with center at P and 3–cm radius$\}$ **12.** $\{3$ pt. intersection of lines 2 cm above and below l with circle
with center at P and 7–cm radius$\}$ **13.** $\{4$ pt. intersection of lines 2 cm above and below l with circle
with center at P and 9–cm radius$\}$ **14.** empty set
15. circle concentric to given circle with 7–in. radius
17. 2 circles concentric to given circle, one with 5–ft
radius, other with 9–ft. radius **19.** $\{2$ pts. as in
Example 5; p. 448$\}$ **21.** $\{4$ pts.; 2 on $\angle$ bisectors
5 in. above r, 2 on $\angle$ bisectors 1 in. below $r\}$
23. $\{$pt. on line midway between m and n and 8 in.
from $P\}$

PAGE 452

1. $\{$pt. on bis. of $\angle A$ and d in. from $A\}$ **3.** $\{4$ pts.,
2 on each $\angle$ bis. and x units from $A\}$ **5.** Case I: $h>$
$\frac{1}{2}d$; $\{2$ pts., each on $\perp$ bis. of $\overline{AB}$ and h in. from $A\}$.
Case II: $h=\frac{1}{2}d$; $\{$midpt. of $\overline{AB}\}$. Case III: $h<\frac{1}{2}d$;
empty set **7.** Denote by A and B the given pts. and
by l the line midway between the parallel lines. Case I:
$\perp$ bis. of $\overline{AB}$ intersects l; $\{1$ pt.$\}$ Case II: $\perp$ bis. of $\overline{AB}$
$\parallel l$; empty set. Case III: $\perp$ bis. of $\overline{AB}$ is l; locus is l.
9. See Oral Exercise 7, p. 452. **11.** Let d be the
distance between the given pts.; see Example 3, p. 451.
13. Consider possible intersection of a pair of $\perp$ lines
($\angle$ bisectors) with a pair of parallel lines. **15.** $\{$inter-
section of the bisectors$\}$ **17.** Consider possible intersections of a line ($\perp$ bis. of line joining 2 given pts.)
with a circle concentric to given circle and the
center of the circle.

ALGEBRA REVIEW

1. $\{-3, 1\}$ **4.** $\{\frac{3}{2}, 4\}$